WOMEN AND DEPRESSION

WOMEN AND DEPRESSION

PAULA HERNANDEZ
AND
SARA ALONSO
EDITORS

Nova Science Publishers, Inc.
New York

NOTICE TO THE READER

The Publisher has taken reasonable care in the preparation of this book, but makes no expressed or implied warranty of any kind and assumes no responsibility for any errors or omissions. No liability is assumed for incidental or consequential damages in connection with or arising out of information contained in this book. The Publisher shall not be liable for any special, consequential, or exemplary damages resulting, in whole or in part, from the readers' use of, or reliance upon, this material.

Independent verification should be sought for any data, advice or recommendations contained in this book. In addition, no responsibility is assumed by the publisher for any injury and/or damage to persons or property arising from any methods, products, instructions, ideas or otherwise contained in this publication.

This publication is designed to provide accurate and authoritative information with regard to the subject matter covered herein. It is sold with the clear understanding that the Publisher is not engaged in rendering legal or any other professional services. If legal or any other expert assistance is required, the services of a competent person should be sought. FROM A DECLARATION OF PARTICIPANTS JOINTLY ADOPTED BY A COMMITTEE OF THE AMERICAN BAR ASSOCIATION AND A COMMITTEE OF PUBLISHERS.

Library of Congress Cataloging-in-Publication Data

Women and depression / Paula Hernandez and Sara Alonso (editors).
  p. ; cm.
 Includes bibliographical references and index.
 ISBN 978-1-60456-647-5 (hardcover)
 1. Depression in women. I. Hernandez, Paula. II. Alonso, Sara.
 [DNLM: 1. Depressive Disorder--etiology. 2. Depressive Disorder--psychology. 3. Depressive Disorder--complications. 4. Sex Factors. 5. Women--psychology. WM 171 W8715 2008]
 RC537.W657 2008
 616.85'270082--dc22
                            2008013801

Published by Nova Science Publishers, Inc. ✦ *New York*

Contents

Preface

Depression is a serious medical illness affecting 5 to 8 percent of the adult population in a given year. Unlike normal emotional experiences of sadness, loss, or passing mood states, major depression is persistent and can significantly interfere with an individual's thoughts, behavior, mood, activity, and physical health. Among all medical illnesses, major depression is the leading cause of disability in the U.S. and many other developed countries.

Depression occurs twice as frequently in women as in men, for reasons that are not fully understood. More than half of those who experience a single episode of depression will continue to have episodes that occur as frequently as once or even twice a year. Without treatment, the frequency of depressive illness as well as the severity of symptoms tends to increase over time. Left untreated, depression can lead to suicide. This new book presents the latest research in the field.

Short Communication - *Background*: Smoking rates are elevated in psychiatric samples in general, rendering smoking a significant concern in this population. Moreover, women with psychiatric illness may be more likely to smoke cigarettes compared to men, in contrast with the higher rate of smoking for men in the general population. To extend our understanding of smoking in individuals with psychiatric illness, the authors studied a sample of patients seeking treatment, most of whom suffered from Major Depressive Disorder (MDD), assessing smoking history and, among current smokers, willingness to be contacted about a smoking cessation program.

Methods. The authors conducted a retrospective study of 129 outpatients (88 women, 41 men). Seventy-eight percent of the sample was diagnosed as having MDD (53% with MDD only, 15% with comorbid MDD and anxiety disorder, and 10% with comorbid MDD and dysthymia). Fourteen percent were diagnosed with an anxiety disorder only, and the remainder had diagnoses such as Bipolar Disorder, Mood Disorder NOS, etc.

Results: Overall, 33% of our sample were current smokers and 12% were ex-smokers. Current smokers had completed significantly fewer years of formal education than the never smokers. Smoking rate was elevated in female patients (34%) compared to women in the community (16%), as well as a lesser increase in smoking rate in male patients (29%) compared to men in the community (20%). Seventeen percent of men and 10% of women were former smokers (ns), suggesting that nearly half of all psychiatric patients may smoke at one time or another and yielding a low quit ratio (percent of eversmokers who have quit) of

28%. Thirty-three percent of current smokers were willing to be contacted about a smoking cessation program, not differing by sex. Among current smokers, those willing to be contacted about a smoking cessation program had smoked more years, were older, had a higher Heaviness of Smoking Index, and had expressed a greater desire to quit when compared to current smokers who were unwilling to be contacted about a smoking cessation program.

Conclusions: Smoking poses a significant health risk, and the increased prevalence of smoking in psychiatric samples, combined with a decreased likelihood of quitting, results in even greater risks among those with psychiatric illness. A third of women in our sample were current smokers, placing this population at particular risk. The authors encourage endeavors to better understand differential mechanisms behind higher smoking rates in psychiatric samples, particularly in women, to develop more specific tools for smoking cessation programs. On a promising note, about 33% of those who currently smoke were willing to be contacted about a smoking cessation program, an ideal target group for such programs.

Chapter 1 - Dyslexia is a life-long condition (without a known cure), affecting approximately 10-15% of the population. It is medical in origin but educational in treatment. It affects the ability to communicate (e.g. writing, spelling), compute mathematical concepts (e.g. algebra) and other aspects of life which require using short-term memory and co-ordination.

Those with dyslexia who are not assessed/treated in early childhood are highly susceptible to emotional manifestations due to low self-esteem and low perceived ability caused by peers, parents and educators who misread their learning difficulties for laziness and lack of motivation. In fact ignoring or misreading a child's learning disability is a form of abuse which reaches far into today's educational systems. Gender has yet to be a major focus in the study of dyslexia, however there is growing evidence that it is an important factor in understanding why some dyslexics are resilient and others are affected emotionally.

There are three research projects included in this chapter. These aim to build personality profiles for dyslexic males and females according to the severity of their dyslexia. Depression and withdrawal emerge as key personality traits amongst these groups. A second study using this same data investigates profiles to successful (degree educated) dyslexics and how personality differences emerge amongst those who are diagnosed and undiagnosed. Diagnosis, gaining remedial help or support, meant that such individuals were more optimistic and did not doubt past events, compared to those who were undiagnosed and went through life thinking something was wrong but were unable to pinpoint the problem. It may also be the case that their coping strategies were successful enough to mean that their difficulties were not highlighted, however the emotional cost was great.

Lastly there was an interview study for dyslexics who were also diagnosed with clinical depression. Strong gender differences were identified with females using more withdrawal and self-blame than males who tend to use helplessness. Their life stories indicate neglect by teachers and parents which lead them to use perfectionism as a defence mechanism. Their difficulties led a number of them to contemplate suicide as there were no other perceived options available to them to deal with the anxiety from having an invisible learning disorder.

Chapter 2 - In the preceding chapter (Alexander-Passe, 2008) gave an understanding of what dyslexia is and how it affects both adults and children in settings from school to the workplace. Both the empirical and the three research studies highlighted the emotional manifestations that come from having a learning disability, such as dyslexia. This chapter continues the investigation from first reviewing empirical evidence concerning stress, coping, avoidance and Defence mechanisms before suggesting a hypothetical model of 'Dyslexia Defence Mechanisms (DDMs)'. Such a model is based on the work of Vaillant (1992) Messiner (1980) but as dyslexics are a unique population, several aspects of normal Defence mechanisms are inappropriate. For example, the DDMs are split in Emotional and Behavioural, being predominately split by gender (Females-Emotional and Males-Behavioural). Avoidance of writing long words has been identified as a key coping strategy before DDMs are chosen, teachers, parents and practioneers should identify this as the start of a long negative path for children at school. Teachers are advised that when children fail in more tasks than they succeed in, such children will perceive learning and school as threats to their self-esteem and self-concept. They will seek out ways to protect themselves and Defence mechanisms may explain what mechanisms are chosen. Defence mechanisms have never been investigated with dyslexic populations, however reviewing empirical data they seem ideal candidates for such investigation.

Chapter 3 - The results from epidemiological studies suggest that adolescence is a critical period for understanding the development of depression for two reasons (Avenevoli, Knight, Kessler, & Merikangas, 2007). First, although during childhood, sex differences in depression are not reliably found, during the transition from early to middle adolescence (i.e., ages 12-15) sex differences emerge with girls reporting higher levels of both depressive symptoms (Angold, Erkanli, Silberg, Eaves, & Costello 2002; Twenge & Nolen-Hoeksema, 2002) and depressive disorders (Costello, Mustillo, Erkanli, Keeler, & Angold, 2003; Hankin, Abramson, Moffitt, Silva, McGee, & Angell, 1998) than boys. Second, during the transition from middle to late adolescence, there is a dramatic, six-fold increase in depression rates (Hankin et al., 1998). Prevalence rates remain at similarly high levels throughout adulthood with adult depression typically being preceded by adolescent depression (Kim-Cohen, Caspi, & Moffitt, 2003). Although it is well established that both of these epidemiological shifts occur during adolescence, little research has examined the factors that underlie them. In the current chapter, the authors will examine both the emergence of sex differences in depression and the surge in depression rates in adolescence from the perspective of cognitive vulnerability-stress theories of depression.

Chapter 4 - *Background*: Differences in emotion processing during Major Depressive Disorder (MDD) have not been well explored as a potential explanation for age and gender disparities in rates of depression and depressive symptoms. Early studies by our group demonstrated that those with MDD underperform in emotion processing of faces, although recently the authors showed a selective decrement in younger women with MDD. The authors now extend this study of gender differences in facial emotion processing during MDD to the full age spectrum. The authors assessed emotion processing performance using posed facial emotional expressions in those with early (age 18- 35) and middle/ late (age 36-73) MDD as well as in women and men to determine if there was differential impact of MDD in these four groups. The authors hypothesized that knowledge about gender, age, and emotion processing performance differences might increase understanding of risk for and expression of MDD in women and in those with later onset MDD.

Methods: Participants included 161 individuals in younger age groups (YA; 123 women, 38 men) and 150 individuals in middle/ elder age groups (MEA; 100 women, 50 men) diagnosed with MDD, as well as 97 healthy control YAs (60 women, 37 men) and 35 healthy controls MEAs (24 women, 11 men). A conservative age classification $\leq$ age 35 was used to separate YAs from MEAs in order to be to be confident that potential causes of middle-late onset MDD (e.g., cardiovascular) were less likely to be present in the younger MDD groups.

Results: There was an interaction between age, gender, and MDD status for response time, with slower response times in YA MDD patients compared to their age-matched control groups. This effect of slower response time was not detected in the comparisons between MEAs with and without MDD. MEA women, YA women, and MEA men with MDD made significantly more errors than did their same-age, same-gender control counterparts ($ps < .05$), whereas YA men with MDD performed similarly to same-age control men ($p > .26$). Further, although MEA women and men with MDD performed more poorly in facial perception relative to same age control cohorts, MEA men with late onset MDD performed worse than MEA men with early onset MDD, in contrast to no difference between performance of MEA women with late and early onset MDD.

Conclusions: These findings suggest that YA men with MDD may have a different neurobiological etiology of depression compared to YA women. In contrast, MEA men and all women with MDD appear to have similar difficulties with emotion processing, suggesting overlap in brain regions affected, albeit likely through different mechanisms. Notably, MEA men with late onset MDD appear to have a greater burden of emotion processing decrement compared to other depressed groups.

Chapter 5- Literature on psychiatric comorbidities in neurologic diseases (including stroke, multiple sclerosis, Parkinson disease, Alzheimer dementia) are generally consistent about the prevalence of female gender in depression in most of these illnesses. These data are in agreement with those of functional depression, in which female preponderance in depression rates appears to be a consistent finding. In the literature, several possible explanations have been suggested and investigated, such as biological, social and psychological factors. However, existing data on the role of gender in depression in neurological comorbidities is, to our knowledge, only exhaustive for post-stroke depression (PSD) and less exhaustive for other diseases.

Chapter 6- The Latino/Hispanic population is the fastest growing ethnic group in the United States. The proportion of Latino/Hispanics in the population grew by 14.2% in fourteen years, from 6.4% in 1980 (14.6 million) to an estimated 12.5% (35.5 million) in 2001(with a 58% increase during the 90's). These numbers do not include illegal migrants, a number that is difficult to establish. It is well known that most of the migrating populations that arrive in the USA are of Latino/Hispanic origin, being Mexican Americans the largest subgroup, Puerto Ricans the second, and Cuban Americans the third largest subgroup. Some of them leave their country of origin to pursue the "American dream", which for many of them is synonymous to having freedom, better educational and economic opportunities, and prosperity. Others have to do so because of threats or political issues.

A recent trend is the fact that more women have been entering the migration stream, which had been primarily male. Latino/Hispanic women, especially migrants, have been identified to be at a higher risk for mental health problems due to the myriad of acculturation issues and economic hardships they may suffer with the migration process. Frequently, Latino/Hispanics are identified as a high-risk group for serious physical and mental health conditions, particularly depression, anxiety, substance abuse, cardiovascular disease and diabetes. These problems tend to be more prevalent among women. Furthermore, research has demonstrated that Latino/Hispanic ethnicity emerged as a risk factor for depressive symptoms, mainly among disadvantaged subgroups experiencing serious hardship (i.e., higher poverty) in the context of their historical, political, and societal reality. Given that by 2020 depression is expected to be the second largest health care problem after heart disease worldwide, the scope of this problem will be enormous among Latino/Hispanic women.

There is a need for continued research of the various factors associated with the depression phenomena in Latino/Hispanic women. Given that Latino/Hispanic women are not a homogenous group, the design and development of linguistically and culturally sensitive and effective interventions that may serve for the prevention of depression in that group needs to be considered in a more specific manner.

It is crucial to pay attention to the significant differences between the Latino/Hispanic subpopulations. Programs intended to reduce feelings of isolation, lack of support, power, language barriers and economic hardship need to be developed by private and public agencies. This can include activities to enhance assertiveness and communication skills, empowerment, and financial independence in order to diminish risk factors for the development of depression in Latino/Hispanic women.

For being effective, interventions need to have a grassroots origin. Interventions that address issues in a more sensitive way, taking into consideration cultural factors, will be more readily accepted by Latino/Hispanic women and will reduce the resistance these women may have and will give them a higher probability of improving their quality of life and adaptation to the host society.

Chapter 7 - *Background:* There is large evidence that major depressive disorder (MDD) has prevalence rates almost twice as high in females as in men. However, few studies have investigated in MDD the regional cerebral blood flow (rCBF) differences between genders. The aim of the study was to identify the influence of gender on the rCBF distribution in a group of depressed patients. This was performed by means of Volume of Interest (VOI) analysis and Principal Component Analysis (PCA), this latter exploring functional brain connectivity and transforming a number of correlated variables by clustering them into functionally uncorrelated factors

Methods: A group of 76 major depressed patients (36 males and 40 females) were investigated by ^{99m}Tc-HMPAO and SPECT. Analysis of covariance (ANCOVA) and PCA were performed on 54 VOIs. Neuropsychiatric tests (MADRS, SCID, CFQ, KSP) were also carried out to assess disease severity without finding any gender differences.

Results: VOIs analysis identified in females as compared to males a significantly higher rCBF distribution ($F(1,73)=10.875$; $p=0.002$). A significant VOI*Gender interaction was also found ($F(26,1898)=2.180$; $p=0.001$) revealing that 10 regions belonging to the frontal, temporal, parietal and occipital cortex were particularly involved in gender differences. An overall effect of gender was also found for PCA ($F(1,73)=8.814$; $p=0.004$). The significant PCs*Gender interaction ($F(12,876)=3.258$; $p<0.000$) revealed lower rCBF distribution in males as compared to females in 6 PCs. Such PCs, grouped brain regions belonging to parietal-limbic cortex (PC3; p=0.033), parieto-temporo-occipital cortex (PCs 8 and 9; p=0.001), fronto-parietal cortex (PC10; p=0.017), fronto-temporal cortex (PC12; p=0.001) and hippocampi (PC 13; p=0.017). Age related hippocampal differences were found in PC13 in female only.

Conclusion: PC8 grouped two areas involved in linguistic processing, the angular and the supramarginal gyrus of the left hemispheres for which gender differences are widely accepted. PC9 with the right angular gyrus was also likely to show rCBF differences since females are known to be more bilaterally organized. Gender differences in hippocampi confirmed previous findings. However, medial prefrontal cortex (anterior cingulate) bilaterally and right dorsolateral prefrontal cortex, regions known from the existing literature to be implicated in MDD, were grouped by PCA into different PCs (PC1 and PC4, respectively) but did not show any sex difference speaking against specific gender related rCBF changes in major depression.

PCA grouping functionally connected brain regions increased the depth of the analysis yielding more information on the processes underlying perfusion distribution measurements in MDD.

Chapter 8 - Depression is the most common psychiatric disorder worldwide. No single antidepressant has been shown to be more effective than any other in lifting depression, and the effectiveness of any particular antidepressant in an individual is difficult to predict. Thus, doctors must prescribe antidepressants based on trial and error. Single nucleotide polymorphisms (SNPs) can be used in clinical association studies to determine the contribution of genes to drug efficacy. In addition, some findings suggest that women respond differently to antidepressant treatment than men. In this chapter, the authors review gender differences, pharmacogenomics, and gene-gender interactions with the drug efficacy of antidepressants in depression. First, the authors survey the SNPs and genes identified as genetic markers that are correlated and associated with the drug efficacy of antidepressants. Evidence is accumulating to suggest that the efficacy of antidepressants results from the combined effects of a number of genetic variants, such as SNPs. Although there are not enough data currently available to prove this hypothesis, more and more genetic variants associated with antidepressant response are being discovered. Secondly, the authors investigate the recent reports that antidepressants may work somewhat differently in men and women. Some theoretical reasons have been suggested for suspecting that gender differences in antidepressant response exist. Thirdly, the authors study gender-specific SNP and gene contributions to antidepressant treatment response and demonstrate pattern recognition approaches to evaluate the epistasis among genes and gender. These techniques may provide tools for clinical association studies and help find genes and SNPs involved in responses to therapeutic drugs or adverse drug reactions.

Chapter 9 - High rates of depression are often reported among women with HIV (Cook et al. 2002). Factors contributing to depression among persons with HIV have been identified as greater, age, physical symptoms, comorbid health conditions, loneliness, substance abuse, stigma, and other stressors (Jones et al., 2003; Heckman et al., 2001; Oursler et al, 2006; Rabkin et al., 2004; Riley et al., 2003; Vance, 2006). Factors mitigating depression in this population include effective coping strategies, social support, and spirituality (Coleman et al., 2006; Heckman et al., 2001; Heckman et al., 2002). However, despite the growing aging population living with HIV, the impact of depression on older women with HIV has received limited attention in the research literature. The success of antiretroviral therapy has moved HIV into the category of chronic disease. In New York City, the epicenter of HIV in the United States, 33% of the 100,000 people living with this virus are now over the age of 50 (New York City Department of Health and Mental Hygiene, 2007). This pattern is seen throughout the United States, where it is expected that one-half of those with HIV will be 50 years or older by 2015. This graying population of persons with HIV will confront the challenges of physical and mental health comorbidities, coupled with the panoply of psychosocial challenges that are associated with aging. The present study is one of the first to examine the effects of stressors on depressive symptoms among a large sample of women 50 years and older living with HIV.

The sample consisted of 264 women, 50 to 76 years old (M age = 55 years). Approximately one-third had post-high school educations, 58% were Black, 34% were Hispanic, and 5% were White. To examine the impact of health-related and psychosocial stressors, the conceptual model employed for analysis was a modified Stress and Coping Model (Folkman and Lazarus, 1984). The multivariate model explained 48% of the variance in depressive symptoms. The number of comorbid conditions and the need for assistance as a result of HIV infection were positively related to greater depressive symptoms, as were both loneliness and stigma. Higher cognitive functioning and spirituality were significantly related to lower levels of depression. These findings support the need for interventions to address depression, health, and psychosocial stressors among older women with HIV. In addition, programs to increase access to spiritual resources for older women with HIV may help to ameliorate depression in this population.

Chapter 10 - Between 11 and 30% of older people worldwide suffer from depressive symptoms, and approximately 17 to 35% of depressed patients suffer cognitive loss. Community samples show a doubling of comorbid mood disorder and cognitive deficits every 5 years after the age of 70 until by age 85, approximately 25% of older individuals demonstrate both conditions. Women have almost double the risk of men for suffering these comorbid conditions before the age of 80.

Research on the biological and physiological changes associated with unipolar major depression center on the prefrontal lobes and the fronto-striatal neural loops that are associated with emotional responsiveness, cognition, and behavior. With the advent of new advances in neuroimaging techniques, researchers can explore the anatomical, biochemical and physiological substrates of late-life depression. Imaging studies report that some regions within the prefrontal cortex are selectively reduced in volume during late-life depression. Stable relationships between cognition and brain biochemicals that are seen in healthy elderly are disturbed in depressed individuals, and myelination of white matter tracts appears compromised. This chapter will discuss the 1) diagnosis of late-life depression and how late-onset differs from early-onset depression, 2) medical context in which late-life depression often occurs, 3) neurocognitive profiles of depressed patients, 4) associated anatomic and physiologic brain abnormalities, 5) putative links between late-life depression and the emergence of dementing syndromes, and 6) effects of pharmacological and psychotherapeutic intervention. Knowledge about the characteristics of late-life depression and successful interventions can mitigate and sometimes reverse the onset of a downward spiral in functioning and physical health that frequently accompanies late-life mood disorders.

Chapter 11 - Diabetes and depression are both significant public health concerns for women. Depression is a risk factor for incident type 2 diabetes, and it also increases risk for poor diabetes outcomes. Research linking depression to health risks is limited in several important ways, particularly by common practices employed to measure depression. In this chapter the authors review evidence linking depression and diabetes in women, and describe limitations of the extant literature. The authors then review our own work that begins to address these limitations. The authors conclude with a review of the treatment literature and recommendations for addressing depression in women with diabetes.

Chapter 12 - The psychological and physical challenges associated with cancer often result in considerable distress and symptoms of depression. Major Depression is a significant mental health concern among patients with cancer, as it affects 20 – 25% of all patients diagnosed with cancer. This chapter examines the factors that both increase and decrease the risk of developing depression following a cancer diagnosis. Cancer related variables including the type of cancer, stage of disease, and level of pain and physical impairment are examined as they relate to depression in women with cancer. Other risk factors including age, prior history of depression, and coping style are also examined. In addition, spirituality and religiosity, as well as level and quality of social support are discussed as buffering factors against the negative effects of a cancer diagnosis. Knowledge and understanding of these factors are imperative for appropriate assessment and diagnosis of depression in oncology patients, and the implications and limitations of this body of research are briefly examined.

Chapter 13 - Converging evidence suggests that patients affected by epilepsy show a considerably higher incidence of depression than the average population (about 65% versus 25%). Since women are twice as likely as men to suffer from depression, female gender could be considered a major risk factor to develop this condition, although gender-related epidemiological data are somewhat controversial. Overall, it is recommended that clinicians pay particular attention, when dealing with women with epilepsy, to examine for early signs of depression. With regards to the neurobiological and psychological underpinnings of these conditions, the key elements to be considered are the partial overlapping in neuro-chemical mechanisms involved both in depression and epilepsy, and the large number of interlinked psychosocial determinants, including clinical features of epilepsy such as seizure type, frequency, and cortical focus. Moreover, sex hormones are important, since they are known to contribute remodelling the hippocampus, a structure which plays a pivotal role in both epilepsy and depression. In women, as opposed to men, the levels of sex hormones are more relevant because of their physiological cyclic fluctuations. Estrogens, rather than other ovarian hormones, show an effect similar to antidepressant drugs by stimulating hippocampal synaptogenesis. With regards to epilepsy, a decrease in estrogen levels is linked to a significant increase in seizures frequency. The exact relationship between epilepsy and depression is not fully understood. However, an emerging picture may suggest potential therapeutic strategies to improve the clinical management of women with epilepsy: first and foremost, an optimal control of seizures can be obtained by using an appropriate pharmacological regimen or neurophysiological devices, such as vagus nerve stimulation. The choice of the antiepileptic drug should take into due account the behavioral profile of the medication, as some of them (e.g. lamotrigine, carbamazepine) can have a positive effect on mood. Selective serotonin reuptake inhibitors and dual-action antidepressant medications are also considered first-line therapy. Finally, electroconvulsive therapy and vagus nerve stimulation can prove useful in selected cases.

Chapter 14 - Temporomandibular disorders (TMD) are characterized as a heterogeneous set of clinical problems involving the masticatory musculature and/or the temporomandibular joint (TMJ). TMD are considered to be one of the musculoskeletal disorders, and are usually subclassified as myogenous, arthrogenous or combined disorders. The symptoms and clinical signs of TMD include joint sounds, TMJ and masticatory muscle pain and restricted mandibular movements.

Several population-based studies indicate that women experience more TMD-related pain than men, usually at a ratio of two to one. The most prominent sex differences have been found at the age of 20-40 years. Altogether, there seem to be both local and central factors involved in the aetiology of TMD. Epidemiological and clinical studies have shown that besides local pain, facial pain is related to pain condition in different parts of the body. It has also been shown that psychological factors are related to TMD, especially those involving muscular problems.

It has been shown that chronic pain conditions and depressive disorders have some pathophysiologic characteristics in common. Additionally, an association between depression and TMD-related pain has been found in several studies, both in clinical and epidemiological ones. It has been suggested that especially TMD pain as part of a generalised pain condition is connected with depression. The comorbidity has been found to be stronger among women than men.

The diagnosis and treatment of TMD pain may be complicated, especially when the condition is linked with psychological problems. Depression may have an effect on the outcome of the treatment of TMD. Especially when TMD are related to chronic pain conditions, a multidisciplinary approach is needed, besides conservative treatment of TMD. Dentists can provide an important contribution to health care by identifying depression in patients and referring them for treatment.

Chapter 15 - Patients and methods. In a prospective study the authors observed which female patients developed depression following an acute and painful vertebral fracture. On the day of diagnosing the vertebral fracture the patients filled the questionnaires 1 and 2. The depression developed in some patients was diagnosed by means of the DSM – IV questionnaire. For the statistical evaluation of questionnaires the authors chose randomly 32 patients with depression (out of 33 patients) aged 51-73, and 32 patients without depression (out of 44 patients) aged 52-70.

The aim of the study: To verify the hypothesis that the patients with more traumatic experience in the anamnesis (Questionnaire No. 1) are more depression prone following the osteoporotic vertebrae fractures and their character features are typical for subjects with higher emotional vulnerability (Questionnaire No. 2).

Statistical analysis: 1. Questionnaires 1 and 2 were evaluated by two statistical methods: a) automatization of mathematical and statistical estimates and tests based on binomial distribution; b) ADALINE Programme.

2. Assessment of relative risk for developing depression.

Results: Questionnaire No. 1 completed by depressed patients contained statistically significant higher number of positive answers to questions defining experienced stress situations (differences in values of weights of questionnaire parameters expressed in percentages within linear combination of the whole group).

Questionnaire No. 2 completed by depressed patients contained statistically significant higher number of positive answers by more depression prone subjects in comparison with non-depressed patients (differences in values of weights of questionnaire parameters.

Patients lapsed into depression most often on the 32nd day following the vertebra fracture.

Proposed questionnaires are according to validity criteria (sensitivity, specificity, prediction value of positive test, prediction values of negative test, test effectiveness) indicated for identification of persons risking the onset of depression following the osteoporotic fracture of vertebrae.

Relative risk (RR) for developing depression in patients with osteoporotic fracture, which answered in Questionnaire No. 1 eight and more questions positive is *7,0 time* higher than in patiens with osteoporotic fracture, which answered in Questionnaire No. 1 less than eight guestions positive. For Questionnaire No. 2 it is *8,5 time* higher.

Conclusion: The authors recommend using questionnaires No. 1 and 2 in female patients with acute painful vertebrae fractures to select patients with the risk of depression development. These patients should be followed more frequently as outpatients and in case of first clinical symptoms of depression should be recommended for special psychiatric care. Early therapy of depression enables to accelerate the mobilisation, rehabilitation and resocialisation of patients, to improve the quality of their lives and to reduce the costs of analgetic treatment of pain, sedatives and rehabilitation.

Chapter 16 - Depression is more prevalent in adult women than men; the etiology of this difference is elusive. Differences in the hormonal milieu of the sexes may play a role, but societal factors may also take their toll. Women physicians and nurses are no exception regarding depression. In the USA although the lifetime prevalence of depression is 12-13% for male and 18-20% for female physicians (the latter being equal to that of the general population), their completed suicide rate is 1.4-2.3 times higher than that of the general population.

Greek society is characterized by close-knit relationships that may also provide a more supportive environment. In the same country the healthcare sector is profoundly iatrocentric and the number of nurses compared to that of physicians is disproportionately low.

Bearing these Greek particularities in mind, the authors have assessed depression and anxiety in medical and nursing personnel and found no overall differences among subjects. However, age and depression scores were positively correlated in female nurses only. Furthermore, in other studies, the authors noted that smoking behavior of physicians (regardless of gender) was more anxiety- than depression-driven. In another study the authors discovered that in nurses their degree of sense of coherence renders them either resistant or vulnerable to depression and burnout.

In conclusion, stress management interventions should be sought in the healthcare workplace, but they should be equally focused on medical and nursing personnel, and particularly women.

Chapter 17 - This study aimed to identify the profile of students from two Nursing courses (Bachelor - diurnal and Teaching Diploma – afternoon) verifying signs of depression and self-esteem levels, comparing these variables. A total of 114 students, properly informed, from the diurnal and afternoon courses at the College of Nursing at Ribeirão Preto participated in the study. The data search was obtained on known, valid and largely used instruments: Brazilian Economic Classification Criteria – CEB; Beck's Depression Inventory –BDI; Janis and Field's Self-Esteem Scale. The data were submitted to analysis of correlation with significance level at 5%. The results show prevalence of 94 women (82,4%), 63% between 20 and 24 years old; 32.06% (Teaching Diploma) are older than 25 years and 32% (Bachelor) are younger than 20 years old; 69.6% (Bachelor) do not work, and 86.1% belong to classes A2 and B; 75.8% (Teaching Diploma) work and 67.4% from the total belong to classes B2 and C. The data show 15.4% (Bachelor) and 28.6% (Teaching Diploma) with signs indicative of depression (three severe cases in the afternoon courses). The self-esteem levels were classified in 97.4% as medium and high. None of the cases indicative of moderate and severe depression presented low self-esteem. The conclusion is that there are significant differences between the profiles of the two groups of subjects especially the higher incidence of depression among the Teaching Diploma students. It is possible that the prestige perceived in the academic context is a resilient factor, positively influencing the students' self evaluation.

Chapter 18 - Compared to men, women are disproportionately subject to both depression and certain adverse cardiovascular outcomes. In this chapter, the authors review a large body of data on women, depression, and cardiovascular disease (CVD). First, the authors highlight epidemiologic data related to women's higher prevalence of depression, and discuss possible explanations thereof. Second, the authors explore findings on the nature and scope of CVD among women. Next, the authors summarize data regarding the status of depression as a risk factor for future CVD and a prognostic indicator for established CVD, emphasizing findings pertinent to women. The authors then examine possible mechanisms underlying the depression-CVD relationship and conclude by exploring a host of treatment issues. Throughout the chapter, the authors offer a variety of recommendations and directions for future research. The present chapter, in its integration of large and diverse research literatures, should serve as a useful resource for professionals interested in the links between women, depression, and CVD.

Chapter 19 - Depression patients characterized by chronobiologic alterations as diminution of locomotor activity, altered sleep architecture, changes in the cyclic pattern of cortisol, growth, and thyroid hormones secretion, all governed by the Suprachiasmatic Nuclei in the hypothalamus. Several previous studies in animals confirmed anatomical and functional relationships between Suprachiasmatic Nuclei and Vestibular Nuclei through Raphe Nuclei in the brain stem. In our research the authors demonstrated that vestibular activity is diminished at the right side in Major Depression and Bipolar Disease patients during the Depression phase of the illness. It is hypothesized that the right Vestibular hypo activity is induced by ipsilateral dysfunction of Raphe Nuclei or Suprachiasmatic Nuclei, two neuronal nuclei that modulate vestibular function. To support this idea the authors analyze, in this chapter, the multiple evidences of anatomical and functional alterations of the serotoninergic Raphe Nuclei and of chronobiologic-suprachiasmatic disturbances in depressed patients, and the authors discuss the importance of studying the right–left asymmetry of activity of both nuclei in the future. The study of the bilateral distribution of cortisol, leptin, orexin and estrogen receptors in Raphe Nuclei is also proposed in order to investigate the possible contribution of those depression-associated hormones in right-left asymmetric Raphe Nuclei activity. In summary, the possibility of an asymmetric modulating effect of Raphe Nuclei on Suprachiasmatic Nuclei could contribute to the development of chronobiologic symptoms including depressed mood, and on the other side, Raphe Nuclei modulating effects on Vestibular Nuclei, could explain the asymmetric vestibular response.

Chapter 20 - The study of depression as a possible risk factor in the incidence of coronary heart disease (CHD) and for recurring coronary episodes or death in previously ill people has a certain tradition in the literature, but publications on this possible relation increased greatly after the appearance of a meta-analysis by Booth-Kewley and Friedman (1987). These authors reviewed 87 studies on the relationship between psychosocial risk factors, especially Type A Behavior (TAB) and its components, and cardiac disease (CD). Among their results referring to the relation between these factors and all types of CD is that greater effect size is produced on analysis of results from studies using TAB measured by the Structured Interview, with depression as a risk factor of considerable weight. Booth-Kewley and Friedman noted that although depression seemed to be reliably associated with CD, it had largely been underestimated. As from the 1980s, and particularly during the 1990s, the number of publications on this as a possible risk factor for CD increased, with a corresponding decline in the number of studies on TAB. Thus Scheidt (2000), in his editorial for a special edition of the Journal of Psychosomatic Research devoted to research on psychosocial factors implicated in cardiovascular diseases, expressed surprise about the absence of contributions to the special edition on TAB as a risk factor for CD.

The importance of depression is particularly great if the authors consider the results of the meta-analysis by Booth-Kewley and Friedman (1987) who found an effect size expressed in z score of 6.44 for the relationship between depression and all types of CD. Effect size was 5.24 for the relationship between depression and myocardial infarction (MI) and 4.29 for the relationship between depression and angina pectoris as an indicator of CHD. Thus it was not unexpected when Lespérance and Frasure-Smith (2000) suggested that it was time to replace TAB with depression as a psychological priority for cardiologists because depression: a) is the fourth most frequent cause of mortality and early invalidity and the second in industrialized countries, only preceded by CHD; b) clearly plays a large part in medical prescription non-adherence and failure to follow recommendations on life-style changes; c) may interfere with and reduce the efficacy of other treatment aimed at ensuring that cardiovascular patients lead active and productive lives. Further weight is added to this issue by the fact that the rate of CHD has increased more rapidly in women than in men since 1984. In addition, estimated mortality for the period 1990-2020 indicates that ischemic cardiopathy and depression are leading factors contributing to world wide mortality (Murray and Lopez, 1997a; 1997b). Thus the authors are dealing with a major health issue, albeit controversial; in spite of the evidence in favor of its association with CHD, depression is not considered a risk factor, as became clear at the annual meeting of the American College of Cardiology held in Bethesda, 2002. The final report listed ten risk factors for CHD, and depression was not included.

From the available etiologic meta-analyses, it may be affirmed that there is a significant association between depression and CHD in the general population. The authors could also affirm a significant association between depression and CHD in women if the authors focus on the crude results of our meta-analysis performed with data obtained from women only. The evidence provided by prognostic studies about the relationship between depression and CHD in the general population is similar to that of etiologic studies, although the data for women only are scarce. The considerable reduction of RR values found using results adjusted for other factors means that the possible effect of depression is closely related with other risk factors for CHD. It is therefore necessary to determine the weight of each of these risk factors and the risk associated to their combination, as well as the type of association and the pathways whereby depression may contribute to the manifestation of CHD. Conclusions based on the results of meta-analyses should, however, be made with reservations due to the limitations of the prospective studies included in them and to the limitations of the meta-analyses themselves. The prevalence of depression after a CHD event seems higher in women than in men, although systematic studies are lacking in this respect. The authors believe that the correct evaluation of all these results is not to negate the possible role of depression in the incidence and recurrence of CHD, but rather to strive for more and better research into this topic.

Chapter 21 - During the last few years our knowledge about disturbed brain function in major depression has been increased mainly due to new possibilities offered by neuroimaging methods like functional Magnetic Resonance Imaging (fMRI). Several key structures were identified to play an important role in major depression, such as the rostral and subgenual parts of the anterior cingulate cortex (ACC), the orbitofrontal cortex (OFC) and the dorsolateral prefrontal cortex (DLPFC). Subcortical regions like the amygdala, the thalamus and the nucleus accumbens also seem to play an important role. In comparison to the large number of studies investigating major depression with neuroimaging methods in general, only a few studies have directly addressed the question of gender-specific differences so far although there are hints that gender specific differences may exist. This review summarizes the most important findings related to neurobiological correlates of gender differences, neural responses in depression and particularly neuroimaging findings for depression in women suggesting new lines of research in this field.

In: Women and Depression
Editors: Paula Hernandez and Sara Alonso

ISBN 978-1-60456-647-5
© 2009 Nova Science Publishers, Inc.

Short Communication

Sex Differences in Smoking Prevalence and Characteristics Associated with Receptivity to Quitting in Psychiatric Patients

Scott A. Langenecker[1,2], Raphaela Finkenauer[1], Sandy M. Snedecor[1], Jon-Kar Zubieta[2], Elizabeth A. Young[2], Sheila M. Marcus[2], Kevin Kerber[2], and Cynthia S. Pomerleau[1,2]

[1]Nicotine Research Laboratory, University of Michigan Department of Psychiatry, Ann Arbor, MI, USA
[2]Department of Psychiatry; University of Michigan; Ann Arbor, Michigan; USA

Abstract

Background: Smoking rates are elevated in psychiatric samples in general, rendering smoking a significant concern in this population. Moreover, women with psychiatric illness may be more likely to smoke cigarettes compared to men, in contrast with the higher rate of smoking for men in the general population. To extend our understanding of smoking in individuals with psychiatric illness, we studied a sample of patients seeking treatment, most of whom suffered from Major Depressive Disorder (MDD), assessing smoking history and, among current smokers, willingness to be contacted about a smoking cessation program.

Methods. We conducted a retrospective study of 129 outpatients (88 women, 41 men). Seventy-eight percent of the sample was diagnosed as having MDD (53% with MDD only, 15% with comorbid MDD and anxiety disorder, and 10% with comorbid MDD and dysthymia). Fourteen percent were diagnosed with an anxiety disorder only, and the remainder had diagnoses such as Bipolar Disorder, Mood Disorder NOS, etc.

Results: Overall, 33% of our sample were current smokers and 12% were ex-smokers. Current smokers had completed significantly fewer years of formal education than the never smokers. Smoking rate was elevated in female patients (34%) compared to women in the community (16%), as well as a lesser increase in smoking rate in male patients (29%) compared to men in the community (20%). Seventeen percent of men and 10% of women were former smokers (ns), suggesting that nearly half of all psychiatric patients may smoke at one time or another and yielding a low quit ratio (percent of eversmokers who have quit) of 28%. Thirty-three percent of current smokers were willing to be contacted about a smoking cessation program, not differing by sex. Among current smokers, those willing to be contacted about a smoking cessation program had smoked more years, were older, had a higher Heaviness of Smoking Index, and had expressed a greater desire to quit when compared to current smokers who were unwilling to be contacted about a smoking cessation program.

Conclusions: Smoking poses a significant health risk, and the increased prevalence of smoking in psychiatric samples, combined with a decreased likelihood of quitting, results in even greater risks among those with psychiatric illness. A third of women in our sample were current smokers, placing this population at particular risk. We encourage endeavors to better understand differential mechanisms behind higher smoking rates in psychiatric samples, particularly in women, to develop more specific tools for smoking cessation programs. On a promising note, about 33% of those who currently smoke were willing to be contacted about a smoking cessation program, an ideal target group for such programs.

Keywords: *smoking, cessation, depression, outpatient, sex*

Smoking rates in psychiatric populations are two to four times as high as in the general population (Grant, Hasin, Chou, Stinson, and Dawson, 2004; Lasser, Boyd, Woolhandler, Himmelstein, McCormick, and Bor, 2000). Evidence that the comorbidity of smoking and depression is stronger in women than in men has recently been reported (Husky, Mazure, Paliwal, and McKee, 2008). Furthermore, individuals suffering from psychiatric illness are less successful in quitting smoking than in quitting alcohol or other drugs (de Leon, Susce, et al, 2005). There is considerable evidence to suggest that smokers with depression or even a history of depression have greater difficulty than others in quitting (e.g., Glassman et al., 1988; Glassman, 1993; Balabanis et al., 2001), although findings to the contrary have also been reported (e.g., Hall et al., 1994; Ginsberg et al., 1995; Hitsman et al., 2003; El-Guebaly, Cathcart, Currie, et al., 2002; Hall et al., 2006). Similarly mixed evidence has been reported regarding abstinence-induced depression, with some studies supporting the existence of this phenomenon (e.g., Glassman, Helzer, Covey, et al., 1990; Covey, Glassman, and Stetner, 1990; 1997; Pomerleau et al., 2001) and others not (e.g., Tsoh et al., 2000; Prochaska et al., 2008).

The explanation for the over-inclusion of smokers among psychiatric patients is unclear (Bonsack et al., 2001), though a number of mechanisms have been proposed, including self-medication (Kasuga et al., 1991), lowered u-opioid receptor density (Scott et al., 2007; Contet, Kieffer, and Befort, 2004), reduction in brain levels of MAO-A and MAO-B (Fowler et al., 1996a; 1996b), and familial/genetic overlap (Kendler et al., 1993; Johnson, Rhee, Chase, and Breslau, 2004; Kalman, Morissette, and George, 2005). Alternatively, it has been proposed that smoking causes or increases vulnerability to depression (Breslau et al., 1998).

The tobacco standard of care (Fiore, Bailey, Cohen et al., 2000) stipulates that medical encounters should include asking about smoking, advising smokers to quit, and arranging for tobacco cessation treatment, yet this is rarely done in the context of psychiatric treatment (El-

Guebaly, Cathcart, Currie, Brown, and Gloster, 2002; Haug et al., 2005; Lasser et al., 2000). Even addiction psychiatrists tend to focus on alcohol, illicit drugs, and prescription drugs first rather than on smoking. To the extent that psychiatrists do offer smoking cessation treatment, it tends to focus on a small minority of psychiatric patients, typically those classically at risk for cardiovascular disease, obesity, hypertension, or diabetes mellitus (Himelhoch and Daumit, 2003). Barriers to the implementation of such programs include lack of training in treatment modalities appropriate for co-occurring diagnosis of mental health and addiction, concerns that smoking cessation will compromise the success of psychiatric treatment, absence of integrated treatment programs, and insufficient integration between psychotherapy and psychopharmacological treatment (Williams and Ziedonis, 2004). Despite the fact that nicotine dependence is "officially" a psychiatric diagnosis, nicotine—in stark contrast to alcohol, illicit drugs, and abused prescription drugs—has minimal behavioral toxicity. On the contrary, nicotine delivered via inhaled tobacco smoke ameliorates psychiatric symptomatology and its absence exacerbates them in dependent smokers. Smoking-related diseases take many years to develop; thus, smoking cessation does not have the same immediacy as other substance abuse problems.

A recent study by Haug, Hall, Prochaska, and colleagues (2005) challenged the implicit assumption that current psychiatric patients are not appropriate candidates for smoking cessation treatment. Participants were 154 psychiatric outpatients in treatment for depression who were recruited to participate in a smoking study involving repeated contact with a counselor. Those who, after counseling, agreed to set a quit date and participate in a trial of behavioral counseling and bupropion as an aid in smoking cessation, were classified as Acceptors (n=53; 34%); those who declined were classified as Refusers (n=101;66%). Among Acceptors, the number of days to treatment acceptance was significantly predicted by stage of change, with those in preparation entering smoking cessation treatment more quickly than contemplators or precontemplators. Accepting treatment was associated with current use of psychiatric medication and perceived success for quitting. Severity of depressive symptoms, duration of depression history, and history of recurrent depression were not related to treatment acceptance.

The goals of the current study were as follows: 1) to determine smoking prevalence of a consecutive sample of male and female outpatients seeking psychiatric treatment for depression and other mood disorders; 2) to determine whether male and female psychiatric patients who were current smokers differed with respect to demographic, clinical, and smoking related variables; and 3) to assess receptivity to a smoking cessation intervention among current smokers. Our sample, unlike that of Haug et al. (2005), consisted of all smokers seeking psychiatric treatment rather than individuals recruited to participate in a trial and motivated by counseling and the promise of bupropion. Since mood disorders are approximately twice as common in women (APA, 1994), we were particularly interested in identifying sex differences that might have implications for addressing and overcoming barriers to smoking cessation in this population.

Methods

Participants

Smoking variables were assessed in 146 consecutive outpatients at their intake interviews at the University of Michigan Depression Center. Of these, 17 were missing demographic data and were excluded from subsequent analyses. Of the remaining 129, 88 (69%) were female and 86% Caucasian. Sixty-five percent were currently taking psychotropic medications. The majority (78%) suffered from Major Depressive Disorder (MDD), including 53% with MDD only, 15% with Comorbid Depression and Anxiety, and 10% with Comorbid Depression and Dysthymia. The remaining 22% were diagnosed with Generalized Anxiety Disorder, Panic Disorder, and a variety of other psychiatric disorders (fewer than 5% each).

Measures

A brief smoking history questionnaire was administered to determine smoking status and current/past use of other tobacco products. Smoking rate (cigarettes/day), desire to quit (rated on a scale of 1 (low) to 10 (high), years smoked, and willingness to be approached about participating in a formal smoking cessation program were assessed in current smokers. Current smokers were also asked to complete the Fagerstrom Test for Nicotine Dependence (FTND; Heatherton, Kozlowski, Frecker, and Fagerstrom, 1991), a brief self-report instrument extensively used in the field of nicotine and tobacco research (Chabrol, Niezborala, Chastan, and de, 2005; John, Meyer, Rumpf, Schumann, and Hapke, 2005; Piper, McCarthy, and Baker, 2006; Weinberger et al., 2006). A score on the Heaviness of Smoking Index (HSI; Kozlowski, Porter, Orleans, Pope, and Heatherton, 1994), a 2-item subset of the FTND, was also derived. Former smokers were asked to indicate how many years they smoked and when they last smoked.

The Patient Health Questionnaire (PHQ; Kroenke, Spitzer, and Williams, 2001; Spitzer, Kroenke, and Williams, 1999) is a nine-item questionnaire used to assess the DSM-IV symptoms of depression. It has been successfully used by our group and others (Balestrieri et al., 2004; Bellantuono, Mazzi, Tansella, Rizzo, and Goldberg, 2002; Dwight-Johnson, Ell, and Lee, 2005; Langenecker et al., 2007; Rizzo, Piccinelli, Mazzi, Bellantuono, and Tansella, 2000). Eight of the nine items were administered prior to the intake session via voice recognition telephone. The self-harm item was removed as responses were not routinely monitored prior to the clinical intake session.

Procedure

Consecutive patients arriving for their first psychiatric appointment with a depression treatment team were included in the study. The Institutional Review Boards (IRB) approved the study protocol, where clinic data from patients was retrieved retrospectively and de-identified with an approved waiver of informed consent, consistent with the Declaration of

Helsinki. After greeting the participant, an assistant explained that the project was designed to expand clinical data available for tailoring treatment options. The participant then completed three cognitive screening measures reported elsewhere (Langenecker et al., 2007), along with the measures described above.

Data Analysis

Exploratory demographic analyses comparing smokers, former smokers, and never smokers were conducted using multivariate analysis of variance for continuous variables and chi square with nominal variables. Analyses based upon sex used t-tests for continuous variables and chi square analyses for nominal variables. Finally, t-tests and chi square comparisons were made within the current smoker group based upon willingness vs. unwillingness to be contacted about a smoking cessation program.

Results

Sample Characteristics

Current smokers constituted 33% of the sample. They had a mean FTND score of 3.3 (2.2), smoked 12.9 (8.6) cigarettes/day, and had been smoking for a mean of 15.1 (10.9) years. Former smokers constituted 12% of the sample. They had quit a mean of 13.5 (15.3) years ago, at the mean age of 28.9 (7.0). Never smokers constituted 55% of the sample.

Demographic and clinical variables for current smokers, former smokers, and never smokers are shown in Table 1. There was a significant difference between groups in years of formal education, with the never-smokers having more years of formal education compared with current smokers. There were no differences in other sample statistics between current, ex-, and never smokers.

Table 1. Sample characteristics

Variable	Current Smokers (n=42)	Former Smokers (n=16)	Never Smokers (n=71)	Statistics and p-value
Age	32.8 (11.2)	40.9 (13.9)	35.9 (10.8)	$F = 2.07$, $p = .06$
Education [a]	14.4 (2.8)	15.4 (2.3)	16.4 (2.6)	$F = 7.27$, $p = .001$
Sex (% female)	71.4%	56.3%	69.0%	$X = 1.28$, $p = .53$
Race (% White, n = 110)	81.6%	92.9%	87.9%	$X = 3.17$, $p = .79$
PHQ-8	14.4 (5.8)	12.2 (6.3)	13.5 (6.4)	$F=0.73$, $p = .48$
Age of Onset Psychiatric Illness	21.2 (11.5)	25.4 (14.5)	23.2 (10.5)	$F = 0.82$, $p = .44$

Table 1. (Continued)

Variable	Current Smokers (n=42)	Former Smokers (n=16)	Never Smokers (n=71)	*Statistics and p-value*
% Taking Psychotropic Medications	64.3%	75.0%	63.4%	$X = 0.80$, p = .67
Number of Family Members with Depression	1.3 (1.4)	1.3 (1.8)	1.5 (1.4)	$F = 0.27$, p = .76
Number of Family Members with any Psychiatric Illness	2.5 (1.9)	2.3 (2.1)	2.4 (1.7)	$F = 0.13$, p = .88

[a] Current Smokers had fewer years of formal education compared to Never Smokers (p = .0001).

Smoking Prevalence by Sex

Smoking prevalence in our sample (33%) was nearly double that of the surrounding community (18%). Smoking prevalence in female patients (34%) did not differ significantly from that in male patients (29%). When population parameters were entered for smokers from the surrounding county (16% in women vs. 20% in men), however, the chi-square analysis was significant, with an interaction between sex, smoking status, and location of sample ($X = 23.9$, P < .0001, WCPHD, 2000). The prevalence of smoking in the study sample, in comparison with smoking prevalence in the local catchment area, is shown in Figure 1.

The quit ratio (percent of eversmokers who have quit) was 23% in women and 37% in men (NS), yielding an overall quit ratio of 28%.

Sex Comparisons in Currently Smoking Psychiatric Patients

Comparisons between male and female current smokers in demographic, clinical, and smoking-related variables are shown in Table 2. Despite the relatively higher rate of smoking in females with psychiatric illness, none of the demographic, clinical, and smoking variables differed between men and women.

Characteristics of Currently Smoking Psychiatric Patients Receptive to a Smoking Cessation Intervention

Percent of current smokers willing to be contacted about a smoking cessation program did not differ by sex, being 33% for both men and women. Table 3 shows characteristics of willing and unwilling groups of current smokers.

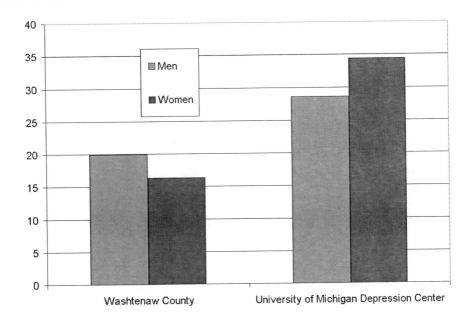

Figure 1. Smoking prevalence in the Study Sample vs. in the Local Population (County Public Health Department, Health Improvement Plan (HIP) survey, 2000).

Table 2. Comparisons between male and female current smokers in demographic, clinical, and smoking related variables

Variable	Women (n = 30)	Men (n = 12)	Statistics and p-value
Age	32.2 (10.7)	34.7 (12.9)	$t = 0.65, p = .52$
Education	14.1 (2.5)	15.1 (3.6)	$t = 0.98, p = .34$
PHQ-8	14.3 (4.8)	14.7 (8.2)	$t = 0.65, p = .52$
Age of Onset Psychiatric Illness	20.4 (10.5)	22.8 (14.0)	$t = 0.87, p = .37$
% Taking Psychotropic Medications	70%	50%	$X = 1.49, p = .22$
Number of Family Members with Depression	1.6 (1.4)	0.8 (1.1)	$t = -1.79, p = .08$
Number of Family Members with any Psychiatric Illness	2.8 (1.9)	1.9 (1.8)	$t = -1.35, p = .19$
Age of Onset Smoking	18.7 (4.8)	17.2 (2.8)	$t = -0.93, p = .36$
Total Cigarettes Smoked per day	11.7 (9.1)	15.5 (7.1)	$t = 1.29, p = .21$
Total Years Smoked	13.5 (10.3)	19.6 (12.1)	$t = 1.54, p = .13$
Fagerstrom Total score	2.9 (2.3)	4.6 (1.7)	$t = 1.78, p = .09$
Heaviness of Smoking Index	1.8 (1.5)	2.7 (1.3)	$t = 1.50, p = .14$
Desire to Quit	5.2 (3.3)	6.2 (3.8)	$t = 0.46, p = .98$

Table 3. Characteristics of current smokers receptive to a smoking cessation intervention

Variable	Willing (n = 14)	Unwilling (n = 28)	Statistics and p-value
Age	39.6 (11.8)	29.5 (9.4)	$t = -3.02$, $p = .004$
Education	14.9 (3.8)	14.2 (2.4)	$t = -0.72$, $p = .47$
Sex (% female)	71.4%	71.4^%	$X = 0.00$, $p = .99$
Race (% White)	84.6%	80.0%	$X = 2.02$, $p = .36$
PHQ-8	15.6 (6.4)	13.8 (5.6)	$t = -0.84$, $p = .41$
Age of Onset Psychiatric Illness	24.5 (14.9)	19.5 (9.4)	$t = -1.25$, $p = .22$
% Taking Psychotropic Medications	64.3%	64.3%	$X = 0.00$, $p = .99$
Number of Family Members with Depression	1.2 (1.8)	1.4 (1.2)	$t = 0.47$, $p = .64$
Number of Family Members with any Psychiatric Illness	2.3 (2.2)	2.6 (1.7)	$t = 0.40$, $p = .69$
Age of Onset Smoking	17.5 (4.7)	18.7 (4.2)	$t = 0.78$, $p = .44$
Total Cigarettes Smoked per day	14.9 (6.3)	11.7 (9.6)	$t = -1.13$, $p = .27$
Fagerstrom Total score	3.9 (2.2)	2.9 (2.2)	$t = -1.24$, $p = .23$
Total Years Smoked	22.4 (11.8)	11.3 (8.5)	$t = -3.33$, $p = .002$
Heaviness of Smoking Index	2.7 (1.5)	1.6 (1.3)	$t = -2.1$, $p = .04$
Desire to Quit	7.9 (2.5)	3.9 (3.1)	$t = -3.93$, $p = .001$

Current smokers willing to be contacted were significantly older, had smoked more years, scored higher on the HSI, and expressed a greater desire to quit smoking than those unwilling to be contacted.

Discussion

The smoking rate in the local community—probably because it includes several large post-secondary institutions—is lower than the national or state average (18% in 2000). Similar to findings in other community samples, the smoking rate among psychiatric patients at intake was nearly double that in the local community (33%), an effect that was particularly pronounced in women (CDC, 2001, 2004). It was also substantially higher than the national rate of the general adult population (20.8%, CDC, 2006), a difference not accounted for by differences in education levels, which were nearly identical in both our sample and that of the community. While smoking rate was elevated in both men and women patients, it was disproportionately high in the women, in contrast to the pattern of higher prevalence for men in the general population. This finding provides support in a clinical sample for the findings of Husky et al. (2008) and is consistent with the possibility that women are more likely than men to use smoking for anxiety/mood modulation (Grant et al., 2004). Further research will be needed to explain and address the apparent excess of smoking among women in treatment for depression. Addressing factors in psychiatric patients that lead to higher rate of smoking, particularly in women, may also be helpful in developing smoking cessation programs tailored to the special needs of this population.

Smokers in our sample had a quit ratio of 28% (23% for women vs. 37% for men, not significant in our small sample. This quit ratio is about half that observed in the general population, which is 56% in Michigan and ranges from 43-59% (mean 44.8) depending upon state (CDC, 2004). Close to half the patients in our sample had been regular smokers at some time in their lives, similar to that in the general population (CDC, 2005). These findings suggest that excess smoking in psychiatric patients may be due to failure to quit rather than excess initiation. The quit ratio in our sample differed substantially between women and men (23% vs. 37%); although this difference did not reach significance in our small and largely female sample, further research is warranted to determine whether women psychiatric patients who smoke are less likely to quit than their male counterparts.

About a third of current smokers expressed willingness to participate in a smoking cessation program. This figure replicates, in a more naturalistic sample, the findings of Haug et al. (2005). The percentage was the same for both men and women, indicating that women are as willing as men to consider smoking cessation treatment.

Regardless of sex, willingness to consider smoking cessation was particularly evident in patients who were older, had been smoking for significantly more years, scored higher on the Heaviness of Smoking Index, and smoked significantly more cigarettes per day. These characteristics are unsurprising and likely reflect recognition by these individuals that they are addicted to nicotine and have experienced some of the negative health effects of smoking. In contrast to the report of Haug et al. (2005), we found no association of medication status on willingness to consider smoking cessation treatment. There were also no main effects for symptoms of depression as measured by the PHQ-8.

Some caveats are in order. First, our sample was small and underpowered for detecting interaction effects based on sex. Second, it should be noted that these patients were not actually offered a smoking cessation program. Thus it is unclear if willingness to be contacted would translate into actual enrollment.

Nonetheless, our findings suggest that psychiatric programs should routinely screen for smoking, which is not typically done, and offer smoking cessation treatment to all smoking patients once clinical symptoms have stabilized. Methods for motivating younger, lighter smokers (for whom cessation should be easier and success rates higher) to accept treatment should be developed and tested.

Most of what is known about response to smoking cessation treatment in individuals with a psychiatric diagnosis has been derived from secondary analyses of smoking cessation trials, comparing outcomes for smokers with depression or a history of depression with those of smokers without such a history (Gutmann, 2004; Hitsman et al., 2003; Munafo et al., 2008). A few studies have also studied smokers recruited for a history of depression or abstinence-induced depression (Glassman, Covey, Stetner, and Rivelli, 2001; Kahler et al., 2003; Niaura et al., 1999; Niaura and Abrams, 2001; Pomerleau, Pomerleau, Marks, et al., 2003). Only a handful of reports have focused on patients actively in treatment for psychiatric illness—for example, Hall et al., 2006), who concluded that smoking cessation interventions used in the general population can be implemented in individuals in psychiatric treatment for depression.

Others (e.g., Pomerleau et al., 2001; El-Guebaly et al., 2002) have suggested that currently depressed smokers might profit more from enhanced programs designed to address their special needs. Our study, combined with that of Haug et al. (2005), should help to dispel the myth that psychiatric patients are "off limits" and open the doors for further research to resolve inconsistencies in the literature and optimize smoking cessation treatment in this population. Since smoking cessation trials in the general population have shown that women are more smoking-treatment-resistant than men (see Perkins, 2001, for a review of this issue), it will also be important to determine whether this trend extends to patients in concurrent treatment for psychiatric illness, and if so, to explore novel approaches to treating this particularly vulnerable population.

Acknowledgments

This research was supported in part by the Rachel Upjohn Clinical Scholars Award to Dr. Langenecker, and internal support from the Depression and Neuropsychology Sections of the Department of Psychiatry, University of Michigan Medical Center. Dr. Pomerleau's participation in this research was supported by DA17640 and DA14662. We thank the University of Michigan Depression Center for assistance with collection of retrospective data following IRB approval of waiver of informed consent. Cognitive data from 92 of these subjects are reported in a separate chapter in this edition (Wright and Langenecker). Thanks to Sara L. Wright, Ph.D. for comments and suggestions about this work. The aid of a number of students and assistants was invaluable in completing this project: Andrew Benway, Rachel Burns, Korey Cantrell, Luis Casenas, Stephen Crocker, Kristen Grabar, Leslie Guidotti, Najat M. Hamid, Jessica Layne, Lawrence S. Own, Rebecca Reiten, and Megan Shaheen.

References

Diagnostic and Statistical Manual for Mental Disorders (1994). 4th ed. Washington, D.C., U.S. American Psychiatric Association.

Balabanis, M.H., Shiffman, S., Winsko, L.A., Gwaltney, C., Waters, A., Paton, S.M. (2001). Depression and the dynamics of smoking: a national perspective. *JAMA-Journal of the American Medical Association, 264*,1541-1545.

Balestrieri, M., Carta, M.G., Leonetti, S., Sebastiani, G., Starace, F., and Bellantuono, C. (2004). Recognition of depression and appropriateness of antidepressant treatment in Italian primary care. *Social Psychiatry and Psychiatric Epidemiology, 39,* 171-176.

Bellantuono, C., Mazzi, M.A., Tansella, M., Rizzo, R., and Goldberg, D. (2002). The identification of depression and the coverage of antidepressant drug prescriptions in Italian general practice. *Journal of Affective Disorders, 72,* 53-59.

Bonsack, C., Camus, D., Kaufmann, N., Aubert, A., Besson, J., Baumann, P., Borgeat, F., Gillet, M., Eap, C. (2006). Prevalence of substance use in a Swiss psychiatric hospital: Interview reports and urine screening. *Addictive Behaviors, 31,* 1252-1258.

Breslau, N., Peterson, E.L., Schultz, L.R., Chilcoat, H.D., Andreski, P. (1998). Major depression and stages of smoking. A longitudinal investigation. *Archives of General Psychiatry, 55,*161-166.

Centers for Disease Control and Prevention. Cigarette Smoking Among Adults—United States, (2006). Morbidity and Mortality Weekly Report [serial online]. 2007;56(44):1157–1161 [cited 2007 Nov 8]. Available from: http://www.cdc.gov/mmwr /preview /mmwrhtml /mm5644a2.htm.

Centers for Disease Control and Prevention. State-Specific Prevalance of Cigarette Smoking and Quitting Among Adults-United States 2004. Morbidity and Mortality Weekly Report [serial online]. 2005; 54(44): 1124-1127 [cited 2008 Feb 6]. Available from:http:// www.cdc. gov/mmwr/preview/mmwrhtml/mm5444a3.htm.

Centers for Disease Control and Prevention, *The Health Consequences of Smoking: A Report of the Surgeon General* (2004). U.S. Department of Health and Human Services, National Center for Chronic Disease Prevention and Health Promotion, Office on Smoking and Health.Centers for Disease Control and Prevention, *Women and Smoking: A Report of the Surgeon General* (2001). U.S. Department of Health and Human Services, National Center for Chronic Disease Prevention and Health Promotion, Office on Smoking and Health.

Chabrol, H., Niezborala, M., Chastan, E., and de Leon. J. (2005). Comparison of the Heavy Smoking Index and of the Fagerstrom Test for Nicotine Dependence in a sample of 749 cigarette smokers. *Addictive Behaviors, 30,* 1474-1477.

Contet, C., Kieffer, B. L., and Befort, K. (2004). Mu opioid receptor: a gateway to drug addiction. *Current Opinion in Neurobiology, 14,* 370-378.

Covey, L., Glassman, A., and Stetner, F. (1990). Depression and depressive symptoms in smoking cessation. *Comprehensive Psychiatry, 31,* 350-354.

Covey, L., Glassman, A., and Stetner, F. (1997). Major depression following smoking cessation. *American Journal of Psychiatry, 154,* 263-265.

de Leon. J., Susce, M. T., Diaz, F. J., Rendon, D. M., and Velasquez, D. M. (2005). Variables associated with alcohol, drug, and daily smoking cessation in patients with severe mental illnesses. *Journal of Clinical Psychiatry, 66,* 1447-1455.

Dwight-Johnson, M., Ell, K., and Lee, P. J. (2005). Can collaborative care address the needs of low-income Latinas with comorbid depression and cancer? Results from a randomized pilot study. *Psychosomatics, 46,* 224-232.

El-Guebaly, N., Cathcart, J., Currie, S., Brown, D., and Gloster, S. (2002). Smoking cessation approaches for persons with mental illness or addictive disorders. *Psychiatric Services, 53,* 1166-1170.

Fiore, M.C., Bailey, W.C., Cohen, S.J., et al. (2000). A clinical practice guideline for treating tobacco use and dependence - A US Public Health Service report. *JAMA-Journal of the American Medical Association, 283,* 3244-3254.

Fowler, J.S., Volkow, N.D., Wang, G.J., Pappas, N., Logan, J., Shea, C., et al. (1996a) Brain monoamine oxidase A inhibition in cigarette smokers. *Proceedings of the National Academy of Sciences, 93,*14065-14069.

Fowler, J.S., Volkow, N.D., Wang, G.J., Pappas, N., Logan, J., McGregor R., et al. (1996b). Inhibition of monoamine oxidase B in brains of smokers. *Nature 379,* 773-776.

Ginsberg, D., Hall, S.M., Reus, V.I., and Muñoz, R.F. (1995) Mood and depression diagnosis in smoking cessation *Experimental and Clinical Psychopharmacology, 3,* 389-395.

Glassman, A.H. (1993). Cigarette smoking: implications for psychiatric illness. *American Journal of Psychiatry, 150,* 546-553.

Glassman, A.H., Covey, L.S, Stetner, F., and Rivelli, S. (2001). Smoking cessation and the course of major depression: a follow-up study. *The Lancet, 357,* 1929-1932.

Glassman, A.H., Helzer, J.E., Covey, L.S., Cottler, L.B., Stetner, F., Tipp J.E., et al. (1990). Smoking, smoking cessation, and major depression. *JAMA-Journal of the American Medical Association, 264,*1546-1549.

Glassman, A.H., Stetner, F., Walsh T., Raizman, P.S., Fleiss, J.L., Cooper, T.B., et al. (1988). Heavy smokers, smoking cessation, and clonidine: Results of a double-blind, randomized trial. *JAMA-Journal of the American Medical Association, 259,* 2863-2866.

Grant, B.F., Hasin, D.S., Chou, S.P., et al. (2004). Nicotine dependence and psychiatric disorders in the United States: results from the national epidemiologic survey on alcohol and related conditions. *Archives of General Psychiatry, 61,* 1107-1115.

Gutmann, L.B. (2004). Outcome research methodology of smoking cessation trials (1994-1998). *Addictive Behaviors, 29*(3), 441.

Hall, S.M., Tsoh, J.Y., Prochaska, J.J., Eisendrath, S., Rossi, J.S., Redding, C.A., et al. (2006). Treatment for cigarette smoking among depressed mental health outpatients: A randomized clinical trial. *American Journal of Public Health, 96,* 1808-1824.

Haug, N.A., Hall, S.M., Prochaska, J.J., et al. (2005). Acceptance of nicotine dependence treatment among currently depressed smokers. *Nicotine and Tobacco Research, 7,* 217-224.

Heatherton, T.F., Kozlowski, L.T., Frecker, R.C., and Fagerstrom, K.O. (1991). The Fagerstrom Test for Nicotine Dependence - A Revision of the Fagerstrom Tolerance Questionnaire. *British Journal of Addiction, 86,* 1119-1127.

Himelhoch, S., and Daumit, G. (2003). To whom do psychiatrists offer smoking-cessation counseling? *American Journal of Psychiatry, 160 (12),* 2228-2230.

Hitsman B, Borrelli B, McChargue DE, Spring B, Niaura R. (2003). History of depression and smoking cessation outcome: a meta-analysis. *Journal of Consulting and Clinical Psycholology, 71(4),* 657-663.

Husky, M.M., Mazure, C.M., Paliwal, P., and McKee, S.A. (2008). Gender differences in the comorbidity of smoking behavior and major depression. *Drug and Alcohol Dependendence. 93,*176-179. [Epub ahead of print].

John, U., Meyer, C., Rumpf, H.J., Schumann, A., and Hapke, U. (2005). Consistency or change in nicotine dependence according to the Fagerstrom Test for Nicotine Dependence over three years in a population sample. *Journal of Addiction and Disease, 24,* 85-100.

Johnson, E.O., Rhee, S.H., Chase, G.A., and Breslau, N. (2004). Comorbidity of depression with levels of smoking: an exploration of the shared familial risk hypothesis. *Nicotine and Tobacco Research, 6,* 1029-1038.

Kahler, C.W., Brown, R.A., Stron, D.R., Loyd-Richardson, E.E., and Niaura, R. (2003). History of major depressive disorder among smokers in cessation treatment: Associations with dysfunctional attitudes and coping. *Addictive Behaviors, 28,* 1033-1047.

Kalman, D., Morissette, S.B., and George, T.P. (2005). Co-morbidity of smoking in patients with psychiatric and substance use disorders. *American .Journal of Addiction, 14,* 106-123.

Kasuga, H., Katsuki, H., Miyagi, O., Mori, W., Takayama, S., and Yanagita, T. (1991). Smoking and health: a review prepared by the Smoking and Health Subcommittee of the Tobacco Industries Council, a council formed by the Minister of Finance of Japan. *International Journal of Addiction, 26,* 423-440.

Kendler, K.S., Neale, M.C., MacLean, C.L. Heath, A.C., Eaves, L.J., and Kessler, R.C. (1993). Smoking and major depression: A causal analysis. *Archives of General Psychiatry, 50,* 36-43.

Kozlowski, L.T., Porter, C.Q., Orleans, C.T., Pope, M.A., and Heatherton, T. (1994). Predicting smoking cessation with self-reported measures of nicotine dependence: FTQ, FTND, and HSI. *Drug and Alcohol Dependence, 34,* 211-216.

Kroenke, K., Spitzer, R.L., and Williams, J.B.W. (2001). The PHQ-9: validity of a brief depression severity measure. *Journal of General Internal Medicine, 16,* 606-613.

Langenecker, S.A., Caveney, A.F., Young, E.A., Giordani, B., Nielson, K.A., Rapport, L.J. et al. (2007). The psychometric properties and sensitivity of a brief computer-based cognitive screening battery in a depression clinic. *Psychiatric Research, 152 (2-3)*: 143-154.

Lasser, K., Boyd, J.W., Woolhandler, S., Himmelstein, D.U., McCormick, D., and Bor, D.H. (2000). Smoking and mental illness – A population-based prevalence study. *JAMA-Journal of the American Medical Association, 284,* 2606-2610.

Munafo, M.R., Hitsman, B., Rende, R., Metcalfe, C., Niaura, R. (2008). Effects of progression to cigarette smoking on depressed mood in adolescents: evidence from the National Longitudinal Study of Adolescent Health, *Addiction, 103,* 162-171.

Niaura R., Britt, D.M., Borrelli, B., Shadel, W.G., Abrams, D.B., and Goldstein, M.G. (1999). History and symptoms of depression among smokers during a self-initiated quit attempt. *Nicotine and Tobacco Research, 1,* 251-257.

Niaura, R., Abrams, D.B. (2001). Stopping smoking: a hazard for people with a history of major depression? *The Lancet, 357,* 1900-1901.

Perkins K.A. (2001). Smoking cessation in women. Special considerations. *CNS Drugs 15,* 391-411.

Piper, M.E., McCarthy, D.E., and Baker, T.B. (2006). Assessing tobacco dependence: a guide to measure evaluation and selection. *Nicotine and Tobacco Research, 8,* 339-351.

Pomerleau, C.S., Namenek Brouwer, R.J., and Pomerleau, O.F. (2001). Emergence of depression during early abstinence in depressed and non-depressed women smokers. *Journal of Addictive Diseases, 20,* 73-80.

Pomerleau, O.F., Pomerleau, C.S., Marks, J.L., Snedecor, S.M., Mehringer, A.M., Namenek Brouwer, R.J., et al. (2003). Prolonged nicotine patch use in quitters with past abstinence-induced depressed mood. *Journal of Substance Abuse Treatment, 24,* 13-18.

Prochaska JJ, Hall SM, Tsoh JY, Eisendrath S, Rossi JS, Redding CA, Rosen AB, Meisner M, Humfleet GL, Gorecki JA (2008) Treating tobacco dependence in clinically depressed smokers: Effect of smoking cessation on mental health fFunctioning. *American Journal of Public Health.* [Epub ahead of print].

Rizzo, R., Piccinelli, M., Mazzi, M.A., Bellantuono, C., and Tansella, M. (2000). The Personal Health Questionnaire: a new screening instrument for detection of ICD-10 depressive disorders in primary care. *Psychological Medicine, 30,* 831-840.

Scott, D.J., Domino, E.F., Heitzeg, M.M., Koeppe, R.A., Ni, L., Guthrie, S., Zubieta, JK. (2007). Smoking modulation of *u*-Opioid and Dopamine D2 Receptor Mediated Neurotransmission in Humans. *Neuropsychopharmacology. 32*(2):450-7

Spitzer, R.L., Kroenke, K., and Williams, J.B.W. (1999). Validation and utility of a self-report version of PRIME-MD – The PHQ primary care study. *JAMA-Journal of the American Medical Association, 282,* 1737-1744.

Tsoh, J.Y., Humfleet, G.L., Muñoz, R.F., Reus, V.I., Hartz, D.T., and Hall, S.M.(2000). Development of major depression after treatment for smoking cessation. A*merican Journal of Psychiatry,157,* 368-374.

Washtenaw County Public Health Department, Health Improvement Plan (HIP) 2000 survey. http://www.ewashtenaw.org/government/departments/public_health/hip/PPT%20Present ations/tobaccousehipdata.ppt#3

Weinberger, A.H., Reutenauer, E.L., Allen, T.M., Termine, A., Vessicchio, J.C., Sacco, K.A. et al. (2006) Reliability of the Fagerstrom Test for Nicotine Dependence, Minnesota Nicotine Withdrawal Scale, and Tiffany Questionnaire for Smoking Urges in Smokers with and without Schizophrenia. *Drug and Alcohol Dependence, 86(2-3),* 278-282.

Williams, J.M., and Ziedonis, D. (2004). Addressing tobacco among individuals with a mental illness or an addiction. *Addictive Behaviors, 29,* 1067-1083.

In: Women and Depression
Editors: Paula Hernandez and Sara Alonso

ISBN 978-1-60456-647-5
© 2009 Nova Science Publishers, Inc.

Chapter 1

Dyslexia, Depression and Gender: Research Studies

Neil Alexander-Passe[1]
School of Psychology, ACS, London South Bank University, London, UK

Abstract

Dyslexia is a life-long condition (without a known cure), affecting approximately 10-15% of the population. It is medical in origin but educational in treatment. It affects the ability to communicate (e.g. writing, spelling), compute mathematical concepts (e.g. algebra) and other aspects of life which require using short-term memory and co-ordination.

Those with dyslexia who are not assessed/treated in early childhood are highly susceptible to emotional manifestations due to low self-esteem and low perceived ability caused by peers, parents and educators who misread their learning difficulties for laziness and lack of motivation. In fact ignoring or misreading a child's learning disability is a form of abuse which reaches far into today's educational systems. Gender has yet to be a major focus in the study of dyslexia, however there is growing evidence that it is an important factor in understanding why some dyslexics are resilient and others are affected emotionally.

There are three research projects included in this chapter. These aim to build personality profiles for dyslexic males and females according to the severity of their dyslexia. Depression and withdrawal emerge as key personality traits amongst these groups. A second study using this same data investigates profiles to successful (degree educated) dyslexics and how personality differences emerge amongst those who are diagnosed and undiagnosed. Diagnosis, gaining remedial help or support, meant that such individuals were more optimistic and did not doubt past events, compared to those who were undiagnosed and went through life thinking something was wrong but were unable to pinpoint the problem. It may also be the case that their coping strategies were

---

1 neil.alexander-passe@inghams.co.uk.

successful enough to mean that their difficulties were not highlighted, however the emotional cost was great.

Lastly there was an interview study for dyslexics who were also diagnosed with clinical depression. Strong gender differences were identified with females using more withdrawal and self-blame than males who tend to use helplessness. Their life stories indicate neglect by teachers and parents which lead them to use perfectionism as a defence mechanism. Their difficulties led a number of them to contemplate suicide as there were no other perceived options available to them to deal with the anxiety from having an invisible learning disorder.

Keywords: *Dyslexia, Depression, Gender, Personality, Success, Degree*

Dyslexia

What is Dyslexia?

Dyslexia is a widespread condition, with an estimated frequency of one dyslexic child in each mainstream school classroom (Miles, 1994). Professor Berlin of Stuttgart (1872) coined the term 'dyslexia', based on the case histories of adults who could read only three to five words, but were of high intelligence. Use of the term has continued to this day, with dyslexia likened to conditions with neurological abnormalities. Initially, it was thought to be purely an acquired condition from accidental brain damage, until Kussmaul (1878) found developmental cases of word blindness. Orton (1937) first noted the main aspects of developmental dyslexia as pronounced reversals (b/d, p/q, on/no and was/saw), orientation difficulties/strong left-handedness and conflicting lateral preference, which forms the basis for many definitions (see Thomson, 1996; Miles, 1994). This study uses the definition from the World Federation of Neurology (1968), which defines dyslexia as 'a disorder manifested by difficulty in learning to read despite conventional instruction, adequate intelligence and socio-cultural opportunity'.

In the UK and many countries in Europe, terms such as 'dyslexia' or 'Specific Learning Disabilities (SpLD)' are used, whilst worldwide and especially in the US, 'Learning Disabled (LD)' and 'Reading Difficulties (RD)' are commonly used terms. 'Dyslexia' and 'SpLD' are more specifically concerned with difficulties that affect most situations (not just reading, e.g., co-ordination and balance) with neurological and phonological epidemiology. Reviews on dyslexia can be found in Thomson (1995) and Miles (1994).

Dyslexia is a negative disorder that affects many life skills (reading, writing, arithmetic) as well as balance and co-ordination, with Miles (1994, p. 189) suggesting that dyslexics show 'an unusual balance of skills'. Individuals with dyslexia can be affected emotionally by being unable to learn as well as their peers, commonly resulting in low self-image, low self-concept and even depression (Alexander-Passe 2004a, b, 2006, 2007; Riddick, 1996; Edwards, 1994; Ryan, 1994). For more than a decade, research has been carried out to identify positive attributes of this disorder; these investigations began with biographical and neurological studies. West (1991) located famous and influential individuals who had school learning difficulties yet had found alternative ways of learning and succeeding in life (e.g.,

Albert Einstein, Leonardo da Vinci), making correlations between these factors and dyslexia, and creativity. Thus, public perception of creativity amongst dyslexics has grown (e.g., 712,000 hits on Google). Since West, the use of famous names (e.g., Charles Schwab, Richard Branson, Tom Cruise, Richard Rogers and so on.) has become widespread (Being Dyslexic 2006; Roehampton University, 2006; British Dyslexia Association, 2006; British Broadcasting Corporation, 2006; International Dyslexia Association, 2006; General Communication Headquarters, 2006, McLaughlin, Fitzgibbon and Young, 1994) to illustrate the career heights that dyslexics can reach. However, this could be misleading and could give false hopes to parents, as a high proportion of dyslexics leave full-time education with few or no qualifications (Grant, 2001)

Neurological investigations started by Geschwind and Galaburda (1985) noting clinical and post-mortem studies indicated atypical symmetrical brains, suggesting dyslexics have larger right (visual processing) brains; however, this conclusion was based on a very small sample of brains. Galaburda (1989) also suggests an 'alternative wiring hypothesis' that some abilities may be strengthened at the expense of others in the re-organisation in the brains of dyslexics. The classic measurement of dyslexia uses the WISC-R (Wechsler, 1974) measures, and the ACID profile (Thomson, 1996) indicates dyslexics show superior performance than verbal skills, in WISC-R subscales. Thus, investigations have since been made into the possibility of superior visual-spatial abilities amongst dyslexics, with many correlating such skills to creativity (Padgett and Steffert, 1999; Wolff and Lundberg, 2002).

Nicolson and Fawcett (1993) note that a skill that would take a normal child 400hrs to develop and learn would take a dyslexic child 20 times longer to achieve. It is interesting that Fawcett and Nicolson (1994, 1996) found in their study that 17yr old dyslexics achieved no better performance in a range of literacy skills than their 8yr old controls (in tests of psychometric, phonological and working memory, balance, motor skills and speed of processing). Fawcett (1995, p. 27) gave an analogy of driving through a foreign country, one can do it but at the expense of constant vigilance and an unacceptable cost in resources. Thus dyslexics can go through mainstream schools without high literacy skills but the emotional cost can be unacceptably high.

Dyslexia and Children's Lives

School

When life goes wrong for a dyslexic at school, it has a knock-on affect to life after school, thus the influence of school is profound (Scott 2004, p.53). At school there are two curriculums: academic and social, failure in either or both will have lifelong effects on the individual and success and can be powerful predictors of later outcomes as intelligence is commonly correlated to academic achievement (Sylva, 1994). Whether you choose to or not in the UK, children must legally attend school for at least ten years and parents are legally required to send them to a recognised institution. Each year at school can be unpredictable and is highly complex for both parents and children e.g. homework, class timetables etc. Integration with others (teachers and peers) can be fraught with danger with bad/good experiences and friendships having lasting impressions.

Several commentators (Fawcett, 1995; Edwards, 1994, Riddick, 1996) view schools as legalised abusive institutions, where children are kept against their will and subjected to the will of teachers. Whilst in the majority of cases children and parents are accepting of such a regime, it does not suit all children and parents, with many choosing to transfer out to the private sector. However, in the private sector more abuse may exist to motivate pupils, with some private school requiring parents to sign forms to permit canning and other abuses, in the name of school ethos and learning.

Scott (2004, p.54) notes 'all dyslexic children – and this is not a loose phase – experience some form of damage from school'. Like all children, some excel in the school environment and others do not. In the case of dyslexics, larger proportions do not excel resulting in high levels of stress and anxiety (and will be discussed later). Dyslexics find school an unpredictable battleground in which they are unskilled to exist. Scott (2004, p.55) notes that 'for the vast majority of dyslexic children and adults, school has been a place of psychological and often physical torture…School for them was destructive and humiliating, nasty, degrading experience, sometimes of raw brutality, of which modern society should be deeply ashamed [of]', comments that others echo (Fawcett, 1995; Edwards, 1994, Riddick, 1996).

Dyslexics fail at school in numerous ways: failure to make friends, failure in literacy, failure to be attractive (to their peers as friends and teachers as receptive to help) and failure to be normal. As school promotes both a social and academic curriculum, failing to make friends and failure to gain literacy are two basic stepping stones needed for development. Due to their learning difficulties they do not come across to others as normal e.g. clumsy and not knowing their left and right which affects play with others.

At school, failure in literacy has huge knock-on effects for the whole academic curriculum and with all subjects. Failing to read and write is a very public failure (Scott, 2004) and begins to propagate the idea that dyslexics are abnormal. This sets off a chain reaction that puts the child in a defensive state of mind and makes them fearful of all learning situations. School becomes a dangerous place and sticking out in class continues to the playground where teasing begins and can lead to unhealthy bullying. Children are very quick to pick-up who is the brightest and dumbest in the class and until a dyslexia diagnosis is made the child begins to self-doubt and believe they are stupid, thinking 'if everyone says I'm slow/stupid I must be'. Teachers prefer easy children, children who do not create problems for them, as this confirms their effectiveness as teachers

Congdon (1995, p. 91) notes the reactions to failure at school 'can vary. Some children lose interest and adopt negative and avoidance attitudes. Others may try harder, spurred on by their teacher and parents, only to discover that the greater effort does not produce the longed for results'. Feelings of disillusionment and mystification sets in, as up to this point the child has been told he was clever by his parents which he believed until now, thus he is now confused and develops self-doubts.

Teacher's Denial of Dyslexia and Teacher Training

Riddick (1996, p. 202) suggests whilst 'dyslexia is physically visible you have to know what it is before you can clearly see it. This explains why it is possible for teachers to claim that they have been teaching for 30 years without coming across a child with dyslexia. As they know nothing about dyslexia they never see a child with dyslexia'. Supporting such a view is Burden (2005, p. 42) noting the typical experiences of children in mainstream schools, with one boy as remarked by his tutor, '[he] said I was nowhere near dyslexic, I was just dumb. So we had about 10 more tests and everyone else said I was dumb. Then I went up to the dyslexia [institute] place in Bristol and they said 'how can anybody miss it''. One could ask, is this teacher denial or just a lack of knowledge on the part of the teacher?

Teachers of varying ages and experiences teach in mainstream schools, due to when and where they were trained and their experiences of children of different abilities. Many young teachers see it's the role of the Special Educational Needs Co-ordinator (SENCO) as used in the UK, to screen, refer and teach children with learning difficulties and avoid dealing with them themselves. Until 2000 in the UK, teacher training made the study of dyslexia optional, resulting in teachers having little or no knowledge about dyslexia (key traits and the best teaching methods). Seeman (2002) found that UK teacher courses for Special Educational Needs still taught that dyslexics have low intelligence, did not cover behavioural problems as a reaction to dyslexia and were packaged together with brain damaged children. Where taught, teachers still failed to accept the existence of dyslexia, preferring to label their dyslexic pupils as 'disruptive' or just 'dim' (Pumphrey and Reason, 1991). Riddick (1996) found that many teachers were 'mystified' by the symptoms of dyslexia and regretted not doing enough for such pupils in hindsight. Whilst Ryan (2004) suggests it is hard to see how hard a dyslexic child is working, teachers commonly perceive dyslexics as 'lazy', 'not trying hard enough', with Burden (2005, p. 43) remarking that commonly dyslexic children are told by their teachers 'you're not trying hard enough'.

Fawcett (2005, p. 13) notes 'this failure to understand dyslexia is not the fault of the teacher, but can be attributed to failure to train teachers adequately in the recognition of dyslexia'. Of course some teachers are highly trained and have taken a personal interest in understanding such conditions, whilst others in spite of training in the warning signs, tend to underestimate the incidence of dyslexia and are unprepared to work with the problem if they ever come across it. Whilst there are many developmental disorders faced in mainstream schools (ADHD, autism etc), dyslexia is by far the most common in western countries (Fawcett, 1995; Jorm, Share, MacLean and Matthews 1986).

Saunders (1995, p. 101) notes that 'many untrained teachers continue to pound away with inappropriate' teaching methods and the dyslexic child has begun to experience what I term as academic abuse'. Edwards (1994) found high frequencies of abuse by teachers amongst her dyslexic sample, whilst such abuse is unjustifiable, it may come from their frustration at teaching children who are 'broken learning machines' (as suggested by Hales, 1994) and who makes them feel ineffective and useless as a teacher.

Miles and Varma (1995) notes that they frequently meet the objection that there is no space in an already crowded teacher-training syllabus to add anything further about dyslexia, but they question the government's sense of priorities.

Osmond (1993, p. 1) indicates that teachers typically dismiss dyslexia early on 'it's far too early to tell. He's a good natured child, very willing and co-operative. We're sure he'll come on. Give him time'. Many parents listen to this and allow their children to waste many additional years of school and learn that failure at school is a way of life. However, Riddick (1996, p. 70) suggests that the vast majority of parents in her study, knew at an early stage that something wasn't right with their child, however they were frequently dismissed by teachers as being over-protective and too biased to make such an opinion, noting 'I just knew something was wrong, but I didn't know what it was', however when faced by teachers who were believed as the experts, commonly parents back down to what they believed was superior knowledge.

Teacher's Expectations

Rosenthal and Jacobson (1968) suggests that teachers treat children expected to do well differently to those that are not expected to do well. The study told teachers that two groups of randomly chosen children had high and low IQ. The results found that the randomly selected children (expected to succeed) grew significantly in IQ over the following 12 months, teachers gave this group more positive attention. Hargreaves (1972) reviewing the results of Rosenthal and Jacobson (1968) suggested that teachers expectations play a large part in how children gain success, even if it is based on inaccurate information. Of course the opposite must also be true, that children expected to fail, commonly do, a form of self-efficiency. Good and Brophy (1982) reviewing all the evidence at that time on teacher expectations concluded that teachers tended to consistently treat high and low perceived achieving pupils differently, with low perceived achieving students being: chosen less often to answer questions even when they volunteered to answer; given less time to answer questions; were seated further away from the teacher; and verbal feedback tended to be more harsh and critical than those perceived to be high achievers who were given more praise. Burns (1982) suggests to avoid these teachers should: interact evenly with all pupils; talk to all their pupils; realistically praise all children and match tasks to individual's abilities.

More importantly 'these expectations can determine the child's level of achievement by confining his learning opportunities to those available in a particular class' (Cohen and Manion, 1995, p. 268). Teachers' expectations of pupils can impact on whether they are placed in a high or low ability set, and thus pupils will achieve to the expectations of his class and peers. It was found that children placed in a low ability-grouped classroom are unlikely to reach their true potential, as the teacher doubts this potential and consequently their achievement and motivation will be affected.

Good and Brophy (1974) similarly suggest that self-fulfilling prophecies play a part in the interactions of teachers and children in the classroom. Cohen and Manion (1995) note that it is natural for teachers to form different attitudes and expectations of their pupils, but these need to be assessed routinely. If not, then the child may get caught in a 'vicious circle of failure' (p. 269).

Teachers make snap judgements about the abilities of their pupils; in many cases (Hargreaves et al., 1975 and Cooper, 1993) these are made on the basis of feedback from other teachers and on the knowledge of the child's parents and siblings.

Scott (2004, p. 72) suggests that 'whilst school is the malign incubator of the dyslexic child's problems, it is the relationship with teachers and peers that provide the nourishment and oxygen for problems. If a dyslexic child had a productive, warm and supportive relationship with a teacher and was valued, played with….he would cope really quite well with his literacy problems. He would also avoid most of the worst long-term effects of his dyslexia….unfortunately; it is the norm that a dyslexic child has significant problems with both teachers and peers at school. These problems, more so than his dyslexia, make him unhappy and store up relationship problems for the future. In fact, it is my position that it is the relationship problems associated with dyslexia – rather than the literacy problems – that cause most of the damage to his psychological functioning'.

It is the teacher that makes the difference between a dyslexic child that learns and enjoys school or one that hates each moment in school and is unhappy. Scott (2004) notes this is can be the difference between a life enjoyed and a life hated, and that dyslexics that succeed in life usually have one teacher which has made the most impact in their lives. She goes on to suggest that teachers are all powerful in four significant ways: the class, the expectation of hope, teaching as power and the power of expectation.

Thomson (1995, p. 37) notes an informed teacher could mitigate the dyslexic's difficulties in many ways: placing him in the front row of the class, repeating instructions, buddying him up with another child who could prompt him where necessary, give extra time without interruption from others to answer questions. But for this to happen the teacher must recognise the learning problem, which is subject to the initial teacher training provided. Thomson also notes that 'even when the teacher is sympathetic and helpful, the dyslexic child may be humiliated by the modified programme devised for him' depending on how it is presented to his class peers (p. 37)

Van den Oord and Rispen (1999) found the psychosocial adjustment of children was more affected by the structure of the class, under the direct control of one teacher, than the ethos of the whole school. Teachers regulate the rules, strictness, conveys praise and criticism and favouritism for a class of young minds, more so in the primary school as one teacher teaches most if not all subjects for that academic year. de Pear (1997, p.19) found that most children expressed a strong need to be accepted and to gain positive attention from their teacher, even more remarkably, this was despite 'few had experienced any real feeling of being seen as competent and responsible by their teacher'. Some teachers are attracted to the power involved in teaching a group of children. This power can be highly dangerous to the child with learning difficulties, as the teacher's power to ridicule is immense and can mean that the child's peers carry this to the playground in the form of bullying. This maybe explained by research suggesting that 75% of teachers were bullied when they were at school (Tattum, 1993); they feel the need to carry on the pain. Teachers can give children either the expectation of hope or the expectation of failure, with high expectations leading to high achievement and self-esteem according to Burns (1979).

Scott (2004), Seeman (2002) and Riddick (1996) found some teachers were found to humiliate dyslexics on a daily basis, sometimes unconsciously, by making them read out loud in class, putting them on slow tables, giving them inappropriate books for their age (whilst it may be appropriate for their reading age) and sometimes just drawing attention to their inadequacies. Osmond (1994, p. 25) exemplifies this with one dyslexic child's experience 'Paul was almost ten years old when I found him crying over a spelling list. He explained that words seemed to move around when he tried to read, that he couldn't copy anything because he was unable to retain the order of the letters in his mind, and that he was being told to look up spellings in the dictionary but found it impossible'.

Stanovich (1986) and Burden (2005) point to the knock-on effect that learning difficulties at school with gaining literacy/numeracy has. They call it the 'Matthew Effect' for the biblical quote 'to those who hath shall be given; from those who hath not shall be taken away'. They note that 'early difficulties at school in establishing the basic skills of literacy and/or numeracy are likely to have a cumulative effect in making it extremely difficult for such children to ever catch up (Stanovich, 1986)

Dyslexic children can be problematic in class, as they are unable to remember tasks and become very needy in very full mainstream classes, the lack of progress in class can make teachers feel failure and they therefore distance themselves from more failure. Teacher's lack of training in identifying a reason for the child's failure is unhelpful and it is much easier to label children lazy and immature than to get to the bottom of any learning problem.

From the moment the dyslexic child enters school, they often are a puzzle to their teachers. Whilst they show high intelligence orally they have problems showing such intelligence when reading or transferring ideas to paper. As teachers hold literacy in such high esteem they begin to reduce their expectations of such children due to their failure in basic building blocks of learning. Thomson (1995, p. 41) notes the reduction of expectations means the dyslexic child is not stretched and that low expectations can lead to low performance. Yet as Thomson notes, these children know they are not lazy or unintelligent, with the resulting performance at high contrast to potential can lead to stress. Their parents are also puzzled which can lead to stress from parents that their child is lazy or not working hard enough. Comparison to non-dyslexic siblings can increase the stress as such comparison is unfair and unproductive. It only reinforces the concept that they are different and a 'broken learning machine' (Hales, 1994).

Edwards (1994, p. 125) notes 'many teachers and parents will be shocked, as I was, by the severity, extent and multiplicity of unpleasant experiences which [dyslexic] pupils in my study had undergone. One obviously did not expect pupils with literacy problems to describe their past school lives in glowing terms, but the skeletons which emerged from the school cupboards of childhood memory were indeed grim and frequently similar across the group'.

Identification of Dyslexia/Special Educational Needs (SEN)

Bentote (2001) investigated UK's Hampshire Local Education Authority's screening and intervention for dyslexia, which followed 360 infant and primary schools over a three-year period and screened children in their first term of school with three different methodologies. These were: Dyslexia Early Screening Test-DEST (Fawcett, Pickering and Nicolson, 1992), Cognitive Profiling System-CoPS1 (Singleton, 1995), and asking teachers which children they thought likely to experience literacy difficulties in the near future. In total, CoPS identified 15.7% of the at risk pupils, DEST identified 20.9% of pupils and teachers identified 37% of the pupils. Despite the teachers identifying more pupils, both the DEST and CoPS 'identified pupils that the teachers had not identified'. It was hoped by the local educational authority that the teachers could identify all 'at risk' pupils themselves without the need for any additional screening tool, but this study suggests otherwise. Arrangements for funding additional provision to meet children's SEN in the early years sector remain incoherent and piecemeal with the conclusion that the older a child is, the more likely he or she is to have a statement (Audit Commission, 2002a, b).

Perceptions of Normal

All children when entering school or nursery perceive themselves as normal, asking 'who am I? (Burden, 2005, p. 5). They have had many years of encouragement by parents from activities on a one to one basis, on entering school they begin to compare themselves to others as others compare themselves to them. They enter school thinking the world is a happy place and very quickly learn that there are winners and losers in life, children who can do things and children who can't. Life changes from a safe and friendly environment to one that they must be on edge to defend themselves not only in classroom, but in the playground as well. In primary and early secondary school, all children wish to be the same and not stick out, as experienced dyslexia teachers noted 'dyslexic children – all children – hate to fail, hate to be different, hate to be singled out as having special needs'.

The undiagnosed dyslexic child sticks out easily as different and their segregation to the slow table or the remedial class does not help the situation. As the world of comparison has put them on edge, due to failure they become hypersensitive to criticism, which is perceived to be a logical reaction to frequent failure, more frequent than their peers (as found by Edwards, 1994 and Riddick, 1996). Cutting and Dunn (2002, p. 856) found 'five year olds:...were sensitive to criticism; they reacted significantly more negatively in response to criticised failure than in response to non-criticised failure'. Such a reaction causes the production of anxiety and lower self-esteem, indicating how fast school failure affects children.

Erikson (1959) notes that our early childhood experiences play a significant part in our attitudes towards ourselves and our place in the world. This shaping is called self-concept and is easily damaged. Rogers (1951, p. 138) discusses self-concept to be 'composed of such elements of the perceptions of one's characteristics and abilities: the perceptions and concepts of the self in relation to others and to the environments; the value qualities which are perceived as associated with experiences and objects; and the goals and ideas which are perceived as having positive or negative valence'. Or as Burns suggests (1982, p. 7) 'self-concept is best regarded as a dynamic complex of attitudes held towards themselves by each person' and has two parts: self-image and self-evaluation. However, Hansford and Hattie (1982) point out that self-concept, self-image and self-esteem are often used interchangeably without adequate definitions and applied without valid and reliable measurement techniques. This comes in part from the hypothesis that self-concept is based on a highly subjective set of constructed attributes and feelings which take on meaning for the individual through evaluation compared to their particular society (Burns, 1982), as also found with self-efficacy.

Morgan and Klein (2001, p. 54) note that 'whilst dyslexia is often referred to as a hidden disability, [as] dyslexic children can't conceal their inability to read and write from their teachers, parents and friends [peers]', frequent negative and confusing labelling has a significant impact on their self-esteem and emerging self-concept. Morgan and Klein (2001, p. 53) also suggest that dyslexics have strong awareness in comparing themselves with their peers and recognise intuitively their undefined and unacknowledged learning difficulties, with many adults noting that they felt this way from an early age. Gilroy (1995, p. 66) notes in her experience that dyslexic students tend to compare themselves unfavourably with their peer group and that Griffiths (1975) found that dyslexic students saw themselves as less intelligent than their peers.

Anxiety and Self-Esteem

Grigorenko (2001), Hales (1994) and Scott (2004) suggest there is clear evidence that dyslexics suffer from anxiety disorders. In addition, Legrand, McGue and Iacono (1996) suggest that approx 20% of all adolescents suffer from anxiety disorders which can exhibit itself in numerous ways: panic attacks, irritability, restlessness, poor concentration, incoherence in speaking, fear, unable to move. Physical features include: dizziness, faintness, sweating, tremor, tension in neck, chest or stomach pain, nausea, shortness of breath, diarrhoea, increased urination, palpitations, hyperventilation and insomnia (Gomez, 1991). It has been linked with alcoholism and drug taking and Scott (2004) suggests that such abuse is higher amongst dyslexics than non-dyslexics.

As Gomez (1991, p. 68) states 'everyone is anxious some of the time - survival depends upon alertness to danger' and one should distinguish between rational human response to real threat, as opposed to the irrational, neurotic and often learned response of excessive anxiety that has become an end in itself. This is particularly relevant for dyslexics who may be experiencing a very real threat to them' (Scott, 2004, p. 169). In studies of children's anxieties (Winkley, 1996; Jacobs, 1986) the follow basic anxieties were found: fear of isolation, abandonment, not understanding, not knowing, and being disoriented in new circumstances and fear of the notion of emptiness. Scott (2004, p. 170) says 'I am struck by how almost every one of these childhood anxieties are particularized in the dyslexic condition'.

The DSM-IV (APA, 1994) defines excessive anxiety or phobia as when an individual's reactions are out of proportion to the demands of the situation, cannot be explained or reasoned away, is beyond voluntary control or lead to an avoidance of the feared situation. Other important signs are that such fears persist over an extended period of time and are unadaptive or are not age or stage-specific. Scott (2004, p. 170) a counsellor to dyslexics notes 'excessive anxiety occurs a lot in dyslexics, and it is a serious and disabling condition...anxiety often leads to panic attacks in both dyslexic children and adults' Thus it could be suggested that dyslexia as a condition is disabling and the excessive anxiety resulting from the condition is also disabling, thus a double whammy!

Studies of dyslexics suggest that low or poor self-esteem is commonly found among this group (Hales, 1994, Riddick, 1996; Humphrey, 2002; Alexander-Passe, 2004a, b, 2006). As Barret and Jones (1996) note 'it would be naive to assume that dyslexics would have good self-esteem given their learning difficulties' As dyslexics are often bullied, there are strong correlations between bullying and poor self-esteem, with particular strong relationships in children with special educational needs (O'Moore and Hillery, 1992, p. 64). Specialist schools for dyslexics have been found to improve self-esteem, especially social and academic self-esteem (Thomson and Hartley, 1980), however segregation in school does not have the same impact as children are identified as different from their peers. Scott (2004) suggests the best improvements in self-esteem comes from literacy and the improvement of literacy breaks the difference between them and their peers, as 'difference' is the core of the problem.

Empirical studies note correlations between low self-esteem/anxiety and academic failure (Burns, 1979), more so with dyslexics, as Humphrey and Mullins (2002, p. 199) notes 'the experience of dyslexics at school has clear and demonstrable negative effects on the self-concept and self-esteem of children'. Riddick et al., (1999, p. 241) indicated 'the powerful mediating effect of literacy performance on how individuals perceive themselves and are perceived by others', suggesting literacy failure can distort the dyslexic's self-perception. As Thomson and Hartley (1980) and Humphrey and Mullins (2002) note, dyslexics acquire a belief that being a good reader is significantly correlated with both happiness and intelligence, with the implication that as they are not good readers they are unhappy and unintelligent. Which leads dyslexics to believe they are out of control in their own learning and destiny, which Burns (1979) found to be the single biggest factor a child needs to progress at school (above that of good teachers, facilities and curriculum). The lack of control can be seen as a predictor of academic success, with striking parallels found between learned helplessness and children with reading difficulties (Butkowsky and Willows, 1980, p. 410) with Hiebert, Winograd and Danner (1984, p. 1139) finding that dyslexic children 'attribute[d] their success to factors beyond their control'. Pumfrey and Reason (1991) suggest that there are many correlations between learned helplessness and how dyslexics cope at school.

Gilroy (1995, p. 66) notes 'it is obvious that past experiences [of failure] leave a deep scar and that many [adult] dyslexic students have a poor self-concept and suffer from low self-esteem. Gilroy also details an interesting observation that in a spontaneous, undirected, general conversation lasting 20 minutes between five adult dyslexic students, the following words and phases were observed: hopeless at (seven times); useless at (five times); could never (three times); mess (twice); typical me (twice); never been any good at (twice). She points to 'typical' and 'never' suggesting deep-rooted poor self-image stretching back to childhood. Post-observation conversation noted four out of the five students 'often felt that they were thick'.

The failing reader must deal with self doubt which becomes 'far from being a secret shame, often becomes a public failure' (Gaines, 1989). Osmond (1994, p. 31) found one boy saying 'I know inside I'm not stupid, but I look stupid to everyone else because all the things that I can't do are the things that you have to do at school'. Another young adult dyslexic noted 'the last person to be convinced I was dyslexic was me. I just thought I was thick at school and that it was my fault. I can remember the anger and frustration I felt, especially earlier on, and I still do I suppose, though not as much. I just felt uptight all the time'. This person had grown up thinking he was thick and stupid!

Riddick (1996, p. 32) one mother notes about her dyslexic son 'it was traumatic for him, incredibly traumatic, every morning I had to pull him up screaming 'I don't want to go to school' and then I had to pull him all the way down to school'. Riddick (1996) indicates there is general empirical consensus that children with reading difficulties are more likely to have behavioural and emotional difficulties (Tansley and Panckhurst, 1981; Gentile and Macmillan, 1987; Hinshaw, 1992).

Brinckerhoff, Shaw and McGuire (1993) identified the lack of positive self-concept as being the one consistent counselling issue that presents itself in people with learning difficulties, with Morgan and Klein (2001) supporting as being the case with dyslexics. Battle (1992) claims that once an individual's level of self-esteem is well established it become difficult to alter and remains relatively stable over time.

Stress and Dyslexics

Stress is the personal perception of how one communicates with the environment around us and is highly subjective. It is normal for pupils to be anxious when taking tests as one wishes to do our best. According to Thomson (1995, p. 33), 'stress appears threatening only when it becomes pervasive and invasive, when it affects too many areas of our lives and when we have neither the strategies nor the energy to cope with it'.

A combination of factors (e.g. lack of strategies or lack of skills) can result in: 'an overwhelming sense of apprehension, incompetence and confusion, sleeplessness and fatigue. It also invites the victim to resort to escape mechanisms which indirectly relieve pressure, to fantasy, obsessive, rebellion or withdraw' in dyslexics at school (Thomson, 1995, p. 33).

Whilst one can't reasonably protect children from all stress, as some measure of it is useful, parents and teachers should monitor stress levels carefully. Thomson (1995, p. 34) notes that 'if stress levels become intolerably high, many dyslexic children develop their own inappropriate strategies, becoming disruptive, aggressive, withdrawn or school phobic'. Some even also enter primary school vulnerable, as they have already learnt in pre-school that are unable to learn as easily as their peers.

As Fawcett (1995, p. 12) notes 'it is hardly surprising that life is stressful for a dyslexic child who is failing within the school system....a useful analogy here might be that of the dyslexic constantly running on a treadmill, just to stay in one place in arrange of skills that others acquire with ease'.

Hales (1994) notes using the 16PF (Cattell, Eber and Tatsuoka, 1970) with 300 dyslexics of mixed age, found that infant aged dyslexic children had scores which indicated that they were tense and frustrated, the middle school, low motivation and high anxiety and at secondary school a desire to keep in the background. Also in the middle school he found there was a noticeable drop in confidence and optimism, especially among girls. He also found an overall inverse relationship between anxiety and IQ, with middle school children with low IQ have the higher levels of anxiety.

Special Schools or Integration into Mainstream Schools?

Scott (2004) supports the view that dyslexic children and other children with disabilities are best served by going to a specialist school, whether it is a boarding or day school. Thomson (1990) notes an increase of self-esteem, especially academic self-esteem from transfer from mainstream to a dyslexic specialist school, with Crozier, Rees, Morris-Beattie and Bellin (1999, p. 34) noting 'children with dyslexia in SpLD units develop more positive self-concepts and levels of self-esteem than those left in mainstream education'. Pumphrey and Reason (1991) suggesting that dyslexics in mainstream school are disadvantaged, with Riddick (1996, p. 150) echoing this stating in 'particularly in schools where dyslexia was not acknowledged, children could feel very isolated', the isolation theme also came out in her studies that there were positives to having a close friend who was dyslexic. Special schools or units have access to full-time specialist teachers, rather than the few hours of specialists support normally given under the terms of a statutory statement of special educational needs, as termed in the UK to mean direct government funding for specialist support. In such units or schools, there is less bullying as no one is deemed to be different or abnormal. Morgan and Klein (2001) suggests that dyslexics attending a specialist school for dyslexia may be able to overcome the feelings of isolation and sense of being different that children in mainstream school experience, however they note that most dyslexics could be happily integrated into mainstream classes and school if appropriate support is given at an early stage of their school careers.

Hales (1995, p. 183) notes one dyslexic boy's experiences 'I was sent to a [specialist] school...all geared up for dyslexics and to my amazement I found I was no idiot but top of the form in my first term. I was very happy there....they made me into a person again', however one could also conclude that special schools have a lower academic curriculum, this boy may have been bottom of the class in mainstream school but top in the specialist school, as expectations were much lower.

Personality Study:
Profiles of General and Successful Dyslexics

Abstract

Dyslexia is a condition which affects many areas of an individual's life, from reading and writing, to poor memory and co-ordination. To date, the majority of researchers have ignored the affects of dyslexia and focussed on ways to help the dyslexic gain literacy. Whilst this stance is positive, it ignores the dyslexic as an individual and as many remedial education teachers have found, until one re-teaches the ability to believe in oneself, most remedial efforts will be in vain. Thus to understand the dyslexic learner, one needs to investigate their personality and especially how different severities of dyslexia affects the creation of extroverted or introverted personality characteristics.

In a sample of N=87 self-diagnosed dyslexic and non-dyslexic adults, a screening measure was used to identify the severity of dyslexia traits and any hidden dyslexia amongst the control sample. Gender and severity of dyslexia were found to be important factors in understanding how dyslexia affects the development of personality attributes (coping strategies) which they have evolved to deal with educational and social failure. Investigations were also made into how the severity of the dyslexia affects the likelihood of attainment at school and in post-school education.

Literature Review

Personality

The origin of the word 'personality' suggests a possible relationship between the dramatic rendering of a playwright's character and the psychologist's attempt to describe it. The word comes from persona, the mask that Greek and Roman actors wore to indicate the characters they played.

Allport and Odbert (1937) suggest the knowledge of an individual's personality attributes will permit us to predict what he is likely to do, even in situations in which we have never observed them. Personality measures were initially devised to supply information that would make such predictions possible. Cronbach (1983) describes the first personality measure, designed to identify emotionally disturbed US Army recruits during World War 1. The measure was an 'adjustment inventory' consisting of questions such as 'do you daydream frequently?' and 'Do you wet your bed?', if they reported many traits they were singled out for psychiatric examination.

Whilst there are similarities between personality and intelligence measures, they are different in how they are validated (intelligence measures can be validated through corrections to age, teacher evaluations and academic performance, personality measures are hard to validate). Many early personality measures (e.g. Minnesota Multiphasic Personality Inventory-MMPI by Hathaway and McKinley, 1942) were created to seek out those with mental illness and were validated from psychiatric samples. Newer measures take a different viewpoint and are better suited for use in the general population (e.g. California Psychological Inventory-CPI by Gough and Bradley, 1996) use high school and college students for validation).

Unstructured personality measures were first suggested in the 1950's, based on asking unrelated questions (asking for their perception and understanding of pictures or images) to inform the questioner to their mental health. One opposing view is that how can one penetrate below the surface to find out what the subject does not know himself? The concept uses tricks to circumvent the subjects own defences against threatening impulses and ideas. Such measures include the 'Rorschach Inkblots' (Zubin, Eron and Schumer, 1965) and the 'Thematic Apperception Test-TAT' (Murray, 1943). According to some experts they have little or incremental validity (Anastasi, 1968; Meehl 1959) for the general population, with only the TAT being of use for psychiatric patients.

Personality – Review of Theories

Whilst personality measures have a practical purpose in aiding diagnosis and counselling, there needs to be empirical support for the theories supporting such measures. These theories generally fall into two categories: Trait, and Humanistic approaches. For this paper 'Trait theory' will be known as 'Attribute theory', to avoid confusion later on in this paper concerning a dyslexia trait measure.

Attribute theories are primarily an attempt to characterise people by reference to some underlying basic attributes. Each sub-theories under the 'attribute' umbrella tries to understand and support different 'basic categorises of attributes'.

One example is in the development of the Cattell 16PF (Cattell 1957; Cattell et al. 1970). The starting point for this measure was 4,500 terms from 18,000 attribute words, with many thrown out by removing difficult and uncommon words and synonyms until 171 attribute names were left. A group of judges then rated subjects to these terms, along with factor analysis to a number of intelligence and performance measures, the results were 16 primary dimensions of personality. Later research now reduced the number to 5 major dimensions, named the 'big five' (Norman, 1963; Brody, 1988; Goldberg, 1993), namely: extroversion, emotional stability, agreeableness, conscientiousness and cultural sensitivity. Eysenck (1953, 1981) suggests just two independent dimensions were required, covered under Norman's five (Neuroticism and Extroversion/Introversion). Eysenck found these two dimensions applied to many different cultures with usage in Bangladesh, Brazil, Hong Kong and Japan (Eysenck and Eysenck 1983). Later Eysenck (Eysenck and Eysenck, 1975, 1983) added a third dimension 'psychoticism' to explain relationships to aggressive, antisocial, cold, impulsive and self-centred attributes for absolute extremes of psychiatric disorders and covers more of Norman's 'big five'.

Researchers have questioned the validity of attribute concept (Mischel, 1968); mainly that situationism is the reason for behavioural inconsistencies. Block (1977) suggests that consistency over time rather than situations is important to attribute theory. Epstein (1980) found that whilst consistency of attributes in situations on a single day basis maybe low, over a number of days it was much higher (from +.30 to +.80), thus suggesting consistency across situations. Moskowitz (1982) noted that whilst manifestations of aggression may differ between childhood, adolescence and adulthood, from boys using fists in childhood to adults shouting, they form the same core attribute, thus consistency.

Another alternative offered is that the 'interaction' rather than 'situation' is the critical factor (Magnusson and Endler, 1977), thus individual perception of anxiety will affect the choice of attributes they use. Endler (1982) suggest that whilst the situation determining a person's behaviour, the person's attributes often determine what situation they find themselves in (a reciprocal effect) – so a chicken and egg situation. There is also biological/genetic support for attribute theory, which suggests that personality is formed from an individual's temperament/anxiety (Buss and Plomin, 1984), as anxiety is an inevitable part of our daily life. This suggests that how an individual deals with anxiety (their pattern of defences) is what makes people different, be it use of alcohol, aggression or emotional - when defences fail, this could modify personality.

Some 50 years ago, a new perspective on human motivation and personality developed, to understand how healthy human beings operate. In their view, psychoanalysts look at people as if they are all emotional cripples, behaviourists as if they are blind and attribute theorists as material to file into sterile pigeonholes. Humanists felt that each of these approaches lost sight of what is truly human about being human (in essence 'feelings'). Maslow (1968) a major theorist of this movement suggested that personality movements to date took a pessimistic and negative view of human beings - always wanting to get away from something (e.g. pain, hunger, sexual tension). He proposed a hierarchy of need, whereas lower order physical needs, needed to be met (e.g. food, water, oxygen then comfort, security and freedom from fear) before higher order emotions could be possible (e.g. love, self-esteem, knowledge, understanding, approval, knowledge) with self-actualization at the top (the desire to realize oneself to the fullest). Rogers (1959) and Jung (1963) developed the term 'self' and 'self-concept' to understand ones sense of oneself who takes or does not take actions. Counselling was the key to Roger's work on the individual and he believed that to grow into emotionally healthy adults, children need warmth and understanding. Many question the empirical basis to the Humanistic movement (Smith, 1996) and view terms of self-esteem and self-actualization as hard to define and measure.

Is there a dyslexic personality?

As Hales (1994) puts it, is there any more blind than a dyslexic personality? The question should really be how does dyslexia affect the individual's personality? Richardson and Stein (1993) conclude, it would be extraordinary if any disorder did not affect the personality profile, where daily life is affected. The dyslexic suffers in varying degrees, from problems tying ones shoelaces, to reading road signs, passing driving tests and reading newspapers and emails. Dyslexia affects every aspect of the dyslexic's life and affects the ability to converse clearly with the outside word.

However, the largest body of research into the personality of dyslexics has been with whose who are successful. This does however put a rosy face on the profile of dyslexics as the vast majority of dyslexics are unsuccessful in education or career environments. As Osmond (1994) found, the majority of dyslexics are still handicapped by their disability and gaining the same heights as their non-dyslexic peers is fraught with difficulty. According to Miller (1998a, b) 50-75% of all disabled adults are unemployed. Some individuals with dyslexia (depending on educational and severity) may find it very difficult, if not impossible, to learn to read, write or do mathematics (Scott, Scherman and Philips, 1992). Frequently, adult dyslexics find they lack adequate academic and emotional skills, but also in interpersonal communication and social skills areas - putting them in a greater risk of a continual cycle of failure.

Successful Dyslexics

Many researchers found successful dyslexics, whilst experiencing success they also: fear failure; over produce; have a very strong personal self-drive for financial freedom; dream about achieving their goals; be control freaks; extremely self-critical; perfectionists; always striving to do better; a need for order, confidence; persistent and show stubbornness (Scott et al. 1992; Wszeborowska-Lipinska, 1997; Reiff, Gerber and Ginsberg, 1997). However, studies of people who go on to become millionaires have shown that the proportion of dyslexics among them is four times the proportion of the general population (Stanley, 2002).

There seems to be counter-arguments concerning self-esteem. Scott et al (1992) suggest successful dyslexics will: lack self-confidence; self-doubt, self-esteem and fear rejection. Whilst Wszeborowska-Lipinska (1997) counters this by suggesting that, as successful dyslexics are not only reaching the heights of their peers but feel the need to surpass them, they therefore require more self-confidence and higher self-esteem than their peers do.

Richardson (1994) and Richardson and Stein (1993) take a different perspective to the personality profile of successful dyslexics, looking at psychological factors. Findings indicate that these individuals use unusual perceptual experiences and strong sense of intuition or belief in paranormal experiences, with 73% of their successful dyslexic sample saying yes to the following question 'Do things sometimes feel as if they were not real?, compared to 49% in controls. They also found that there were significant indications that successful dyslexics were eccentric, extroverted and used unusual perceptual experiences (hunches, gut reactions and delusions) for decision making.

A main difference between successful and unsuccessful dyslexics was found by Scott et al (1992), in that they had at least one person who believed in them (mostly the mother) and encouragement of talents and hobbies (also found by Morgan and Klein, 2001 and Thomson, 1996). Thomson also noticed that successful dyslexics were commonly those who 'got by' by being highly intelligent, but they were often under-achievers, failing to attain their potential and sometimes suffering a lifetime of frustration.

Gerber et al. (1992) believe a 'goodness of fit' and the seeking of support systems are two key external factors for dyslexics to achieve success at work. The 'fit' or 'match' of dyslexic abilities to the employment environment and expectations create success for both employer and employee. Morgan and Klein (2001, p.130) interestingly contemplate that employers need to be 'aware that whilst some dyslexic difficulties seem like incompetence, they need not necessarily be an impediment to doing the job'. Dyslexics doing jobs differently can also have their advantages, as Klein and Sunderland (1998) found with one young dyslexic labelled a 'slow learner' at school. At 16 years old she went to work for a local factory making electrical components for cars. Her role was basic and routine, but within a short time she had re-wired one of the components in such a way that it was more efficient, used less wire and saved the company large amounts of money.

Summary

The literature review has looked at many aspects of 'dyslexic personality', starting with what is currently known, with its implications to childhood and adult reluctant learners and secondly a review of literature concerning 'personality' and the different schools of thoughts. Lastly, a review of 'successful dyslexics' looked at what was known about successful dyslexics and their attributes.

Empirical studies suggests there is a limited knowledge concerning the personality of adult dyslexics, a lack of knowledge concerning how the severity of the disorder affects those who are affected, and little comparison of personality traits over the whole spectrum of sufferers of dyslexia. Turning to the minority of adult dyslexics who are successful, there is a lack of knowledge concerning which type of dyslexics will/will not experience academic success.

The aim of this research study is to:

- Understand how gender and the severity of dyslexia are crucial factors in understanding the personality of adult dyslexics.
- Investigate if any negative secondary manifestations found in children with dyslexia will also be found with adults.
- Investigate if dyslexics with and without school/post-school success will have significantly different personalities and to controls.
- Investigate if there are significant personality differences between dyslexics with and without academic success.

This research study has two parts; Part 1 investigates the 'General Profiles' of dyslexics, as compared to non-dyslexic controls. Part 2 looks at 'Successful Profiles' and aims to understand the personality of dyslexics who experience academic success.

Dyslexia and Personality: General Profiles

Methodology

This study uses three measures:

- A screening questionnaire (Vinegrad, 1994)
- A measure of Emotional Instability vs. Adjustment (Eysenck and Wilson, 1991)
- A measure of Introversion vs. Extroversion (Eysenck and Wilson, 1991)

According to the authors of all three measures, no time restraints are necessary.

The Screening Measure

Vinegrad's (1994) measure has extensively been used to screen for dyslexia (British Dyslexia Association, 2007; Dyslexia Action, 2007; LABDA, 2007). From 20 question, N=679 norm values resulted in mean scores of 12.140 (4.096 SD) for dyslexics and 5.824 (4.637 SD) for non-dyslexics, a 6.316 mean difference with a P value of <.0001.

Items include questions about completing forms, forgetting messages, co-ordination problems etc, all of which are classic traits of dyslexia (Thomson, 1996; Miles, 1994; Morgan and Klein, 2001). The 20 items are indicated in Table 1.

Table 1. Dyslexia screening measure (Vinegrad, 1994)

1. Do you find difficulty telling left from right?
2. Is map reading or finding your way to a strange place confusing?
3. Do you dislike reading aloud?
4. Do you take longer than you should to read a page of a book?
5. Do you find it difficult to remember the sense of what you have read?
6. Do you dislike reading long books?
7. Is your spelling poor?
8. Is your writing difficult to read?
9. Do you get confused if you have to speak in public?
10. Do you find it difficult to take messages on the telephone and pass them on correctly?
11. When you say a long word, do you sometimes find it difficult to get all the sounds in the right order?
12. Do you find it difficult to do sums in your head without using your fingers or paper?
13. When using the telephone, do you tend to get the numbers mixed up when you dial?
14. Do you find it difficult to say the months of the year forwards in a fluent manner?
15. Do you find it difficult to say the months of the year backwards?
16. Do you mix up dates and times and miss appointments?
17. When writing cheques do you frequently find yourself making mistakes?
18. Do you find forms difficult and confusing?
19. Do you mix up bus numbers like 95 and 59?
20. Did you find it hard to learn your multiplication tables at school?

The Emotional Instability vs. Adjustment and Introversion vs. Extroversion Measure

The full Eysenck Personality Questionnaire (EPQ). Consists of items with dichotomous (yes or no) response choices and is comprised of four subscales: Neuroticism; Extraversion; Psychoticism/'tough mindedness'; and Lie/'social desirability'. All of the scales have satisfactory reliability coefficients for normal adults, with test-retest reliabilities of 0.86 and 0.84 for the EPQ-N and EPQ-L scales respectively (Eysenck and Eysenck, 1975). Excellent internal consistency for the EPQ-N scale (Cronbach's alphas of 0.84 for men and 0.85 for women) as well as the EPQ-L scale (Cronbach's alphas of 0.81 for men and 0.79 for women).

Both measures used in this paper are a modified version of the Eysenck Personality Inventory (Eysenck and Wilson, 1991; Eysenck and Eysenck, 1975), reduced in number of questions by a third (from 210 items to 70 for each measure), but for analysis comparison the scores were multiplied by three. Each 70 item version was personally approved by Professor Hans Eysenck for the purpose of this study before he passed away. A review of the EPI and 6, 12 and 20 item versions can be found in Francis and Jackson (2004), which indicates high validity between the full and smaller versions.

The Emotional Instability vs. Adjustment and Introversion measure investigates the following variables (sub scales):

Inferiority feelings/ Self-esteem	low self-opinion, unattractive failures (Low score) confidence in themselves/abilities (High score)
Depression/ Happiness	pessimistic, gloomy and depressed (Low score) cheerful, optimistic and well (High score)
Anxiety/ Calm	easily upset by things that go wrong (High score) resistant to irrational fears or anxieties (Low score)
Obsessiveness/ Casualness	careful, highly disciplined, finicky (High score) casual, easy going, less need for order (Low score)
Dependence/ Autonomy	lacks self-reliance, easy pushed around (Low score) enjoys freedom, independent and realistic (High score
Hypochondrias/ Sense of Health	demands sympathetic attention (High score) seldom ill, carefree (Low score)
Guilt Guilt-freedom	self-blaming, self-questioning of life (High score) does not regret past actions/behaviour (Low score)

The Introversion vs. Extroversion measure investigates the following variables (sub scales):

Inhibition Expressiveness	reserved, even tempered, detached (Low score) sentimental, volatile, sympathetic (High score)
Inactivity Activity	physically inactive, lethargic (Low score) active and energetic (High score)
Responsibility Irresponsibility	reliable, trustworthy, bit compulsive (High score) careless, late, unpredictable (Low score)
Sociability Unsociability	enjoys socializing, meet people easily (High score) few special friends, enjoys solo activities (Low score)

Carefulness Risk-taking	prefers familiarity, safety, security (Low score) live dangerously, gamblers, likes risk (High score)
ImpulsivenessControl	make hurried, premature decisions (High score) systematic, orderly, cautious (Low score)
Reflectiveness Practicability	likes ideas, discussions, and speculations (High score) likes doing rather than talking about it (Low score)

Sample

N=87 adults were recruited, N=44 self-reported dyslexics and N=43 adult controls. The gender split included N=21 males and N=25 females for self-reported dyslexics and N=17 males and N=26 females for controls. The mean age for the self-diagnosed dyslexics was 35.64yrs (S.D. 11.543) and 43.41yrs (S.D. 8.180) for the controls. This study did not diagnose dyslexia, but relied on them to indicate their own diagnosis. Thus, a screening measure was introduced to firstly confirm diagnosis and secondly screen for likely dyslexics in the (N=43) control sample.

Results – Dyslexia and Personality: General Personality

By using the screening measure with the N=87 sample, four groups were created according to the number of traits scored: 0-4 traits (N=18, 20.4%), 5-9 traits (N=23, 26.1%), 10-14 traits (N=30, 34.1%) and 15-19 traits (N=16, 18.4%). This study will compare those with low traits (0-4) with those with moderate (10-14) and high traits (15-19) to assess the core differences between dyslexics (of varying severity) and non-dyslexics controls.

The raw data for the Emotional Instability vs. Adjustment Measure and Introversion vs. Extroversion results is located in Appendix 1.

Graph 1 indicates how this sample, sorted by gender, compares to the 50% percentile score of the general population (Eysenck and Wilson, 1995; Eysenck and Eysenck, 1975). It indicates that this sample is similar to population norms (norm shown in grey) but are lacking in self-esteem, can be more easily pushed around, more pessimistic, have fewer friends and prefer less risk in their lives. It could be suggested that this profile is weighted towards those who find life hard and thus even though the sample was split 50% self-diagnosed dyslexics and 50% controls, however there are early indicators of dyslexia among the control group, maybe in the form of unidentified dyslexia – which is unbalancing the gender data.

Appendix 1 indicates that gender personality differences are significant in this study, but do these results correlate with known gender differences? The resulting profile of Males, with significant differences compared to females is: more confidence; more independence; more optimistic; more high disciplined; resistant to fears/anxieties; less ill; and make more hurried decisions

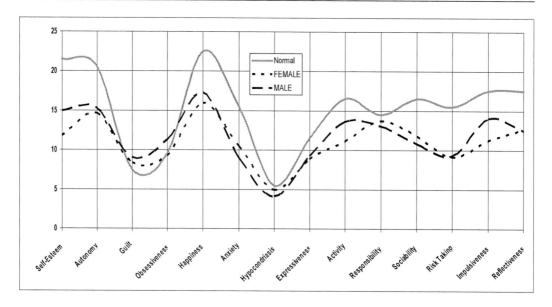

Graph 1. Gender data, compared to population 50% percentile scores.

Empirical gender stereotypes (Edley and Wetherell, 1995; Kilmartin, 1994) suggestions are indicated in Table 2. Social theories do not ascribe to a single meaning of maleness (Hearn, 1994) and Social constructivist theories of masculinities recognise that gender is achieved through and by people and their context (Stolenberg, 1989), thus it could be argued that gender is not something we are, but something we do in social interactions.

Studies of men with cancer (Moynihan, 1998; 2002) found that it was 'crucial for men to be controlled and silent about their emotional life…also the men needed to control when and where any emotion was shown'. They felt happier to cry away from family, often in their cars where they felt 'enclosed and safe'. Male patients felt happier when male doctors referred to their illness on male terms (as machines, controllable and controlled) e.g. cases of testicle cancer 'a plane flying on one engine and landing safely…..one cylinder is as good as two' - holding their mind and body as separate and estranged. That said, men feel unable to cry in hospitals for sadness but are able to cry and hug team mates on the football pitch (Moynihan, 1998)

Whilst difficult, constructs of gender are possible in loose generic terms; those indicated in this study are supported as within normal ranges.

Traits

Graph 2 indicates the profiles of each of the four sub groups, divided by traits (0-4, 5-9, 10-14 and 15-19). 0-4 is classified as non-dyslexic to 15-19 being classified as severely dyslexic. Along with Appendix 1, a profile emerges.

Table 2. Gender Stereotypes

Masculine	Feminine
Inexpressive	Emotional
Aggressive	Expressive
Ambitious	Compassionate
Analytical	Childlike
Assertive	Gentle
Successful	Loyal
Competitive	Sensitive
Forceful	Tender
Independent	Understanding
Dominant	Yielding
Strong Personality	Gullible
Athletic	Refined
Invulnerable	Warm

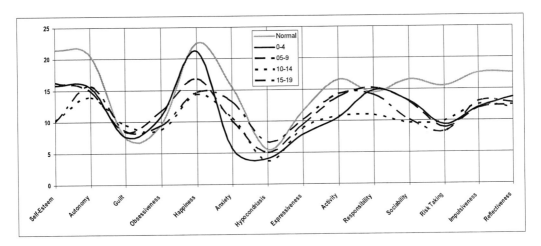

Graph 2. Chart of the whole sample, separated by the number of screening (dyslexic) traits.

But how do the sub groups compare to 50% percentile normative data?

Comparison of normative scores (shown in grey) in Chart 4 indicates that norm differences, with all the sub groups (lacking self-esteem, can be more easily pushed around, more pessimistic, has fewer friends and prefers less risk in their lives), the only exception seems to be in Happiness, with the low trait group being as cheerful, optimistic and well as norm values. Even the control group doesn't fit the norm profile completely, thus there is a possibility the modified versions of the EPI requires the norms to be re-calibrated, possibly from the 0-4 trait data?

Compared with those with low (0-4) of traits (categorised as controls for this study), the sample with high number (15-19) of traits (categorised as severely dyslexic for this study) are more pessimistic, gloomy, depressed and easily upset when things go wrong, and feel unattractive failures with low self-esteem. They also lack self reliance, feel easily pushed around, self-blaming, demand sympathetic attention, more sentimental, volatile, active, energetic with few friends and enjoy their own company rather than group activities/socializing.

Reflecting the data the other way, those with low traits (0-4) compared to those with high traits (15-19) are more confident in themselves and their abilities, cheerful, optimistic, resistant to irrational anxieties, reserved, even tempered, seldom ill, carefree and physically inactive. They also do not regret past actions, are careful, disciplined, enjoy socializing, like risk and can make hurried decisions.

The high trait profile suggests that personality is affected by having a learning difficulty, such as dyslexia. Many adult dyslexics have difficulty completing forms for job applications or housing benefit (Scott et al., 1992; Morgan and Klein, 2001). Whilst, children and teenagers with dyslexia are affected by a rigid school system which relies on literacy, adults have more choices in defining how dyslexia affects their lives. Adults can choose to either face difficulties head on or empower themselves e.g. Richard Branson, Charles Schwab etc. (externalise their difficulties) or see their difficulties as debilitating (internalization) and use avoidance to limit the exposure of their self-esteem to failure and difficulties. The results indicated in this study suggest the majority use the latter. The profile for the low trait control group seems logical and makes them more likely to be resilient in mainstream education.

These profiles are useful and confirm many empirical studies concerning the secondary effects of having a disability like dyslexia (Alexander-Passe, 2006, 2007; Hales, 1994; Edwards, 1994; Riddick, 1994, Burden, 2005). To date there has been little quantitative evidence concerning personality to support many views held but unsubstantiated by educationalists and parents.

Traits and Gender

Graphs 3 and 4 describe the two test measures by the number of traits, split by gender. Comparison to norm data (shown in grey) suggests that Males (Graph 3) in general are closer to the norm profile, than Females (Graph 4) which seem erratic, but neither hugs the norm profile completely, and this is especially true for the Inferiority feelings/Self-esteem, Sociability/Unsociability, Risk-taking/Carefulness, Impulsivity/Control and Reflectivess/Practicability sub scales. As mentioned earlier, it maybe a case that this modified version of the EPI measures require new recalibrated norm values.

Two questions were posed. What are the differences between high trait (15-19) males and females and what are the differences between low trait (0-4) male and females? The following profiles of difference are indicated below (with significant and major differences):

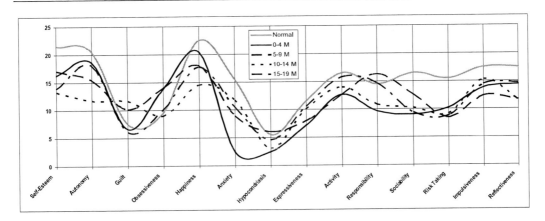

Graph 3.The Male sample, separated by the number of screened (dyslexic) traits.

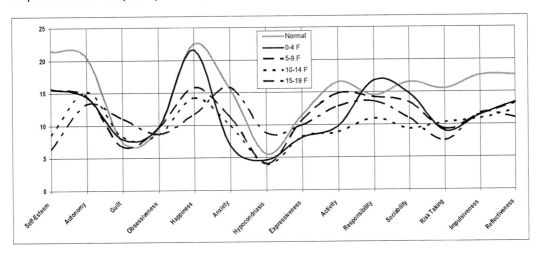

Graph 4. The Female sample, separated by the number of screened (dyslexic) traits.

High trait (15-19) adult males, compared to high trait (15-19) females were found to be:

- Significant differences
  - More confident in themselves/abilities
  - More cheerful, optimistic and well
  - Enjoys freedom, independent and realistic
  - Do not regret past actions/behaviour
  - Resistant to irrational fears or anxieties
- Major differences
  - Careful, highly disciplined, finicky
  - Make hurried, premature decisions
  - Likes ideas, discussions, speculations
  - Seldom ill, carefree
  - Active and energetic

Comparison of low trait (0-4) adult males, compared to low trait (0-4) females suggests the following profile:

- Significant differences
  - Enjoys freedom, independent and realistic
  - Resistant to irrational fears or anxieties
  - Careless, late, unpredictable
  - Few special friends, enjoys solo activities
- Major differences
  - Careful, highly disciplined, finicky
  - Active and energetic
  - Make hurried, premature decisions

The above profiles suggest that overall both high and low trait males are more confident and resilient than females. Gender profiles between high and low trait males and females which would be more useful in understanding how personality is affected by severe dyslexia (high frequency of dyslexia trait), these are described below:

Females – high traits (15-19) compared to low traits (0-4) were found to include:

- Significant differences
  - Low self-opinion, feel unattractive failures
  - Pessimistic, gloomy and can feel depressed
  - Easily upset by things that go wrong
  - Demand sympathetic attention
- Major differences
  - Self-blaming, self-questioning of life
  - Active and energetic
  - Careless, late, unpredictable
  - Have few special friends and enjoy solo activities

Males - high traits (15-19) compared to low traits (0-4) included:

- Significant differences
  - Easily upset by things that go wrong
  - Reliable, trustworthy, bit compulsive
- Major differences
  - Have a low self-opinion and feel unattractive failures
  - Sentimental, volatile, sympathetic
  - Active and energetic

Combining both sets of data, both profiles (high trait Males and Females) share many similar aspects:

- Significant/major differences
    - A low self-opinion and feel unattractive failures
    - Can be easily upset by things that go wrong
    - Active and energetic

The above profiles for high (15-19) trait dyslexic adults are interesting as not only do they describe dyslexic adults but researchers and educationalists will recognise many aspects of the school-aged dyslexic. Thus the question must be asked, how much of this profile is developed in childhood? The literature review suggests that many of these emotional manifestations are commonly found in the secondary effects of dyslexia amongst school-aged children/teenagers (Alexander-Passe, 2006, 2007; Hales, 1994; Edwards, 1994; Riddick, 1994, Burden, 2005). So the development of the introverted dyslexic profile could very well start in childhood and it could be suggested that their experiences at school, from interactions with both teachers and peers could be the cause.

Conclusions

This first research study investigated the general personality of adult dyslexics, looking at the personality attributes of those with low trait (controls) to moderate and severe trait dyslexics and split by gender. Profiles were created for these groups, which should aid practioneers by generalizing personality attributes.

Dyslexia and Personality: Successful Profiles

Introduction

As discussed earlier, successful dyslexic adults are said to have strong traits (Gregg et al., 1992; Scott et al., 2002; Reiff et al., 1997) including perfectionism, Obsessiveness, persistence, stubbornness, self-doubt and the need for controlling the finest details. The findings of the first study (General Personality) suggests the severe dyslexic (15-19 traits) sample did not have these successful traits. Of the N=16 (N=8 Males and N=8 Females) with high traits (15-19), N=4 took O'levels (25%), N=5 took only CSEs at school and N=7 left school with no qualifications. Many dyslexics achieve post-school and from this N=16 sub group only 25% achieved a degree (with another 44% achieving other post school certificate/diploma/other qualification to assist their careers, this left 31% with no post school qualifications.

In the UK, where this study took place, until the late 1990's adolescents took O'Level (ordinary) examinations at 15-16yrs, A' Level (Advanced) examinations at 18ys and proceed to university at 18yrs. Those unable to deal with the academic demands took CSE's, where the highest grade is comparable to a C grade at O'level standard.

Whilst it is true that many dyslexics do well post-school, the traits of successful dyslexia are not commonly found in the general dyslexic population. Alexander-Passe (2007) and

Grant (2001) noted that there is much public misinformation about dyslexia which misleads dyslexics into the false hope that they can achieve to the heights of fame and fortune of individuals paraded as 'dyslexic and proud', such as Tom Cruise, Albert Einstein and Richard Rogers. Thus, it could be suggested that severe dyslexics in this study may lack overall the traits of academic success – however, this does not exclude non-academic success.

Turning to data in Appendixes 2 and 3, we investigate the highly dyslexic, but not severe dyslexics with 10-14 traits; do they have the success traits? Features of those with moderate traits (10-14) compared to low traits (0-4) which are not found in the high (15-19) traits sample, included:

- Significant differences
    - Careless, late, unpredictable
    - Live life dangerously, gamblers, likes risk
    - Seldom ill, carefree

- Other differences
    - Enjoys freedom, independent and realistic
    - Casual, easy going, less need for order
    - Likes doing rather than talking about it

Breaking down the data more, by gender, female with moderate traits (10-14) compared to low trait (0-4) which are not found in the high (15-19) traits sample, include:

- Significant differences
    - Careless, late, unpredictable
    - Few special friends, enjoys solo activities

Males with moderate traits (10-14) compared to low trait (0-4) which are not found in the high (15-19) traits sample, include:

- Significant differences
    - Sentimental, volatile, sympathetic
    - Likes doing rather than talking about it
    - Lacks self-reliance, easy pushed around
    - Casual, easy going, less need for order

- Other differences
    - Reliable, trustworthy, bit compulsive
    - Make hurried, premature decisions

The above indicates the unique aspects of personality for the moderate (10-14) trait group. Of the N=30 with medium (10-14) traits (N=11 Males and N=19 Females), N=23 took O'levels (76.7%), N=3 took only CSE at school and N=5 (18%) left school with no qualifications. As already noted, many dyslexics achieve post-school and from this a N=16 sub group (53% of the 10-14 trait sample) achieved a degree (N=5 were postgraduates and N=1 with a PhD) with another N=10 (33%) achieving a non-degree post school certificate/diploma/ other qualification to assist their careers, leaving only N=4 (13.3%) with no post school qualifications. Thus, education data suggests that the moderate (10-14) trait group are far more successful educationally than those with severe dyslexia (15-19) traits. Even with 10-14 traits of dyslexia, which still suggests significant life difficulties (as Vinegrad, 1994 found the mean score for dyslexics was 12.140, S.D. 4.096), they seem to have survived school and post school life well – thus education was a positive experience. Comparison should be made to the N=18 (N=5 Males and N=13 Females) categorised as controls (with 0-4 traits) who N=18 (100%) took O'levels. N=9 (50%) achieved a degree (N=4 were postgraduates) with another N=7 achieving a post school certificate/diploma/other qualification to assist their careers, leaving only N=2 (11.1%) with no post school qualifications.

It could be argued this group of medium trait self-diagnosed dyslexics (10-14) succeeded on par with their peers (educationally) and whilst they do not display all of the traits which researchers (Gerber et al., 1992; Scott et al., 2002; Reiff et al., 1997) describe as successful in type, they do however display traits unlike those of their more severe dyslexic peers, who don't succeed academically and on par with their peers. These include: unpredictability, risk taking, independence and realistic thinkers. It is hypothesised that these extroverted traits are important to teach children with dyslexia, to assist them in their ability to be resilient during and after mainstream schooling.

A second research study sample of academic successful dyslexics was created from the data of the first research study (General Personality) to investigate academic success e.g. the ability to gain a degree. In our literacy-based society, everyday success, rather than exceptional success (e.g. genius level achievement) for dyslexics is measured by academic achievement and thus is the basis for this second study.

The adult sample used in the first research Study (N=87) was then sub-divided into those who had gained a degree (N=40: 30 females and 10 males) and those without a degree (N=47: 23 females and 24 males), and then divided again by traits and gender

Results - Dyslexia and Personality: Successful Dyslexics

Appendix 4 and Graph 5 indicate the differences between moderate dyslexics with and without degrees. The data suggests differences in the guilt, obsessiveness, happiness, and risk-taking scales between the groups and suggest such differences are enough for further study.

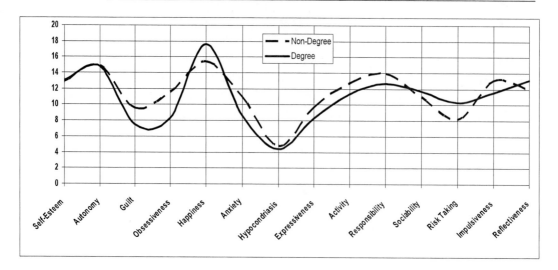

Graph 5. Degree vs. Non-degree populations (10-14 traits).

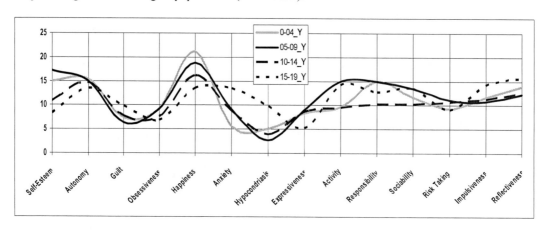

Graph 6. Degree educated, split by traits (all trait groups)

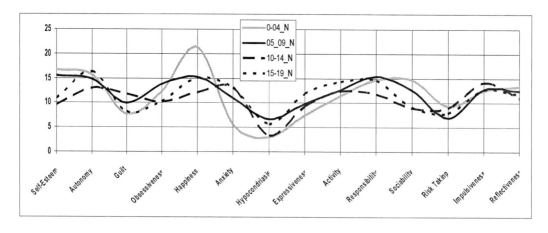

Graph 7. Non-degree educated, split by traits (all trait groups).

Graph 6 indicates the differences between the degrees educated samples, split by dyslexic traits. The results suggest those with higher traits (15-19) have a lower self-opinion and feel unattractive failures; are more pessimistic, gloomy and depressed; are easily upset by things that go wrong; demands sympathetic attention; are sentimental, volatile, sympathetic; and are more systematic, orderly, cautious, than individuals with mild or moderate traits and controls. This suggests that to reach university standard there has been an emotional cost. The sample with moderate (10-14) traits are closer to the low (0-4) trait norms, however with greater reliability, trustworthiness and enjoys socializing, meet people easily than the norms, which might suggest their coping strategy.

Graph 7 investigates the non-degree educated sub sample, split by dyslexic traits. The data suggests the low (0-4) trait norms are significantly different to the rest of the samples, with greater happiness and less anxiety scores. It is interesting that the 10-14 trait group are more pessimistic, gloomy and depressed but more reliable, trustworthy than the 15-19 trait group, which may suggest that being less severely dyslexic might make them more frustrated in their inability to reach academic heights of their peers, whereas the high (15-19) trait group have come to terms that they would not reach the academic heights of those around them.

Degree Educated

Appendix 2 data suggested that moderate trait (10-14) males, compared to females who gain academic success are significantly easier going, resistant to irrational fears/anxieties and are less sporty. Other major differences are in their greater confidence, greater freedom, optimism, risk taking and the ability to discuss and speculate. The inverse profile suggests (with non-degree educated males with moderate traits) a need for order, have irrational fears/anxieties and use of sport as a way to maintain self-esteem. In comparison, degree educated female compared to non-degree educated female dyslexics (both with 10-14 traits), do not regret past actions, are optimistic, are resistant to irrational fears/anxieties but are systematic and require order.

Academically successful males compared to females (10-14 traits) were found to be more confident socially, generally more confident, likely to be easy going, more optimistic, enjoy risk and unpredictability and to a lesser extent, can question their actions.

The difference between male low trait controls (0-4) with a degree and those without a degree, suggest degree educated males don't regret past actions, are more easy going, resistant to irrational fears, feel happy to take risks. Interestingly they also have a lower self-opinion, are unpredictable and volatile. The data suggests that dyslexics with moderate (10-14) traits and especially males have a more suitably equipped personality, compared to severe (15-19) trait dyslexics, to succeed academically in our current literate based society. One could argue that either they had these qualities first, or academic success has developed these personality traits, but what seems important is that dyslexic adults can achieve academically, and can succeed on par with their non-dyslexic peers. However data (O'level/GCSE) suggests school success on par with non-dyslexic peers is not apparent, only post-school, which might indicate that post-school diagnosis is stronger, especially at university.

It is also interesting that the differential between degree and non-degree educated females is not as great as among males, would suggest that opportunity rather than ability/personality are more crucial factors (parents, teachers and cultures have stereotypically perceived girls as not being as career dependant as boys, thus the pressure for academic success was not as great).

Non-Degree Educated

The data presented in Appendix 3 compares non-degree educated moderate trait (10-14) males, compared to low trait (0-4) males, suggest that moderate dyslexia trait males are significantly more upset by things that go wrong (e.g. when their dyslexia makes them make mistakes) which makes them volatile and sentimental. They also feel unattractive failures, can be easily pushed around, self-blame, are pessimistic, have few friends and can make hurried decisions in the heat of the night. This may indicate they doubt their own abilities and will withdraw from situations where their dyslexia maybe embarrassing (e.g., situations requiring reading and writing like promotion at work or reading/answering questions for a quiz). It is interesting, but not wholly unexpected that they are more sporty, prefer doing than talking about things (are more practical) which would suggest they try and find personal success in practical (e.g. creative or engineering) careers (as also found by Alexander-Passe, 2006).

The profiles above suggest that non-degree dyslexic educated males use sport as a means to maintain a positive self-esteem but indicates a profile of avoidance in situations that highlight their difficulties, as well as being volatile and unpredictable when faced with situations that require literacy and numeracy.

Is diagnosis a positive step?

Appendix 4 investigates degree educated moderate trait (10-14) dyslexic group, looking at personality differences amongst those who are diagnosed dyslexic (N=9) and those who are not (N=7). There are significant differences between the two groups, Graph 8 indicates that those (degree educated with moderate 10-14 traits) who are diagnosed are extroverted, as they are significantly more independent, do not regret past actions, more optimistic, resistant to irrational fears, carefree and even tempered. Less significantly, they have self-confidence, like to take a risk with life, and are orderly and reliable. This suggests that diagnosis was a positive aspect of having dyslexia. The flip side is those who without diagnosis are introverted and are pessimistic, gloomy and lack self-confidence. It could be postulated that those without diagnosis have gone through life thinking 'what if' rather than achieving their full potential – thus diagnosis should be encouraged.

The data from Appendix 5 suggests that if you investigate the sub sample of individuals with moderate (10-14 traits) traits further, especially those who are degree educated but undiagnosed using gender as criteria. The results suggest, even though the sample is extremely small (N=1 females and N=5 males) that the female compared to the male: has significantly less self-esteem and feels inferior; lacks self-reliance; easily pushed around; self-blames; significantly obsessive and careful, highly disciplined, finicky; significantly more pessimistic, gloomy and depressed; significantly more outgoing and expressive; highly active; significantly more responsible; takes many more risks; are more impulsive and enjoys discussing ideas and speculating. There are several aspects of this personality that would suggest such females are highly depressive, are obsessive and self-blame amongst other traits.

Whilst she enjoys academic success, the emotional cost of gaining a degree has been high and empirical studies suggest such individuals have fought every step of the way, whilst thinking there was something odd about their inability to learn as per their peers. Further research is needed to investigate if this result is a one off or that further samples can confirm such findings.

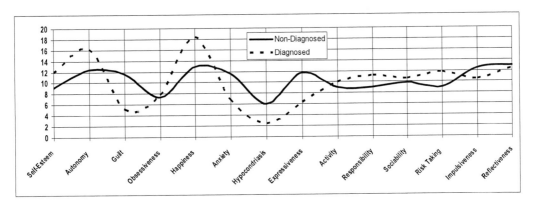

Graph 8. Moderate (10-14) trait dyslexics (degree-educated) split by those diagnosed and those who are not.

Conclusion

The first part of this research study begun by investigating empirical knowledge concerning dyslexia and personality. Difficulties were found in forming generalizations, due in part to the limitations of empirical studies, in that gender and severity of disorder were ignored as dominant factors. Whilst the majority of researchers into dyslexia choose to study diagnosis and remedial frameworks for dyslexics, few look at secondary (emotional) manifestations from having a disorder, such as dyslexia. Ignoring such factors, especially when teaching dyslexics at school, ignores those that suffering human feelings, and can place difficulties in the learner/teacher dialogue. This has major repercussions in post-school learning situations, as learners can re-experience feelings of classroom failure. This study took the view that a screening measure was needed to firstly identify unidentified/ diagnosed dyslexia amongst the control sample and secondly be a means to measure the severity of the disorder. Investigations into personality were made using an experimental version of Eysenck's Personality Inventory (Extroversion-Introversion and Neuroticism-Emotional Stability scales). Investigations, concerning gender and severity of dyslexia traits suggest that profiles can be created to aid understanding of this group. Gender was an important variable and personality traits varied significantly, with males being more confident and females being more depressive. Those with moderate dyslexia (10-14 traits) were more likely to attain academic success on par with peers, than severe dyslexics (15-19 traits).

The second research study looked at post-school achievement. The ability to gain a degree was found by 46% of the whole sample (44% among those in the 10-19 trait groups, deemed to be dyslexic), and again personality was found to be a differential, along with gender and trait severity. It was interesting that there were much fewer differences between dyslexic females with and without a degree, compared to males, which could have more to do with opportunity than ability or severity of difficulty. Lastly it was investigated amongst degree educated with moderate (10-14) traits if there was differential of personality amongst those diagnosed, to those undiagnosed, the later hypothesised to have coped without additional assistance and considerable self doubt due to ignorance of their disorder. Results indicate wide differences, significantly those diagnosed were being more independent, not regretting past actions, more optimistic, resistant to irrational fears, carefree and even tempered. Thus it was concluded that diagnosis is important for resilience amongst dyslexics.

The data suggests a depressive profile for moderate (10-14) trait individual who have gained a degree without diagnosis. This suggests they will be introverted, pessimistic, gloomy, lack self-confidence and will self-doubt. Such a profile even after attaining an academic qualification that many dyslexics and non-dyslexics do not gain, suggests the huge emotional cost of gaining such a qualification and growing up that they weren't quite normal without any apparent reason or support. Appendix 5 took the data one stage further and found that there were huge gender differences with the Female (however there was only N=1, compared to N=5 Males) having a more extreme and depressive personality profile, thus such a conclusion should be taken with caution.

Table 3 creates profiles for academically successful and unsuccessful adult dyslexics with moderate (10-14) traits. As noted earlier, those with severe dyslexia (15-19 traits) would have more extreme personality profiles. Table 3 suggests a framework for those dealing with adult and child dyslexics, which will suggest traits suitable for academic success/resilience and what secondary traits failure promotes.

To conclude, the measures used in both research studies were been successful in creating credible and likely profiles for both successful and unsuccessful dyslexics. Distinctions can now be made between dyslexics of varying severity and genders - allowing an insight to coping strategies (personality attributes) are developed by dyslexic adults. Investigations of academically successful and unsuccessful dyslexics resulted in profiles highlighting fewer personality attribute differences between successful and unsuccessful females, compared to males. The data suggests the emotional cost of having a learning disability such as dyslexia seems huge and those who are highly intelligent are frustrated, and develop certain abnormal personality traits or coping strategies to gain academic recognition along with their peers. Females seem to pay a high emotional cost in gaining academic recognition and this is an area which needs further invest.igation.

Table 3. The dyslexic adult personality (academically successful and unsuccessful)

ACADEMICALLY SUCCESSFUL DYSLEXIC MALES	ACADEMICALLY SUCCESSFUL DYSLEXIC FEMALES
Physically inactive and lethargic Casual, easy going and have less need for order Resistant to irrational fears or anxieties Confidence in themselves/abilities Enjoys freedom, independent and are realistic about abilities Does not regret past actions/behaviour Cheerful, optimistic and mentally healthy Careless, late and unpredictable Enjoys socializing and meets people easily Lives dangerously, can be gamblers and enjoys taking risk Likes ideas, discussions and speculations	Does not regret past actions/behaviour Cheerful, optimistic and mentally healthy Resistant to irrational fears or anxieties Systematic, orderly and can be cautious
ACADEMICALLY UNSUCCESSFUL DYSLEXIC MALES	**ACADEMICALLY UNSUCCESSFUL DYSLEXIC FEMALES**
Careful, highly disciplined and finicky Easily upset by things that go wrong Active and energetic Has low self-opinion and feel unattractive failures Lacks self-reliance and can be easy pushed around Self-blaming and can be self-questioning of life Pessimistic, gloomy and depressed Reliable, trustworthy and a bit compulsive Few special friends and enjoys solo activities Prefers familiarity, safety and needs security	Self-blaming, and self-questioning of life Pessimistic, gloomy and can be depressed Are easily upset by things that go wrong Can make hurried and premature decisions

Appendix 1. Results for the Emotional Instability vs. Adjustment Measure and Introversion vs. Extroversion Measure

trait group	N	Self-Esteem/ Inferiority	Autonomy/ Dependence	Guilt /Guilt-Free	Obsessiveness/ Casualness	Happiness/ Depression	Anxiety/ Calm	Hypochondriacs/ Sense of Health	Expressiveness/ Inhibition	Activity/ Inactivity	Responsibility/ Irresponsibility	Sociability/ Unsociability	Risk Taking/ Carefulness	Impulsiveness/ Control	Reflective-ness/ Practicability
Females (All)	51	11.74 (8.17)	14.57 (5.56)	8.36 (5.00)	9.26 (3.36)	15.92 (7.47)	10.53 (7.46)	4.94 (5.64)	8.87 (5.38)	11.08 (6.66)	13.65 (6.24)	11.71 (6.24)	9.12 (5.08)	11.19 (5.28)	12.58 (5.23)
Males (All)	38	14.88 (7.53)	15.21 (6.51)	8.97 (5.41)	11.29 (6.51)	17.26 (7.65)	9.00 (7.75)	4.06 (4.72)	9.26 (5.69)	13.62 (6.93)	12.97 (6.30)	10.74 (6.87)	9.24 (4.63)	14.03 (5.60)	12.44 (5.70)
Controls	43	12.88 (7.8)	13.53 (5.29)	8.72 (4.50)	11.09 (5.93)	16.60 (7.58)	9.88 (7.64)	4.63 (5.64)	10.07 (6.19)	12.14 (7.47)	14.24 (6.56)	11.31 (7.85)	8.67 (5.05)	12.50 (5.47)	12.07 (5.61)
Dyslexics	44	13.05 (8.32)	16.07 (6.29)	8.48 (5.74)	9.05 (5.72)	16.30 (7.56)	9.98 (7.57)	4.57 (4.99)	8.00 (4.50)	12.02 (6.28)	12.57 (5.87)	11.34 (6.87)	9.64 (4.72)	12.14 (5.69)	12.95 (5.20)
50% Percentile (Eysenck and Wilson (1991))		21.5	20.5	7.5	9.5	22.5	15.5	5.5	11.5	16.5	14.5	16.5	15.5	17.5	17.5
0-4 Traits	18	15.83 (7.41)	15.50 (5.27)	7.56 (3.43)	10.83 (4.62)	21.22 (4.88)	5.67 (5.90)	4.00 (4.83)	7.83 (5.16)	10.50 (6.53)	14.78 (6.86)	13.17 (9.72)	9.33 (6.16)	12.06 (5.92)	13.61 (5.33)
5-9 Traits	23	16.22 (7.27)	14.91 (5.81)	8.35 (5.42)	11.74 (6.33)	16.78 (7.40)	10.13 (7.86)	4.96 (5.59)	9.39 (5.37)	13.68 (7.03)	15.18 (5.80)	13.00 (7.11)	8.86 (5.19)	11.96 (5.36)	12.36 (4.90)
10-14 Traits	30	10.27 (7.35)	13.90 (6.38)	9.47 (5.78)	8.67 (5.83)	14.30 (6.85)	10.63 (6.30)	3.60 (4.41)	8.83 (5.21)	10.70 (6.39)	10.87 (5.86)	9.63 (6.31)	12.43 (6.05)	12.43 (6.05)	11.87 (5.56)
15-19 Traits	16	10.13 (8.75)	15.63 (6.22)	8.50 (5.22)	9.38 (6.38)	14.63 (9.29)	13.13 (9.35)	6.63 (6.47)	10.19 (6.59)	14.25 (7.31)	14.06 (5.77)	10.13 (5.78)	8.13 (3.38)	13.00 (4.82)	12.75 (6.05)
0-4 Female Traits	13	15.69 (7.16)	14.31 (5.63)	7.92 (3.75)	9.69 (4.09)	21.54 (4.88)	6.92 (6.17)	4.62 (5.42)	8.08 (5.80)	9.69 (6.50)	16.77 (6.46)	14.77 (9.99)	9.00 (5.87)	11.38 (6.04)	13.31 (5.36)
5-9 Female Traits	12	16.50 (7.44)	14.50 (6.38)	6.75 (4.63)	9.67 (6.26)	15.75 (7.79)	11.25 (7.14)	4.00 (5.33)	10.75 (6.20)	14.73 (7.64)	14.18 (5.71)	13.36 (7.02)	9.27 (5.10)	11.45 (5.66)	13.09 (3.62)
10-14 Female Traits	19	8.58 (6.43)	15.16 (6.15)	8.21 (5.82)	8.53 (5.22)	14.21 (6.62)	9.95 (6.56)	3.95 (5.01)	8.11 (4.46)	8.84 (5.05)	10.89 (5.22)	9.32 (6.63)	10.26 (4.51)	10.84 (5.37)	12.05 (5.75)
15-19 Females Traits	8	6.38 (9.81)	13.25 (6.25)	11.00 (4.57)	8.63 (6.30)	11.63 (8.70)	15.75 (9.59)	8.75 (7.32)	9.88 (5.57)	12.75 (7.31)	13.50 (6.99)	10.88 (6.30)	7.50 (4.54)	11.63 (4.37)	10.88 (5.54)
0-4 Male Traits	5	16.20 (8.90)	18.60 (2.51)	6.60 (2.51)	13.80 (5.02)	20.40 (6.37)	2.40 (3.91)	2.40 (2.51)	7.20 (3.42)	12.60 (6.84)	9.60 (5.37)	9.00 (8.49)	10.20 (7.53)	13.80 (6.86)	14.40 (5.77)
5-9 Male Traits	11	17.00 (7.36)	15.36 (5.39)	10.09 (5.89)	14.00 (5.85)	17.91 (7.15)	8.91 (8.76)	6.00 (6.15)	7.91 (4.09)	12.64 (6.55)	16.18 (5.98)	12.64 (7.53)	8.45 (5.50)	12.27 (5.27)	11.64 (6.02)
10-14 Male Traits	11	13.18 (8.22)	11.73 (7.88)	11.64 (5.28)	8.91 (7.02)	14.45 (7.57)	11.82 (5.53)	3.00 (3.29)	10.09 (6.33)	13.91 (7.38)	10.82 (7.13)	10.18 (5.98)	9.09 (4.78)	15.18 (6.42)	11.55 (5.47)
15-19 Male Traits	8	13.88 (5.99)	18.00 (5.56)	6.00 (4.81)	10.13 (6.79)	17.63 (9.41)	10.50 (8.93)	4.50 (5.07)	10.50 (7.86)	15.75 (7.48)	14.63 (4.66)	9.38 (4.66)	8.75 (1.75)	14.38 (5.13)	14.63 (6.30)

Appendix 2. Successful Dyslexics – Degree Educated

trait group	N	Self-Esteem/ Inferiority	Autonomy/ Dependence	Guilt /Guilt-Free	Obsessiveness/ Casualness	Happiness/ Depression	Anxiety/ Calm	Hypochondriacs/ Sense of Health	Expressiveness/ Inhibition	Activity/ Inactivity	Responsibility/ Irresponsibility	Sociability/ Unsociability	Risk Taking/ Carefulness	Impulsiveness/ Control	Reflective-ness/ Practicality
0-04 F	6	15.43 (8.38)	14.14 (7.29)	8.29 (3.25)	9 (4.90)	20.29 (5.44)	7.29 (5.15)	6 (6.48)	8.14 (6.18)	9 (6.48)	17.43 (7.30)	12.86 (8.25)	8.14 (6.41)	10.71 (5.71)	14 (5.83)
0-04 M	3	13.5 (14.85)	19.5 (2.12)	4.5 (2.12)	10.5 (6.36)	24 (4.24)	0.00	1.5 (2.12)	9 (4.24)	12 (0.00)	6 (4.24)	7.5 (10.61)	13.5 (10.61)	15 (4.24)	13.5 (2.12)
05-09 F	7	14.57 (6.58)	12.43 (4.04)	6.43 (4.72)	8 (6.78)	15.86 (7.29)	10.71 (6.90)	2.14 (3.34)	8.57 (.58)	15.86 (7.24)	14.14 (6.41)	11.14 (7.43)	9.86 (4.81)	9.43 (5.59)	12.43 (4.04)
05-09 M	4	23 (3.46)	21 (6.00)	6 (3.00)	11.67 (5.51)	25.67 (2.31)	5.33 (4.73)	4 (1.73)	10 (4.58)	13 (6.93)	17 (6.24)	19 (8.66)	14 (3.46)	14 (6.24)	12 (5.20)
10-14 F	12	9.08 (6.93)	14.77 (5.26)	7.15 (5.81)	8.54 (4.88)	15 (7.04)	9 (6.82)	3.92 (5.39)	8.15 (5.08)	9.46 (3.84)	10.85 (5.13)	9.23 (5.80)	10.15 (4.34)	10.08 (6.13)	12.31 (6.94)
10-14 M	4	16.5 (5.74)	14.25 (5.12)	9.75 (4.50)	4.5 (3.87)	19.5 (3.87)	8.25 (2.87)	3.75 (2.87)	9.75 (5.66)	9.75 (6.65)	8.25 (10.78)	13.5 (6.24)	12 (4.90)	15 (10.39)	13.5 (5.20)
15-19 F	3	5 (8.66)	11 (6.24)	12 (5.20)	8 (3.46)	11 (6.24)	16 (9.17)	11 (4.58)	7 (4.58)	14 (6.93)	14 (10.54)	14 (6.93)	9 (3.00)	11 (1.73)	16 (1.73)
15-19 M	1	18 (0.00)	21 (0.00)	3 (0.00)	3 (0.00)	21 (0.00)	6 (0.00)	6 (0.00)	0 (0.00)	15 (0.00)	9 (0.00)	12 (0.00)	9 (0.00)	24 (0.00)	15 (0.00)

Appendix 3. Unsuccessful Dyslexics – Non-Degree Educated

trait group	N	Self-Esteem/ Inferiority	Autonomy/ Dependence	Guilt /Guilt-Free	Obsessiveness/ Casualness	Happiness/ Depression	Anxiety/ Calm	Hypochondriacs/ Sense of Health	Expressiveness/ Inhibition	Activity/ Inactivity	Responsibility/ Irresponsibility	Sociability/ Unsociability	Risk Taking/ Carefulness	Impulsiveness/ Control	Reflective-ness/ Practicality
0-04 F	6	16 (6.20)	14.50 (3.51)	7.50 (4.55)	10.50 (3.15)	23 (4.10)	6.50 (7.89)	3 (3.79)	8 (5.90)	10.50 (7.04)	16 (6.90)	17 (12.10)	10 (5.59)	12.17 (6.85)	12.50 (5.17)
0-04 M	3	18 (6.00)	18 (3.00)	8 (1.73)	16 (4.58)	18 (5.20)	4 (4.58)	3 (3.00)	6 (3.00)	13 (9.64)	12 (5.20)	10 (9.17)	8 (6.24)	13 (7.55)	15 (7.94)
05-09 F	5	16.80 (9.15)	17.40 (8.32)	7.20 (5.02)	12 (5.20)	15.60 (9.34)	12 (8.22)	6.60 (6.84)	13.80 (4.55)	12.75 (8.96)	14.25 (5.12)	17.25 (4.50)	8.25 (6.18)	15 (4.24)	14.25 (2.87)
05-09 M	8	14.75 (7.27)	13.25 (3.54)	11.63 (6.09)	14.88 (6.08)	15 (6.00)	10.25 (9.78)	6.75 (7.13)	7.13 (3.91)	12.50 (6.69)	15.88 (6.29)	10.25 (5.97)	6.38 (4.66)	11.63 (5.18)	11.50 (6.63)
10-14 F	6	7.50 (5.61)	16 (5.25)	10.50 (5.61)	8.50 (6.41)	12.50 (5.82)	12 (6.00)	4 (4.52)	8 (3.10)	7.50 (7.29)	11 (5.90)	9.50 (8.78)	10.50 (5.28)	12.50 (2.95)	11.50 (5.82)

Appendix 4. Successful Dyslexics – Degree Educated, Diagnosed and Undiagnosed Dyslexics

Degree_D	N	Self-Esteem/ Inferiority	Autonomy/ Dependence	Guilt /Guilt-Free	Obsessiveness/ Casualness	Happiness/ Depression	Anxiety/ Calm	Hypocondriasis/ Sense of Health	Expressiveness/ Inhibition	Activity/ Inactivity	Responsibility/ Irresponsibility	Sociability/ Unsociability	Risk Taking/ Carefulness	Impulsiveness/ Control	Reflective-ness/ Practicability
Non-Diagnosed	7	9.14 (7.15)	12.43 (5.0)	11.57 (4.04)	7.29 (4.54)	12.86 (7.69)	11.57 (4.72)	6 (6.24)	11.71 (6.21)	9 (5.20)	9 (6.48)	9.856 (4.88)	9 (3.46)	12.43 (7.63)	12.86 (7.88)
Diagnosed	9	12 (7.48)	16.20 (4.73)	5.10 (4.91)	7.80 (5.33)	18.30 (4.99)	6.90 (6.33)	2.40 (3.09)	6.30 (3.86)	9.90 (4.01)	11.10 (6.79)	10.50 (7.11)	11.70 (4.79)	10.40 (7.32)	12.40 (3.86)

Appendix 5. Successful Dyslexics – Degree Educated, Undiagnosed by Gender

Degree Dyslexic and undiagnosed by gender	N	Self-Esteem/ Inferiority	Autonomy/ Dependence	Guilt /Guilt-Free	Obsessiveness/ Casualness	Happiness/ Depression	Anxiety/ Calm	Hypocondriasis/ Sense of Health	Expressiveness/ Inhibition	Activity/ Inactivity	Responsibility/ Irresponsibility	Sociability/ Unsociability	Risk Taking/ Carefulness	Impulsiveness/ Control	Reflective-ness/ Practicability
Females	7	21	21	15	0	24	9	6	21	18	0	15	6	18	21
Males	9	6.8 (5.89)	11.4 (3.91)	10.8 (4.55)	8.4 (3.91)	10.2 (6.91)	12 (5.61)	6 (7.65)	11 (5.24)	6.6 (3.23)	12 (4.74)	8.4 (4.45)	9 (3.67)	9 (5.61)	12 (8.49)

Limitations

This study was quantitative in nature and thus the measures chosen, data collected and interpreted have certain limitations, including: (1) The study used self-reported dyslexics and non-dyslexic controls. Due to the limitations of time, no paperwork was gained to confirm their diagnosis, which was why a dyslexia screening measure was used. This also helped to screen likely and undiagnosed dyslexics from the control sample; (2) The personality measures were experimental in nature, however as they were personally approved by Professor Eysenck, the measure creator, it was thought to be valid enough for the study. Subsequent data suggests the norm data from the original measure was incompatible, with the 0-4 trait sample data (from this study) as a more likely norm to work from; (3) The study took place by mail using freepost envelopes. Whilst the measures were not time based, this methodology might have affected the results given. However as the marking was highly complex, it would have been hard for most participants to pre-judge their results; (4) The personality measures were chosen for a number of reasons such as respectability and having numerous sub scales, however commentators might suggest other or more modern measures with similar respectability and sub scales; (5) The resulting data used to make the generalization concerning depression in undiagnosed degree educated individuals, with moderate (10-14) dyslexic traits with gender personality differential was based on a very small sample and should be taken with caution.

Interview Study

Abstract

There has been a distinct lack of research investigating the emotional aspects of having dyslexia, compared to studies on the sources of dyslexia and treatment. Whilst a few researchers are now looking at emotional manifestations, both gender and depression have been areas with little or no empirical research.

This paper took the view that prior research suggests that gender is an important factor in how dyslexics deal with failure, academic difficulties and difficulties affecting all interactions with society, specifically that females cope more emotionally than males and that depression was more likely in females than males.

This study interviewed N=7 adult dyslexics with clinical depression (N=4 females and N=3 males) to create profiles of how they cope and have coped in relation to their dyslexia from childhood to adulthood. Each interview lasted for at least 45 minutes. Overall the study found that females experienced feelings of perfectionism, isolation, withdrawal and self-blame, whilst males tended to use denial and helplessness forms of defence mechanisms. In all cases avoidance of writing and tasks (that would highlight difficulties) were found and that dealing with their child's teachers was problematic and brought back highly emotional feelings from their childhood. Such feelings came from the smell, small chairs and layout of schools along with feeling belittled by teachers – as if they were still a helpless child. The majority were university educated and to reach such a level in education there had been a huge emotional cost, which in some cases had lead to self-harm and attempted suicide attempts.

Methodology

This project was instigated to study adult dyslexics diagnosed with clinical depression, and investigate if other variables are important in understanding why depression is triggered as a coping strategy. These may include: gender, task avoidance, isolation and family relationships.

The sample was gained from three yahoo email mail groups in the fields of dyslexia and mental health which the investigator had been tracking for at least a year prior to requesting volunteers. On two occasions between October and December 2007 an email poster was sent to the mailing list requesting men and women with dyslexia who had suffered or are suffering from clinical depression, for a research study. The investigator either required copies of dyslexia and depression diagnosis or sufficient evidence to confirm such criteria for inclusion in the study. Whilst the total size of the three mailing groups is unknown, it is estimated to be in excess of 250 email addresses. In total N=7 volunteers took park (N=4 females, aged 25, 27, 29, 34 and N=3 males, aged 48, 50, 58), whilst the aim was N=10 (N=5 males and N=5 females). However due to the depth of interviews, the number gained was deemed to be sufficient for the study.

A Semi-structured interview was selected for this study as it allowed flexibility to evolve the interview script where needed. Such techniques have already been used with dyslexics (Riddick, 1996; Alexander-Passe, 2004a, b), as it removes the need for reading and writing. However, as this study group may have problems recalling events, an option of sending the transcript to participants to check and amend was given and noted at the start of each interview. Confidentiality was reiterated at several points (in the initial email poster, setting the date and time for the telephone interview, and at the start and end of each interview). Participants were told that their names and personal details would be changed/camouflaged and that they would receive a copy of the final paper. Out of the N=7 interviews, N=6 were conducted over the phone from the more emotionally secure surroundings of their home environment. The remaining interview took place via email with the interview script sent to be completed, with additional questions emailed to gain clarification where needed. interviews took between 45-60 minutes each and were audio taped, these were transcribed and emailed to participants to check and amend if they wished.

The N=26 items for the experimental semi-structured interview (See Table 4) were selected from the author's prior research on dyslexia, coping and depression (Alexander-Passe, 2004b, 2006), interview studies by other researchers (Riddick, 1996; Edwards, 1994) and empirical studies concerning triggers relating to depression and education (Frydenberg, 1997; Aldwin, 2000).

Table 4. Semi-Structured Interview Script

1. Please describe how you are feeling today? Are you taking any depression medication at present?
2. Please describe your life/yourself? (I need to create a description of you e.g. age, education, job, character, personality etc)
3. Do you enjoy life?
4. Please describe your childhood? Was it happy? (e.g. with your family)
5. Do you have any siblings? Do you think you were treated fairly/unfairly to your siblings?
6. Please describe your time at school? Was it enjoyable?
7. Did you ever get frustrated from your learning difficulties?
8. What does dyslexia mean to you?
9. Is dyslexia something positive or negative?
10. How does dyslexia affect your daily life?
11. What classic dyslexia symptoms to you have?
12. Do you think your hobbies help you? Giving you self-confidence?
13. Do you ever blame your dyslexia for things?
14. Do you/have you ever resented your teachers at school for not seeing your difficulties?
15. Do you ever feel rejected? Please explain?
16. How does failing or getting things wrong affect you?
17. Do you ever say why me? Why am I dyslexic?
18. Do/Did you self-harm? Why? What are the triggers?
19. Have you ever thought about or tried to commit suicide? Why? What were the triggers?
20. Do you think dyslexia and depression are correlated (linked)?
21. Do you think men and women have the same chances in life? Please explain?
22. Does being women have any bearing on your depression? Please explain? Could dyslexia be linked to your triggers?
23. Do you think more men or more women get depressed?
24. Did you ever truant/run away from home?
25. How do you feel going into schools now, what triggers any negative emotions?
26. Do you enjoy being you? Please explain?

Case Studies

Andrew, aged 50yrs describes himself as average, tolerant, scatty, quick witted, honest, intelligent, caring and passionate about things to do with equality and justice. He is university educated, married with children and works as a disability employment advisor for a government body that helps others to seek re-employment. He was medicated with Prozac at the time of the interview which he says 'takes the edge of stress, incidents triggered and gives me a neutral feeling' and had been taking such medication for several months prior to the interview.

As the middle of five children he describes a 'good but poor [low-income] home life [upbringing]', but found infant and primary school an 'absolute nightmare' and was in the remedial class from his last year at primary school till the end of secondary/high school. In fact he was sent to a small remedial secondary/high school for problems with behavioural children due to his frustration at school. They first thought his learning problems were due to eye sight problems but after getting glasses, his reading and writing still didn't improve. Placing him in a remedial class was humiliating and along with being labelled lazy and stupid he felt dumped in the 'spaz' class for those too thick to learn. He coped by being aggressive and was excluded from school on numerous occasions.

Andrew feels that the problems concerning dyslexia are 'socially constructed' and is optimistic about dyslexia being a positive attribute. As he works for a government agency he is very fortunate to get 16 hours of support each week for his learning difficulties, but doesn't feel it is a real compensation in life. He uses a spell-checker at work and feels the word processor and email has improved his life; however he wishes to break the straightjacket of having a colleague checking his work for spelling mistakes before being released to the general public.

His dyslexia traits include a poor short-term memory, data overload and organisation problems; however he uses hobbies to increase 'learning, determination and focus'. His partner is relied upon to organise bills and all other paperwork. However he feels that he suffers daily from frustration, embarrassment, rejection from his difficulties, which 'gets him down' and can be subject to mood swings when he gets things wrong, he gets 'very angry with myself', however has never self-harmed as a result.

He notes one of his strongest memories from childhood is a time when he was the only child in his class who was unable to write his own name of the blackboard at school and was made to miss playtime until he could. He notes he felt 'so frustrated, angry and very sad', he definitely thinks that his dyslexia and depression are linked and even thinking back to his unhappy school life for the interview is giving him physical stress reactions. He recalls being an insomniac, having nagging foot and stomach pains as a child, and being 'anxious and frightened'. Whilst he never truanted, it was due to having an older sibling at the school and strict parenting, but remembers always wanting to 'run out of school, to scream and shout when I [he] didn't understand' things. Even now returning to school as a parent, brings back emotive feelings 'the smell of the school, I hate it, the small chairs, the paintings in the corridors…it reminds me of being outside the headmasters office, in trouble again'.

Jack, aged 58yrs describes himself as very happy, fulfilled, eccentric, perfectionist but troubled with back problems. He is university educated, married with children and is a home tutor for dyslexics. He is not taking any depression medication, has not for the last 16yrs and describes his as reactive depression.

Describing his childhood he says that his parents were uneducated but gave him a 'lovely and supportive environment' to grow up in. He describes his time at grammar school as generally enjoyable but he had and still has major problems with mathematics. He attributes his learning to read at 8yrs old to a teacher called 'Mr Malcolm', which would suggest that his learning to read was a long and hard battle, and he found progress reports sent to his parents as 'quite frightening'. Whilst there were no reports of truancy there was no mention of his years at primary school which may suggest repressing such painful memories, although his attending secondary grammar school (a select school) would suggest a certain degree of academic performance at primary school.

Jack comes over as highly confident but sees dyslexia as 'not a gift, [but] a poisoned cup and a double edged sword', whilst acknowledging that many see positive attributes such as 'imaginative stuff and lateral thinking'. He has more difficulties than he would like to admit to including short term memory, left/right confusion and data overload.

As a teacher he says that he was a master at avoiding paperwork 'avoided paperwork, like crazy', he used to either ignore forms or get others to do them for him. His downfall leading to depression was the introduction of the UK's 'National Curriculum' which created more paperwork than he was able to avoid, noting 'the demands went up and the back-up and all collapsed'. He says that he 'literally burst into tears' when he was faced with it. His depression lasted for three years suggesting the long-term effects of avoiding for so long are hard to repair. He notes that he hates repetitive clerical work and form filling and will avoid it like the plague, but notes he is meticulous keeping teaching records regarding students. He also uses his 'long suffering wife as a secretary and reminder'.

Jack mentions that when he found out his daughter was dyslexic and wasn't getting the help needed at school, his anger at the school brought him out of his depression 'my wife said I whipped out my depression at a rate of knots…because I wanted something done'. He comes across as using humour as a means to externally cope and disguise his dyslexia creating a defensive persona.

Whilst he notes the correlation between dyslexia and depression he suggests that his chronic back problem from a traffic accident and being of mixed Irish decent may also be strong variables.

Peter, aged 48yrs initially describes himself as relaxed and happy but as soon as the interview develops it is evident that he is unhappy with mood swings and unfulfilled in life. Whilst married with children, he keeps himself busy to avoid thinking about things 'If I don't keep busy I tend to sit around doing nothing and that's when the depression sort of sets in', he lacks hobbies and seems socially introverted. He is educated to diploma level and has changed careers several times from nursing to training, noting bullying in the work place. Whilst not mediated at present, his last course of depression mediation was only two and a half years ago.

Peter's childhood was not enjoyable, with bullying both at school and socially. Whilst he is unable to pin-point why he was the victim, it may be the case that he took a 'poor me' stance at school as a cry for help but was seen as easy prey by his peers. He felt singled out at school when put into remedial classes and felt misunderstood by both teachers and parents. He recalls dreading school reports to his parents, as they always noted 'could do better, doesn't try, underachieves, and doesn't take care'. Having non-dyslexic brothers meant unfair comparison at home and his parents writing him off which made home life difficult. He recalls that his brothers were supported at home and academically (by his parents), whilst he wasn't, such comparison meant complict with his brothers and encountered abuse from his father for underachieving.

Peter sees dyslexia meaning 'I struggle a lot with things', be it reading, writing, spelling, short term memory, poor concentration and uses several techniques to protect himself from humiliation by being a perfectionist. 'I write anything, say a letter or an essay I leave it for a while and then get back to it again and re-read it, and probably rewrite it, and do the same several times before I think it's right'. He also avoids feared situations by spending a lot of time by himself and has only one close friend.

He feels his depression is highly related to his difficulties at school and clearly resents his teachers for not identifying his problems. Even when he was identified at 19yrs old and asked to attend remedial classes at college he was unwilling to go, due to perceptions of repeating the feelings of school failure. As an adult he feels rejected and gets angry with himself for making silly daily mistakes. He blames his dyslexia for lack of academic success leading to a well paid career, however he uses self-blame 'I will not achieve it, I will not get it' if left to think too much.

As a child he used to truant and run away from home as a means to escape school work and bullying pressures. All his emotions from school have affected his ability to enter school as a parent for his own children, noting the smells and layout as bring back all the emotions of fear and panic. Looking back, with his two grown up children he only entered the school two or three times as the triggers childhood memories were so great.

Suzanne is 27yrs old and describes herself as creative, sensitive, artistic, thoughtful, emphatic and currently in a long-term relationship. She is currently taking citalopram and olanzapine for depression. Due to her current symptoms she is only working part-time as a nanny and hasn't worked full time for over a year.

Growing up in a family with two younger siblings, she had a rocky relationship with her parents who she felt resulted in her becoming rebellious and moody, as a teenager was as a reaction to her parent's constant fighting and the extra responsibility to take care of her younger siblings as her parents worked long hours. This may suggest extra pressure to an already pressurised school life, enough to tip individuals over the emotional edge.

She notes frustration and difficulty with reading at school at the age of 12 which would suggest her strategies were sufficient for primary school but not for secondary school. She notes her dyslexia wasn't diagnosed till she left school and was at college, due to struggling at Advanced level (pre-university examination) stage. Her interview suggests that she worked extremely hard to overcome her learning difficulties and this has had an effect on her emotional wellbeing. On the surface she comes over as competent and intelligent but internally she has been screaming for help resulting in self-harm from 4yrs old, from the anger and frustration, cutting her arms and belly with 'scratching my hands or bang parts of my body like my head', and is now 'having therapy which is addressing this issue'. More recently overdosing this summer and alcohol damage as escapism suggest that current effects of dyslexia as an adult are still emotionally damaging.

Suzanne is creative and uses her creative talents to maintain her self-confidence with hobbies in poetry, painting and learning to play the violin. Such hobbies are used to express her emotions and deal with her daily struggles.

Due to her dyslexia she struggles with reading, word comprehension, getting muddled up and mathematics which causes her embarrassment and lack of confidence in speaking to others. She is unsure if her dyslexia is related to her dyslexia and notes being a female and hormonal as other reasons for her emotional turmoil. She notes no negative feelings about entering school and aims to retrain as a teacher next year.

Nancy is 29yrs old and describes herself as an outgoing, caring, considerate person. Whilst not married she has three children and is studying for a degree in social work. Whilst diagnosed as depressive by her GP and prescribed medication she has never actually taken any, preferring to manage it herself.

Her childhood was an unhappy time for her as she was not diagnosed dyslexic till she was 23yrs old. She remembers thinking she was really stupid growing up as she couldn't learn like her peers and just didn't feel she fitted in at school or home. She was an only child with a mother with depression, suggests isolation as a variable to her depression. She dreaded parent evenings and school reports as her parents were never satisfied with her level of effort which she gives as a reason for her first being depressed at 6-7 yrs old. Overall my parents were unsympathetic to my problems and just thought I was stupid or lazy. She found school pointless, however she was very good at hiding her problems by 'keeping my head down and avoided, I avoided writing a lot….I was avoiding both words and writing'. She was put into the bottom class for all her GCSE subjects and this she felt just confirmed her low self-opinion of herself and led to bullying. She notes no positive feedback given by teachers.

Nancy struggles constantly with her dyslexia (e.g. problems with short-term memory, left/right confusion and data overload) and any failure makes her feel stupid and leads her into a spiral of despair, triggering childhood feelings of helplessness. She perceives dyslexia as both negative and positive and talks about how it makes her feel continuously stupid leaving her emotionally drained, When asked to name the positives and negatives she was able to list loads of negatives but few positives.

Whilst no physical hobbies were noted she has enjoyed in the past, volunteering to help others less fortunate than herself, she found the positive contribution and interaction with people helpful and enjoyable. Which would suggest empathy towards other people who have struggled in their lives and this has been useful in putting her own difficulties into perspective?

Whilst resenting her old teachers for not identifying her learning difficulties, she notes how complex her avoidance strategies were, even to the point of losing books that needed to be submitted in for marking. She would rather be thought as careless for loosing books than stupid for being able to read and write. She only had a small group of friends at school and felt isolated and rejected by her peers. Even now she feels rejected by her group at university as she needed to learn in other less noisy rooms, which is misunderstood by her peers.

Nancy's main coping strategy is perfectionism and she will spend days writing and re-writing assignments as any imperfection or bad mark is perceived as complete failure and she beats herself up about such things. Such perfection is linked to her need for control, without that control her depression and feelings are inadequacy are triggered. She notes no self-harm or suicide but mentions that whilst she didn't truant or run away from home she felt forced out of her family home at 16yrs old, but feels she would have left of her own choice at around that age due to hostility at home. She correlates her depression to her dyslexia, due to the emotional wreckage of coping with the symptoms.

On a positive note she has a good relationship with her child's teachers and feels no triggers of despair visiting their school. Also she notes the advances in help for children at her children's school with special needs, as they are helped inclusively in a warm and friendly atmosphere.

Louise is 25yrs old, single and describes herself as very motivated, perfectionist and enthusiastic but a stubborn person who enjoys life. She is a college trained health worker and a former school health educator working for the NHS. She feels more comfortable working in a structured environment and has not taken any depression medication for 12 months, when she was prescribed Anitripatine to deal with an unhappy and stressful working environment with drug addicts.

Her childhood home life was complex as she has three brothers and a mother suffering with depression, and her parents divorced when she was 13yrs old, which helped to release the tension at home, she then lived with her father. However as her father worked long hours, she felt she was spending too much time taking care of her siblings, running the home and cleaning up her brothers mess as a surrogate mother figure. She enjoyed primary school but ran into trouble at secondary school when her coping strategies were not developed enough to deal with the increased academic pressures. She was later diagnosed dyslexic at university which meant a childhood of growing up thinking she was lazy and stupid. She was sent to a very academic technology secondary school which she notes was a mistake as she is more vocational in nature. She was forced into taking 13 GCSEs which is a lot by anyone's standards and was required to attend summer school to catch-up she felt unable to confide in anyone that she was unable to cope, noting the extra burden (time and effort) of doing academic work with an underlying undiagnosed learning problem. The workload was huge along with constant pressure of deadlines which lead her to take an overdose at 14yrs old.

Her problems were made worse by the fact she verbally comes across as intelligent which meant rather than being put into remedial classes she was put in the top streams for subjects. Things changed after her attempted suicide, she was bullied at school and common knowledge of her attempt made her easy prey in the playground.

She feels that dyslexia is an excuse 'for not doing things', but paradoxically she feels it's a reason to explain why she struggles with tasks. Whilst clearly noting her perfectionist tendencies, she sees dyslexic as an excuse for not being good enough at things. Her difficulties affect her daily life, especially short term memory, concentration, left/right, directional, writing backward and data overload problems. Lstly she notes 'it makes you feel kind of, well inferior because if I wasn't dyslexic it would be easier, [well…] I think it would be'.

Louise does a lot of voluntary work in supporting homeless women which she finds enjoyable as it's a contrast to her work, noting 'you can se their needs are more intense [greater and this] makes you feel better about your own life'. Whilst this helps her self-confidence it also could be seen as escapism from difficulties which can at times get her down, especially when they relate to work pressures.

Given the choice, Louise feels she would prefer not being dyslexic and whilst she is creative, it is not a large enough compensation for the difficulties experienced and the lack of support given growing up, 'all I knew is that it made me think I was stupid without a reason for it'. Whilst acknowledging that she would not be in the job she was in if she hadn't had the empathy for other children going through problems and experiencing some anger and frustration growing up.

Comparison to her non-academic brothers meant that they received the support and help needed and she was seen as attention seeking which she perceived unfair and annoying, but she intellectualises that such behaviour is normal in large families. She does however note one tutor at secondary school who gave her the support she needed and dealt with unsympathetic teachers. Whilst never truanting from school she left home when she was 18 and never returned which suggests that the pressures at home were great.

She felt growing up that she was a problem child without anyone to help her and her coping strategy has been perfectionism to avoid getting things wrong and getting adverse feedback. When she does get things wrong she beats herself up about it and has self-harmed as a result. She finds life hard when there are big life changes and when life gets repetitive and these are triggers for her depression. Louise feels that her dyslexia and depression are related and that had she had not struggled at school growing up she would never have got depressed and self-harmed at 14yrs old.

Mary is 34yrs old and describes herself as an emphatic, artistic and anxious person. She is a mother and a mature student studying for a PhD. She has not taken any of her Cromosona depression medication for the last two weeks as she has run out and is trying to survive non-medicated. This anxiety medication was prescribed 6 months ago when she felt isolated, frustrated and intense about things.

She describes her childhood as both good and very isolated, as she had a kidney illness growing up which she feels delayed her normal development, regularly knocked her in confidence and resulted in her 'finding social situations very awkward and something I would shy away from'. Due to her health problems her learning difficulties were camouflaged and 'my mum and dad didn't understand what was wrong with me so they sort of wrapped me up in cotton wool, if something happened they would hide me away from the world as well'. She has a sister without any health or learning problems and felt that from childhood had been unfairly compared to her and still feels the ugly ducking compared to her. Her parents were unable to brag about her to friends and always said 'poor Mary, she's not quite right, not normal and made it into a bigger issue than it was'. Her parents are still impressed by the fancy job and money of her sister and this is unhelpful for her emotional stability.

At school she was taken out of class and put into remedial units to learn basic reading and writing but this segregation made her feel isolated, a target for bullies and for peers to laugh at her. The remedial class was full of disruptive pupils who were there more for behavioural than learning reasons. At school and now at university she excels in art, but her abilities are constantly questioned as she was unintellectual in her other school subjects 'they don't believe I've done it [created such a good painting], it's not possible – there must be a reason behind it (cheating etc)' as she has difficulty getting her message across verbally and on paper due to her dyslexia. It makes her angry and upset and she finds that she must 'constantly prove yourself all the time, that's it's my work and it is me that has done it, you constantly have to fight and it can make you feel very isolated'.

Rather than lashing out she took the abuse internally until one point in her twenties where it became too much and she exploded 'I was sort of psychotic and I just had enough, I just had enough of everybody and I went inside myself and I went external and lashed out'.

Whilst presently feeling happy about being dyslexic, she expressed in the past that she hated it and wished she wasn't dyslexic. She is now at a university which she perceives as un-dyslexic friendly, however remarking 'when you get to masters and doctorate level, any dyslexia support is less structured'. She perceives dyslexia as an inability to deal with structure and lateral thinking, she personally has difficulties with reading and writing, short-term memory, word recall, spelling, balance, left and right and mathematics. Whilst she writes daily in her note books, she avoided writing at school and will still avoid writing if required for tutor/examination assessment. She has just completed an art based masters and feels that she needs to solve problems visually and creatively, at home, university and life.

Mary deals with life by being a perfectionist and when she was psychotic in her twenties she was advised to learn to be imperfect, in that the pressure to get everything right is too much for some people. However in a very academic environment she feels ridiculed and that the ability to read and write is perceived as a sign of intelligence. Recently she went for a part-time cashier job with a leading supermarket and failed the basic literacy test, she felt humiliated and 'felt herself shrinking' and the interviewer could not understand how she was doing a PhD and couldn't spell. She commonly beats herself up and calls herself stupid if she gets things wrong; however more recently she is learning to let things go and say its other people's ignorance. However when she fails in things it triggers issues from childhood concerning withdrawing, isolation and frustration.

She has attempted suicide many times when she has thought to rid the world of her herself and her problems. She also ran away from home when she was 16yrs old after feeling bullied at home, but when she returned it just re-enforced the idea that she was dependent on others for help and support and this made her even more depressed. Even as a mother, she questions how much her dyslexic abilities affect her ability to be a mother and organise all the things needed for son's interaction with school. 'Going back into school, for my son, brings back feelings of my time there. He tells me off for some of the things I say, as it does trigger off my anxiety about [my time] being at school' luckily her son's school is better than her own and her doing a PhD is a role model for her son as they are both dyslexic. She notes the smell and size of chairs are the triggers to her school anxiety and still finds herself changing back to a small child when she talks to her son's teachers.

Discussion

A number of themes develop from the interviews which will now be discussed along with the original hypothesis that gender, task avoidance, isolation and family relationships might be important variables in understanding why dyslexics get clinically depressed.

The project began by asking participants to complete both a pre-interview questionnaire and a number of standardised measures to assess coping, depression and locus of control before the interview took place. The pre-interview pack contained a lot of forms requiring substantial reading. This was designed to assess the ability to communicate both in these measures and in our form based society. Interestingly only two of the males (66%) and only one of the females (25%) returned the pre-interview pack, along with one female withdrawing from the study after being sent the pre-interview pack, which may statistically suggest male dyslexics are more able to survive in today's word based society, alternatively it could be argued that the females prioritised their lives and these forms were deemed to be unnecessary or they felt they would trigger their anxiety and thus defended against it.

From the interviews, gender differences are suggested in a number of areas: (1) isolation seems to be a key to why females get depressed in that they seem to withdraw when they can't cope with the academic demands of school; (2) self-harm seems to be predominant among the females of this study suggesting self-hate and limited ability to externalise their anger; (3) Males tend to use humour as a coping strategy and this allows them to deflect internalizing anger; and (4) Females in this study commonly choose volunteering as a hobby in environments that suggests their empathy with others who also experience problems with life.

The vast majority name perfectionism as a coping strategy which they feel helps them reduce exposure to criticism and the spiral of despair that adverse marks or failure would bring. However the extra stress that they put themselves under to get forms and letters to a certain standard is immense. Participants have noted rewriting essays several times and photo copying forms and redoing them several times before submitting a final version. Such stress is likely to confirm their inability to communicate fluently. Perfectionism is a learnt strategy developed at school which may have worked back then, but as adults is unsuitable for our modern fast moving society (e.g. emails). Children develop such strategies along with avoidance of tasks, losing homework and books and hiding in class as defence mechanisms to escape ridicule and exposure that they are different from their peers. Children at school commonly strive to be 'normal', and perception of abnormality is both traumatic and emotionally damaging. As noted earlier, Scott (2004) have suggested such trauma is similar to that of Post Traumatic Stress Disorder (PTSD) in that the long term stress and trauma can be as damaging as single episode car crashes and experience of death, with similar long-term psychological and emotional effects.

A key finding is that all participants were diagnosed with dyslexia after leaving mainstream education, which suggests that schools have failed many dyslexics and as noted by several in this study, if they had been diagnosed earlier they may not have got depressed and have experienced personal failure to such an extent. Another common feature is that participants were put into remedial classes at school which were full of children with behavioural rather than educational problems, which not only confirmed in their eyes the concept that they were thick and stupid but isolated them from their peers and made them a target for bullies.

The majority of the participants commonly used camouflage of their difficulties as a coping strategy. Most are also university educated and therefore such a strategy could be seen as successful. However, a number went to university as mature students and were only identified as dyslexic in adulthood, thus camouflaging has delayed their diagnosis. Such camouflaging has also meant that their cries for help are unseen and may have caused them to regress to depression as a greater cry for help. Also in the case of Suzanne, which was conducted via email, her response to the questions was much more guarded and positive than those conducted over the phone. Suzanne may have had the time to camouflaging responses. On reading about her childhood one is initially struck to why she was depressed leading to self-harm and suicide at 14yrs old, as her rewriting of her childhood may have been to block out such painful and emotional thoughts of her childhood or a total denial that anything adverse ever happened. It is the author's opinion that Jack also used humour to camouflage his denial of painful school events, as this would upset the carefully rewritten story of childhood which allows his extremely strong present day ego to stay intact; however it may be that if he unlocked his Pandora's Box of childhood memories he may trigger his depressive again.

Conclusions

The overriding theme of this study is that the stress of both the academic and social curriculum of school is driving some dyslexics to depression, and in some cases self-harm and attempted suicide. In every interview one sees that either cries for help have been ignored or that the participants have not had anyone to confide in. Depression only happens after a large number of strategies have failed to produce the help needed and is either a last desperate cry for help or a total rejection of help offered, and that ridding society of their problems would be the best for everyone concerned (suicide attempt).

All of those taking part in this study were diagnosed as dyslexic in adulthood and thus to a greater or lesser extent they experienced a childhood of thinking they were stupid and suffered in the hands of the numerous of teachers they have passed through. It is really surprising that apparently none of the ten or fifteen teachers they would have had, and formed a close relationship throughout their childhood, never realised the child in their care had learning problems and attempted to ensure that something was done. This can serve to illustrate the problems encountered in our mainstream educational system.

The total breakdown of help experienced by the participants of this study, along with parents lack of faith in their own knowledge that their child had problems, needs to be highlighted. Whilst educators may have the experience of teaching children, large classroom sizes mean that their ability to give one-to-one assessments is greatly limited. Riddick (1996) and the Audit Commission (2003) suggest that parents are more able to assess their child's learning difficulties than their child's teachers and that when these parents questioned their child's teachers concerning assessment they were commonly ignored and dismissed.

Camouflage and denial were found to help participants deal with present day life and such rewriting of their childhoods correlate with the defence mechanisms and strategies as found by Vaillant (1977). This was first highlighted in the email response to the interview by Suzanne but also by unpicking the interview of Jack.

This study suggests that the secondary manifestations of dealing with a learning disorder such as dyslexia maybe a significant factor for understanding why some individuals develop depression and others do not. The study has identified gender differences which suggest that female dyslexics who develop depression, feel isolated by their peer group, withdraw and then self-blame, whilst male dyslexics who develop depression may use denial and helplessness. In both genders avoidance of words, tasks and situations were commonplace and that any failure can bring back childhood memories of 'I'm stupid and unworthy'. Returning to school later to meet their own child's teachers was fraught with danger as the smell and layout of the buildings made childhood feelings resurface with many choosing to avoid such situations.

Limitations

This study was qualitative in nature and thus the data collected and interpreted have certain limitations, including: (1) the study aimed to gain N=5 Males and N=5 Females, however due to time constraints for the study only N=4 Females and N=3 Males were located. Locating dyslexics with diagnosed clinical depression proved to be very difficult. However the earlier study suggest un-diagnosed depression maybe more common; (2) The study aimed to use both paper based quantitative and qualitative measures to build profiles of participants, however as many dyslexics mentioned they avoided forms in their interviews, only 4 quantitative measure packs were returned. This may confirm their phobia towards form filing; (4) all except for one interview took place over the phone which allowed for further questioning where needed. The remaining interview took place via email and this allowed denial and camouflaging of painful childhood memories to take place which would have been less likely over the phone, depending on their defence mechanisms; (5) the samples varied in ages, with the Females much younger than the Males. There seems little difference between the samples in their ability to describe their childhood and school and thus the author concluded the age differences were negligible.

Chapter Conclusions

The chapter began by taking a look at empirical studies on dyslexia. These included: what is dyslexia; school life; teacher denial and teach training; teacher expectations; the identification of dyslexia; perceptions of normal; anxiety and self-esteem; stress; and special schools versus integration. The overriding view taken by researchers is that whilst dyslexia maybe a treatable disorder affecting both children and adults through their lives, it is how they are treated in mainstream education that can make the difference between the condition being identified and remediated giving the individual a sense of being normal and having equal chances in life, or being ignored and punished for a disability they are unable to treat themselves, leading to a sense of failure, stress, low self-concept and unequal chances in life.

The personality study drew on a sample of N=87 (N=44 self-reported dyslexics and N=43 controls) using the Eysenck Personality Inventory. The first part of this study looked at the general personality of adult dyslexics and significant gender differences were found, whilst using a severity measure several unidentified dyslexics were identified amongst the control sample. Such a result suggests that many children and adults go through life thinking they are stupid and abnormal, rather than being identified and helped early in their educational careers. Gender was an important variable and personality traits varied significantly amongst those with moderate and high dyslexic traits, suggesting males were more confident and females were more depressive. The data also suggests those with moderate and high dyslexic traits, compared to those with low trait controls, were: pessimistic; gloomy; depressive; easily upset when things go wrong; have lower self-esteem; and feel unattractive failures. The second part of the study investigated academic success and the personality attributes amongst those with dyslexic attributes. It was found that individuals with significant (moderate 10-14 traits) but not severe dyslexic attributes were most likely to have the personality traits required to gain academic success. Gender was investigated and insignificant personality trait differences were found between females with and without university degrees, suggesting that other variables such as opportunity were more likely reasons for their lack of academic progression. The study concluded by investigating if diagnosis made a difference to the personality traits of university educated dyslexics. The data indicates wide differences. Significantly those diagnosed were: more independent; did not regret past actions; more optimistic; resistant to irrational fears; more carefree; and even tempered. Thus it was concluded that diagnosis is important for resilience amongst dyslexics. Further investigations were made among those individuals who were undiagnosed and degree educated, the resulting profile suggests a difference between males and females, with females having an obsessive and depressive personality profile. Table 12 suggests profiles to identify the personality traits of academically successful and unsuccessful males and females, which should be helpful for educationalists.

The Interview study was a commissioned for this book. Based on a small N=7 sample of adult dyslexics with depression (N=4 females and N=3 males), it used a semi-structured interview script to investigate dyslexia, diagnosed clinical depression and gender. Case studies were summarised which illustrated their life struggles. There were several themes that came out from the study, firstly all participants were identified as dyslexic in adulthood and this could suggest a total breakdown of identification in mainstream UK schools. These individuals were highly intelligent with the vast majority being university educated, but had struggled through school with unidentified learning difficulties and this pressure had been the overriding reason for their depression. One main coping strategy was perfectionism, however these individuals took such strategies to an extreme level by rewriting and drafting several times everything from job application forms to work reports. Such a strategy may have been possible at primary school, with ample time to redraft homework, but from secondary school onwards when the work demands rise, and time available for redrafting reduces – pushing them over the emotional edge resulting in self-harm and suicidal attempts as cries for help. Isolation was also especially seen amongst the females, which suggests that they had few or no dyslexic friends or peers growing up and took the logical step of labelling themselves as 'abnormal'. Alternatively their difficulties meant that they withdrew to protect their self-concept but this turned into a double edge sword and meant that they were isolated even more from their peer group.

As adults, many found returning to school to meet their child's teachers triggered their childhood emotions of fear from the smell and layout of small chairs - many avoided such situations. There was also a strong sense that dyslexia still caused them problems as adults and any setback caused them to return to childhood thoughts that they were as stupid and helpless.

To summarise the chapter in a paragraph is difficult, however certain themes can be found which are beneficial and these include: (1) The empirical evidence points to dyslexics having considerable difficulties at school and these can lead to stress and anxiety if their underlying difficulties are not diagnosed and remediated at an early stage of their school career, with commentators suggesting the first term of mainstream school is the ideal identification point, to avoid the child learning that failure is a way of life; (2) The personality study identified that adult males and females with high and moderate levels of dyslexic traits have different personality profiles and these suggest that females are more likely to have depressive and obsessive profiles, compared to males who are more laid back and rely on sociability profiles to cope; (3) Further investigations of degree educated individuals with moderate dyslexic traits suggest a profile comparable with empirical evidence for successful dyslexics, however those who are undiagnosed have suffered a life of doubt and this has taken an emotional cost, with significant gender differences identified. Diagnosis was seen as a positive strategy to gain support and this was indicated in more resilient personality profiles; (4) The interview study of adult dyslexics with clinical depression found that gender differences could be identified, with females being more obsessive, self-blaming and withdrawn, compared to males who used more helplessness and humour as defence mechanisms. The interview and personality studies highlight similar themes, that the depression amongst the general dyslexic population, especially in females is likely.

The research studies contained in this chapter provide a framework of understanding how dyslexia affects the lives of those suffering in adulthood with dyslexic. What is needed is a framework to understand why dyslexics choose certain coping strategies, and will be investigated in the next chapter (Alexander-Passe, 2008).

Acknowledgements

The author would like to thank his wife Andrea for the help and support she has given over the years for my research. The author would also like to thank his four children in their understanding that sometimes daddy can be busy and that you can attain seemingly impossible goals in life if you are willing to put I the effort.

Bibliography

Aldwin, C.M. (2000). Stress, Coping and Development: An integrative perspective. London: Guilford Press

Alexander-Passe, N. (2004a). How Children with Dyslexia Experience School: Developing an Instrument to Measure Coping, Self-Esteem and Depression. Unpublished MPhil Thesis. The Open University

Alexander-Passe, N. (2004b). A Living Nightmare: An investigation of how dyslexics cope in school. Paper presented at the 6th British Dyslexia Association International Conference. Retrieved 10th January 2006 from: www.bdainternationalconference.org /2004/presentations/mon_s6_d_12.shtml.

Alexander-Passe, N. (2006). How Dyslexic Teenagers Cope: An investigation of self-esteem, coping and depression. Dyslexia, 12: 4, 256-275.

Alexander-Passe, N. (2007). The sources and manifestations of stress amongst school aged dyslexics, compared to sibling controls. Published Online: 1 Oct 2007 Dyslexia, 10.1002/dys.351. http://www3.interscience.wiley.com/cgi-bin/abstract/116323773 / ABSTRACT?CRETRY=1andSRETRY=0

Alexander-Passe, N. (2008). Dyslexia, Gender and Depression: Dyslexia Defence Mechanisms (DDMs). In Paula Hernandez, P. and Sara Alonso, S. (Eds.) Women and Depression. Novo Science, New York (In press).

Allport, G. W. and Odbert, H. S. (1936). Trait names: A psycholexical study. Psychological Monographs, 47, 211.

American Psychiatric Association (1994). Diagnostic and statistical manual of mental disorders. DSM-IV (4th. Ed.). Washington, DC: Author

Anastasi, A. (1968). Psychological testing (2nd Ed.). New York: Macmillan.

Audit Commission (2002a). Managing special educational needs: A self-review handbook for local educational authorities. London: Audit Commission.

Audit Commission (2002b). Policy focus. Statutory assessment and statements of SEN: In need of review? London: Audit Commission.

Barrett, H. and Jones, D. (1994). The inner life of children with moderate learning difficulties, in Varma, V. P. et al. (Eds.) The Inner Life of Children with Special Needs, London, Whurr.

Battle, J. (1992). Culture-Free Self-Esteem Inventories. Austin, Texas: Pro-Ed.

Being Dyslexic (2006). Famous Dyslexics. Retrieved December 16, 2006, from http://www.beingdyslexic.co.uk/information/famous-dyslexics.php.

Bentote, P. (2001). SIDNEY (Screening and Intervention for Dyslexia, Notably in the Early Years). Paper at the 5th BDA International Conference (www. bdainternational-conference. org/presentations/thu_s3_a_1).

Berlin, R. (1872). Eine Besondere Art der Wortblindheit (Dyslexia). Wiesbaden.

Block, J. (1977). Advancing the science of personality: Paradigm shift or improving the quality of research. In D. Magnusson and N. Endler (Eds.), Personality at the crossroads: Current issues in interactional psychology (pp. 37–64). Hillsdale, NJ: Lawrence Erlbaum.

Brinckerhoff, L., Shaw, S., and McGuire, J. (1993). Promoting postsecondary education for students with learning disabilities: a handbook for practioners. Austin, Texas, Pro-Ed.

British Broadcasting Corporation (2004). Dyslexia. Retrieved December 16, 2006, from http://www.cbeebies/grownups/special_needs/dyslexia/teacher/index.shtml?article_page 3.

British Dyslexia Association (2006). What is Dyslexia? Retrieved December 16, 2006, from http://www.bdadyslexia.org.uk/whatisdyslexia.html#difficulties.

British Dyslexia Association (2007). British Dyslexia Association. Retrieved 16th April 2007. http://www.bdadyslexia.org.uk/adultchecklist.html

Brody, N. (1988). Personality: in search of individuality. Academic Press, New York

Brophy, J.E., and Good, T.L. (1986). Teacher behaviour and student achievement. In M.C. Wittrock (Ed.), Handbook of research on teaching (3rd Ed, pp. 328-375). New York, NY: Macmillan.

Burden, R. (2005). Dyslexia and self-concept: Seeking a dyslexic identity. London: Whurr.

Burns, R. (1982). Self-concept development and education. London: Holt, Rinehart, and Winston.

Burns, R.B. (1979). The self-concept: theory, measurement, development and behaviour. London, Longman.

Buss, A., and Plomin, R. (1984). Temperament: Early personality traits. Hillsdale, N.J.: Erlbaum.

Butkowsky, T.S. and Willows, D.M. (1980). Cognitive-motivation and characteristics of children varying in reading ability: Evidence of learned helplessness in poor readers. *Journal of Educational Psychology* 72(3): 408-22.

Cattell, R. B. (1957). Personality and motivation: Structure and measurement. New York: Harcourt, Brace and World. Journal of Personality Disorders, 19(1):53-67

Cattell, R. B., Eber, H. W., and Tatsuoka, M. M. (1970). Handbook for the Sixteen Personality Factor Questionnaire (16PF). Champaign, IL: IPAT.

Cohen, L. and Manion, L. (1995). A guide to teaching practice, 3rd edition. London: Routledge.

Congdon, P. (1995). Stress factors in gifted dyslexics. In Miles, T., Varma, V. (Eds.). Dyslexia and Stress. London, Whurr.

Cooper, P. (1993). Effective schools for disaffected students: Integration and segregation. London: Routledge.

Cronbach, L.J. (1983.) Fundamentals of psychological testing, NY Harper.

Crozier, W. R., Rees, V., Morris-Beattie, A., and Bellin, W. (1999). Streaming, self-esteem and friendships within a comprehensive school, Educational Psychology in Practice, 15(2), 128-134.

Cutting, A. L., and Dunn, J. (2002). The cost of understanding other people: Social cognition predicts young children's sensitivity to criticism. *Journal of Child Psychology and Psychiatry,* 43, 849-860.

De Pear, S. (1997). Excluded pupils' views of their educational needs and experiences. Support for Learning, 12 (1), p. 19-22.

Dyslexia Action (2007). Dyslexia Checklist. Retrieved April 16, 2007, http://www.dyslexia-inst.org.uk/pdffiles/checklist.pdf.

Edley, N. and Wetherell, M. (1995). Men in Perspective: Practice, Power and Identity. Hemel Hempstead: Prentice Hall/ Harvester Wheatsheaf.

Edwards, J. (1994). The scars of dyslexia: Eight case studies in emotional reactions. London: Cassell.

Endler NS. (1982). Interactionism comes of age. In Consistency in Social Behaviour: The Ontario Symposium, Vol. 2, Zanna MP, Higgins ET, Herman CP (Eds.). Erlbaum: Hillsdale, NJ; 209-249.

Epstein, S. (1980). The stability of behaviour: II. Implications for psychological research. American Psychologist, 35, 790-806.

Erikson, E. (1959). Identity and the life cycle. New York, IVP.

Eysenck, H. J. (1981). A Model for personality. New York: Springer-Verlag, 1981

Eysenck, H. J., and Eysenck, S. B. G. (1983). Recent advances in the cross-cultural study of personality. In C. D. Spielberger and J. N. Butcher (Eds.), Advances in personality assessment. Hillsdale, New York: Erlbaum (pp. 41-69).

Eysenck, H.J. (1953). The structure of human personality. New York: Wiley

Eysenck, H.J., and Wilson, G.D. (1975). Know your own personality. Harmondsworth, Penguin.

Eysenck, H.J., and Eysenck, S.B.G. (1975). Manual of the Eysenck Personality Questionnaire. London: Hodder and Stoughton.

Fawcett, A. (1995). Case studies and some recent research. In Miles, T.R. and Varma, V. (eds.) Dyslexia and stress, London: Whurr, 5-32.

Fawcett, A., and Nicolson, R. (1994). Naming speed in children with dyslexia. *Journal of Learning Disabilities*, 27, 641-646.

Fawcett, A., and Nicolson, R. (1996). The Dyslexia Screening Test and Dyslexia Early Screening Test. London: Harcourt, Brace and Company.

Fawcett, A.J.; Pickering, S. and Nicolson, R.I. (1992). Development of the DEST test for early screening for dyslexia. In Wright, S.F. and Groner, R. (eds.) Facets of dyslexia and its remediation. Amsterdam: North Holland/Elsevier.

Franci, L.J., and Jackson, C.J. (2004). Which versions of the Eysenck Personality Profiler is best? 6-, 12- or 20-items per scale. Personality and Individual Differences. 37, 1659-1666.

Frydenberg, E. (1997). Adolescent coping: Theoretical and research perspectives. London: Routledge.

Gaines, K. (1989). The use of reading diaries as a short term intervention strategy. Reading. 23(3), 141-145.

Galaburda, A.M. (1989). Ordinary and extra-ordinary brain development: Anatomical variation in developmental dyslexia. Annals of Dyslexia 39, 67-80.

Galaburda, A.M.; Sherman, G.F.; Rosen, G.D.; Aboitz, F. and Geschwind, N. (1985). Developmental dyslexia: Four consecutive patients with cortical abnormalities. Annals of Neurology 18, 222-33.

General Communication Headquarters (2006). GCHQ disabilities toolkit leads the way. Retrieved December 16, 2006, from http://www.gchq.gov.uk/press/pdf/ disabilities _toolkit.pdf.

Gentile, L.M., and Macmillan, M.M. (1987). Stress and reading difficulties: research assessment and intervention. Newark, DE, International Reading Association.

Gerber, P.J.; Ginsberg, R. and Reiff, H.B. (1992) Identifying alterable patterns in employment success for highly successful adults with learning disabilities. *Journal of Learning Disabilities* 25: 475-87.

Gilroy, D. (1995). Stress factors in the college student. In Miles, T.R. and Varma, V. (Eds.) Dyslexia and Stress. London, Whurr.

Gilroy, D. (1995). Stress factors in the college student. In Miles, T.R., and Varma, V. (Eds.) Dyslexia and Stress. London, Whurr Publications.

Goldberg, L. R. (1993). The structure of phenotypic personality traits. American Psychologist, 48, 26-34.

Gomez, J. (1991). Psychological and Psychiatric problems in men. London, Routledge.

Good, T.L., and Brophy, J.E. (1987). Looking in classrooms (4th Ed.). New York, Harper and Row.

Gough, H. G., and Bradley, P. (1996). CPI manual (3rd Ed.). Palo Alto, CA: Consulting Psychologists Press.

Grant, D. (2001). That's the way I think – Dyslexia and Creativity. Paper presented at the 5th British Dyslexia Association International Conference. Retrieved 10th January 2006 from: http://www.bdainternationalconference.org/2001/presentations/sat_s6_b_4.htm

Griffiths, A.N. (1975). Self-concepts of dyslexic children. Academic Therapy. 11, 83-90.

Grigorenko, E. (2001). Developmental dyslexia: an update on genes, brains and environments. *Journal of Child Psychology and Psychiatry*. 42(1), 91-125

Hales, G. (1994). Dyslexia Matters. London: Whurr

Hales, G. (1995). The human aspects of dyslexia. In Hales, G. (ed.) Dyslexia Matters. London: Whurr, 184-198.

Hansford, B.L., and Hattie, J.A. (1982). The relationship between self and achievement/performance measures. Review of Educational Research. 52, 123-142.

Hargreaves, D.; Hester, S. and Mellor, F. (1975). Deviance in Classrooms. London: Routledge and Kegan Paul.

Hargreaves, D.H. (1972). Interpersonal Relations and education. London, Routledge and Kegan Paul.

Hathaway, S. R., and McKinley, J. C. (1942). A multiphasic personality schedule (Minnesota): III The measurement of symptomatic depression. *Journal of Psychology,* 14, 73-84.

Hearn, J. (1994). Research in Men and Masculinities: Some Sociological Issues and Possibilities. *Australian and New Zealand Journal of Sociology,* 30, 1: 47-70.

Hiebert, E., Winograd, P., and Danner, F. (1984). Children's attributions for failure and success in different aspects of reading. Journal of Educational Psychology. 76(16), 1139-1148.

Hinshaw, S. P. (1992). Externalising behaviour problems and academic underachievement in childhood and adolescence, Psychological Bulletin, 111, 125-155.

Humphrey, N., and Mullins, P. (2002). Personal constructs and attribution for academic success and failure in dyslexics. *British Journal of Special Education*. 29(4), 196-203

Humphrey, N. (2002). Self-concept and self-esteem in developmental dyslexia: implications for theory and practice. Self-concept research: driving international research agendas. Retrieved 1st November 2007, http://self.uws.edu.au/Conferences/ 2002_ CD_ Humphrey.pdf.

International Dyslexia Association. (2006). Other well-known people thought to have dyslexia or other learning disabilities, Retrieved December 26, 2006, from http://www.interdys.org/well-known.html.

Jacobs, M. (1986). The presenting past: an introduction to practical psychodynamic counselling. Buckingham: Open University Press.

Jorm, A.F., Share, D.L., MacLean, R., and Matthews, R. (1986) Cognitive factors at school entry predictive of specific reading retardation and general reading backwardness. *Journal of Child Psychology and Psychiatry* (27): 45-54.

Jung, C.G. (1963). Memories. dreams, reflections. New York: Pantheon Books.

Kilmartin, C. T. (1994). The Masculine self. New York: Macmillan.

Klein, J. and Sunderland, H. (1998) SOLOTEC dyslexia good practice guide. London: Language and Literacy Unit.

Kussmaul, A. (1878). Word-deafness and word-blindness. In von Ziemssen, H. (ed.) Cyclopaedia of the Practice of Medicine, Vol. 14, Diseases of the nervous system and disturbances of speech. London: Sampson Row, Maston, Searle and Rivington.

Leeds and Bradford Dyslexia Association. (2007). Adult Dyslexia Checklist. Retrieved April 16, 2007, from http://www.labda.org.uk/.

Legrand, L., McGue, M., and Iacono, W. (1999). A twin study of state and trait anxiety in childhood and adolescence. *Journal of Child Psychology and Psychiatry.* 40(6), 953-958

Life Long Learning (2004). Freedom to Learn. Retrieved 10th February 2007. http://www.lifelonglearning.co.uk/freedomtolearn/rep08.htm

Magnusson, D., Endler, N.S. (Eds.) (1977). Personality at the Crossroads: Current Issues. In International Psychology. Erlbaum: Hillsdale, NJ.

Maslow, A.H. (1968). Toward a psychology of being (second edition). Princeton: Van Nostrand.

McLoughlin, D., Fitzgibbon, G., and Young, V. (1994). Adult Dyslexia: Assessment, Counseling and Training. London: Whurr.

Meehl, P.E. (1959). Structured and projective tests: Some common problems in validation. *Journal of Projective Techniques,* 23, 268-272

Miles, T.R. (1994). Dyslexia: The pattern of difficulties. London: Whurr.

Miles, T.R. and Varma, V. (1995). Dyslexia and stress. London, Whurr.

Miller, P.S. (1998b). Genetic Discrimination in the Workplace, 26 J.L. Med. and Ethics 189

Miller, P.S. (1998a). Genetic Discrimination in the Workplace, in Contemporary Issues in Business Ethics, (Joseph R. DesJardins and John J. McCall, eds., Wadsworth)

Mischel, W. (1968). Personality and assessment. New York: Wiley.

Morgan, E., and Klein, C. (2001). The dyslexic adult in a non-dyslexic world. London: Whurr.

Moskowitz, D. S. (1982). Coherence and cross-situational generality in personality: A new analysis of old problems. *Journal of Personality and Social Psychology,* 43, 754–768.

Moynihan, C. (1998). Theories of Masculinity. *British Medical Journal,* 317, 1072 – 1075.

Moynihan, C. (2002). The psychosocial aspects of men with cancer. Cancer Topics, 11(9), 8-11.

Nicolson, R. I., and Fawcett, A. J. (1993) Children With Dyslexia Classify Pure-Tones Slowly. Annals of the New York Academy of Sciences. *682,* 387-389.

Norman, W. T. (1963). Toward an adequate taxonomy of personality attributes: Replicated factor structure in peer nomination personality ratings. *Journal of Abnormal and Social Psychology,* 66, 574-583.

O'Moore, A., and Hillery, B. (1992). What do teachers need to know? In Elliott, M (Ed.) Bullying: a practical guide to coping for schools. Harlow, Longman.

Orton, S. T. (1937). Reading, writing and speech problems of children. New York: Norton.

Osmond, J. (1994). The reality of dyslexia. London: Cassell.

Padgett, I., and Steffert, B. (Eds.) (1999). Visual Spatial Ability and Dyslexia, a research project [Electronic version]. London: Central St Martin's College of Art and Design.

Pumphrey, P.D., and Reason, R. (1991). Specific learning difficulties (dyslexia): challenges and response. Windsor, NFER-Nelson.

Reiff, H.B.; Gerber, P. and Ginsberg, R. (1993). Definitions of learning disabilities from adults with learning disabilities: The insiders' perspectives. Learning Disability Quarterly 16: 114-25.

Reiff, H.B.; Gerber, P. and Ginsberg, R. (1997) Exceeding expectations: Successful adults with learning disabilities. Austin, Texas: Pro-Ed.

Richardson, A.J. and Stein, J.F. (1993). Personality characteristics of adult dyslexics. In S.F. Wright and R. Groner (Eds.) Facets of dyslexia and remediation. Amsterdam: Elsevier.

Richardson, J. T. E. (1994). Mature students in higher education: Academic performance and intellectual ability. Higher Education, 28, 373-386.

Riddick, B. (1996). Living with dyslexia: The social and emotional consequences of specific learning difficulties. London: Routledge.

Riddick, B.; Sterling, C.; Farmer, M. and Morgan, S. (1999). Self-esteem and anxiety in the educational histories of adult dyslexic students. Dyslexia 5, 227-48.

Roehampton University (2006). Famous Dyslexics. Retrieved December 16, 2006, from http://www.roehampton.ac.uk/dyslexia/famous-dyslexics.asp.

Rogers, C.R. (1959). A theory of therapy, personality and interpersonal relationships, as developed in the client-centered framework. In S. Koch (Ed.). Psychology: A study of science. (pp. 184-256). N.Y.: McGraw Hill.

Rosenthal, R. and Jacobson, L. (1973). Pygmalion in the classroom. New York, Holt, Rinehart and Winston.

Ryan, M. (1994). Social and emotional problems related to dyslexia. *The Journal of Adventist Education. Perspectives,* spring 1994, Vol. 20, No. 2

Ryan, M. (2004). Social an Emotional Problems Related to Dyslexia. International Dyslexia Association, Downloaded 19th October 2006, www.IDonline.org/article/19296.

Saunders, R. (1995). Stress factors within the family. In Miles, T., and Varma, V. (Eds.) Dyslexia and Stress. London, Whurr Publications.

Scott, M.E.; Scherman, A. and Philips, H. (1992). Helping individuals with dyslexia succeed in adulthood: Emerging keys for effective parenting, education and development of positive self-concept. Journal of Instructional Psychology 19(3): 197-204.

Scott, R. (2004). Dyslexia and Counselling. Whurr, London.

Seeman, L. (2002). The sociological implications of untreated dyslexia: linkage of dyslexia with crime. Available: seeman@netvision.net.il.

Singleton, C.H. (1995). Cognitive profiling system CoPS-1. Staythorpe, Newark, Notts: Chameleon Assessment Techniques Ltd.

Smith, R.C. (1996). The wounded Jung. Evanston, Illinois: Northwestern Press.

Stanley, T.J. (2002). The millionaire mind. London, Bantam.

Stanovich, K.E. (1986). Matthew effects in reading: some consequences of individual differences in the acquisition of literacy. Reading Research Quarterly. 21, 73-113.

Stewart-King, S. (2004). The Adult Dyslexia and Personal Training course. Paper at 6th British Dyslexia Association International Conference, Warwick University.

Stoltenberg, J. (1989). The Profeminist Men's Movement: New Connections, New Directions. Changing Men: Issues in Gender, Sex and Politics, 20, Winter/Spring.

Svensson, I.; Lundberg, I. and Jacobson, C. (2001). The prevalence of reading and spelling difficulties among inmates of institutions for compulsory care of juvenile delinquents. Dyslexia 7: 62-76.

Sylva, K. (1994). School influences on children's development. *Journal of Child Psychology and Psychiatry*. 35(1), 135-170.

Tansley, P., and Panckhurst, J. (1981). Children with specific learning difficulties: a critical review. Windsor, NFER-Nelson.

Tattum, D. (1993). Understanding and managing bullying. London, Heinemann.

Thomson, M. (1996). Developmental dyslexia: Studies in disorders of communication. London: Whurr.

Thomson, M., and Hartley, G.M. (1980). Self-esteem in dyslexic children. Academic Therapy. 16, 19-36.

Thomson, P. (1995). Stress factors in early education. In Miles, T.R. and Varma, V. (eds.) Dyslexia and stress. London: Whurr, 5-32.

Thomson, P. (1995). Stress factors in early education. In Miles, T.R. and Varma, V. (eds.) Dyslexia and stress (pp. 5-32). London: Whurr.

Van den Oord, E., and Rispen, J. (1999). Differences between school classes in preschoolers' psychosocial adjustment: evidence for the importance of children's interpersonal relations. *Journal of Child Psychology and Psychiatry*. 40(3), 417-430.

Vinegrad, M. (1994). A revised adult dyslexia checklist. Educare 48: 21-4.

Vogel, S. A., and Adelman, P. B. (1990). Extrinsic and intrinsic factors in graduation and academic failure among LD college students. Annals of Dyslexia, 40, 19-137.

Wechsler, D. (1974). Manual of the Wechsler Intelligence Scale for Children. Revised. New York: Psychological Corporation.

West, T. (1991). In the Minds Eye: Visual Thinkers, Gifted people with learning difficulties, Computer Images, and the ironies of creativity. Buffalo, NY: Prometheus Books.

Winkley, L. (1996) Emotional problems in childhood and young people. London, Cassell.

Wolff, U., and Lundberg, I. (2002). The prevalence of dyslexia among art students. Dyslexia, January-March; 8(1), 34-42.

World Federation of Neurology (1968). Report of research group on developmental dyslexia and world illiteracy. Bulletin of the Orton Society, 18, 21-22.

Wszeborowska-Lipinska, B. (1997). Dyslexic students who succeed. Unpublished paper. University of Gdansk.

Zubin, J., Eron, L. D., and Schumer, F. (1965). An experimental approach to projective techniques. New York: John Wiley and Sons.

In: Women and Depression
Editors: Paula Hernandez and Sara Alonso

ISBN 978-1-60456-647-5
© 2009 Nova Science Publishers, Inc.

Chapter 2

Dyslexia, Depression and Gender: Dyslexia Defence Mechanisms (DDMs)

Neil Alexander-Passe[2]
School of Psychology, ACS, London South Bank University, London, UK

Abstract

In the preceding chapter (Alexander-Passe, 2008) gave an understanding of what dyslexia is and how it affects both adults and children in settings from school to the workplace. Both the empirical and the three research studies highlighted the emotional manifestations that come from having a learning disability, such as dyslexia. This chapter continues the investigation from first reviewing empirical evidence concerning stress, coping, avoidance and Defence mechanisms before suggesting a hypothetical model of 'Dyslexia Defence Mechanisms (DDMs)'. Such a model is based on the work of Vaillant (1992) Messiner (1980) but as dyslexics are a unique population, several aspects of normal Defence mechanisms are inappropriate. For example, the DDMs are split in Emotional and Behavioural, being predominately split by gender (Females-Emotional and Males-Behavioural). Avoidance of writing long words has been identified as a key coping strategy before DDMs are chosen, teachers, parents and practioneers should identify this as the start of a long negative path for children at school. Teachers are advised that when children fail in more tasks than they succeed in, such children will perceive learning and school as threats to their self-esteem and self-concept. They will seek out ways to protect themselves and Defence mechanisms may explain what mechanisms are chosen. Defence mechanisms have never been investigated with dyslexic populations, however reviewing empirical data they seem ideal candidates for such investigation.

Keywords: *Dyslexia, Depression, Gender, Defences, Avoidance, Denial*

---

2 neil.alexander-passe@inghams.co.uk.

Empirical Review

Stress

Stress, what is it? According to the Oxford English Dictionary (2006) it has been in common language since the 18th century both as a noun and a verb. Initially it is understood to refer to external events, negative ones spring to mind e.g. unemployment or career based pressures. Aldwin (2000) suggests it refers to negative life events but these may turn out to be positive after the intervention of stress e.g. it may show what is possible if an individual is pushed a little out of their comfort zone.

Mason (1975) and Forman (1993) identified three types of definitions of stress or three ways one can understand how the term stress is used: (1) stimulus-based definitions; (2) response-based definitions; and (3) transactional definitions.

The first definition of stress refers to both the physiological and emotional reactions to stress, such as war, earthquakes, divorce, failing an examination. Modern studies now look at stresses such as chronic strain of a bad marriage, childbirth, parenting and daily hassles of everyday life in society (Aldwin, 2000). However, Aldwin notes that whilst the common assumption is that stress has negative physiological effects, it would be more accurate to perceive stress as having an activating effect, which at times can be positive and other times negative, depending upon various personal and contextual factors. Emotional reactions to stress include negative feelings such as anxiety, anger and sadness, although shame, guilt or feeling bored may also be seen as a reaction to stress (Lazarus, 1991). The limitations to this type of definition is that it fails to account for individual variations in the perception of stress and the ability to deal with it, e.g. one adolescent may withdraw following acute stress, whereas another may manifest behaviour problems. (Frydenberg (1999, p. 14)

The second type of definition to stress comes from an individual's biological and psychological response to environmental demands (Selye, 1974). It is widely used to understand the health effects of stress and how each demand disrupts the body's careful chemical balance, with the response as a way to achieve balance again (e.g. sweating to cool down our bodies). Dienstbier (1989) suggests that stress causes a chemical reaction and if such stress is intermittent, then the body has time to recover. Where stress is continuous and no time for recovery is allowed, it can lead to the chemical reaction of exhaustion (Selye, 1956). Studies have found that alcohol and drugs may give an individual stress-reducing capacities but use may have negative long-term effects (Gray, 1981, 1983; Vaillant, 1983), with Aldwin (2000) suggesting that continuous stress can lead also to the weakening of the immune system. As the stress is triggered the body sends round adrenalin which increases pulse rate, blood pressure and blood sugar levels. Selye (1991) notes that as the body reacts to stress, it sends alarm signals all around the body and will do so until the stress is removed or the body is exhausted, this turns to distress (when the body's response is too intense or lasts too long).

The third definition of stress looks at the experiences arising in individuals between the environment and the person, especially when there is a mismatch between the two. As Lazarus and Folkman (1984) note, it is the individual's appraisal of stress to whether the stressor poses as a threat or challenge which must be present for any emotional or physiological reactions to occur. Lazarus (1966, 1993) notes three components to stress, where each situation is assessed/appraised according to: (1) harm (e.g. whether the psychological damage has already been done); (2) threat (e.g. where harm is anticipated); and (3) challenge (e.g. where the response made to the demands is made with confidence). Lazarus and Bandura (1982a; b) suggest that a positive frame of mind is required for combating stress and facilitating coping, with Bandura (1982) noting that people avoid tasks that exceed their perceived capabilities.

This chapter is interested in stress as an interaction between the individual and their environment, as Lazarus and Folkman (1984) and Lazarus (1991) note, what is stressful for one individual may not be stressful for another and what is stressful at one point in time may not be stressful at another time, e.g. the stress of losing a job at 20yrs old when it is your first job, may be different to losing it at 64yrs old. The former may feel the loss is a crisis, but for the latter it might be perceived as a welcome opportunity to just settle down and take life easier. Stress can come from running late for a meeting to missing a plane and can range from a minor irritation to affecting an extended period of time. The key to understanding stress comes in how individuals deal with the stress and stressors they face, and this comes with understanding the individual's appraisal system. In Lazarus and Folkman's (1984) theory there are five types of appraisals: harm, threat, loss, challenge or benign. However, Aldwin (1990) notes there may be others such as concern over other's problems (e.g. a mother getting stressed about their child's problems etc.). Lazarus and Folkman (1980) and Hobfall (1989) note that in the appraisal process there is continual re-appraisal and allowances made concerning the environment and the stressor taking place (e.g. awareness of the limitations of the environment or tools available to deal with the threat). Whilst Aldwin (2000) notes that if the stressor reoccurs, the individual will develop coping strategies to deal with such situations more effectively, however as Lazarus (1991, p. 153) notes these are due to two types of assigning appraisal to a situation, 'one conscious, deliberate and under volitional control and the other automatic, unconscious and uncontrollable'. Thus, if a situation is experienced more than once, automatic and unconscious appraisal can happen (e.g. in a phobia, the appraisal of threat is made very fast as a threat, with little or no re-appraisal taking place of the appropriateness of the coping strategy to fear)

What are Normal Levels of Stress?

From an early age we experience stress. This starts from the inability to communicate with others that we are hungry and thirsty (Bower, 1977). However, Cleaver, Unell and Aldgate (1999) note that it is common for pregnant mothers to avoid certain types of food or loud parties as it annoys their foetus, their displeasure can be seen by the foetus kicking the mother until the stressor is changed. Children will cry when experiencing distress and can modify their parent's behaviour towards them (Bell and Harper, 1977). Other stress reducing activities can involve sucking their thumb, having a comfort blanket and continuous crying until they manage to stand up or move from one end of the room to their favourite toy (Murphy and Moriarty, 1976). As a preschooler they have more skills but are still unable to master all skills they require to feed themselves and to activate all toys or electronic apparatus they want, at this stage the frustration can turn into temper tantrums and blind anger. At school or nursery, children learn about the world around them and more about what is socially acceptable behaviour. The question posed is what is a normal amount of stress? The answer may lie with the environment one exists in - society sets the tone of what is 'normal'.

Children learn at different rates, so what might be stressful to one child may not be to another. It is only with integration with ones peers that we can judge what is normal. From these environments children learn about differences, expectations and this impacts on their cognitive development. With the development of abilities to verbalize and differentiate their feelings comes the dramatic increase in emotion-focused strategies (Altschuler and Ruble, 1989; Band and Weisz, 1988) and their ability to regulate their own emotions until they become overwhelming (Aldwin, 2000). Through childhood to adolescence and then to adulthood they develop a range of coping strategies to deal with the thousands of stressors they encounter (e.g. school work pressures, puberty, dating, examinations, socialising, marriage, children and home/work balance, getting old etc).

Thus, if society deems your learning to be abnormal (not normal), then stressors increase (pressure to learn as one's peers). Thus, an individual's appraisal system will choose whether such pressure is a threat or not. From such an appraisal the body puts into action a number of strategies to progress from point A to point B.

Aldwin (2000, p. 240) believes that strategies 'serve a homeostatic function whereby emotions are managed, problems are solved, and life returns to normal. The more I study stress and coping processes, the more I am convinced that adaptation simply does not work in that way....in order to better understand why some people break and others flourish'. Linear models (e.g. emotions are managed, problems are solved, and life returns to normal) are now being challenged with the concept that the stressful experience changes the individual and thus transformational (Stouffer, 1949; Menninger, 1963) to either positive or negative effect (Dienstbier, 1989; Antonovsky, 1987; Taylor and Brown, 1988). The results are often named coping strategies (if positive), others are called defensive strategies or mechanisms (if negative). If the result of either is deemed to be positive and is reinforced on a long term basis it is called resilience. If in the long-term the effect is negative then it is called vulnerability. Resilience is described as the positive aspects or effects of stress and the study of both allows understanding of the processes involved, it is including factors such as age, gender, social class, family dynamics, social support, temperament, self-efficacy and coping skills (Elder, 1974; Garmezy and Masten, 1986; Rutter, 1983; Werner and Smith, 1992).

Arguments for stress being an impetus for developmental growth include philosophical, psychoanalytical and immune perspectives. Kierkegaard (1985) believes that despair is an absolutely essential precondition for development in adulthood, as only by facing and fulfilling the demands can one achieve the despair necessary to develop emotionally, as also noted by Erikson (1950). In the psychoanalytical perspectives by Freud (1966), stress is generated by unfulfilled or unfulfillable demands requiring the development of new and more adaptive strategies, as also found by Jung (1966). The conflicts encountered from infancy, to childhood, then to adolescence then to adulthood are important and necessary to learn limits and capacities.

Current thinking suggests that it is best to try and protect children from all harm (Miller, 1990); however Aldwin (2000) suggests that it is really not possible to remove all stress from a child's life and it may not be desirable anyway as stress drives emotional development. If it was removed it would be an even greater shock when individuals are removed from the protective shell as adults. Not withstanding, the overwhelming majority of studies into stress finds negative effects (see Rutter, 1983; Berlinsky and Biller, 1982 for reviews). However other studies show that resilient children can bounce back (Felsman and Vaillant, 1987; Werner and Smith, 1992) and can show enhanced functioning in later life as a result of earlier stress (Anthony, 1987a, 1987b). More recently there have been studies into the resilience of children who by all accounts are highly vulnerable due to having sick or handicapped parents or live in poverty (Masten, Best and Garmey, 1990; Garmezy and Masten, 1986; Werner and Smith, 1992), suggesting three main factors to such resilience: cognitive skills, temperament and social integration. Others have highlighted higher intelligence to find better coping strategies (Anthony, 1987b), although intelligence and gender may be questionable as with adolescent girls, intelligence may be an additional stressor (Gilligan, Lyons and Hamer, 1990). Studies into temperament have often found children with sunny dispositions may be protected from depression and thus resilient (Garmezy, 1983). Researchers have noted that social integration plays an important role in resilience, with one supportive adult either inside or outside the family as vital (Werner and Smith, 1982; Wyman, Cowen, Work and Parker, 1991, Vaillant, 1993) which may come from stability.

Wolin and Wolin (1993) questions whether such resilience comes from the supportive adult rescuing the child, they believe that the resilient child actually seeks out the social support, sometimes with innovative strategies and that the support relies on effort both ways. They note resilient children and adults feature several strategies: they build on their own strengths, they wish to improve on their parent's lifestyle; married into consciously strong and healthy families; and worked hard to build a cohesive family. From clinical observations they created seven categories of resiliency (Insight, Independence, relationships, initiative, creativity, humour and morality). However Anthony (1987a) notes that there is no such thing as a child completely invulnerable to stress, rather a child who has a checkerboard of competence and vulnerability that may change over time (Murphy and Moriarty, 1976; Luthar and Zigler, 1991; Rutter, 1983). Wolin and Wolin (1993) also identified a number of strategies leading to vulnerability, these include: dwelling on the past, blaming parents for their own failures and seeing oneself as hopeless and a victim.

From Stress to Coping

As mentioned earlier, the third type of stress definition is that of a 'transactional' mechanism, in that after appraisal, the individual will respond or avoid as per the level of threat posed. Coping research has been closely linked to stress research due to its association with the transactional model. In coping terms it is generally called the 'stimulus-response' (S-R) model which related to behavioural responses to any stressful stimulus. Newer models suggest a 'Stimulus-Organism-Response (S-O-R) model, where the 'O' stands for individual (organismic) variation in responses to the same stressful stimulus, which accounts to why two people may respond differently to the same stressor. A key component to the S-O-R model is of self-efficacy (Bandura, 1977a, 1982, 1991), where self-efficacy denotes and explains how the individual perceives their capacities, based on past performance in similar tasks (history of behaviour) rather than on actual capacities at the time of the new stressor. As Roskies and Lazarus (1980) note, it is not enough to posess the skills required to fulfil the task, but one must believe one has them. Frydenberg (1999, p. 27) suggests 'self-efficacy is the hallmark of people who judge themselves as being able to handle situations that would otherwise be intimidating or overwhelming' to others.

The Lazarus (1968; 1991) model of coping is important for understanding the field of coping research, noting three key aspects: (1) coping is context-bound rather than primarily driven by stable personality characteristics; (2) coping strategies are defined by effort; and (3) coping is seen as a process that changes over time during a particular encounter. The model emphasises cognitive appraisal as an intrinsic component of the coping process, with continuous appraisal taking place, starting with 'primary appraisal' (what is at stake to me, harm or benefit?) then 'secondary appraisal' (what can I do about it, what are my options?). Secondary appraisal looks at the possible options available and this is based in part on the organismic/variation as part of the S-O-R model. Personal variation will give a battery of possible responses for the individual to choose from. For example, which weapon should a soldier use for a situation? Grenade, rifle, tank, talking etc, some choices will be too extreme for the situation, some will be unsuitable or ineffective and others will be ideal. Past experience (self-efficacy) will guide the option or options chosen.

In one explanation by a 15yr old girl, noted in Frydenberg (1999, p. 48), 'coping means different things to different people. It means adapting, dealing with problems, arriving at solutions, getting knowledge and trying out things. Some people can do it better than others'. There are a range of options available to all and the study of coping measures is a good starting point in isolating the types of coping options available, these may include: seeking social support, focussing on solving the problem; working hard; worrying; investing in close friendships; seeking to belong; wishful thinking; not coping; tension reduction; social action, ignoring the problem; self-blame; keeping feelings to oneself; seeking spiritual support; focussing on the positive; seeking professional help; seeking a relaxation diversion; or physical recreation) as noted as the sub-scales for the Adolescent coping scale (Frydenberg and Lewis, 1993). Individuals may use a number of options together or one at a time and continual appraisal will mean the options, variations and stressors may change or vary.

Bednar and Peterson (1999) suggest that the essence of coping is the ability to tolerate psychological risk taking: the risks are to self-esteem; injury to one's reputation; loss of approval from others; greater vulnerability; increased anxiety; increased pulses and emotions; and open rejection from others. There are two parts to the risk involved with coping, one is intrapsychic and the other interpersonal. The first is a risk to one's self-concept (e.g. being unable to deal with the risk), the second is a risk to one's public persona (e.g. will people see I'm not as clever as I tell everyone I am). Bednar and Peterson (1999) suggest that the greatest learning and personal growth comes from the greatest risk to one personally.

From Coping to Avoidance

The concept of avoidance plays a central role in general psychology theory (psychotherapy, psychotherapy, concepts of normality and abnormality, and personality development).

Looking at psychological avoidance from the viewpoint that humans are reactive beings, these theories based on past conditioning, determine how an individual will deal with the future. Thus humans are creatures of habit and predictable. Psychological terms found in such theories of Beck, Steer and Brown (1996), Meichenbaum (1977) and Mahoney and Thoresen (1974) will include: reinforcement; conditioning, drive reduction, stimulus and environmental determinism. Such theories are based on individuals avoiding feared stimulus (object, event, thought, situation or feeling) becomes a means of preventing the unpleasant experience or fear or anxiety. Avoidance is a learned maladaptive response, which can be quickly learned and reinforced when it is the means by which stress and anxiety are successfully avoided. However as Bednar and Peterson (1999, p. 72) note it is a self-defeating behaviour pattern because it prevents the individual from re-approaching the feared stimulus and learning that such fears are exaggerated and irrational, they note that 'avoidance is a psychological attribute that one would not wish to possess to any significant degree'.

For a second view point, Freud (1961) suggests that avoidance of anxiety plays a key part in neurosis, as the individual's attempts to avoid such feared stimulus using varied and elaborate defence mechanisms with terminology to protect the ego such as: deny, distort, repress, displace, sublimate and disguise. Overall it is the means by individuals attempting to excuse themselves from facing unpleasant psychological events.

A third point of view is involved with the production of optimism, with the following terminology commonly used: personal identity; self-direction; personal growth; individual accountability; and free will. Based on personal experiences which guide and directs the self into a self-fulfilling future (Rogers, 1959), avoidance as a defence works as individuals distort their perception of events so that they are more conducive to their self-concept. Bednar and Peterson (1999, p. 74) remark that unfortunately many of the terms used are based on vague definitions and thus it is hard to define what exactly is involved.

As noted earlier, Normality or the lack of definite definition of normal and abnormal behaviour means that the study of coping is a confusing and subjective area of psychology. Debate has been continuing for over 60 years (Korchin, 1976; Bednar and Peterson, 1999) and has been based on the following four questions: (1) What are psychological disturbances, and how can their presence be reliably ascertained? (2) What is psychological health, and how can its presence be ascertained reliably? (3) Are there essential differences between psychological health and disturbance, and can these differences be ascertained reliably? and (4) Are the attributes that define and differentiate psychological health and abnormality culture bound, or can they be applied on a cross-cultural basis?

As Wegrocki (1939) suggests abnormality is based on two assumptions: (1) abnormality can be considered to be any behaviour that is different from an accepted norm and deviating from the ordinary or natural type; and (2) it cannot be defined in terms of conformity to social standards, values, or expectations; all of these are contaminated by arbitrary cultural considerations. Bednar and Peterson (1999, p. 80) suggest that 'any behaviour that is culturally determined and reinforced simply cannot be considered abnormal in the true sense of the word' and that 'one of the quintessential qualities of abnormality is avoidance – avoidance motivated by fear and anxiety', with the 'underlying function of avoidance is virtually always the same: to defend and protect the individual from unpleasant or unwelcome psychological experiences'

McCall (1975, p. 81) suggests 'the moment we choose avoidance over coping, we openly and undeniably announce to ourselves (and to any others who care to observe) that we have detected impulses within that are so unacceptable that they cannot be faced realistically' and 'obviously, the prospects for personal growth are virtually non-existent when the individual's response to threat is' to avoid and deny they existed.

Use of avoidance influences individual's self-perceptions, and as all definitions agree that avoidance is an escape from unpleasant psychological events as they exist as fear and anxiety, with their avoidance is an escape from a conflict between how they see the world (in a bubble) and one that really exists, thus denial. Whilst the opposite of avoidance would be coping and avoidance is the essence of abnormality, coping must therefore represent normality and the ability to deal with psychologically threat successful. It is not just the ability to deal successfully with psychological threats, but the ability to tolerate with more anxiety-laden conflicts in difficult situations with but evasive (avoidance) actions.

From Avoidance to Defensive Strategies

As noted earlier, there are different reactions to stress and what is stressful for one may not be for another: some may shrug off being reprimanded; whilst others may take it personally withdrawing to cry; some might get angry and lash out; and others might take on board the comments and try and improve from it. According to Lazarus and Folkman (1984) and Aldwin (2000) there are four main approaches to coping: (1) person-based approaches; (2) Situation-based approaches; (3) Interactionist approaches; and (4) Transactionist approaches.

The study of coping strategies has its roots in psychoanalytic descriptions of defence mechanisms, which are concerned with internal conflict. Whilst Freud (1961) began the work of defence mechanisms in 1924, his daughter A. Freud (1966) did the majority of the work on the basis in which they are now understood. Specifically, how the ego is the moderator between the id (devil on your shoulder) and the superego (angel on your shoulder). It is explained that when the ego has a difficult time making the id and superego happy, it will employ one or more defence mechanisms.

Vaillant (1977, p. 10) identifies five major functions of defence mechanisms: (1) to keep affects within bearable limits during sudden life crises (e.g. following a death); (2) to restore emotional balance by postponing or channelling sudden increases in biological drives (e.g. at puberty); (3) to obtain a time-out to master changes in self-image (e.g. following major surgery or unexpected promotion); (4) to handle irresolvable conflicts with people, living or dead, whom one cannot bear to leave; and (5) to survive major conflicts with conscience (e.g. killing in wartime, putting a parent in a nursing home). Valliant's notion of defence is far more broad than that of Freud's since it includes conscious defences.

Holmes (1984) notes three central features of defence mechanisms: (1) avoidance or reduction of negative emotional states; (2) distortion of reality to various degrees, from mild to blatant; (3) and lack of conscious awareness in using defence mechanisms. As noted in the DSM-IV (American Psychiatric Association, 1994, p. 751) 'defence mechanisms (or coping styles) are automatic psychological processes that protect the individual against anxiety and from the awareness of internal or external stressors. Individuals are often unaware of these processes as they operate. Defence mechanisms mediate the individual's reaction to emotional conflicts and internal and external stressors'.

Kreitler and Kreitler (2004, p.203) suggest that coping strategies differ from defence mechanisms in four way: (1) they are performance programs rather than conflict resolution programs, (2) they may be, and often are, enacted overtly rather than internally; (3) they may be applied consciously; (4) they deal with major defined threat or stress that endangers the individual's physical or psychological survival or both. Similar aspects of the two are denial, displacement and rationalization. Cramer (1998, 2000) adds that defence and coping can be differentiated based on psychological processes, but not based on outcome.

A. Freud (1966) identified several major defence mechanisms: suppression, denial, projection, reaction formation, hysteria, obsessive-compulsive behaviours and sublimation. These are understood to mean: suppression and denial are similar but in varying forms, in that the individual will refuse to acknowledge an event or feeling. Those using suppression will not think about the event, whilst those using denial won't even acknowledge there was ever such an event; The hysterical person will inappropriately focus on the event and may spend all day crying about it; The obsessive-compulsive will spend so long checking and rechecking for the event that he/she may miss it; Projection and reaction formation are similar in that they both externalise the problem. Individuals using projection will see the event as wrong and project his anger at others. With reaction formation they will invert their own feelings or anger into admiration and think how great the people running the event are; lastly those using sublimation will learn from the event for the future. With these models, the environmental stimulus has very little or nothing to do with the coping strategy chosen, rather the defence strategy chosen aims to reduce anxiety by what ever means possible. The behaviours, feelings and cognitions evoked by the stressful event situation are determined by the individual's personality structure and developed in early childhood and are not easily modified. Aldwin (2000) suggests that defence mechanisms can either be used fleetingly and only under great stress or can be habitual. And Shaprio (1965) suggests that people can be characterised by their predominate use of a particular mechanism, e.g. the obsessive-compulsive is characterised by being rigid, distortion of the experience and the loss of reality. Paranoids also suffer a loss of reality and are typically characterised by suspicious thinking. Hysterical individuals are characterised by being repressive and hyperemotional, and impulsives are characterised by rapid, thoughtless action and lack of planning. Whilst these maybe useful they are all based on negative coping, other theories by Vaillant (1977) and Haan (1977) look at both positive and negative mechanisms which will now be discussed.

Vaillant's study tracked 100 men from 1930 to the modern day indicating a range of unconscious adaptive styles at different stages of these men's lives. He notes that even strategies involving planning and anticipation are unconscious and are concentrated on the regulation of emotion and the preservation of ego integrity, and were termed as projective, immature, neurotic and mature.

Vaillant (1977) explains them as: level-1 projective mechanisms (denial, distortion and delusional projection); level-2 immature mechanisms (fantasy, projection, hypochondriasis, passive aggression and acting out); level-3 neurotic mechanism intellectualization, isolation, obsessive behaviour, undoing, rationalization, repression, reaction formation, displacement and dissociation); and level-4 mature mechanisms (sublimination, altruism, suppression, anticipation and humour).

The adaptative styles that Vaillant theories are based on, are explained in everyday life dealing with both everyday events and trends from childhood, with going beyond the pathological only defence mechanisms as detailed by A. Freud (1966). Vaillant demonstrated over a period of time that: defences are stable over time; largely independent of the person's environment, and associated with a host of meaningful social, personal and biological characteristics. His defence mechanisms have been incorporated into the current DSM-IV (American Psychiatric Association, 1994) as they have been called 'the most thorough and systematic investigation of Defence mechanisms ever undertaken' (Draguns, 2004, p. 58). However Conte, Plutchik and Draguns (2004) question what constitutes a defence, as the number of defences vary widely among researchers according to their models (Brenner, 1993; Vaillant, 1977; Wong, 1989; Plutnick, Kellerman and Conte 1979), these include: 10 defences according to A. Freud (1966); 8 defences according to Vaillant (1971); 11 defences according to Brenner (1973); and 31 defences included in the DSM-IV (APA, 1994). Critics of Vaillant, not only point to the lack of females in his study, but also the lack of investigation of problem solving techniques over the life course, however the later were included at later parts to his study. Vaillant's study does however document how learning, heredity, love and social support play major roles in the choice of defences chosen unconsciously by individuals over time.

In contrast to the work of Vaillant, Haan (1977) attempted to create a more straightforward approach to understanding how conscious and unconscious defences are chosen and used, maintaining that defence mechanisms are inherently pathological and constructed a hierarchy of adaptation based upon the extent to which the strategies used reflect conscious or unconscious processes. Haan identifies ten basic or generic ego processes that can be expressed in three modes (coping, defence and fragmentary processes): coping (conscious, flexible, purposive and permits moderate expression of emotion); defensive (compelled, negating, rigid and is directed towards anxiety rather than the problem); and fragmentation or ego failure (distorts 'intersubjective reality' and is automated, ritualistic and irrational). The ten generic processes are then divided into four functions: cognitive, reflexive-intraceptive, attention-seeking and attention-impulsive regulation. The processes are not only used to reduce anxiety but also regulate cognitive processing, provide self-reflective capacity and focus attention.

Haan (1977, p. 49) notes that coping processes happen when assimilation and accommodation are evenly matched or unpressured, defensive processes happen when there are marked imbalances between assimilation and accommodations, and fragmentation happens when the imbalances between the assimilation and accommodation are so great that the individual retreats as the requirements are not only beyond the person's capability but irrefutably contradicts and confuses their self-constructions and makes a retreat to another reality preferable. Haan notes that generally a mixture of coping and defensive strategies are used with healthy development, moving from defensive to coping modes, described as gaining progressive control over behaviour. Critics of Haan question her assertion that rational coping can only happen when individuals are under normal stress, as those at war and fighting a fire can make rational and good judgements (Aldwin, 2000; Horowitz, 1986). Both Hann's study at Berkeley with men and women and Vaillant's with only men at Harvard are supportive of each other and suggests that defence and coping are both adaptive.

Cramer (1991) taking an alternative view identifies three main defence mechanisms: denial, projection and identification. She explains these as: 'denial' inhibits thought or emotion by the attachment of a negative marker to the idea or affect; 'projection' as a defence is complex, involving three steps: differentiating between internal and external; comparing the thought or feeling with internal standards; and attributing unacceptable thoughts/feeling to an external source. This displacement onto another avoids the shame or guilt of owning the emotions; and 'identification' being the most complex of the three, requiring the capacity to differentiate self from others, to differentiate among others, to form inner representations of others, and to adopt some qualities of import person (whilst rejecting others) in the process of identification. Thoughts and feelings are not inhibited, but taken over from others and incorporated into the self, protecting the self through affiliation.

Cramer (2004) suggests that defences mechanism use varies with age and that younger children use denial the most. In a study of three main defences (denial, projection and identification), 'denial' was construed as the developmentally early defence, reaching an early peak. 'Projection' rose to its highest level in late childhood and pre-adolescence, and declined thereafter. The developmental progression for 'identification' exhibited a progressive ascent all the way to late adolescence. Roecker, Dubow and Donaldson (1996, p.351), like Cramer found that Junior high school children report distancing/denial mechanisms to deal with interpersonal conflicts. These studies were corroborated in part by Smith and Danielsson (1982) with Swedish samples and Dias (1976) with Swiss samples. However, Wertlieb, Wiegel and Feldstein (1987, p. 351) and Donaldson, Prinstein, Danovsky and Sprito (2000) suggest that school-aged children use more wishful thinking to deal with school and sibling difficulties. Their study found that whilst the level of use of a particular strategy may vary across situations (school, peers, siblings, family), it did not alter the overall pattern of strategies chosen. Wishful thinking topped all other strategies (followed by emotional regulation, problem solving, cognitive restructuring and distraction) and was stable over gender, type of stressor reported or age (early of middle adolescence). Older adolescents used a much wider range of strategies but were related to those found chosen in early and middle adolescence. Stark, Spirito, Williams and Guevremont (1989, p. 351) noticed that adolescents use more self-criticism with school problems than with parent or friend problems. Whilst Donaldson et al. found these mechanisms were stable over stressors, Band and Weisz (1988) found they did not, thus such a conclusion needs further investigation.

Cramer and Gaul (1988) also found that children who experience failure tend to rely on maladaptive and immature defences whilst children who experience success tend to utilize more mature defences. Accordingly, given that perfectionists are generally intolerant of failure and have an elevated fear of failure (Flett, Hewitt, Blankstein and Mosher, 1991), changing a child's defences will be easier when they begin to experience successful outcomes and develop a heightened sense of self-efficacy (can control ones destiny), rather than when they are fully developed and reinforced in adulthood.

Another alternative model is found in Meissner (1980) who suggests a greater range of defence mechanisms, about double those of Vaillant (1992) and has a greater concentration of immature mechanisms, including regression.

Others have also investigated defence mechanisms, White (1974, p. 55) notes that coping has three important functions: (1) keep securing adequate information about the environment; (2) maintain satisfactory internal conditions for both action and for processing information; and (3) maintain the organism's autonomy or freedom of movement, freedom to use its repertoire in a flexible fashion. White's main contribution to the debate is to 'recognise the importance of obtaining information about the environment and defence processes are necessary prerequisites for gathering information and acting upon the environment', they are also seen as supporting problem-solving activities. Thus defence mechanisms are a necessity rather than pathological component to coping/adaptation, and are developmental for the higher goal of autonomy and freedom.

There are various empirical theories and models in the area of defence mechanisms. Once the use of defence mechanisms is understood in individuals it allows greater understanding of suitable remedial options available. In the case of dyslexics, if coping or defence mechanisms are understood it will allow adverse secondary manifestations to be understood for what they are – cries for help and a means to deal with the stressful tasks or environments they face in daily life, e.g. at school, university, home, socially and in the workplace.

Dyslexic Defence Mechanisms (DDMs)

Conceptual Model

The hypothetical model (See Table 1) proposed is based on personal experience, recent research (Alexander-Passe, 2004a, 2004b, 2005, 2006, 2007, 2008) and supporting empirical evidence, as discussed earlier.

All children when entering education, be it at nursery or primary school, would have been encouraged by their parents on a one to one basis and feel the world is their oyster. As soon as they enter school or nursery they begin to see differences between themselves and others, but most importantly they will either experience success or failure in any new tasks presented to them. Where encouragement results in success in more cases than failure, they will learn that tackling new tasks is exciting and enjoyable. Where they experience failure more times than success, they will feel that learning is an activity they are unable to control, with failure being perceived in the majority of learning environments as something negative and to be feared. However, progressive educational techniques (Montessori, 1965) encourage failure and perceive any failure as an expected aspect and encouraged part of the learning process; in mainstream UK education such views are not valued. Failure and especially public failure is seen as socially unacceptable.

Table 1. Hypothetical Model of 'Dyslexia Defence Mechanisms'

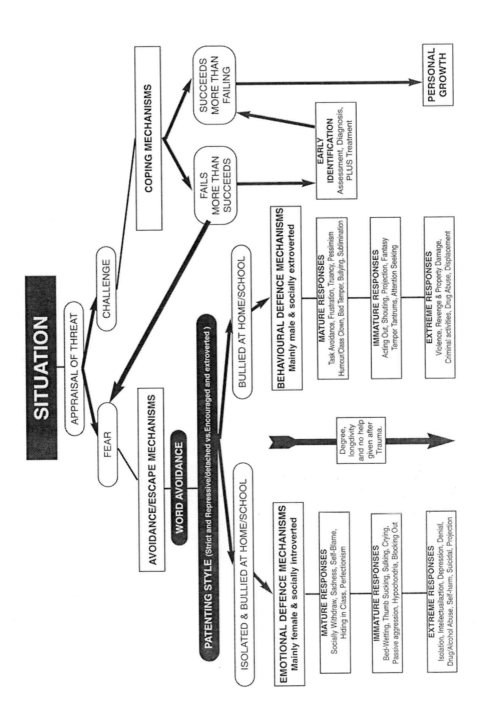

Early screening of children as soon as they enter school (the first 6 weeks of their first term of their first year at school) is seen as a powerful tool in screening for learning difficulties such as dyslexia, ADHD etc (See Appendix C). Such screening is a means to monitor, diagnose and treat educational difficulties before a child learns that education establishments can be threatening environments. Research suggests that early assessment and correct specialist dyslexia treatment where required, can dramatically reduce adverse reactions to mainstream schools.

Fear of failure is such a powerful psychological concept and can be extremely potent in changing an individual's whole basis of pre-judging new learning situations, or any situation that may risk public ridicule. Once the appraisal is of fear, the body aims to avoid or escape from such threat in various ways; however parental example and the reaction of parents to their own and child's difficulties have a strong impact on how they act themselves. If the parenting style is understanding and supportive, then the child may be encouraged to try and risk again, if the parenting style is strict, repressive and unsupportive, then the child will develop mechanisms to reduce their exposure to any feared stimulus.

First they will try basic word avoidances (e.g. writing less and using simple words); however this commonly is not sufficient to deal with school demands. Mature defensive mechanisms are first likely to be developed and are classed as either Emotional or Behaviourial, with the former being social withdrawal, self-blame, perfectionism, hiding in class and feeling sad. The later are likely to include task avoidance, truancy, frustration, bad temper, bullying, pessimism and sublimation. These are classed as mature responses according to empirical studies (Vaillant, 1977 and Meissner, 1980). Scott (2004, p. 257) notes from clinical experience that dyslexics are outstanding at defence mechanisms and 'the subtext is that you [counsellors] get lost in the smoke screen of the dyslexic's behaviours [Defence mechanisms] and do not notice the failure and vulnerability beneath'. With counsellors noting that you never forget a dyslexic client as they are very cunning, 'refined and slippery' and that commonly their defences can isolate them from others, noting 'in short, we have to notice when the iron defences turns into iron cages'. Alexander-Passe (2006) suggests that clear Emotional or Behaviourial differences exist among dyslexics, with gender splits being evident.

The key is understanding why some children choose Emotional or Behaviourial defensive strategies. Experience suggests that children with strict and repressive parents choose emotional strategies, whilst those with parents displaying aggression encourage their children to replicate such aggression at school (aggression begets aggression). Such children learn that its okay to display anger and a bullied child is more likely to bully others or even younger siblings.

However in the primary school, immature Emotional strategies may be evident, these include bed wetting, delayed or regressive language skills, sulking, thumb sucking and crying, hypochondria, passive aggression and blocking out (See Appendix C). These regressive strategies are direct responses to difficulties at school and a wish to return to their mother's safety as an infant. Regressive strategies are less common in late primary school however regressive language skills such as stammering are habit forming and can be life-long complaints. Other immature Behaviourial strategies may also be evident during primary school years with shouting, acting out, temper tantrums, biting, and attention seeking, as a means to ward away feared stimulus (See Appendix F).

Whilst it is unclear how much is too much fear, children and adolescents with dyslexia experience high levels of stress as their dyslexic difficulties also evolves from the classroom into the playground and to socialising outside of school (the whole school experience). Any defence strategies used are cries for help; however these secondary manifestations are commonly treated without looking at the primary causes.

When the fear gets too much and mature and immature mechanisms are ineffective e.g. unable to protect the individual from threats, the individual will look for more complex escape mechanisms, either extreme Emotional or Behaviourial defensive mechanisms, with isolation, intellectualization, depression, projection, escapism, drug abuse to numb the pain and self-harm by those using Emotional mechanisms (See Appendix F).

Such responses are perceived by them as the only means left to them to escape or control the risk in their hostile world and can lead to suicidal tendencies. Those who use Behavioural mechanisms are likely to turn to revenge on teachers leading to violence, displacement, criminal activities, not only repaying the hostility they themselves have experienced from a society they feel excluded from, but also as a means to gain self-esteem from material gain. Alcohol and drug abuse is also common for ticks, voyeurism and part of taking enlarged risks in life (See Appendix F).

There are three main keys to this hypothesis: (1) how does parenting style and other factors make individuals choose between Emotional and Behavioural defensive strategies? (2) What factors are needed for individuals to move from mature, to immature and extreme Emotional and Behavioural responses in dealing with situations? (3) are Emotional and Behavioural defensive strategies exclusive or can combined responses be found?

How does Parenting Style and other Factors Make Individuals Choose between Emotional and Behavioural Defensive Strategies?

Children learn explanatory styles from those around them, if parents or peers are aggressive towards them, then they have been shown successful mechanisms which they then will replicate in similar stressful situations. The same is true for parents and peers who are relaxed and show concern for their child's learning problems, the child will learn such lessons well and will replicate in similar situations. One question that is always posed is how much influence does a parent have when their child goes to school? Whilst their child's peers have a strong influence (especially from late primary school onwards), a parent can support or make it difficult for their child to mix socially with any undesirable peers, however the parenting style seen before a child goes to school can instil a basis for their coping mechanisms. Factors such as bullying in the classroom by teachers and in the playground by peers can teach behavioural coping to vulnerable children. Isolation in the playground and after school can made a vulnerable child turn to emotional defences as a means to cope with their feelings; it can also confirm a child's concept that they are unloved and unwanted.

How parents deal with homework and allowing their child to relax after school is important and can provide a safe haven from a hostile and threatening day at school.

A main factor can be gender, in that more girls turn to emotional defences than boys, with boys choosing more macho behavioural mechanisms. Not only at home but at school, gender is a strong factor and is reinforced in the classroom, playground and role-play. Brody (1985) reports that parents encourage sons to be more aggressive but unemotional, but encourage daughters to be emotional but non-aggressive. Feschbach (1970) therefore suggests that girls believe it is inappropriate to express anger openly, as compared to boys and that boys will tend to think it is inappropriate to express fear so will use internal attempts to control or hide that fear. Gender differences are apparent in both dyslexic and norm population and suggest that females will choose more emotional and males will choose more behavioral defence mechanisms (Alexander-Passe, 2006).

What Factors are Needed for Individuals to Move from Mature, to Immature and Extreme Emotional and Behavioural Responses in Dealing with Situations?

When a child starts to use defence mechanisms they are saying to themselves and others 'I can't cope, help me', whilst some defences are shouting, others are whispering and thus if they are not heard and responded to then the feelings of failure are reinforced. Factors such as the degree and longevity of the trauma (e.g. a bad supply teacher may only be there a week) are important factors. However, if the trauma is continuous (e.g. bullying or unfair teacher/tutor), then extreme responses may be used to escape the threat.

Scott (2004) suggests a child can be bullied twice, first by the actual bully and secondly by parents/teachers ignoring the cries for help. If help is not given their feelings of poor-concept (e.g. 'I'm stupid, I'm lazy') are confirmed and they then go further down a spiral of lower self-concept to a point of no return. Such points either turn to depression, suicide if they blame themselves or criminal activities if they blame others and society for the injustice in their lives.

Are Emotional and Behavioural Defensive Strategies Exclusive or can Combined Responses be Found?

It is hypothesised that initial mature responses may be interchangeable between Emotional and Behavioural defence mechanisms, however as each is reinforced they begin to separate into strongly Emotional or strongly Behavioural. Some mature responses may be found by both defensive mechanism models, as it is the basis of avoidance for dyslexics. This may take the form of writing less, choosing to use shorter easier to remember words in essays, losing books and forgetting homework assignments. Whilst some may be attributed to core dyslexic deficits e.g. short term memory problems, on the whole they are suppressive defence mechanisms.

Could the Decision to Choose Emotional or Behavioural Defence Mechanisms Happen at Childhood?

As discussed earlier, empirical studies (Donaldson et al, 2000) suggest that defence mechanisms are stable over age and gender. However, Vaillant (1992) suggests differences in age appropriate defense mechanism, with: 'psychotic' (or extreme) defenses being in healthy individuals till 5 years old and common in adult dreams and fantasies; 'immature' defenses in healthy individuals between 3-15 years old; 'neurotic' (or extreme) defenses in healthy individuals between 3-90 years old; and 'mature' defenses mechanism in healthy individuals between 12-90 years old. Whilst there is very little difference in Valliant's scales, it cannot be taken for granted that all defenses are stable over time.

A recent study (Alexander-Passe, 2007) compared the sources and manifestations of stress with dyslexic and non-dyslexic siblings, using a standardized measure by Helms and Gable (1989). The data shown in Tables 2 and 3 has been re-analyzed to investigate both gender and age. Table 2 results indicate that the manifestations of stress vary according to age. High emotional and physiological manifestations are found in the primary school group suggesting immature emotional defence mechanisms are used e.g. fear, shyness, loneliness, nausea, tremors because of the school experience. In the early secondary school group there is no clear manifestation differential, thus, it is difficult to assess their primary defence mechanism and these are similar to the sibling control data. However the late secondary school group suggests that emotional manifestations or defence mechanisms are used again as their primary strategy e.g. fear, shyness, loneliness. Interestingly in the control (late secondary school) group, behaviour e.g. acting out and being disrespectful was their primary manifestation and defence mechanism.

Table 3 results investigate the data with gender and age variables. Whilst these sub-groups are small, they suggest no gender differences at an early age (primary school group) because of the school experience. The results were due to high teacher, academic stress with a poor academic concept. However, there is no real control data for comparison.

In the early primary school group, dyslexic females show high behavioural manifestations e.g. being hurtful, disrespectful or striking out as a defence mechanism, compared to dyslexic males. The data suggests that this defence mechanism is used up to the point of leaving school. Interestingly the data suggests that dyslexic males use less behavioural and more emotional and physiological manifestations at the point of leaving school e.g. fear, shyness, loneliness, nausea, tremors as a result of the school experience.

Another study Alexander-Passe (2006) suggests gender coping differences amongst dyslexic teenagers, using standardized measures of coping (Endler and Parker, 1999) and depression (Beck et al., 1996), see Tables 4 and 5. Females scoring higher in emotional coping and depression than dyslexic males, who preferred Task-orientated coping. It is interesting that the Females scored high in all three forms of Avoidance (General, Distraction and Social Diversion), suggesting that withdrawal is a main defence mechanism at this age. Such a result has also been found in the preceding chapter in both the personality and interview studies Alexander-Passe (2008).

One explanation may come from Hales (2001) who has studied post-private educational psychologist diagnosis of dyslexia. He found that the mood in nearly half of all those diagnosed changed to denial, depression and resentment and that this might be caused by a large percentage of schools ignoring the diagnosis. Severe and immature defences may be used in the primary school as dyslexics are getting to know and deal with a world they have difficulty interacting with. Bu earlu secondary school, dyslexics they are hopeful of the changes in help following assessment, however when this does not happen, they become emotionally defensive again (as found in the late secondary school data).

In Hales (1994) a study was conducted with various aged dyslexics (6-8, 8-12, 12-18 and 18+years) using the Cattell Sixteen Personality Factor Questionnaire (Cattell, Elber and Tatsuoka, 1970) on N=300 dyslexics (75% Male and 25% Female), ranging from 6 to 58 years old. A selection of the results shown in Table 6 have been drawn from his published diagrams and are approximate, but indicate gender and age differences in how dyslexics cope from childhood to adulthood.

Taking a global view, dyslexics in all age groups score in the average range, except for 8-12year old dyslexic females who score very high in the apprehension scale suggesting they worry about things, feel anxiety and insecurity; this may indicate difficulties changing to secondary school, difficulties making new friends and dealing with the increased academic pressures. High self-confidence scores for 6-8 year old dyslexic males suggest they enter school with high confidence and optimism, however this dramatically drops to average levels as they come to terms with having learning difficulties, however to norm levels. Hale's analysis of the full data suggests that children between 6-8 years old feel tense, frustrated, inferior to peers and lack an obligation to conform to society's value schemes which may be due to their inability to conceive why they find school difficult and others do not. At between 8-12 years old they have already resigned themselves to having learning difficulties, and are unmotivated and anxious due to demands made on them. He also notes they are unmotivated to control their own emotions and may have fits of anger. Children with this score are normally have problems socially with peers and problems interacting in the classroom as these are repeated chances for them to appear inadequate. In the 12-18 year age group, the scores still indicate they prefer to work by themselves and show high independence. With the 18+ year group, high dominance scores suggest such a group are more assertive and independent-minded, however also solemn, unconventional and rebellious. Hales remarks these this may be part of their coping strategy to reduce hostile environments that would affect their self-esteem.

The data from Hales (1994) indicates defence strategies are already being used from an early age (6-8 yrs) and that school is perceived as a threatening environment that needs to be controlled, results also suggest that withdrawal in both school and social environments and signs of perfectionism confirm several of the aspects found in the hypothetical model. Overall, there is evidence that DDMs develop early on in childhood and these vary according to age and gender, with many males choosing behavioural and females emotional defence mechanisms to deal with the hostilities they face.

Table 2. Dyslexic siblings (N=78) vs. Control siblings (N=77) sorted by school year and gender, scoring on the School Stress Survey (Helms and Gable, 1989), re-analyzed data from Alexander-Passe (2007). Stress scale - Low =1, Medium=2, High=3

DYSLEXICS		SOURCES OF SCHOOL STRESS				MANIFESTATIONS OF SCHOOL STRESS		
		Peer Interaction	Teacher Interaction	Academic Stress	Academic Self Concept	Behaviour	Emotion	Physiological
Primary school N=19	Mean	2.263	2.526	2.368	2.526	2.158	2.737	2.421
	Std. Deviation	0.653	0.772	0.684	0.612	0.688	0.562	0.692
Early secondary school N=43	Mean	2.163	2.279	1.651	1.953	2.279	2.279	2.209
	Std. Deviation	0.721	0.826	0.613	0.688	0.766	0.734	0.804
Late secondary school N=17	Mean	2.353	2.294	1.824	2.647	2.176	2.412	2.294
	Std. Deviation	0.862	0.772	0.728	0.606	0.809	0.712	0.686

CONTROLS		SOURCES OF SCHOOL STRESS				MANIFESTATIONS OF SCHOOL STRESS		
		Peer Interaction	Teacher Interaction	Academic Stress	Academic Self Concept	Behaviour	Emotion	Physiological
Primary school N=14	Mean	1.714	2.357	1.929	2.071	2.071	2.071	1.929
	Std. Deviation	0.469	0.497	0.475	0.616	0.730	0.829	0.730
Early secondary school N=37	Mean	1.973	2.189	1.703	1.676	2.297	2.216	2.135
	Std. Deviation	0.726	0.739	0.618	0.669	0.777	0.750	0.855
Late secondary school N=28	Mean	1.786	1.929	1.714	1.357	2.393	2.250	2.107
	Std. Deviation	0.686	0.858	0.535	0.559	0.685	0.701	0.956

Table 3. Dyslexic siblings (N=78) vs. Control siblings (N=77) sorted by school year and gender, scoring on the School Stress Survey (Helms and Gable, 1989), re-analyzed data from Alexander-Passe (2007). Stress scale - Low =1, Medium=2, High=3

DYSLEXICS			SOURCES OF SCHOOL STRESS				MANIFESTATIONS OF SCHOOL STRESS		
			Peer Interaction	Teacher Interaction	Academic Stress	Academic Self Concept	Behaviour	Emotion	Physiological
Primary school	Females (N=2)	Mean (Std. Deviation)	2 (0)	2.5 (0.71)	2.5 (0.71)	3 (0)	2 (0)	3 (0)	2.5 (0.71)
N=19	Males (N=10)	Mean (Std. Deviation)	2.29 (0.69)	2.53 (0.8)	2.35 (0.7)	2.47 (0.62)	2.18 (0.73)	2.71 (0.59)	2.41 (0.71)
Early secondary school	Females (N=13)	Mean (Std. Deviation)	2.23 (0.6)	2.23 (0.93)	1.46 (0.66)	1.92 (0.76)	2.54 (0.66)	2.31 (0.75)	2.15 (0.9)
N=43	Males (N=30)	Mean (Std. Deviation)	2.13 (0.78)	2.3 (0.79)	1.73 (0.58)	1.97 (0.67)	2.17 (0.79)	2.27 (0.74)	2.23 (0.78)
Late secondary school	Females (N=7)	Mean (Std. Deviation)	2.57 (0.79)	2.71 (0.49)	1.57 (0.53)	2.71 (0.49)	2.57 (0.53)	2.29 (0.95)	2.14 (0.69)
N=17	Males (N=10)	Mean (Std. Deviation)	2.2 (0.92)	2 (0.82)	2 (0.82)	2.6 (0.7)	1.9 (0.88)	2.5 (0.53)	2.4 (0.7)

Table 3. (Cotinued)

CONTROLS			SOURCES OF SCHOOL STRESS				MANIFESTATIONS OF SCHOOL STRESS		
			Peer Interaction	Teacher Interaction	Academic Stress	Academic Self Concept	Behaviour	Emotion	Physiological
Primary school	Females (N=9)	Mean (Std. Deviation)	1.56 (0.53)	2.44 (0.53)	2 (0.5)	2 (0.71)	2 (0.87)	2.22 (0.83)	2 (0.71)
N=9	Males (N=0)	Mean (Std. Deviation)	-	-	-	-	-	-	-
Early secondary school	Females (N=26)	Mean (Std. Deviation)	2 (0.75)	2.27 (0.72)	1.65 (0.56)	1.69 (0.68)	2.35 (0.8)	2.31 (0.74)	2.31 (0.79)
N=27	Males (N=1)	Mean (Std. Deviation)	2	3	2	2	3	3	3
Late secondary school	Females (N=17)	Mean (Std. Deviation)	1.76 (0.75)	1.76 (2.44)	1.71 (0.59)	1.12 (0.33)	2.29 (0.77)	2.12 (0.78)	1.76 (0.97)
N=23	Males (N=6)	Mean (Std. Deviation)	2 (0.63)	2.17 (0.75)	1.67 (0.52)	1.83 (0.41)	2.67 (0.52)	2.67 (0.52)	2.67 (0.52)

Table 4. Beck Depression Inventory (Beck et al., 1996) – raw mean scores (SD) in a study of N=19 Dyslexic teenagers in Alexander-Passe (2006)

	BDI Raw Scores
Males N=12	6.2 (5.6)
Females N=7	20.1 (12.8)

Table 5. Coping Inventory for Stressful Situations (Endler and Parker, 1999) - percentile mean scores (SD) in a study of N=19 Dyslexic teenagers in Alexander-Passe (2006)

	Task	Emotion	Avoidance	Distraction	Social diversion
Males N=12	70.1 (23.7)	56.1 (39.0)	34.8 (23.1)	34.5 (23.2)	39.6 (29.3)
Females N=7	55.4 (27.8)	70.3 (28.8)	60.7 (32.4)	55.9 (35.9)	67.9 (16.0)

Table 6. Data taken from Hales (1994) Dyslexics of various ages in measures from the Cattell 16 Personality Factor Questionnaire. Range 1=low and 10-high, 3.5-7.5=average

	Dominance	Tension	Independence	Emotional Stability	Apprehension	Self-confidence	Super-ego strength
Females							
6-8yrs	5.25	6.25	5.6	5.5	5.25	6	5.6
8-12yrs	4.5	6.1	6.7	4.25	9.4	4.25	5.25
12-18yrs	6.5	5	5	4.5	6	5.75	5.5
18+yrs	7.5	6.5	4.5	5	6.5	6.5	3.75
Males							
6-8yrs	5.5	6.75	4	4.8	6.75	7	3.75
8-12yrs	5.5	5.5	5	4.6	4.5	5.5	4.1
12-18yrs	5.6	5.2	6.25	5.4	5	5.75	5
18+yrs	6.7	5.4	4.4	5.4	4.75	6	5.4

How Dyslexic Defence Mechanisms (DDMs) Compare to those of other Researchers?

The DDMs as conceptualised have been developed from various research studies (Alexander-Passe, 2004a, b, 2005, 2006, 2007) and the studies contained in the previous chapter (Alexander-Passe, 2008). They suggest that dyslexics will either predominantly use Emotional or Behavioural coping strategies/defence mechanisms. The closest defence mechanism models to that of the findings of empirical studies and the DDM are specifically those of Vaillant (1977) and Meissner (1980); however they suggest no difference between Emotional and Behavioural mechanisms in their immature, mature and neurotic models. Even though Vaillant's model is now incorporated in to the DSM-IV (APA, 1994), it was created from investigating a small sample of 100 male Harvard graduates, and thus are still questionable if such models can be generalized to not only male and female as a whole, but specifically dyslexic populations. Both Vaillant's and Meissner's models proved problematic in the case of dyslexics (child, adolescent and adult models) and thus modifications were made. In addition, an initial strategy of using word avoidances has been suggested which is used when first faced with possible challenges to their self-concept. Dyslexics, due to the reactions of educators and peers to their invisible learning difficulties and the resulting emotional reactions to maintain their self-esteem, are a unique group and it is hypothesised they require a modified framework in understanding how such individuals deal with constant stressors. The three models are compared in Appendix B.

The DDM framework notes the importance of early identification and how important it is for teachers to identify children failing more than they are succeeding in the classroom. Studies support self-efficacy in the classrooms (Bandura, Pastorelli, Barbaraneli and Caprara, 1999; Cramer and Gaul, 1988; Burns, 1982; Frydenberg, 1999) suggests that children whose belief system is positive are more able to apply themselves to the curriculum and access the support they need.

Supporting Evidence

The supporting evidence included within this chapter aims to document evidence by other researchers who have made unconnected parts to the puzzle.

Appendix A gives an explanation of terms used within the hypothetical Dyslexia Defence Mechanisms (DDMs) and aims to aid the identification in individuals.

Appendix B is a chart comparing the DDMs to the Defence Mechanisms of Vaillant (1992) and Meissner (1980).

Appendix C investigates overriding factors at school which influence the development of DDMs: such as early identification, bullying, isolation and word avoidance.

Appendix D looks at Emotional Defence Mechanisms: Mature, Immature and Extreme.

Appendix E looks at Behaviourial Defence Mechanisms: Mature, Immature and Extreme.

Chapter Conclusions

An empirical review of coping, stress, avoidance and defence mechanisms began to make sense of both the personality and interview studies in the previous chapter (Alexander-Passe, 2008) and suggest how such findings could be used to make generalizations to aid practioneers and educationalists in helping dyslexics for the future. The second part of the chapter suggests a hypothetical framework which could explain how dyslexics cope in life and why they would choose defensive mechanisms over those which might aid their learning. To date, there has been no attempt to understand the mechanisms which drive the dyslexic's reactions to constant difficulties at school, university, workplace and society as a whole.

The framework suggests that early identification is the key to helping dyslexics choose mechanisms that will aid further learning. Where early identification is not made, dyslexics will fail in more tasks that they succeed in and thus learning becomes a fearful activity and word avoidance is first used to reduce their failure rate. Where basic word avoidance alone is ineffective and parents are unhelpful in their approach to their child's difficulties, the child will choose either Emotional or Behavioural defence mechanisms. In the extreme these may lead to depression, suicide and crime, but it is hoped that only a small percentage are pushed to such a degree in dealing with life as a dyslexic. All these defence mechanisms are cries for help and if their cries are unheard then they will move from mature, to immature to extreme mechanisms to deal with stressful situations presented to them. Such situations may not be seen as stressful to many (e.g. completing a form, remembering a telephone number or reading a newspaper) but to those with dyslexic difficulties, they are significant challenges which most people in society can handle with ease.

The hypothetical model suggests how dyslexics cope by using defence mechanisms is based the work by Vaillant (1977, 1992) and Meissner (1980), but evolved with a pre-defence of word avoidance and defences separated into Emotional and Behaviour defences, as supported by evidence from both empirical evidence and the three studies included in the previous chapter (Alexander-Passe, 2008). Such a framework it is hoped will aid educationalists, psychologists and counsellors in understanding what defences are used and why, along with noting that all are cries for help from a learning difficulty that has life long effects.

The model suggests that teachers and parents need to be aware that if children fail in more tasks than they succeed in, then children will find learning fearful and develop defensive mechanisms. Early identification is vital in young learners and will make a huge difference not only to academic results but their for self-esteem and self-concept as well.

Further Research

The author notes that supporting the hypothetical model will require substantial research into the use of the defence mechanisms by dyslexics, especially with gender and age samples. As dyslexics, as a group tend to avoid form based measures, it will therefore be a challenge to develop interview structures that suitable for this task. Future research is suggested with different groups of dyslexics who might be known to use Emotional or Behavioural mechanisms e.g. dyslexics who truant or have been in prison, and those who are successful and unsuccessful in their adult careers.

Acknowledgements

The author would like to thank his wife Andrea for the advice, proof-reading and support she has given over the many years, which have cumulated in the hypothesis detailed in this chapter.

Appendix A

Explanation of Terms Used in the Dyslexic Defence Mechanisms (DDMs) and Chart 6

PRE-DEFENCE MECHANISM	
Word Avoidance	Avoiding words that are hard to spell and avoiding writing too much.
EMOTIONAL DEFENCES	
Mature Mechanisms	
Socially withdrawn	Avoiding situations that require remembering, reading, writing and spelling e.g. avoiding visits to cinemas as they are unable to read bus numbers or read lists of films shown.
Sadness	Feeling sad when getting things wrong.
Self-blame	Self-blaming and internalizing when getting bad marks
Hiding in Class	Sitting at the back of the class and not putting your hands up, to avoid their learning difficulties being highlighted e.g. when asked to read aloud in class or answer a question from the books given.
Perfectionism	Working painstakingly long on an assignment to avoid getting bad marks and losing face by failing in tasks.
Immature Mechanisms	
Bed-wetting	Regressive manifestations from stress that show helplessness
Stammering	This is another regressive defence mechanism where speech patterns return to infant states. This can be temporary or a long-term habit. It is sometimes used to look weak and gain sympathy.
Thumb sucking (pen sucking)	Regressive manifestations which returns individual to womb or infantile emotional and comfort states

Explanation of Terms (Continued)

Sulking	Regressive manifestations which says 'it's not fair' and is a toddler stage responses of the world as unfair.
Crying	Regressive manifestations which show complete helplessness and returns to a state of infantile and toddler hood that they need someone else to fix things for them.
Passive aggression	Internalizing feelings. An early form of depression.
Hypochondria	Physical manifestations of emotional stress and trauma e.g. phantom pains in legs as soon as tests approach or vomiting. This is an extreme cry for help and attention.
Blocking out	Try not to think about the feared stimulus. Thinking that it will go away if it is not thought about, without realising it won't.
Extreme Mechanisms	
Isolation	A self-protecting mechanism to withdraw to an environment that is safe and non-threatening.
Intellectualization	Logically thinking about the threat and taking a superior at attitude to the feared stimulus. I'm not wrong, he/she is.
Depression	An extreme state of helplessness and indicates that all strategies have failed and need to be rebuilt to progress
Denial	A self-protecting state that refuses to believe or accept actions that conflict with internal values. Altering facts to fit into belief systems.
Drug or Alcohol Abuse	An extreme reaction to stress that the individual uses abuse to escape painful realism by using drugs/alcohol to alter mental states to a safe haven. Addiction may follow that is life threatening.
Self-Harm	An extreme reaction to anxiety that aims to control their own bodies in a world they are unable to control any other aspects of their lives. It can involve controlling food intake as in bulimia, causing bodily harm as a means to inflict pain on the self as punishment or a means to control the bodies reactions to stress, e.g. cutting oneself can be a tension release.

Suicide or attempted suicide	Used when the individual feels completely helpless and decides that the burden they create is too great for others and wish to rid the world of themselves.
Projection	Taking an extreme emotional stance that the feared stimulus is out to get them.
BEHAVIOURIAL DEFENCES	
Mature Mechanisms	
Task Avoidance	Avoiding homework or work assignments that would highlight their inabilities and make them open to public ridicule e.g. losing homework books on purpose or forgetting to bring books to school.
Frustration	Getting frustrated from failing or being unable to understand tasks due to dyslexia. E.g. unable to read or understand homework.
Truancy	A more extreme form of task avoidance. Avoiding classes or school when there are tests or stressors e.g. teacher that bullies them.
Humour and Class Clown	Using humour to deflect the adverse affects of dyslexia e.g. being the class clown to divert peers attention from their inability to read or playing drunk to avoid misreading bus numbers.
Bad Temper	This is an advanced form of frustration and is a lesser form of anger. The individual diverts attention from their difficulties by blaming others e.g. bad teacher or bad luck.
Pessimism	Rather than risk failing at tasks, the individual will prejudge the task and protect themselves by prejudging they will do badly or fail at a test. This however stops the individual from trying their best.
Bullying	A form of anger. The individual will choose a weaker target and project their hostility onto them. This is another expression of frustration. Commonly they were or are bullied themselves by others
Sublimination	Using clever means to gain revenge on the feared stimulus, a way to get one over them in a way they might not get into trouble by doing. A clever form of revenge.

Immature Mechanisms	
Acting Out	An advanced form of bad temper. The individual seeks to either divert attention to their difficulties by picking on someone else (projection) or it is an expression of their frustration.
Shouting	Another expression of frustration. This is related to bullying in that it is either directed at a weaker individual or as a response to hostility towards them e.g. a parent shouting at the child that they aren't trying hard enough.
Biting	Regressive manifestations relating to helplessness and infancy as an inability to express ones hostility in words.
Temper Tantrums	Regressive manifestations also relating to helplessness and infancy as an inability to express ones frustration.
Attention Seeking	This manifestation aims to gain the attention of others by any means possible e.g. shock, crying, anger
Fantasy	Imagining causing harm to the individual e.g. in a day dream. This can help to relieve the pressure to injure.
Extreme Mechanisms	
Violence	An extreme form of frustration where the individual chooses a target weaker than them to express their frustration and anger. This is a form of projection causing bodily harm
Revenge and Property Damage	Another extreme form of frustration and can mean projection of anger from suffering at the hands of others. It can be directed at property damage or individuals e.g. setting fire to a school or a library or letting down the tires on teachers cars in revenge on teachers who bullied them
Criminal Activities	Another extreme expression of frustration. This is a means to improving self-esteem by gaining in monetary terms by stealing or mugging as their only means to earn money. As they are unable to gain employment, as per their peers.
Drug Abuse	Drug abuse is a means to take high risks to gain self-esteem; this can include high drug doses or being an adrenaline junkie. Addiction may follow that is life threatening.
Displacement	Rather than causing physical damage, property of the individual is chosen as a new target for the anger and threats e.g. their car.

Appendix B.

Differences between Defence Mechanisms Theories (Vaillant, Meissner and Alexander-Passe)

Vaillant (1992)		Meissner (1981)		Alexander-Passe	
No Defence	I hate my teacher	No Defence	I hate my teacher	No Defence	I hate my teacher
				PRE-DEFENCE	
				Word Avoidance	I will avoid getting bad marks by avoiding hard to spell words
				IMMATURE	
				(EMOTIONAL)	
		Regression (IMMATURE DEFENCE)	I wet my bed from worry	Bed wetting	I wet my bed from worry
		Regression (IMMATURE DEFENCE)	I will gain sympathy from stammering	Stammering	I will gain sympathy from stammering
		Regression (IMMATURE DEFENCE)	I wish I wasn't in class and at home in safety	Thumb/pen sucking	I wish I wasn't in class and at home in safety
				Sulking	I hate going into my teachers class, it's not fair
		Regression (IMMATURE DEFENCE)	I cry as I feel so helpless. I want my mummy	Crying	I cry as I feel so helpless. I want my mummy
Passive aggression	I hate myself (suicidal)	Passive aggression (IMMATURE	I hate myself (suicidal)	Passive aggression	I hate myself (suicidal)
Hypochondria	I have leg pains and feel	Hypochondria (IMMATURE DEFENCE)	I have leg pains and feel nausea	Hypochondria	I have leg pains and feel nausea
		Blocking (IMMATURE DEFENCE)	I'm not thinking about him	Blocking Out	I'm not thinking about him
		Somatization (IMMATURE DEFENCE)	I have a headache (psychic derivations)		
		Introjection (IMMATURE DEFENCE)	I love/like my teacher		
				(BEHAVIOURIAL)	
Acting Out	Without reflection I hit	Acting Out (IMMATURE DEFENCE)	Without reflection I hit children in the	Acting Out	Without reflection I hit children in the playground
				Shouting	I shout answers back at my teacher
Projection	My teacher hates me	Projection (IMMATURE DEFENCE)	My teacher hates me	Projection	My teacher hates me
				Temper Tantrums	I refuse to go into his classroom
Passive-aggressive	I tell everyone I hate him			Attention Seeking	I tell everyone I hate him so much
Fantasy	I daydream of killing	Schizoid Fantasy (IMMATURE	I daydream of killing him	Fantasy	I daydream of killing him
				EXTREME	
				(EMOTIONAL)	
Isolation	I won't answer questions	Isolation (NEURISSISTIC DEFENCE)	I won't answer questions in class	Isolation	I won't answer questions in class
Intellectualization	I disapprove of my	Intellectualization (NEUROTIC	I disapprove of my teachers teaching methods	Intellectualization	I disapprove of my teachers teaching methods
				Depression	I get depressed as I'm with him all year!
Denial (PSYCHOTIC)	I don't have that teacher	Denial (NARISSISTIC DEFENCE)		Denial	He isn't really my teacher, he is only temporary
				Drug or Alcohol Abuse	I take drugs to help me escape my daily hell
		Controlling (NEUROTIC DEFENCES)	I don't eat so I can show how much he affects me	Self-harm	I don't eat so I can show how much he affects me
				Suicide attempt	I'm getting out of his class one way or another
Repression	I do not know why I feel	Projection (NARISSISTIC DEFENCE)	He is out to get me	Projection	He is out to get me
		Rationalization (NEUROTIC DEFENCE)	Its because he knows nothing about dyslexia		
		Repression (NEUROTIC DEFENCE)	I don't hate him anymore		
		Sexualisation (NEUROTIC DEFENCE)	I want to have sex with him		
		Somatization (NEUROTIC DEFENCE)	I have leg pains and feel nausea--check		
		Distortion (NARISSISTIC DEFENCE)	I wish he was dead or leaves the school		

Differences between Defence Mechanisms Theories (Continued)

Reaction Formation	I love my teacher or hate	Reaction formation (NEUROTIC)	I deal with my anger by other means
Displacement	I hate my teachers car		
		Displacement (NEUROTIC DEFENCES)	I hate my teachers car
		Dissociation (NEUROTIC DEFENCES)	I'm a different person so I don't hate this teacher
		Inhibition (NEUROTIC DEFENCES)	I play by myself in the playground
		Externalization (NEUROTIC	The teachers hates how I act in class
		Anticipation (MATURE DEFENCE)	Planning how to act in the next class
		Asceticism (MATURE DEFENCE)	I'm good in class but others are not
		Anticipation (MATURE DEFENCE)	Planning how to act in the next class
Dissociation	I tell my teacher jokes	Humour (MATURE DEFENCE)	I make jokes in class so he likes me
Suppression	I am cross at my teacher	Suppression (MATURE DEFENCE)	I am cross at my teacher but will not tell him
Altruism (MATURE	I make friends with other	Altruism (MATURE DEFENCE)	I make friends with other teacher haters
Sublimation	I beat my teacher at	Sublimation (MATURE DEFENCE)	I beat my teacher at football

(BEHAVIOURAL)

Violence	I kick him on the playground
Revenge/Property Criminal Activities	I knife the tyres down on his car or scratch his car / I steal his coat
Drug Abuse	Taking drugs makes me feel better about myself
Displacement	I hate my teachers car

MATURE DEFENCES

(EMOTIONAL)

Socially withdraw	I play by myself in the playground
Sadness	I'm sad and quiet
Self-Blame	It's my fault he hates me
Hiding in class	I hide in his classroom, so he won't pick on me
Perfectionism	I redo my work until it's perfect to not get bad marks

(BEHAVIOURAL)

Task Avoidance	I avoid working in his class
Frustration	I get tense about being in his class
Truancy	I avoid his class and truant
Humour/Class clown	I make jokes in class so he likes me
Bad Temper	I'm angry about being in his class but won't tell him
Pessimism	I will never get another teacher I make friends with other teacher
Bullying	I take my anger out on someone else in the playground
Sublimation	I beat my teacher at football

Appendix C: Overriding School Factors

Early Identication

Ideally, all dyslexic children would be identified upon entering primary schools, and help would be given at this stage. Silver and Oates (2001) found that early identification positively reduced secondary associated problems such as emotional and behavioural manifestations. Gardner (1994, p. 85) notes that 'there is ample evidence that the earlier a child's difficulties are diagnosed, and appropriate treatment given, the better the prognosis for remediation'. Fawcett (1995) also notes that screening at entry to mainstream education is the goal for helping each dyslexic avoid failure and gain literacy, as their peers. This view is supported by Edwards (1994) and Osmond (1994) and this diagnosis could run alongside of the normal medical screenings for eyesight and hearing.

The case for assessing children on entry to school was put forward by Blatchford and Cline (1992, 1994) with four main arguments: (1) getting a profile of new entrants to inform of subsequent pedagogy for each child; (2) identification of children who may have difficulties; (3) getting a picture of the new intake as a whole, compared to norm data; and (4) using it as a measure of the impact of the school (value-added). There is debate to whether baseline assessment can adequately address each of these requirements (Drummond, 1993; Lindsay, 1997). Wolfendale (1993) notes concerns at every level (theoretical, ideological, practical and financial). Lindsay (1997, p. 26) notes 'baseline assessment is potentially a very useful addition to the education system – but only if developed and used widely'.

The UK Education Act (HMSO, 1997) launched the statutory Baseline assessment scheme, starting in September 1998. It aimed 'to provide information to help teachers plan effectively to meet children's individual learning needs' and 'to measure children's attainment, using one or more numerical outcomes which can be used later in value-added analyses of children's progress' (School Curriculum and Assessment Authority, 1997). The assessments should start as soon as children start school, in their first seven weeks of starting primary school, at ages 4 to 5 years. The tests will examine both literacy (speaking, listening, reading and writing) and numeracy/maths (applications, counting and shape). In most cases the assessments will be made by the teachers as part of their usual teaching and learning process, in either the nursery or reception classes or when the child starts mainstream education (primary school).

It is interesting that the UK government used dyslexia as a means to sell the 'baseline assessment' concept to the public; one government source noted 'it could help to tackle dyslexia, for example. We think the parents will want this' (Brown, 1998). Jacqui Smith, the UK's Minister for Education also noted the link between dyslexia and baseline assessments (Hansard, 2000)

The Scottish government review of early intervention (when children start school) programmes (Fraser, 1997) was a review of UK educational policy. The study concluded that 'early intervention falls within the broader category of equal opportunities for all' and that 'early intervention is more effective than later remediation with six years being the most commonly recommended age for specific intervention' (p. v). Fraser (1997) notes that teachers involvement is crucial noting Stoll (1991) that the key to he success of school improvements lie with the teachers responsibility to make it work. Noting that teacher assistants should only be used as an extra pair of hands rather than a replacement for a fully trained teacher in helping children with reading difficulties, with the best improvements coming from teacher one-to-one involvement. Fraser (1997, p. 7) notes 'research evidence in general favours early intervention...if children are identified in their first or second year at school there seems a greater chance of success...and that preventing later reading problems seems to be easier than dealing with them after they have become established'. Slavin, Karwit and Wasik (1992) notes that whilst early success in school does not guarantee later success, early failure virtually guarantees later failure.

In Britain, Sylva and Hurry (1995) notes a reluctance in the 1990's to intervene early as it was felt that children with real reading problems cannot be identified early, Fraser (1997, p. 9) remarks 'this position seems no longer tenable. [As] it is [now] possible to discriminate the attainment in reading of children of five or six years'.

The Scottish Office Education and Industry Department (1996) viewed the current policy for children with special educational needs (SEN) in school with unease (p. 4), for three reasons: (1) teachers were not prepared/trained enough to deal with pupils with SEN; (2) there is a lack of support for teachers teaching SEN pupils; and (3) some pupils have reported experiencing high levels of isolation (or over-protection) within mainstream classrooms. They also note that SEN pupils receive a much reduced school curriculum.

In a government review (Brooks, 2002, p. 3) of 40 early intervention schemes for literacy in the UK, notes that 'ordinary teaching (no intervention) does not enable children with literacy difficulties to catch up....working on children's self-esteem and reading in parallel has definite potential and ....that some children with severe literacy difficulties need extra help to catch up, in the form of skilled, one-to-one tuition'.

However in September 2002, the Foundation Stage Profile (QCA, 2001) was launched in England (not Wales or Scotland) to replace the Baseline assessment. This was due to the following reasons: (1) It identified boys falling behind girls; (2) The workload was too high as each baseline assessment took 60-90 minutes (however the 90 schemes reviewed before the single national scheme was introduced they only took 20-30 minutes); (3) Too many children were identified with learning difficulties and as the results were used to request extra funding for SEN needs there were insufficient funds available (SMSR, 2001). However, Local Educational Authorities (LEA) were still encouraged to use Baseline assessments whilst not being statutory. One such LEA is Brent in London (England), and where they still assess children's needs in the first few weeks at school. However, in Wales and Scotland Baseline assessments are still statutory, which suggests there is still justification for its use.

The 'Foundation Stage Profile', based assessment on a review at the end of the foundation year (i.e. the first year of a child's primary school), as by the end of the foundation stage all pupils should have reached a certain standard in six areas of learning. Testing for the basic skills of speaking, listening, reading, writing, mathematics and personal and social development were established as a minimum.

Early years specialists and the vast majority of practitioners argue that leaving assessments to the end of the foundation stage is 'too late to identify special educational needs or other needs' (SMSR, 2001, p. 37). Thus, as this 'Foundation Stage Profile' stands, early identification will be delayed and children will suffer. There are also concerns about young children being coached to pass tests rather than failing the profile. Practioners were against the change as it left identification to the end of the first year of school and allowed teachers to teach pupils to pass the test, rather than allow baseline assessments at the time of entering school, which would be in their best interests, noting 'there are bright children who will not fare well in the (first 7 weeks) assessment, due to reading and writing difficulties' (SMSR, 2001, p. 32). Such bright children would suggest those with dyslexic/ADHD.

SMSR (2001, p. 37) also notes 'across many groups, there was a feeling that if the different assessments were to relate, then baseline assessment should act as a trigger only, leading practitioners towards particular, more detailed, assessment measures where necessary'.

As noted earlier, empirical evidence supports early screening and intervention, as noted in the UK's Special Educational Needs Code of Practice (Department of Education, 2000, 5.2) 'the importance of early identification, assessment and provision for any child who may have special educational needs cannot be over-emphasised. The earlier the action is taken, the more responsive the child is likely to be. However, Dockrell, Peacey and Lut (2002) notes that early identification is only useful if it leads to intervention or support. Thus, when a need is identified, it needs to be acted on effectively and with the right teaching methods. Unless young children receive appropriate instruction, over 70% who are at risk of reading failure at year one will continue to have reading problems into adulthood (Lyon 2001).

Although some schools have good literacy support, without fully recognising dyslexia they miss out vital parts of the puzzle within the child's overall curriculum difficulties. In the majority of cases, local educational authorities require a deficit of at least two years in reading before assessment is considered. The UK's Office of Standards in Education (1999) found that deficits of four years plus were not uncommon. This delay can affect dyslexic children's relationships with their parents, siblings and peers (Riddick, 1996). Importantly, such a delay creates disaffection towards learning, teachers and school. This disaffection lies at the heart of this investigation, as it affects the dyslexic's ability to cope.

Dyslexic children who are identified early and, importantly, helped early will be able to cope with their specific educational difficulties, as their schoolwork would be tailored to their needs (Gardner, 1994). The ability to cope comes from not only understanding their difficulties, but having been taught strategies to overcome them in the classroom, e.g. use of a computer, dictation, visual support, being provided with classroom and course notes etc.

Bullying

Empirical studies suggest that bullying happens in both the classroom and playground. McDougall (2001) found that 48% of a sample of dyslexics had been bullied at school, but only 10% in a non-dyslexic control group, with Scott (2004) finding the figure to be as high as 80% which is between two and three times the national average (Rigby, 2002). Whitney, Smith and Thompson (1994) and Nabuzoka and Smith (1993) note that children in remedial classes of mainstream schools were: more likely to be victims of bullying, particularly frequent bullying; were teased significantly more than mainstream pupils; and formed fewer friendships than their peers. Unfortunately, it is their difference which is perceived to be the reason for them being selected as a victim. Scott (2004) notes that dyslexics are still being victimised with both physical and verbal abuse. Riddick (1996, p. 149) noted 'many of the children lived with the constant fear of being teased about their difficulties and put a lot of their energies into covering up their difficulties or trying to divert attention away from them'. Elliott (1999) notes bullied children: feel bad about themselves; get upset if told they are good; destroy their own work; say no one likes them; become over sensitive; lack humour; and can be startled easily. Rigby (2002) also notes children who are bullied: have a low self-worth; are non-assertive; have poor social skills; psychologically introverted; relatively uncooperative; uncompetitive; and not group orientated. Scott (2004) suggests that concerns by dyslexics regarding bullying are generally ignored and this attitude could be classed as secondary bullying, first bullied by their peers and then by adults not helping them. This confirms to the dyslexic that they are helpless, unimportant, worthless and abandoned.

Osmond (1994, p. 30) notes the comments of one dyslexic boy 'other children often made fun of me and call me names. I am picked on a lot and a gang used to make fun of me because they said I was too thick to do anything about it. I was called thicko and much worse things'. This would suggest transferral of what teachers are saying in class to the playground. If the teachers were sympathetic and were aware of dyslexia, such things may not happen.

Isolation

Scott (2004) suggests that isolation is an important factor in understanding the resilience of dyslexics. She notes that those that escape isolation are more socially integrated, however those who suffer from isolation are at a much greater risk of depression and associated manifestations.

Dyslexics are susceptical to isolation due to three main reasons: their outward communication is complicated by processing problems and thus can be perceived to be 'broken', unresponsive or at times autistic; They find it hard to process all the data around them 'data overload' (Hales, 1994) and can give wrong and inappropriate responses and; problems with literacy can mean that they are segregated at school for special remedial classes, thus they can be bullied for being 'thick' or called names such as 'spas[tic]'. Such problems can cause dyslexics to become anxious and depressed due to rejection and bullying which can make friendships difficult at school. Tur-Kaspa, Weisel and Segev (1998, p. 54) found dyslexic boys had significantly higher levels of loneliness than their non-dyslexic peers and had 'high expectations of being lonely – in their future, in general and in new situations in particular', thus they had accepted that such loneliness would not improve. Isolation seems to start when the dyslexic child starts school and has its roots with peer relationships and as Leach (1994, p. 156) notes 'many aspects of development depends on the mutual aid of peer interaction – pleasant and unpleasant' and thus Scott (2004) notes it should not be understated that to be accepted or rejected by ones peer group can determine a happy or unhappy childhood, as children spend a lot of time with their peers growing up. Vanzetti and Duck (1996) notes that 7-11yr old children spend 40% of their spare time with friends, if children are isolated and rejected by their peers they are alone or lonely for a huge amount of time.

Peers can be very inventive in their play and thus can unfortunately be very inventive in the ways they can hurt and reject others, including: stopping interaction; preventing friendships; exercising control; domination, aggression ;or invoking a third party to do or say something hurtful, according to Deater-Deckard, 2001, p. 566). According to Scott (2004, p.198) dyslexics commonly take a 'victim' stance and is the 'most common form of maladaptive behaviour among dyslexic adults and children. Whether from bullying or learned helplessness, it is evident in over 80% of referrals'. Scott (2004, p. 1999) goes on to suggest it 'is chosen, learned and then becomes useful'. And can be powerful way to gain attention, friendships and this can re-enforce the victim identification. In some case 'victims' propagate situations to confirm their 'poor me' status, whilst much is unconscious it can be a conscious decision to not change the status.

Scott (2004, p. 64) notes that isolation is an enduring feature for the majority of dyslexics and a recurring theme in their lives, 'sometimes they feel as if they are alone on the planet' and Riley and Rustique-Forrester (2002, p. 32) found in interviews with young people that they remark that 'school was a profoundly sad and depressing experience', their images and depictions were powerful suggesting that school was similar to a prison in which children continually try to escape from with themselves depicted as small voices without influence.

Thomson (1995, p. 41) notes that dyslexic and ADHD children suffer from being unpopular at school due to unpredictable reactions to events due to their difficulties which children find annoying. They also are isolated both inside and outside of school in normal social situations such as not being invited in the home of peers, ostracised in the school playground, teased or bullied by exasperated peers. After a while, dyslexics get used to the isolation and prefer to work on their own (Hales, 1995).

Edwards (1994, p. 116) notes that the majority of her sample of dyslexics felt isolation along with being unduly competitive or anti-competitive with the minority developing a clinical psychosomatic illness as a reaction to the stress and trauma from their experiences of being dyslexic at school. Such isolation of children between 7-13yrs old resulted in them: 'cutting themselves off within their own distress, hiding, crying, wanting to die, or just feeling completely alone with their disability and unable to fit in – a rejected outsider' (p. 141).

Pre-Defence Mechanisms (Word Avoidance)

Avoidance strategies deflect attention from low academic ability and under-performance, and teachers see these avoidance strategies very differently, with perceptions such as laziness and lack of parental support. Riddick's (1996) study found that children avoided words daily, especially those words that were difficult to spell or pronounce, and had difficulty in focusing enough to start new work, such as homework. In a study of dyslexic school children (primary and secondary), Riddick (1996 p. 130) also found pupils commenting that they 'daily avoided using difficult words to spell, wrote less (avoiding making mistakes) and put off starting work as coping strategies'. In fact, out of 45 noted strategies, avoidance featured in 35. The other 10 were characterised by asking classmates to help. These findings are similar to those of Mosely's (1989) study concerning adults and children with general spelling difficulties.

Pollock and Waller (1994) found that dyslexic children were perceived as immature (in their vocabulary choice and mode of expression) by schoolteachers and examination board markers, as they preferred using words they knew how to spell. But, if they do use words where the spelling is uncertain, they are accused of being careless and risk lower self-esteem. Thus word avoidance has attractive advantages to young dyslexics – they think it is better to be seen more immature than to risk embarrassment. Studies by Alexander-Passe (2004, 2007) and the interview study in the last chapter (Alexander-Passe, 2008) note that avoidance of words is a primary coping strategy used and covered all school subjects in both male and female teenage samples. The strategy included writing less, choosing easier to spell words and putting off the task of writing. At school they have consistently lost work books or homework to avoid submitting work which they thought would give them lower marks.

Appendix D: Emotional Defence Mechanisms

Mature Responses

Social Withdrawal, Sadness

Many of the participants in the interview study featured in the last chapter (Alexander-Passe, 2008) and Alexander-Passe (2004) have noted that they avoid many situations which would increase their vulnerability due to their dyslexia. These have included avoiding socialising in peer based activities such as a debating club, as each takes turns writing up the minutes for meetings. In another case a teen dyslexic's enjoyment of music was prevented due to their inability to read music. Thus they have both abstained from much enjoyed hobbies. In class they avoided participating in activities or tasks which would put them in jeopardy by highlighting their disability, they have instead hid in the back of the classroom and abstained from putting up their hands in a learning environment that should be safe. In some case, individuals have become the class clown to avoid work, as humour is more acceptable to their peers than the inability to read and write. In other cases dyslexics have withdrawn from social activities outside of school which might highlight their inability to read and write, these might include visits to the swimming pool or to see a film, as they are unable to read a bus number, road sign correctly or the choose from a list of films on a notice board. Non-dyslexics find it hard to understand how much of society is inaccessible to those who are unable to read, write and remember instructions.

Edwards (1994, p. 61) also noticed that some dyslexics suffer from competitiveness disorders, with many withdrawing both academically and socially 'Gareth only tries hard if he thinks he can win, if not he merely gives up…. Nevertheless, he had to be very sure of his good standard before making himself vulnerable again'. In large schools, this avoidance of competing or reaching potential goes unnoticed, compared to smaller schools. This extreme non-participation through lack of confidence is a recurring characteristic in dyslexics.

Nearly half of Riddick's sample (1996, p. 147) openly avoided telling their friends and other school pupils that they were dyslexic. Reasons for not telling included 'I don't want to tell anyone, because I think they'll tell everyone else, and then everybody might tease me…. Some people I do tell, some I don't. Most of them would just make fun of me… Only my best friend knows'. Riddick (p. 149) also found that half of her school-aged dyslexic sample had been teased specifically about school difficulties related to dyslexia, thus giving a foundation to their fears. Others commented, 'she (member of her peer group) kept saying I was thick because I was always last on our table (to copy things down)'. Scott (2004); Seeman (2002) and Riddick (1996) note the public shame many dyslexics feel at school, by teachers publicly drawing attention to their inadequacies. Seeman (2002) noted sadistic tendencies among teachers towards dyslexics

Self-Blame

When unidentified dyslexics find school hard and are at a loss to the reasons for their difficulties, the first place they look is to themselves. Is it me? The interview study in the last chapter (Alexander-Passe, 2008) investigated seven dyslexics who also had dyslexia. There were several individuals who used self-blame as a strategy to deal with why they were having difficulties in life. Whilst as adults they knew they were dyslexic and would have such problems, as soon as they failed they beat themselves up about failing, calling themselves 'stupid' and in some cases self-harmed. Self-blame is perceived by some as logical reasoning, as who else could be at fault. However, in these cases it leads to a self-perpetual conceptualisation that their teachers were right and 'that they would never amount to anything in life'. Self-blame could be positive as it can be used to remonstrate oneself to do better next time.

In Butkowsky and Willows' (1980) study, poor readers (including diagnosed and undiagnosed dyslexics) gave up more easily in the face of difficulties. Average to good readers attributed their success to their ability, while poor readers attributed their success to luck. Poor readers tended to blame themselves by attributing failure to their own incompetence, and success to environmental factors such as luck. There are also correlations to 'learnt helplessness' and 'attribution style' (Diener and Dweck, 1978; Miller and Norman, 1978).

Alexander-Passe (2006) investigated three types of coping among dyslexic teenager, the resulting factors included: Task, Blaming and Avoidance. It was hypothesised that the Blaming factor needed to be divided into self-blame and blame others, to deal with the results of the parallel interview study (Alexander-Passe, 2004b). The results suggested that beating yourself up about your difficulties is natural to some and when one is unaware of dyslexia or have no dyslexic friends and peers, internalization is a nature way to find meaning in a world without meaning (Edwards, 1994; Scott, 2004). Dyslexic peers are important to a young dyslexic, as they learn they are not alone. This is even more important when there is non-dyslexic sibling, as parental comparison is likely.

Hiding in Class

This is discussed under task Avoidance in Appendix E.

Perfectionism

Perfectionism is a means to which dyslexics feel they can protect themselves from the outside word by correcting and recorrecting drafts of essays or forms until such a point they feel willing to let others see them and make judgement. In the case of dyslexics who have problems with reading, writing and spelling this can mean: making sure they have read the question correctly and read it many times; to making sure the writing is neat enough and with the correct punctuation and thus rewriting the essay or form several times; to spending an inordinately large amount of time checking every word in a dictionary to make sure they are all spelt correctly (as also found by Alexander-Passe, 2008 and Scott, 2004). Such strategies may be possible when the academic workload is low but as children move from primary to secondary school and university to the workplace, such a time consuming task is not possible. The stress dyslexics put themselves under to avoid stress via perfectionism is high and can turn out to be a double edge sword. Because the work produced is too a high standard, teachers are unaware of the huge workload needed for such productions and disregard any notion of unidentified learning difficulties. They might be better served to fail and get low marks with the resulting low self-esteem and thus be visually disabled than to continue putting themselves under such stress with resulting anxiety and possibly depression, by hiding their difficulties.

Immature Responses

Bed-Wetting

Nocturnal enuresis is a condition in which a person who has bladder control while awake urinates whilst asleep. The condition is commonly called bed-wetting and it often has a psychological impact on children and their families. Children with the condition often have low self-esteem and weak interpersonal relationships, poor quality of life, and poor performance at school (Von Gontard, 2004; Van Hoecke, Hoebeke, Braet and Walle, 2004). Von Gontard (1998) linked enuresis with delayed speech, motor and speech milestones (each correlate to dyslexia). Miles (1994, p. 144) noted a case of an 8 yr old dyslexic child who was 'still bed-wetting and full of nervous twitches'. Scott (2004, p. 171) postulates that '30% of dyslexic children suffer from enuresis, some of it very severe including total soaking of the bed, every night, for months on end'.

If parents are aware that a bed-wetter has no medical problems but is having difficulty with: paying attention in school; concentrating on academic material; impulsive behaviour; fidgetiness; intermittent explosive tantrums; or conduct disorder, then dyslexia may be the underlying problem. Therapeutic Resources (2004) notes that in a study of 1822 children with attention-deficit hyperactivity disorder, (a condition with co-morbidity to dyslexia, see Fawcett and Peer, 2004; Gilger, Pennington and DeFries, 1992; Ramus, Pidgeon and Frith, 2003), 48% had been bed-wetters.

Watkins (2004) believes '…sometimes enuresis (bed-wetting) may be due to anxiety, a change in the home situation (such as the birth of a sibling) or an emotional trauma. We particularly look for emotional factors in children who were previously dry and start to wet again. A child with shaky bladder control may be more likely to revert to wetting when under stress'

Scott (2004, p. 171) suggests that bed-wetting (enuresis) in dyslexic children is common (approx 30% of all dyslexic children) and usually starts when they start to have problems at school and can go on for months at a time. Miles (1993) notes two cases along with Thomson (1995) and Von Gothard (1998) suggests an association between delayed motor and speech milestones, which can be found in dyslexics. There is double stress from the bedwetting, firstly from the act itself and secondly from the reactions of others, including peer and sibling teasing. Rutter (1983) and Rutter, Tizard and Whitmore (1970) suggest a third of such children also have emotional or behavioural problems and a higher rate of psychiatric disorders (Von Gontard).

Riddick (1996, p. 136) notes a teachers giving one of her pupils 20 hard spellings a week as a form of bullying, the child's mother commented that 'he was worrying himself sick before the spelling test. In fact, he started bed-wetting because of the pressure of the spelling test, she destroyed his confidence'.

Povey and Todd (1993) suggests that at 7yrs old, dyslexic children first begin to be a cause of concern to both parents and teachers experience difficulties at school, this corresponds with the peak of requests for dyslexia assessments (8-11yrs) according to Scott (2004). This age responds with the Freudian change from 'latency' to 'age of industry' stages of child development (Freud, 1961; Erickson, 1968). Trauma at this age can affect the progression from one stage to the next. Jacob (1986) suggests problems at this stage can cause: negative self concept; feelings of inadequacy; feelings of inferiority; confused values; dependency among others; and can cause a regression to the 'genital' stages of development as seen as a toddler, recognised as clinging to family and mother for safety.

McLoughlin et al., (2002) and Patton and Holloway (1992) and Scott (2004) suggest that dyslexics are generally immature and slow developers, even as adults they are still passive to their parents and allow them an unhealthy control over their lives. They suggest that they resist the notion of growing up as an empowerment decision. Scott (2004) suggests that this happens in several ways: firstly all major organisations helping dyslexics are run by non-dyslexics (as seen by the British Dyslexia Association) and thus they are perceived to be incapable of standing up for themselves; secondly due to their difficulties they are unable to protest in printed media and thus only use verbal media (how a toddler protests in a world of adults); dyslexia is the only disability defined by school learnt abilities of children and thus until they have mastered the abilities of children they can't be adults; as mothers are the main saviour of the dyslexic child, they remain in adulthood 'mummy's little child'; the dyslexic is often seen as creative and this is seen as the one consolation prize for dyslexia, however trapped by this concept they are unable to live in the real adult world of newspapers with political status and education; lastly work published by dyslexics is done unedited and without changing incorrect spelling and grammatical mistakes, thus they are perceived to be childish. Thomson (1995, p. 41) notes the stress from a school that doesn't assist the dyslexic child can spill into homelife and can result in manifestations such as temper tantrums, aggression and bed wetting.

Congdon (1995, p. 93) notes other manifestations in dyslexics of 'emotional disturbance arising from the problem are: enuresis (bed-wetting); stammer; sleep-waking; asthma; and various physical symptoms, such as vomiting and recurrent abdominal pains for which no physical cause can be found'.

Riddick (1996, p. 48) notes a 7yr old boy who had a new teacher unsympathetic to his dyslexic difficulties, he became distressed and his behaviour at school deteriorated, his mother noted he cried himself to sleep each night, he started to wet the bed and came home shaking (with fear) if he had a spelling test to revise for the next day, his mother was frequently contacted about his bad behaviour at school but by then his behavioural problems were seen as the main source of concern. When asking his teacher whether his behaviour could be down to a learning difficulty, the response received was 'rubbish he's just very immature, when he learns to behave properly and knuckles down to the work he'll be ok'. The next year his teacher was more sympathetic and identified him as dyslexic, helped him and his behaviour improved again.

Stammering

According to Glauber (1958) stammering is a defence mechanism where personality is disturbed and speech reverts to its infant pattern. The causes of stammering are still unclear, with many researchers looking at the condition as a neurosis, caused by anxiety, as a learned behaviour, or as an organic disorder (genetic, central nervous system, sequencing and timing, temporal programming).

Children turning to regression as a defensive mechanism would have experienced numerous stressful situations where they had tried to cope, but failed. When the situation gets just too much for the young preschooler, regression starts and they turn inwards to protect themselves, just as a turtle will when sensing danger. Blood, Blood, Frederick, Ertz and Simpson (1997) found that stammerers scored high on communication apprehension and use of emotion-based coping strategies. Alexander-Passe (2006) found high emotion-based coping among dyslexics, compared to the general population.

Stammering is a psychological and physical cry for help, and sadly these secondary symptoms are often treated without investigation of the primary cause. Thus continuous regression is likely in many cases. Unfortunately, such symptoms become a life long 'hard-to-break' habit (Van Riper, 1982, Conture and Caruso, 1987, Starkweather, 1987), and many perceive anxiety as the cause of stammering (Messenger, Onslow, Packman and Menzies, 2004; Ezrati-Vanacour and Levin, 2004; Bloodstein, 1987). Individuals react to situations and academic pressures differently; thus, it should be noted that what may be stressful to one may not be to another. One could ask, is the person disfluent because of the anxiety, or is the anxiety the result of the act of being disfluent?

Johnson (1961) found that disfluent children often came from families where the parents placed strong demands on them to achieve – speech is a major milestone and thus could be interpreted to be a predictor of later achievement. However, not all children from demanding homes become disfluent and visa versa, so there must be other factors (such as possible dyslexia).

Both dyslexics and stammerers are affected by their conditions (avoidance of difficult tasks such as reading, writing and speaking situations). Their avoidance strategies could be explained as defences against unexplained and inappropriate anxiety.

Importantly, Van Riper (1982) noted that, 'The neurosis symptoms (stammering) may at first alleviate the unpleasantness (by reducing academic pressures) but soon contribute towards it (further unhappiness)', in a form of 'conflict and trap' scenario, which has also been noted by Starkweather (1987).

Orton (1937) one of the pioneers of dyslexia study suggests that speech delay and stuttering were more common than usual in a sample of dyslexic individuals examined by him, as supported by the famous 'Isle of Wright study by Rutter, Tizard, Graham and Whitmore (1976) with later support from Snowling (1987) and Stackhouse (1990). In contrast, Scott (2004, p. 195) notes 'stuttering is not a commonly observed problem in dyslexics'; what is more common, in her experience, is that some dyslexics can't get their words out quickly enough. Whilst not fully supporting the hypothesis in this paper, she does support the regression and enuresis aspects of the hypothesis.

Riddick (1996, p. 104) describes one mother's comments that her son in French lessons…'He's never going to be academic, that's not him anyway. But he's got disheartened and upset because he wanted to get good results like the other children and he wasn't. Then he stammers, and it's an emotional stammer. It comes and goes. But really it's more there than the times it's not'. This suggests that a stammer is an emotional reaction to failure and can become habit forming.

Fawcett (1995, p. 6) notes that when her dyslexic son entered school 'he became withdrawn and introverted, to the extent that his first teacher questioned whether or not he could speak…it soon became clear that something was wrong…with many broken nights...crying with pains in his legs, coupled with poor reports of his progress at school....after diagnosis he regained his talkativeness'. His reaction to his first teacher at school was to develop a stammer (p. 8) as a defensive mechanism to stress at school and feelings of anxiety and fear of failure, as the teacher thought he 'simply refused to complete his work' (p. 8). Fawcett also notes that at the end of the year after external diagnosis his teacher admitted that she misunderstood his problem and had assumed that he was being difficult when he failed to follow instructions. It is interesting to note that as a mother, she allowed her son to stay away from school at times of class testing to 'avoid humiliation which we felt would be counterproductive' (p. 9).

Fawcett (1995, p. 19) also notes a second nervous dyslexic boy that had developed a stammer as a defensive mechanism, however 'his attendant stress and the amount of effort that he constantly needed to input into his work to try and achieve his potential took its toll....by the time he reached GCSE level, he suffered a nervous breakdown, and was simply no longer able to maintain the level of effort needed to keep up'. As a result, his parents removed all stress from his life and are unsure if he will ever obtain work.

Gilroy (1995, p. 65) also noted that two of her adult dyslexic students developed a stammer as a reaction to stress along with another one that lived on bananas and milk 'as it did not make any demands on her' to deal with supermarket shopping.

The cognitive learning theory by Conture and Caruso (1987) suggests that stammering is a result of the relationship a child has between their abilities and their environment; thus, if a child's abilities fall short of what their environment requires (parents, peers or teacher), then they will learn behaviours that will either lower the requirements (e.g. a parent expects less from someone with a known disability such as a stammer) to cope (a threat/response scenario). So disfluency could be a learnt behaviour, especially in situations children perceive as anxious. Thus disfluencies could lower these parental predictions (stress), thus reinforcing the stammer as a useful coping strategy.

Studies (British Stammering Association, 2003) suggest that most children who develop a stammer in early childhood (possibly as a coping strategy for attention) have spontaneous recovery in 2 out of 3 cases. A third recovers within 18 months of the onset of the stammer and another third before adulthood (both cases possibly as a reaction to the readjustment of academic expectations).

Stuttering could be explained as a learnt behaviour (operant conditioning) as a consequence of punishment and reinforcement. According to Shames and Sherrick (1963), repetitions in stammering which produce desired consequences (e.g. gaining parental attention) will increase in frequency until they become a major feature of communication. However, if the child gets punished, he will take steps to avoid speaking.

Thumb Sucking, Sulking, Crying and Passive Aggression

There is little empirical evidence that dyslexics use immature coping strategies such as thumb-sucking, sulking, crying, and passive aggression. However as dyslexia has not been easily identified in young children (until only recently in under 5yr olds), it is difficult to identify how pre-school children manifest their frustrations at not being able to learn normally at kindergarten. Vaillant (1992) suggests that immature defence strategies are used from birth to approx 9-11yrs old. As Riddick (1996, p. 103) notes comments by a mother of a dyslexic child 'She was like a different child once she started school. There were tears and tantrums, she used to beg me to not send her, and it was hell really. I didn't know what to do for the best'. Riddick also comments from her research that tantrums are common features of general early childhood and cannot necessarily related to a symptom of dyslexia, however they are a sign of frustration.

Scott (2004, p. 258) notes that she has found 'sucking of fingers and clothing, curling into balls under desks, bed-wetting and soiling, rocking, holding of genitals and the constant company of furry toys. When these infantile behaviours appear in an older child, they represent a signal that he is no longer coping' and are symptoms of real distress.

Hypochondrias

There are very few cases of reported hypochondrias in dyslexics, these include Edwards (1994, p. 110) who found children that developed psychosomatic disorders or other illnesses to avoid school: 'I used to pretend I was sick, make myself puke, and say I don't wanna go today', one dyslexic teenager commented. A powerful example of psychosomatic pain is the following story of a 12-year-old dyslexic: Trevor developed a pain in his right leg requiring crutches. To him it felt like a rare disease. The hospital doctor concluded that he was dyslexic but intelligent, was therefore frustrated, and that the frustration was expressed as pain in the right thigh, which occurred about once every six months and could last 10 days at a time. Strangely enough, this same teenager was reluctant to be truant, as he felt there would be 'repercussions and (that it) was pointless anyway' (p.39).

This suggests a main difference between normal truants and dyslexics avoiding school (social conscience). Another 12-year-old called Gareth used to get into fights with larger or other (dyslexic) kids to get off school. The injuries were for mutual avoidance reasons, not anger, and usually meant two to three days off school.

Blocking out

When the dyslexic has nowhere else to turn, blocking out is a form of fantasy and denial. They hope that if the deny that the feared stimulus is really there and close their eyes, it will go away. Such an immature strategy may make more sense to an infant and young child, than one that has developed more.

Extreme Responses

Isolation (of self)

This is an extreme form of social withdrawal. It requires the individual to shut themselves away, Scott (2004) suggests in many ways their peers isolate dyslexics as they are different, however she found many choose this as a coping strategy for self-preservation. See Appendix C for a full description of Isolation in dyslexics.

Intellectualization

The human instinct is to try and make sense of the world, this is no different for dyslexics and they come to the conclusion, as they are frequently isolated from other's with similar problems, that it is either their problem or those around them are the problem. If they conclude that they are normal, they begin to resent the outside world which makes life hard for them (Edwards, 1994). This can also mean they take a superior attitude to those around them to gain some power, status and self-esteem. If they conclude they are the problem, this may lead to self-harm or depression.

Depression

Scott (2004) suggests that whilst externalising (aggression) strategies are more common in dyslexic males, internalizing strategies such as depression and withdrawal are most commonly found in dyslexic females. Support comes from Alexander-Passe (2006, 2008) and Wilcutt and Pennington (2000), with Hales (1994) finding that dyslexic females scored higher than controls on anxiety and depression, with Riddick (1996) speculating at the levels of self-blame, sensitivity to others and over perfections of others amongst dyslexic females and their particular vulnerability to adjustment problems.

Scott (2004) hypothesises that dyslexics either internalizing or externalizing the psychological effect of having dyslexia or suffering the effects of having a learning disability, with the former more likely. Support comes from Griorenko (2001, p. 112) suggesting 'internalizing, effects include stress, depression and anxiety and, on balance, are those most widely associated with learning disabilities'.

Humphrey and Mullins (2002, p. 197) conclude that the experience of dyslexia has clear and demonstrable negative effects, adding 'the parallels between leaned helplessness (Seligman, 1991) and children with reading difficulties is striking'. Butkowsky and Willows (1980) claim that good and bad readers have different attribution style, leading poor readers more likely to blame themselves for failure and attribute success to luck, with poorer expectations of success and responding more negatively to failure than good readers. Such poor attribution style has been correlated with depression (Gilbert, 1992; Seligman, Abramson, Semmel and Baeyer, 1979). Bandura et al., (1999) found a significant negative relationship between children's feelings of social and academic efficacy and levels of depression, academic achievement and problem behaviour.

According to Scott (2004) all dyslexics have some form of stress-related disorder and there is no such thing as a 'stress-free dyslexic' (p. 158). She suggests that a useable way forward for counsellors is to treat dyslexics as having either a 'post-traumatic stress disorder' (PTSD) or with the theory of 'daily hassles'.

Duane (1991) and Fawcett (1995, p. 14) note 'in terms of emotional stability, the literature suggests a threefold increase in psychiatric diagnosis in children with dyslexia, in particular of conduct disorders and depression'. Fawcett suggests that such problems are a natural sequence of year-on-year school failure.

Osmond (1994, p. 28) notes one dyslexic child, 'I would get stuck again and again. I couldn't understand why I couldn't do the work when everyone else could. I just wanted to cry and I thought 'I am thick'. I started to get depressed. I would stand in a queue waiting for my book to be marked, watching all the others getting ticks for their work. It would be my turn and I'd get Xs and be told to redo the work. I would still get Xs and I'd be told that I wasn't trying'....I never knew that I'd done it wrong...I felt angry at times and I wanted to scream or even hit out but I didn't because I'd end up in trouble and there would be a letter sent to my mum and dad and they would be angry with me'.

Depression is a frequent complication in dyslexia, according to Ryan (1994), Burden (2005) and Scott (2004). Although most dyslexics are not clinically depressed, children with this type of learning difficulty are at higher risk of intense emotional feelings of pain and sorrow (as found in Alexander-Passe, 2004b, 2007). Evidence suggests that dyslexics commonly manifest low self-esteem, explaining why many dyslexics (especially female) internalise such sorrow and pain. Depression in school-aged children may be manifested by their being more active in order to cover up painful feelings (extrovert) or their being loathe to enjoy anything from their day (introvert). Both types will manifest negative thoughts about themselves and see the world in a very negative way.

Ryan (1994) notes that depressed dyslexic children tend to have three similar characteristics: (1) they tend to have negative thoughts about themselves, i.e., a negative self-image; (2) they tend to view the world negatively. They are less likely to enjoy the positive experiences in their lives. This makes it difficult for them to have fun; and (3) most depressed youngsters have great trouble imagining anything positive about the future. The depressed dyslexic not only experiences great pain in his present experiences, but also foresees a life of continuing failure.

There is very little research that actually investigates a correlation with dyslexia; the majority of empirical references are based on observations (Scott, 2004; Ryan, 2004; Duane, 1991; Rutter, 1983) rather than actual studies. Two such studies exist which investigated depression with dyslexic children and teenagers. Boetsch, Green and Pennington (1996) found that the reports of depression by parents and teachers with primary school children, were not confirmed by children's own self-reports of depressive symptomatology. The second study, by Alexander-Passe (2006) used the Beck Depression Inventory (Beck et al., 1996), The Coping Inventory for Stressful Situations (Endler and Parker, 1999) and The Culture-Free Self-Esteem Inventory (Battle, 1992) measuring N=19 teenage dyslexics. Results strongly suggested gender differences, with females using more emotional and avoidance based coping, resulting in lower percentile scores in general and academic self-esteem with moderate depression. Males tend to use more task based coping resulting in normal percentile self-esteem levels and minimal depression.

However, Grigorenko (2001) has observed that learning disabilities are observed in individuals with depression and has also commented that depressive disorders are elevated in youth with learning disabilities. In addition he notes that between 14-32% of youth with learning disabilities are depressed, but it also means that between 78-86% are not. Scott (2004) asks what variable is missing in understanding such a correlation, she suggests that social isolation is the missing variable. As Kennedy et al (1989, p.562) notes depressed children often have 'deficits in social skills and interpersonal relationships' due to being rejected or isolated by their peers. Thus it is the dyslexics who are isolated and rejected by their peers who will be the most vulnerable to depression.

PTSD and Daily Hassles

'Post-traumatic stress disorder' (PTSD) in children can come from various factors, these include: the sudden exclusion from their peer group; intense anger from a teacher or parent, physical bullying at school; realisation that something unrecognisable is wrong (maybe realising that they are abnormal or unable to learn normally, or being called stupid, lazy etc). There are two forms of PTSD, which Scott (2004) suggest dyslexics suffer. The first is Type 1 (an acute, single-impact traumatic event) and Type 2 or complex PTSD (a series of traumatic events or prolonged exposure to a stress or stressor), both are listed in the DSM-IV (APA, 1994). PTSD is a widely researched aspect of psychology (see Rose, 2002; Stallard, Karwit and Wasik, 1999 for reviews). PTSD is categorised by being the sudden and irrevocable perceptive change of the world from one that is safe and predictable to one that is dangerous and random. Individuals are as traumatised as if they had been in a major car crash. The behavioural effects of PTSD come from repetitive and intrusive thoughts and can be triggered by vision, sound and smell (as noted by Miles and Varma, 1995; Riddick et al., 1999). Yule, Bolton, Udwin, Boyle, O'Ryan and Nurrish (2000) found only 25% of PTSD sufferers had recovered after five years, 33% after eight years and 59% warranted a lifetime diagnosis.

Whilst Perrin, Smith and Yule (2000) note correlations between a sufferer with PTSD with concentration, memory and reading problems, it is unclear if the PTSD caused such difficulties or whether they were there before, a 'chicken and egg scenario'. Tsui (1990) suggests that PTSD is related to academic performance and that the PTSD was the cause. Scott (2004) suggests this is not clear cut and that the PTSD might have been caused by the secondary effects of having dyslexia, a view this author supports.

The second theory presented by Scott (2004, p. 164) is that of 'daily hassles', an opposite concept of PTSD, in that the stress of daily inconveniences are 'even more perilous in the stress lexicon than major life events'. As noted by Lu (1991), Lazaraus (1984), Chamberlain and Zika (1990) the risk of persistent hassles that are endlessly present in the sufferers life are a powerful predictor of psychological distress and have been likened to 'living permanently in a cloud of small, biting mosquitoes' (Scott, 2004 p. 164). Morgan and Klein (2000) observed that even adults with minor dyslexic symptoms are placed under extra stress from the constant effort needed to perform ordinary daily tasks, such as reading instructions to understanding conversations. To support such a concept, Winkley (1996) asked dyslexics at junior school to rank the most stressful things that they can think of, 12 of the 16 stressors mentioned are related to the experience of being dyslexic (getting lost, being left alone, being ridiculed in class, tests and examinations, breaking or loosing things, being different, performing in public). Harrison (1995, p. 116) herself a dyslexic, suffered high levels of stress in her own life, in work with a group of PTSD sufferers she noticed 'the similarities struck me; although I realise they are not as extreme for me. The social dysfunctionality also is, in them exaggerated, but nevertheless comparable to my own experiences and those I have known with other dyslexics'.

Denial

Louise in the interview study in the preceding chapter (Alexander-Passe, 2008) is a classic example of dyslexic denial. Even as she acknowledges that she self-harmed and attempted suicide at 14yrs old, she is in denial to the actual causes of her difficulties. Scott (2004, p. 258) suggests, being dyslexic is not fun or cool for children or adolescents and many take the view that they don't have a problem - this is a classic form of denial. Scott suggests that real intervention only happens when denial stops, and they realise that they do have learning problems. McLoughlin et al., (2002) suggests that many dyslexics at school hide their spelling difficulties with messy handwriting as a form of denial, as also found by Riddick (1996).

Drug Abuse

There is very little empirical evidence to rely on to investigate drug abuse amongst dyslexics. Scott (2004, p. 169) suggests that, in general, 60% of alcoholics, mainly men, start drinking due to anxiety. As a counsellor to dyslexics, Scott found high frequencies of drug and alcohol-related anxieties amongst child and adult clients. She postulates that dyslexics are more likely than non-dyslexics to use drink and drugs to cope with anxiety. Scott found a significant proportion of dyslexic children, as young as 13 years wishing to beat their addiction to tobacco, cocaine, marijuana, ecstasy, drink and anti-depressants. She has also come across drug, drink and food abuse as a means to reduce anxiety amongst children and adolescents with dyslexia. In girls anorexia and bulimia are used which represents a need to exert personal control their bodies, in a world where they are unable to control any other segment of their lives (e.g. school and home life). It may also be used as a cry for help as having such disorders gains the attention of parents and health officials, but in similar ways to truancy and behaviour manifestations, health and educational professionals will commonly treat the manifestation without looking for the initial root cause. Dyslexics who use drugs with as part of an Emotional defence mechanism are looking to escape their daily hell of being abnormal.

Suicide and Self-Harm

In a world where dyslexics are unable to control many aspects of their lives (more so in young dyslexics), self-harm by diet or alcohol abuse or cutting themselves is a common means to have control over their bodies, as noted in Alexander-Passe (2008) and Scott (2004).

When children begin to withdraw or are extremely quiet or highly active and agitated, suicide may be seen as an option to dyslexic children, as a result of excessive bullying and rejection (Winkley, 1996). Scott (2004) suggests that problems related to dyslexia maybe a cause of suicide, whilst real numbers are unknown. However as little research has been conducted in this area, numerous newspaper reports and anecdotes are the only real data to go on. Correlations between bullying, school failure, pressure to achieve academically, peer rejection, feelings of frustration, depression, guilt and hostility have been correlated with children's suicide (Thompson and Rudolph, 1996; Harrington, Bredenkamp, Groothues, Rutter, Fudge and Pickles, 1994). Thompson and Rudolph (1996, p. 446) go on to note that children with 'learning disabilities or other learning difficulties that cause constant frustration are more likely to attempt suicide...gifted children may attempt suicide because their advanced intellectual ability makes relating to children their own age difficult'. It has been found that attempts of suicide increase during school term and decrease during school holiday (Winkley, 1996) and that the attempts increase in May and June to correspond with GCSE examinations.

Alexander-Passe (2008) found that dyslexics may choose an attempt of suicide to not only end their daily hell of being perceived abnormality, but also to to rid the world and their parents of the strain of dealing with an abnormal learner and the associated pressures that arise from having a disabled child. Lastly there are feelings of not being worthy to be members of their family or society, such a perception is connected to their low self-worth or self-image.

Peer (2002, p. 32) notes that the six cases presented to him from a dyslexic forum suggests that such children are fragile, vulnerable and feel the ramifications for failure are enormous. Riddick (1996, p. 107) describes how the problems encountered because of dyslexia was enough for dyslexic children to want to kill themselves, noting one mother 'he wanted to be dead, there was nothing for him. He wanted his tie so that he could hang himself'. Scott (2004) notes that many cases of dyslexia led suicide are not recorded as the children are unable to write suicide notes.

Projection

This stance suggests that an extreme and feared stance, with perceptions that someone or something is out to get (a form of paranoia). There is no research at present that looks directly at the mental health of dyslexics. However Alexander-Passe (2008) noted with dyslexics who also suffered from clinical depression, that some women in his study felt the world was out to get them. One man noted that he needed to keep busy to shut out thoughts coming into his mind, which were negative and gets him down, these included 'I'm useless, I'm no good and I will never amount to anything'. As noted earlier, dyslexia commonly hide their difficulties from others, as they have perceptions that they would be perceived as disabled, odd or just thick (Scott, 2004; Alexander-Passe, 2004b; Riddick, 1996).

Appendix E: Behavioural Defence Mechanisms

Mature Responses

Task Avoidance

Sasse (1995, p. 113) noted the best way to avoid class input in subjects that he found difficult or impossible as a dyslexic 'the best place [to sit in class] was out to the side near the back where I was not in the teacher's direct line of sight'. 'As so many dyslexics find, after a point, the harder you try, the worse it seems to get. I often ended up in tears! While trying to correct errors I just spelt differently but still not correctly. It wasn't only the teacher who became frustrated!'

'She told me he sometimes deliberately broke the point of his pencil 10 times a day', mother of a dyslexic in Van der Stoel (1990). Such techniques are aimed at spending the maximum time off-task and consequently less time at the desk doing work, although dyslexics (especially females) tend to prefer less obtrusive ways to avoid academic work, by rarely putting up their hands or choosing to sit at the back of classes to be invisible (i.e. not picked on by teachers to take part in the class). Riddick (1996, p. 131) suggests 'by secondary (school) age all children claim that they avoid difficult to spell words and over half of them claim that they put off or avoid doing writing'.

If academic success cannot give dyslexics self-worth, then they begin to withdraw from classroom activities (negative environments), according to Morgan (1997). There is a growing body of evidence to suggest that children with dyslexia avoid tasks that highlight their difficulties. High on the list of causes are the ways in which teachers and schools deal with failure (Fontana 1995, p. 168): 'Too often the teacher instils in children a fear of making mistakes and of showing their failure to understand, and this leads to conservative and stereotyped patterns of learning which inhibit reflective thinking and a genuine grasp of the principles upon which knowledge is based'.

Frustration, Bad Temper, Pessimism

Frustration has been discussed earlier in this chapter and is one of the most common manifestations found in dyslexics, when they seek other means to deal with daily struggles at school. This can be seen in manifestations of bad temper and being pessimistic about their inability to change their rate of success at school. Such views are similar to learned helplessness as found by Seligman (1975). As Harrington (1995, p. 125) notes 'learned helplessness occurs when a person has learned expectations that external events are largely beyond his control and that unpleasant outcomes are probable'. Scott (2004) notes that learned helplessness and pessimism happens when dyslexics feel out of control and see no change in sight, and later tend to associate success in others as associated to be related to external factors (e.g. the teachers likes them etc) than to internal factors such as ability (Humprey and Mullins, 2002), thus success is attributed to factors out of their control (Hiebert, Winograd and Danner, 1984, p. 1139).

School Phobia, Attention-Seeking and Truancy

Whilst there is no direct empirical data to support the concept that dyslexia and school phobia are correlated, supporting evidence suggests that many dyslexics are phobic. Riddick (1996) noted in a study of primary and secondary pupils, that 70% dreaded going to school, Scott (2004, p. 67) also suggests the percentage is high and feels it is not unrealistic to find large numbers of dyslexics amongst a school phobic sample.

There are two types of school absence: truancy and school phobia. Truancy refers to those who are not particularly worried about school and who wish engage in delinquent and destructive acts and the distinguishing feature is that they try and conceal such school absence from their parents. School phobia was once seen as a form of separation anxiety (separation from the mother); more recently the term 'school refuser' is used when truancy is not the case. Anxiety and depression are key features of school phobia/school refuser, with it not being a single psychiatric diagnosis but a collection of symptoms (Elliott, 1999). Psychological and physical symptoms are normally found to include: stomach ache, dizziness, headaches and nausea which swiftly disappear if the child is allowed to stay at home. A conservative feature of 20,000 children or 1-2% of the school population has been sited from 2000 data (Scott, 2004, p. 68) for school phobia.

Gardner (1994) found that dyslexics are prone to withdraw from situations in which they perceive they cannot cope (e.g. spelling tests). This withdrawal can be both from specific lessons and for whole days. Withdrawal for long or frequent periods can also be caused by a reaction to certain teachers who humiliate them in front of their peers.

Blagg (1992, p. 121) suggests that school refusal is a rational response to the child who is continuously subject to ridicule and criticism from peers or teachers, with Elliott (1999) quoting research that many school-phobic children were afraid of strict, sarcastic teachers or academic failure. Scott (2004, p. 70) suggests that 'school refusal is a rational learning response' which can be replaced by other, less maladaptive coping strategies. Scott notes these children see the home as safe and the school an unsafe environment, thus they return to their parents when they feel frightened or uncertain, where the mother/dyslexic child bond is seen to be strong.

Sasse (1995, p. 113) notes whilst reflecting growing up as dyslexic 'they say that school days should be the happiest days of your life; that was certainly not true in my case. It was not a total nightmare but I soon learned to take precautions. Precise strategies were quickly evolved and a standard set of excuses were trundled out on a regular basis. The best, undetectable avoidance strategy was a serious stomach ache fifteen minutes before I had to leave for school'. Fawcett (1995) suggest that many parents, as she has, turn a blind eye to such truancy, especially on days where school tests or examinations would cause them high levels of anxiety and stress.

Humour/Class Clown

Morgan and Klein (2001, p. 72) notes that some adults use different strategies to avoid tasks and disguise and distract their inabilities to do tasks at school, being the class clown is a comment noted by several researchers (Edwards, 1994; Riddick, 1996). It is also noted that this use of humour or cheekiness is used in adulthood to cover the embarrassment from misreading words and other dyslexic errors. Morgan and Klein (2001) suggest that using humour in this way results in reducing anxiety by using existing strengths, however it means that the dyslexic is always guarding against making socially inexcusable errors.

Fantasy

This strategy allows the individual to progress through life; however there is no dyslexia research that would support such a strategy. The closest would be Richardson and Stein (1993) where they noted. Richardson (1994) and Richardson and Stein (1993) take a different perspective to the personality profile of successful dyslexics, looking at psychological factors. Findings indicate that these individuals use unusual perceptual experiences and strong sense of intuition or belief in paranormal experiences, with 73% of their successful dyslexic sample saying yes to the following question 'Do things sometimes feel as if they were not real?, compared to 49% in controls. They also found that there were significant indications that successful dyslexics were eccentric, extroverted and used unusual perceptual experiences (hunches, gut reactions and delusions) for decision making.

Immature and Exreme Responses

It is hypothesized that the differences between immature and extreme behaviour responses as defence mechanisms are more about extremes of response. The anger, shouting, biting and attention-seeking are the more basic forms which in their extremes lead to aggression, conduct disorders and property damage.

Alm and Anderson (1997, p. 247) believes that dyslexics turn away from a world that is inconsistent and difficult to handle. That acting out and acts of revenge can be understandable, as many dyslexics feel marginalised by society and have limited or no means to gain the material wealth that their peers seem to gain without much effort. Scott (2004, p. 178) suggests that 'crime becomes both a coping strategy and a useful ego-defence for a resourceful dyslexic'. Morgan (1996, 1997) notes that many dyslexics who get into problems with the police for several reasons, including: misreading legal documents such as credit agreements or police statements; are unable to remember where they were and or turn up to probation; or court meetings at the wrong times or dates; or are confused about the social signals around them.

Acting out and Displacement

Morgan and Klein (2001, p. 61) found that a lack of understanding at school and home and bullying by teachers and peers can lead to violent reactions. One dyslexic tutor recalled her own experiences at school (as a dyslexic); she actually stabbed a teacher's hand with the sharp end of a compass, because 'she called me stupid once too often'. Van der Stoel (1990) reported that one dyslexic commented concerning his time at school 'I was forever being told off and was the laughing stock of the class. Turns at reading aloud were a disaster. Well then I really threw in the towel! I'm quite a spitfire and my self-control went completely'. Critchley (1968), Jorm, Share, Maclean and Matthews (1986), Rosenthal (1973), Rutter et al. (1970), and Pianta and Caldwell (1990) all found correlations between acted out anti-social aggression and problems in reading.

Edwards (1994, p. 139) noticed in her sample of severe dyslexics that all exhibited behavioural manifestations from their experiences at school. Examples of these acts ranged from 'hitting other pupils' to 'fights with other pupils'. Edwards found that this was often linked to a dislike of the teachers' methods, boredom with the subject taught, inability to do the class task required and conflict with the class teacher.

Deviant Behaviours

One explanation is that offered by Svensson, Lundberg and Jacobson (2001, p.63), 'early failure on a socially, highly valued skill such as reading would cause an almost traumatic frustration leading to aggression, acting out behaviour and eventually, in severe cases, to conduct disorders'. Fergusson and Lynskey (1997) also suggest that a reversed relationship might also be true, i.e. that 'social, emotional and conduct problems can lead to reading difficulties'.

There are suggestions that both unrecognised and recognised dyslexics receiving insufficient or inappropriate support can feel devalued at school and turn to deviant behaviour. This is a response to their sense of low self-esteem induced by school, and as a way of gaining recognition from their peers (Kirk and Reid, 2001). Riddick et al. (1999, p. 78) suggests that low self-esteem amongst dyslexics may 'lead to a pattern of anti-social or maladjusted behaviour, which could lead to more serious forms of deviant behaviour and ultimately imprisonment'.

Delinquency

Alm and Andersson (1995), Antonoff (1998), Kirk and Reid (2001) and Morgan (1996) have all identified very high percentages of dyslexic adults and young people amongst offenders.

Morgan's (1997) study of delinquent/criminal dyslexics found that when dyslexic children fail to keep up at school, their self-esteem drops as they begin to question their academic abilities (develop inferiority complexes). Nearly Morgan's entire dyslexic (criminal) sample felt they were not given appropriate remedial support at school, and by the time they reached their teens, they voted with their feet, played truant and mixed with delinquents. Similar findings concerning dyslexics and crime have been found by Devlin (1995). This would suggest that many young dyslexics could be prevented from drifting into crime by better support at school. Edwards (1994) also found that school avoidance/refusal/truancy started at primary school, and that the extra time on such children's hands meant they were at the mercy of boredom, deviant company, street culture and crime. The Dyspel Pilot Project (Klein, 1998), which identified dyslexia among offenders, found that only 5% had also been diagnosed as dyslexic at school

This suggests a main difference between normal truants and dyslexics avoiding school (social conscience).

Aggression and Violence

Scott (2004) hypothesises that externalising effects, such as conduct disorders and crime are to come a from comorbidity to ADHD. Hill (2002) suggests that children with reading problems exhibit more frequent emotional and behavioural difficulties than children without reading problems. Willcutt and Pennington (2000, p. 1045) also found 'significant elevations of all measures of internalizing and externalizing symptoms' amongst those with a reading disability, however one cannot always take reading disabilities to mean dyslexia, as Farrell, Critchley and Mills (1999) found that only 12.3% of children in their sample with Emotional and Behavioural Difficulties (EBD) were dyslexic. Riddick (1996) suggests that whilst the vast majority of dyslexics she sees have behavioural problems exhibited by inattentiveness and restlessness, conduct disorders were less commonly found.

Scott (2004) notes that dyslexics as a product of their problems begin to use defensive mechanisms (frustration and in some cases anger), whilst experienced teachers see through these for what they are (a reaction to learning difficulties), other teachers read them as negative and obtrusive. Cooper, Smith and Upton (1994, p. 93) notes that children 'avoid the experience of repeated failure by acting out or challenging behaviour in the classroom', as they have no other perceived means to express their intense feelings.

Fawcett (1995, p. 16) notes how a 7yr old undiagnosed dyslexic changed from a compliant and delightful boy on entering school, in a few years to one that was stubborn and angry, lost large amounts of weight due to the stress, then became withdrawn and suffered with blinding headaches, attacks of weeping and finally reluctant to attend school. As soon as he was helped and diagnosed, he regained his lost weight and began to enjoy school again and achieved academically.

Fawcett (1995, p. 18) also notes a boy that developed behavioural problems as a mask to his learning problems, so much so, that his problems with literacy were not recognised until he was 9 yrs old. 'His school had been unable to identify the real cause of the problem, because he had used bad behaviour as a smoke screen, to hide his inability to cope with literacy skills', even his dyslexic father was unable to see the literacy problems which would suggest how strong he camouflaged his learning difficulties.

Miles and Miles (1999) warn against the danger of confusing primary and secondary difficulties. If a child with a primary impairment of dyslexia develops behavioural manifestations, it is important that the behavioural manifestations are not seen as the primary and the reading difficulties as the secondary, although by now they may be a contributing factor.

Morgan and Klein (2001, p. 85) notes that one girl encountered [Isobel] was so bored in her class, felt unable to access the school curriculum and so began to be disruptive, she felt 'being placed with a peer group of non-achievers in the bottom sets [of school] reinforced the lack of incentive to work hard. Isobel did not feel she belonged there and this added to her mounting frustration', she felt punished for her bad behaviour, rather than getting help for her learning difficulties.

Revenge, Property Damage and Displacement

In dealing with their problems, dyslexic's anger and frustration 'may take the form of temper tantrums, aggression or destructiveness' (Congdon, 1995, p. 93). Edwards (1994, p. 139) notes that all her dyslexic sample were prone to behaviour problems, these included 'hostile, disruptive actions towards teachers, aggression and cheekiness were already being exhibited at primary school in five cases, ranging from sabotaging the ladies' loo [toilet] as revenge on teachers to hitting other pupils to playing dangerous practical jokes'. Classroom disruption was confessed to by all her eight subjects, 'with varying motives, but often linked to dislike of the teacher's methods, boredom with the subject matter, inability to do the task in hand, or direct mutual confrontation and conflict with the class teacher. Impertinence in class, diverting attention away from literacy difficulties by clowning, and trouble in the playground were common comments from school'.

Criminal Activities

Studies by Svensson et al., (2001), Seeman (2002), Miles (2001), Lundberg (1985), Kirk and Reid (2001), and Turner (2000) suggest a correlation between dyslexia and criminal activity with a high percentage of dyslexics among prison populations - as high as 31% in some cases. It is suggested that limited school attendance and poor self-esteem, 'public humiliation in front of peers and violent outburst in response to frustration at not learning and being mocked, humiliated and called stupid' (Morgan and Klein, 2000, p. 60) to be among the contributing factors. Literacy programs have been highly successful in not only screening for dyslexia and recruitment for remedial programs, but also reducing reconviction rates (seen in both the UK and USA) and increasing the self-esteem and self-confidence of those completing the course (Meridan, 2002; Breir, 1994).

Studies have investigated the reasons behind the high frequency of dyslexics in prisons. Alm and Andersen (1997, p. 247) and Morgan (1997) suggest that dyslexics turn away from a world that is 'inconsistent and difficult to handle', they act out to boost self-esteem, use revenge and use crime as a 'useful ego-defence' as a coping strategy (Scott, 2004, p. 178). As their ability to earn is reduced by their dyslexic abilities (or lack of them), turning to crime can give them access to money for status building (the ability to purchase items of value, as per their peers). Morgan (1997) a probation officer suggests that the short-term memory deficit found in dyslexics and their inability to remember court dates or where they were at times means they are less credible witnesses of crime, along with their inability to read and understand police statements they are asked to sign, concluding that they are disadvantaged in the criminal system.

Correlations between dyslexia and ADHD also mean dyslexics are susceptible to conduct disorders.

Drug Abuse

The difference with drug abuse (See Appendix D) between Emotional and Behaviourial defence mechanisms, is that in Behaviourial defence mechanisms, it is used for frill seeking and voyeurism to gain self-esteem (Edwards, 1994), whereas for Emotional defence mechanisms it used for escapism from their perceptions of daily hell (Scott, 2004).

References

Aldwin, C.M. (2000). Stress, Coping and Development: An integrative perspective. London: Guilford Press

Alexander-Passe, N (2004a). How Children with Dyslexia Experience School: Developing an Instrument to Measure Coping, Self-Esteem and Depression. Unpublished MPhil Thesis. The Open University

Alexander-Passe, N. (2004b). A Living Nightmare: An investigation of how dyslexics cope in school. Paper presented at the 6th British Dyslexia Association International Conference. Retrieved 10th January 2006 from: www.bdainternationalconference. org/ 2004/presentations/mon_s6_d_12.shtml.

Alexander-Passe, N. (2005). Pre-school unidentified Dyslexics: Progression, Suppression, Aggression, Depression and Repression. http://www.spld-matters.com/article8.html (English version), at http://www.dyslexia.co.il/irit/article12.html (Hebrew version)

Alexander-Passe, N. (2006). How Dyslexic Teenagers Cope: An investigation of self-esteem, coping and depression. Dyslexia, 12: 4, 256-275.

Alexander-Passe, N. (2007). The sources and manifestations of stress amongst school aged dyslexics, compared to sibling controls. Published Online: 1 Oct 2007 Dyslexia, 10.1002/dys.351.   http://www3.interscience.wiley.com/cgi-bin/abstract/116323773/ ABSTRACT?CRETRY=1andSRETRY=0

Alexander-Passe, N. (2008). Dyslexia, Gender and Depression: Research Studies. In Paula Hernandez, P. and Sara Alonso, S. (Eds.) Women and Depression. Novo Science, New York (In press).

Alm, J. and Andersson, J. (1995). Reading and writing difficulties in prisons in the county of Usala. The Dyslexia Project, National Labour Market Board of Sweden at the Employability Institute, Usala.

Altschuler, J.A., and Ruble, D.N. (1989). Developmental changes in children's awareness of strategies for coping with uncontrollable stress. Child Development. 60, 1337-1349.

American Psychiatric Association (1994). Diagnostic and statistical manual of mental disorders. DSM-IV (4th. Ed.). Washington, DC: Author

Anthony, E.J. (1987a) Risk, vulnerability, and resilience: an overview. In E.J. Anthony and B.J. Cohler (Eds.). The invulnerable child (pp. 3-48). Guilford Press; New York.

Anthony, E.J. (1987b). Children at high risk for psychosis growing up successfully. In E.J. Anthony and B.J. Cohler (Eds.). The invulnerable child (pp. 3-48). Guilford Press; New York.

Antonoff, J. (1998). Conference on Juvenile Justice, Dyslexia and Other Learning Disabilities (2nd) New York

Antonovsky, A. (1987). Health, stress and coping, San Francisco, Jossey-Bass

Band, E.B., and Weisz, J.R. (1988). How to feel better when it feels bad: children's perspectives on coping and everyday stress. Developmental psychology, 24, 247-253.

Bandura, A. (1977). Self-efficacy: toward a unifying theory of behavioural change. Psychological Review. 84: 191-215

Bandura, A. (1982). Self-efficacy mechanism in human agency. American Psychologist. 31(2), 122-47.

Bandura, A. (1991). Self-regulation of motivation through anticipatory and self-reactive mechanism. In R.A. Diensbier (Ed.) Nebraska Symposium on motivation 1990: perspectives on motivation, Vo. 38, 61-164.

Bandura, A., Pastorelli, C., Barbaranelli, C., and Caprara, G.V. (1999). Self-efficacy pathways to childhood depression. *Journal of Personality and Social Psychology.* 76, 258-269.

Battle, J. (1992). Culture-Free Self-Esteem Inventories. Austin, Texas, Pro-Ed.

Beck, A.T.; Steer, R.A. and Brown, G.K. (1996). Beck Depression Inventory - 2nd ed. San Antonio: The Psychological Corp.

Bednar, R.L., and Peterson, S.R. (1999). Self-esteem: Paradoxes and Innovations in clinical theory and practice. 2nd Edition. Washington, American Psychological Association.

Bell, R.A., and Harper, L.V. (1977). Child effects on adults. Hillsdale, NJ, Erlbaum.

Berlinsky, E.B., and Biller, H.B. (1982). Parental death and psychological development. Lexington, MA, Heath.

Blagg, N. (1992). School phobia. In Lane, D., Miller, A. (Eds.) Child and Adolescent Therapy: A handbook. Buckingham, Open University Press.

Blatchford P., and Cline T., (1992). Baseline Assessments for School. Entrants, 7, 247 – 270

Blatchford, P., and Cline, T. (1994). Baseline Assessment: Selecting a Method of Assessing. Children on School Entry, 3 (13) 10 – 15, (1994)

Blood, G.W.; Blood, I.M.; Frederick, S.B.; Ertz, H.A., and Simpson, K.C. (1997). Cortisol responses in adults who stutter: coping preferences and apprehension about communication, Perceptual Motor skills, Jun, 84 (part 1 of 3), 883-9

Bloodstein O. (1987). A handbook on stuttering. Illinois, National Easter Seal Society.

Boetsch, E.A., Green, P.A., and Pennington, B.F. (1996). Psychosocial correlates of dyslexia across the life span. *Development and Psychopathology*, 8, 539–562.

Bower, T.G.R. (1977). A primer of infant development. San Francisco, Freeman.

Breir, N. (1994). Targeted treatment for adjudicated youth with learning disabilities: effects on recidivism. *Journal of Learning Disabilities.* 27, 215-222.

Brenner, C. (1973). An Elementary Textbook of Psychoanalysis (rev. Ed.). Anchor Books. Pp. 91-93; Lefton, Lester A. 1994. Psychology (5th edition). Allyn and Bacon. Pp. 432-433.

British Stammering Association (2004). General information on stammering www.stammering.org/generalinfo.html

Brody, L. R. (1985). Gender differences in emotional development: *A review of theories and research Journal of Personality,* 53, 102-149.

Brooks, G. (2002). What works for children with literacy difficulties? The effectiveness of intervention schemes, Research brief No. 380, Nottingham, DFES Publications

Brown, C. (1998). Children to be tested in first year of school. The Independent (London), 31st August.

Burden, R. (2005). Dyslexia and self-concept: seeking a dyslexic identity. London, Whurr.

Burns, R. (1982). Self-concept development and education. London: Holt, Rinehart, and Winston.

Butkowsky, T.S. and Willows, D.M. (1980). Cognitive-motivation and characteristics of children varying in reading ability: Evidence of learned helplessness in poor readers. *Journal of Educational Psychology* 72(3): 408-22.

Cattell, R.B., Elber, H.W., and Tatsuoka, M.M. (1970). Handbook for the sixteen personality factor questionnaire. Champaign, IL, Institute for personality and ability testing.

Chamberlain, K. and Zika, S. (1990). The minor events approach to stress: support for the use of daily hassles. *British Journal of Psychology.* 8(4): 469-481

Cleaver, H., Unell, I. and Aldgate, J. (1999). Children's needs - parenting capacity: The impact of parental mental illness, problem alcohol and drug use, and domestic violence on children's development, London, The Stationary Office

Congdon, P. (1995). Stress factors in gifted dyslexics. In Miles, T., Varma, V. (Eds.). Dyslexia and Stress. London, Whurr.

Conte, H.R.; Plutchik, R.; Draguns, J.G. (2004).The measurement of ego Defences in clinical research. In Hentschel, U; Smith, G; Draguns, JG; Ehlers, W (Eds.), Defence Mechanisms: Theretical, Research and Clinical Perspectives, (393-414), Advances in Psychology, 136, New York., Elsevier.

Conture, E.G. and Caruso, A.J. (1987). Assessment and diagnosis of childhood disfluency. In L. Rustin, D. Rowley and H. Purser (Eds.) Progress in the Treatment of Fluency Disorders. London: Taylor and Francis.

Cooper, P., Smith, C.O., and Upton, G. (1994). Emotional and Behavioural Difficulties: Theory to Practice. Routledge: London.

Cramer, P. and Gaul, R. (1988). The effects of success and failure on children's use of Defence mechanisms. *Journal of Personality,* 56, 729-742

Cramer, P. (1991). The development of Defence mechanisms: theory, research and assessment. New York: Springer-Verlag

Cramer, P. (1998). Threat to gender representation: identity and identification. *Journal of Personality,* 59, 335-357.

Cramer, P. (2000). Defence mechanisms in psychology today: further processes for adaptation. American Psychologist, 55, 637-646

Cramer, P. (2004). Stress, autonomic nervous system reactivity, and Defence mechanisms. In Hentschel, U; Smith, G; Draguns, JG; Ehlers, W (Eds.), Defence Mechanisms: Theoretical, Research and Clinical Perspectives, (pp. 325-352), *Advances in Psychology,* 136, New York, Elsevier.

Critchley, M. (1968). Developmental dyslexia. Paediatric Clinics of North America 15, August: 669-76.

Deater-Deckard, K. (2001). Annotation: recent research examining the role of peer relationships in the development of psychopathology. *Journal of Child Psychology and Psychiatry,* 42(5), 565-579.

Department for Education and Employment (1998). Baseline assessments. London: DfEE.

Department of Education (2000). Freedom to Learn: Basic skills for learners with learning difficulties and/or Disabilities. London, DfEE.

Devlin, A. (1995). Criminal classes: Offenders at school. Winchester: Waterside Press

Dias, B. (1976). Les mechanisms de Defence dans la genese des norms de conduite. Etude experimentale basee sur le TAT (Measurement of Defence in the course of development of norms of conduct. An experiment study based on the TAT). Fribourg, Switzerland: Editions Universitaires.

Diener, C.I. and Dweck, C.S. (1978) An analysis of learned helplessness: Continuous change in performance, strategy and achievement following failure. *Journal of Personality and Social Psychology* 36, 451-62.

Dienstbier, R.A. (1989). Arousal and physiological toughness: Implications for mental and physical health. Psychological Bulletin. 96, 84-100.

Dockrell, J.; Peacey, N. and Lunt, I. (2002). Literature reviews: Meeting the needs of children with special educational needs. London: Institute of Education, University of London.

Donaldson, D., Prinstein, M.J., Danovsky, M. and Spirito, A. (2000). Patterns of Children's coping with life stress: implications for clinicians. *American Journal of Orthopsychiatry*, 70 (3), July 2000 (351-359)

Draguns, J.G (2004). Defence mechanisms in the clinic, the laboratory, and the social world: towards closing the gaps. In Hentschel, U; Smith, G; Draguns, JG; Ehlers, W (Eds.), Defence Mechanisms: Theretical, Research and Clinical Perspectives, (55-76), Advances in Psychology, 136, New York, Elsevier

Drummond M.J., (1993). Assessing Young Children's Learning. David Fulton, London, (1993)

Duane, D. (1991). Dyslexia: Neurobiological and behavioural correlates. Psychiatric Annals. 21, 703-708.

Edwards, J. (1994) The scars of dyslexia: Eight case studies in emotional reactions. London: Cassell.

Elder, G.H. (1974). Children of the great depression. Chicago, University of Chicago Press.

Elliott, J.G. (1999). School refusal: issues of conceptualisation, assessment, and treatment. *Journal of Child Psychology and Psychiatry.* Oct, 40(7):1001-12

Endler, N. S., and Parker, J. D. A. (1999). Coping inventory for stressful situations: CISS manual (2nd Ed.). New York: Multi-Health Systems.

Erickson, E. (1968). Identity: Youth and Crisis. New York, Norton.

Erikson, E. (1950). Childhood and society. New York, Norton.

Ezrati-Vinacour, R. and Levin, I. (2004). The relationship between anxiety and stuttering: a multidimensional approach. *Journal of Fluency Disorders.* 29(2), 135-48.

Farrell, P., Critchley, C., and Mills C. (1999). The educational attainments of pupils with emotional and behavioural difficulties, *British Journal of Special Education*, 26, pp. 50-53.

Fawcett, A. (1995). Case studies and some recent research. In Miles, T.R. and Varma, V. (eds.) Dyslexia and stress, London: Whurr, (pp. 5-32).

Fawcett, A. and Peer, L. (2004). Research Reviews. BDA http://www.bda-dyslexia.org.uk/main/research/doc/Research_Reviews_Part1_and_Part2.pdf

Fawcett, A.J. (1995). Case studies and some recent research. In T. Miles and V. Varma, (Eds.), Dyslexia and Stress. London: Whurr

Felsman, J.K. and Vaillant, G.E. (1987). Resilient children as adults: a forty year study. In E.J. Anthony and B.J. Chohler (Eds.). The invulnerable child (pp 289-314). New York, Guilford Press

Fergusson, D.M. and Lynskey, M.T. (1997). Early reading difficulties and later conduct problems. Journal of Child Psychology and Psychiatry 38(8), 899-907.

Feshbach, N. (1989). The construct of empathy and the phenomenon of physical maltreatment of children. In D. Cichetti and V. Carlson (Eds.), Child Maltreatment: Theory and Research on the Causes and Consequences of Child Abuse and Neglect, (pp. 349-373). Cambridge, MA: Cambridge University Press.

Flett, G.L., Hewitt, P.L., Blankstein, K.R. and Mosher, S.W. (1991). Perfectionism, self-actualization, and personal adjustment. Journal of Social Behaviour and Personality, 6, 147-160

Fontana, D. (1995). Psychology for teachers (psychology for professional groups). London: Palgrave Macmillan.

Forman, S.G. (1993). Coping skills interventions for children and adolescents. San Francisco, Jossey-Blass.

Fraser, H. (1997). Early Intervention: Keys issues from research. No. 50. Research and Intelligence Unit. Scottish Government Research.

Freud, A. (1966). The ego and the mechanisms of Defence (Rev Ed.). New York, International Universities Press.

Freud, S. (1961). The ego and the id. In J. Strachey (Ed.), The standard edition of the complete psychological works of S. Freud (Vol. 19, pp. 3-66). London: Hogarth Press (originally published in 1923).

Frydenberg, E. (1999). Adolescent coping: theoretical and research perspectives. London, Routledge.

Frydenberg, E., and Lewis, R. (1994). Coping with different concerns: consistency and variation in coping strategies used by children and adolescents. Australian Psychologist, 29, 45-48

Gardner, P. (1994). Diagnosing dyslexia in the classroom: A three-stage model. In Hales, G. (ed.) Dyslexia matters. London, Whurr.

Garmezy, N. (1983). Stressors in childhood. In N. Garmezy and M. Rutter (Eds.) Stress, coping and development in childhood (pp. 43-84). New York, McGraw-Hill.

Garmezy, N., and Masten, A.S. (1986). Stress, competence, and resilience: common frontiers for therapist and psychopathologist. Behaviours Therapy. 17, 500-521.

Gilbert, P. (1992). Depression: the evolution of powerlessness. Hillsdale, NJ, Erlbaum.

Gilger, J.W.; Pennington, B.F. and DeFries, J.C. (1992). A twin study of the etiology of comorbidity: Attention deficit-hyperactivity disorder and dyslexia. Journal of the American Academy of Child and Adolescent Psychiatry. 31(2), 343-8

Gilligan, C., Lyons, N.P., and Hammer, T.J. (Eds.) (1990). Making connections: the relational world of adolescent girls at Emma Willard School. Cambridge, MA, Harvard University Press.

Gilroy, D. (1995). Stress factors in the college student. In Miles, T.R., and Varma, V. (Eds.) Dyslexia and Stress. London, Whurr Publications.

Glauber, I.P. (1958). The Psychoanalysis of Stuttering. In J, Eisenson (Ed.) Stuttering: A Symposium. New York: Harper and Brothers, 71-119.

Gray, J.A. (1981). The psychology of fear and stress. New York, McGraw-Hill.

Gray, J.A. (1983). Anxiety, personality and the brain. In A. Gale and A. Edwards (Eds.), Physiological correlates of human behavior: Vol. III. Individual differences and psychopathology (pp. 31-43). London, Academic Press.

Grigorenko, E. (2001). Developmental dyslexia: an update on genes, brains and environments. Journal of Child Psychology and Psychiatry. 42(1), 91-125

Haan, N. (1977). Coping and defending. New York: Academic Press

Hales, G. (1994). The human aspects of dyslexia. In Hales, G. (Ed.) Dyslexia Matters (pp. 172-183) London: Whurr.

Hales, G. (2001). Chickens and eggs. The effect of the erosion of self-esteem and self-image by treating outcomes as causes. Paper at The sixth British Dyslexia Association International Conference, York.

Hansard (2000). Education and Employment. Parliamentary debate, House of Commons. 18th December, 2000. UK, Houses of Parliament.

Harrington, R. (1995). Depressive disorder in childhood and adolescence. Chichester, Wiley.

Harrington, R., Bredenkamp, D., Groothues, C., Rutter, M., Fudge, H., and Pickles, A. (1994). Adult outcomes of childhood and adolescent depression. III, Links with suicidal behaviours. Journal of Psychology and Psychiatry, 35(7), 1309-1319

Harrison, S. (1995). Letter. In T.R., Miles and V. Varma. Dyslexia and Stress. (pp. 115-117). London, Whurr.

Helms, B. J and Gable, R. K (1989). School Situation Survey: Manual. Palo Alto, CA: Consulting Psychologists Press

Hiebert, E., Winograd, P., and Danner, F. (1984). Children's attributions for failure and success in different aspects of reading. *Journal of Educational Psychology.* 76(16), 1139-1148.

Hill, J. (2002). Biological, psychological and social processes in the conduct disorders. *Journal of Child Psychology and Psychiatry.* 43(1), 133-164.

HMSO (1997). UK Education Act. London, HMSO.

Hobfall, S. (1989). Conservation of resources: a new attempt at conceptualizing stress. American Psychologist. 44: 513-524.

Holmes, D. (1984). Meditation and Somatic Arousal Reduction: A Review of the Experimental Evidence. American Psychologist, 39(1), 1-10.

Horowitz, M.J. (1986). Stress response syndromes, Northvale, NJ: J. Aronson

Humphrey, N., and Mullins, P. (2002.) Personal constructs and attribution for academic success and failure in dyslexics. *British Journal of Special Education.* 29(4), 196-203

Jacobs, M. (1986). The presenting past: an introduction to practical psychodynamic counselling. Buckingham: Open University Press.

Johnson, W. (1961). Stuttering and what you can do about it. Danville, IL: Interstate Publishers.

Jorm, A.F., Share, D.L., Maclean, R. and Matthews, R. (1986). Cognitive factors at school entry predictive of specific reading retardation and general reading backwardness. *Journal of Child Psychology and Psychiatry* (27), 45-54.

Jung, C.G. (1966). Two essays on analytical psychology. Princeton, Princeton University Press.

Kierkegaard. S. (1985). Fear and Trembling. London: Penguin Books Ltd.

Kirk, J. and Reid, G. (2001). An examination of the relationship between dyslexia and offending in young people and the implications for the training system. Dyslexia 7, 77-84.

Klein, C. (1998). Dyslexia and offending. London, Dyspel.

Korchin, S.J. (1976). Modern clinical psychology. New York, Basic Books.

Kreitler, S and Kreitler, H (2004). The motivational and cognitive determinants of Defence mechanisms. In Hentschel, U; Smith, G; Draguns, JG; Ehlers, W (Eds.), Defence Mechanisms: Theoretical, Research and Clinical Perspectives, (pp. 195-238), Advances in Psychology, 136, New York, Elsevier.

Lazaraus, R.S. (1984). On the primacy of cognition. American Psychologist. 39, 124-129.

Lazarus, R. S., and Folkman, S. (1984). Stress, appraisal, and coping. New York: Springer-Verlag.

Lazarus, R.S. (1968). Emotions and adaptation: conceptual and empirical relations. In W.J. Arnold (Ed.) Nebraska Symposium on motivation, (pp. 175-266) Lincoln: University of Nebraska Press.

Lazarus, R.S. (1991). Emotion and apation. New York, Oxford University Press.

Lazarus, R.S., and Folkman, S. (1980). An analysis of coping in a middle-aged community sample. *Journal of Health Soc. Behaviour* 1980 Sep; 21(3):219-39.

Leach, R. (1994). Children first: what society must do – and is not doing – for children today. London, Penguin

Lindsay G.A., (1997). Baseline Assessment: A Positive or Malign Initiative? Institute of Education, University of Warwick, Coventry, (1997)

Lu, L. (1991). Daily hassles and mental health: A longitudinal study. *British Journal of Psychology*. 13(1), 441-447

Lundberg, I. (1995). Trends in Dyslexia research in Sweden. Dyslexia. 1(1), 46-53.

Luthar, S.S., and Zigler, E. (1991). Vulnerability and competence: a review of research on resilience in childhood. *American Journal of Orthopsychiatry*. 61, 6-22.

Lyon, G.R. (2001). Measuring success: Using assessments and accountability to raise student achievement. Washington, D.C.: Subcommittee on Education Reform, Committee on Education and the Workforce. U.S. House of Representatives.

Mahoney, M.J., and Thoresen, C.E. (Eds.) (1974) Self-control: Power to the person Monterey, CA: Brooks/Cole.

Mason, J.W. (1975). A historical view of the stress field. *Journal of Human Stress.* 1, 6-27.

Masten, A.S., Best, K.M., and Garmey, N. (1990). Resilience and development: contributions from the study of children who overcome adversity. Development and Psychotherapy. 2, 425-444.

McCall, R.J. (1975). The varieties of abnormality. Springfield, IL, Charles C. Thomas.

McDougall, S. (2001). Experiences of dyslexia: social and emotional factors associated with living with dyslexia. Dyslexia Review. 12(2), 7-9

McLoughlin, D., Leather, C., and P. Stringer, P. (2002). The Adult Dyslexic. Interventions and Outcomes. London: Whurr.

Meichenbaum, M. (1977). Cognitive behaviour modification: an integrative approach. New York, Plenum.

Meissner, W.W. (1980). Theories of personality and psychopathology: classical psychoanalysis. In Kaplan, H.I., Freedman, A.M|., Sadock, B.J. (Eds.) Comprehensive Textbook of Psychiatry, 3rd Ed. Vol. 1. (pp. 212-230). Baltimore, MD, William and Wilkins.

Menninger, K. (1963). The vital balance: the life processes in mental health and illness. New York, MacMillian.

Meridan (2002). Meridian Broadcasting On Line. That's Esther Fact sheet. Programme 4, 2 October. www.meridian.tv.co.uk.

Messenger, M.; Onslow, M. Packman, A. and Menzies, R. (2004). Social anxiety in stuttering: measuring negative social expectancies. *Journal of Fluency Disorders.* 29(3), 201-12.

Miles, T.R. (1993). Dyslexia: The pattern of difficulties (2nd Ed.). London, Whurr.

Miles, T.R. (1994) Dyslexia: The Pattern of difficulties. London, Whurr.

Miles, T.R. (2001). Editorial: A chain of editorial reflections (crime and dyslexia). Dyslexia. 7(2), 57-61.

Miles, T.R. and Miles, E. (1999). Dyslexia: A hundred years on, 2nd edition. Buckingham: Open University Press.

Miles, T.R., and Varma, V. (1995). Dyslexia and stress. London, Whurr.

Miller, L.W., and Norman, W.H. (1978). Learned helplessness in humans: A review and attribution theory model. Psychological Bulletin 86, 93-118.

Miller, S.M. (1990). To see or not to see: cognitive informational styles in the coping process. In M. Rosenbaum (Ed.), Learned resourcefulness: on coping skills, self-regulation, and adaptive behaviour (pp. 95-126). New York, Springer.

Montessori, M. (1965). Dr Montessori's Own Handbook. New York, Schocken Books.

Morgan, E. and Klein, C. (2001). The dyslexic adult in a non-dyslexic world. London, Whurr.

Morgan, W. (1996). Dyslexic offender. The magistrate magazine 52(4), 84-6.

Morgan, W. (1997). Criminals! Why are so many offenders dyslexic? Unpublished paper.

Mosely, D. (1989). How lack of confidence in spelling affects children's written expressionism. Educational Psychology in Practice, April: 5-6.

Murphy, L., and Moriarty, A. (1976). Vulnerability, coping and growth: from infancy to adolescence. New Haven, Yale University Press.

Nabuzoka, D., and Smith, R. (1993). Sociometric status and social behaviour of children with and without learning difficulties. Journal of Child Psychology and Psychiatry. 34(8), 1435- Office for Standards in Education 1448.

Orton, S.T. (1937). Reading, writing and speech problems of children. New York, Norton.

Osmond, J. (1994). The reality of dyslexia. London, Cassell.

Office for Standards in Education (1999). Report into pupils with specific learning difficulties in mainstream schools. London: HMSO.

Oxford English Dictionary (2006). Paperback Oxford English Dictionary. Oxford University Press; 6th Rev Edition.

Patton, J., and Holloway, E. (1992). Learning difficulties: the challenge of adulthood. *Journal of Learning Difficulties.* 25, 410-415

Peer, L. (2002). Dyslexia – Not a condition to die for. Special children (September), 31-33.

Peer, L. and Reid, G. (Eds.) (2001). Dyslexia: Successful inclusion in the secondary school. London: David Fulton.

Perrin, S., Smith, P., and Yule, W. (2000). Practioneer review: the assessment and treatment of post-traumatic stress disorder in children and adolescents. *Journal of Child Psychology and Psychiatry.* 41(3), 277-289.

Pianta, R.C. and Caldwell, C.B. (1990). Stability of externalising symptoms from kindergarten to first grade and factors related to instability. Development and Psychopathology 2, 247-58.

Plutnick, R.; Kellerman, H.; and Conte, H.R. (1979). The structural theory of ego Defences and emotions. In C. E. Izard (Ed.), Emotions in personality and psychopathology (pp. 229-257). New York, Plenum

Pollock, J. and Waller, E. (1994). Day to day dyslexia in the classroom. London, Routledge.

Povey, R., and Todd, J. (1993). The dyslexic child. In Varma, V (Ed.). How and why children fail. London, Jessica Kingsley.

Qualifications and Curriculum Authority QCA (2001). Foundation profile. London, Qualifications and Curriculum Authority (www.qca.org.uk).

Ramus, F.; Pidgeon, E. and Frith, U. (2003). The relationship between motor control and phonology in dyslexic children. *Journal of Child Psychology and Psychiatry* 44, 5, 712–722

Reid, G. (1988). Dyslexia and Learning Style: A Practitioner's Handbook. Chichester, Wiley.

Richardson, A.J. and Stein, J.F. (1993). Personality characteristics of adult dyslexics. In S.F. Wright and R. Groner (Eds.). Facets of dyslexia and remediation. Amsterdam, Elsevier.

Richardson, J. T. E. (1994). Mature students in higher education: Academic performance and intellectual ability. Higher Education, 28, 373-386.

Riddick, B. (1996). Living with dyslexia: The social and emotional consequences of specific learning difficulties. London, Routledge.

Riddick, B.; Sterling, C.; Farmer, M. and Morgan, S. (1999). Self-esteem and anxiety in the educational histories of adult dyslexic students. Dyslexia 5, 227-48.

Rigby, K. (2002). New perspectives on bullying. London, Jessica Kingsley.

Riley, K., and Rustique-Forrester, E. (2002). Working with disaffected students: why students lose interest in school and what we can do about it. London, Paul Chapman.

Roecker, C.E., Dubow, E.F., and Donaldson, D.L. (1996). Cross-situational patterns in children's coping with observed interpersonal conflict. *Journal of Clinical Child Psychology.* 25, 288-299.

Rogers, C.R. (1959). A theory of therapy, personality and interpersonal relationships, as developed in the client-centered framework. In S. Koch (Ed.). Psychology: A study of science. (pp. 184-256). N.Y.: McGraw Hill.

Rose, S. (2002). Theoretical approaches to psychological trauma: Implications for research and practice. Counselling and Psychotherapy Research 2(1), 61-72

Rosenthal, J.H. (1973). Self-esteem in dyslexic children. Academic Therapy 9(1), 27-30.

Rosenthal, R. and Jacobson, L. (1973). Pygmalion in the classroom. New York, Holt, Rinehart and Winston.

Roskies, E., and Lazarus, R. S. (1980). Coping theory and the teaching of coping skills. In P. O. Davidson and S. M. Davidson (Eds.), Behavioural medicine: Changing health lifestyles. New York: Brunner/Mazel.

Rutter, M, Tizard, J, Yule, W, Graham, P. and Whitmore, K. (1976). 1964-1974 Isle of Wight studies, Psychological Medicine, 6, 313-332.

Rutter, M. (1983). Stress, coping and development: Some issues and some questions. In Garmezy, N. and Rutter, M. (eds.) Stress, coping and development in children. New York, McGraw-Hill, 1-41.

Rutter, M.; Tizard, J. and Whitmore, K. (eds.) (1970). Education, health and behaviour. London, Longman and Green.

Ryan, M. (1994). Social and emotional problems related to dyslexia. *The Journal of Adventist Education. Perspectives,* spring 1994, Vol. 20, No. 2.

Sasse, M (1995). The positive and the negative. In T.R., Miles and V. Varma. Dyslexia and Stress. (pp. 112-115). London, Whurr.

School Curriculum and Assessment Authority (1997). The National Framework for Baseline Assessment. Middlesex: SCAA.

Scott, R. (2004). Dyslexia and Counselling. Whurr, London.

Scottish Office Education and Industry Department (1996). Improving Achievement in Scottish Schools, A report to the Secretary of State for Scotland, Edinburgh: HMSO [Government's Response (1996) Improving Achievement in Scottish Schools]

Seeman, L. (2002). The sociological implications of untreated dyslexia: linkage of dyslexia with crime. Available: seeman@netvision.net.il.

Seligman, M. (1975). Helplessness. San Francisco, CA: Freeman. Singer, J.L. (Eds.), Repression and dissociation. Chicago, IL, University of Chicago Press.

Seligman, M.E.P. (1991). Learned optimism. New York, Knopf.

Seligman, M.E.P., Abramson, L.Y., Semmel, A., and Baeyer, C.V. (1979). Depressive attributional style. *Journal of Abnormal Psychology.* 88, 242-247.

Selye, H. (1956). The Stress of life. London, McGraw-Hill

Selye, H. (1974). Stress without distress. Philadelphia, Lippincott.

Selye, H. (1991). Stress without distress. London, J.P. Lippincott

Shames, G.H. and Sherrick, C.E. Jr. (1963). A discussion of nonfluency and stuttering as operant behaviour. Journal of Speech and Hearing Disorders. Feb; 28, 3-18.

Shaprio, D. (1965) Neurotic styles. New York, Basic Books.

Silver, M. and Oates, P. (2001) Evaluation of a new computer intervention to teach people with autism or Asperger's syndrome to recognise and predict emotion in others. Autism 5(3), 299-316.

Slavin, R.E., Karwit, N.L., and Wasik, B.A (1992). Preventing early school failure; what works? Educational Leadership. 50(4), Dec/Jan 1993, 10-18.

Smith, G.J.W.; and Danielsson, A. (1982). Anxiety and defensive strategies in childhood and adolescence. New York, International Universities Press.

SMSR (2001). Report to QCA: Baseline assessment for the foundation stage – A national consultation. Kingston upon Thames, SMSR.

Snowling, M. (1987). Dyslexia: a cognitive developmental perspective. Oxford, Blackwell.

Stackhouse J. (1990). Phonological deficits in developmental reading and spelling disorders. In: Grunwell P, editor. Developmental Speech Disorders. London: Churchill Livingstone

Stallard P., Velleman, R., Baldwin, S. (1999). Recovery from post-traumatic stress disorder in children following road traffic accidents: the role of talking and feeling understood. *Journal of Community and Applied Social Psychology*. 11(1), 37-41.

Stark, L., Spirito, A., Williams, C., and Guevremont, D. (1989). Common problems and coping strategies I: Findings with normal adolescents. *Journal of Abnormal Child Psychology,* 17, 203-212

Starkweather, C.W. (1987). Fluency and Stuttering. Englewood Cliffs, NJ, Prentice-Hall.

Stoll, L. (1991). School effectiveness in action: supporting growth in schools and classrooms. Effective Schools for All. London: David Fulton

Stouffer, S.A. (1949). The American soldier. Princeton, Princeton University Press.

Svensson, I.; Lundberg, I. and Jacobson, C. (2001). The prevalence of reading and spelling difficulties among inmates of institutions for compulsory care of juvenile delinquents. Dyslexia 7, 62-76.

Sylva, K. and Hurry, J. (1995). Early intervention in children with reading difficulties. London, School Curriculum and Assessment Authority.

Taylor, S., and Brown, J.D. (1988). Illusion and well-being: a social psychological perspective on mental health. Psychological Bulletin. 103, 193-210.

Therapeutic Resources (2004). A history of Bedwetting (primary nocturnal enuresis) is a very strong clue to the diagnosis of ADD/ADHD. http://www.therapeuticresources. com /bedwetting.html

Thompson, C.L., and Rudolph, L. B. (1996). Counselling Children (4th Ed.). Pacific Grove, CA, Brooks/Cole.

Thomson, P. (1995). Stress factors in early education. In Miles, T.R. and Varma, V. (eds.) Dyslexia and stress. London: Whurr, 5-32.

Tsui, E. (1990). Effects of a disaster on children's academic attainment. Unpublished master's thesis. University of London.

Tur-Kaspa, M., Weisel, A., and Segev, L. (1998). Attributes for feelings of loneliness of students with learning disabilities. Learning Disabilities Research and Practice. 13(2), 89-94.

Turner, M. (2000). Dyslexia and Crime. Dyslexia Review. 12(1), 4-5.

Vaillant, G.E. (1971). Theoretical hierarchy of adaptive ego mechanisms. Archives of General Psychiatry, 24, 107-118

Vaillant, G.E. (1977). Adapation to life. Boston, Little, Brown

Vaillant, G.E. (1983) Childhood environment and maturity of Defence mechanisms. In D. Magnusson and V.L. Allen (Eds.), Human development: An interactional perspective (pp. 343-352). San Diaego, CA, Academic Press

Vaillant, G.E. (1992). Ego Mechanism of Defence: A guide for clinicians and researchers. London, American Psychiatric Press Inc.

Vaillant, G.E. (1993). The wisdom of the ego. Cambridge, MA, Harvard University Press.

Van der Stoel, S. (1990). Parents on dyslexia. Clevedon, Multilingual Matters.

Van Hoecke, E.; Hoebeke, P.; Braet, C and Walle, J.V. (2004). An assessment of internalizing problems in children with enuresis. Journal of Urolology. Jun, 171 (Pt 2 of 6), 2580-3.

Van Riper, C. (1954). Speech correction: principles and methods (3rd Ed.). New York, Prentice-Hall.

Van Riper, C. (1982). The nature of stuttering (2nd Ed.). Englewood Cliffs, NJ, Prentice-Hall.

Vanzetti, N., and Duck, S. (1996). A lifetime of relationships. Pacific Grove, CA, Brooks/Cole.

Von Gontard, A. (1998). Annotation: day and night wetting in children – a pediatric and child psychiatric perspective. 39(4), 439-451.

Von Gontard, A. (2004). Psychological and psychiatric aspects of nocturnal enuresis and functional urinary incontinence. Urologe A. 2004 Jul; 43(7), 787-94

Watkins, C. (2004). AD/HD and Enuresis (Bedwetting) http://www. baltimorepsych. com /adhd_and_bedwetting.htm

Wegrocki, H.J. (1939). A critique of cultural and statistical concepts of abnormality. Journal of Abnormal and Social Psychology. 34, 166-178.

Werner, E.E. and Smith, R.S. (1992). Overcoming the odds. Cornell University Press: Ithaca, N.Y.

Wertlieb, D., Wiegel, C., and Feldstein, M. (1987). Measuring children's coping. American Journal of Orthopsychiatry, 57, 548-560

White, R.W. (1974). Strategies for adaptation: an attempt at systematic description. In G.V. Coelho, D.A. Hamburg and J.E. Adams (Eds.), Coping and adaptation (pp. 47-68). New York, Basic Books.

Whitney, I., Smith, P., and Thompson, D. (1994). Bullying and children with special educational needs. In Smith, P., Sharp, S. (Eds.) School Bullying: insight and perspectives. London, Routledge.

Wilcutt, E., and Pennington, B. (2000). Psychiatric comorbidity in children and adolescents with reading difficulty. Journal of Child psychology and Psychiatry. 41(8), 1039-1048.

Winkley, L. (1996). Emotional problems in childhood and young people. London, Cassell.

Wolfendale, S. (1993). Baseline assessment: a review of current practice, issues and strategies for effective implementation. OMEP.

Wolin, S.J., and Wolin, S. (1993). The resilient self: how survivors of troubled families rise above adversity. New York, Ullard Books.

Wong, N. (1989). Theory of personality and psychopathology. In H.I. Kaplan and B.J. Sadock (Eds.) Comprehensive textbook of psychiatry: Vol 1 (5th Ed.) (pp. 356-410). Balimore, Williams and Wilkins.

Wyman, P.A., Cowen, E.L., Work, W.C., and Parker, G.R. (1991). Developmental and family milieu correlates of resilience in urban children who have experienced major life stress. American Journal of Community Psychology. 19, 405-426.

Yule, W., Bolton, D., Udwin, O., Boyle, S., O'Ryan, D., and Nurrish, J. (2000). The long-term psychological effects of a disaster experienced in adolescence: I: The incidence and course of PTSD. Journal of Child Psychology and Psychiatry, and Allied Disciplines 41, 503–511.

In: Women and Depression
Editors: Paula Hernandez and Sara Alonso

ISBN 978-1-60456-647-5
© 2009 Nova Science Publishers, Inc.

Chapter 3

Sex and Age Differences in Adolescent Depression: A Cognitive Vulnerability-Stress Perspective

Irene Zilber, John R. Z. Abela and Reuben Weinstangel
McGill University, Montreal, Quebec, Canada

The results from epidemiological studies suggest that adolescence is a critical period for understanding the development of depression for two reasons (Avenevoli, Knight, Kessler, & Merikangas, 2007). First, although during childhood, sex differences in depression are not reliably found, during the transition from early to middle adolescence (i.e., ages 12-15) sex differences emerge with girls reporting higher levels of both depressive symptoms (Angold, Erkanli, Silberg, Eaves, & Costello 2002; Twenge & Nolen-Hoeksema, 2002) and depressive disorders (Costello, Mustillo, Erkanli, Keeler, & Angold, 2003; Hankin, Abramson, Moffitt, Silva, McGee, & Angell, 1998) than boys. Second, during the transition from middle to late adolescence, there is a dramatic, six-fold increase in depression rates (Hankin et al., 1998). Prevalence rates remain at similarly high levels throughout adulthood with adult depression typically being preceded by adolescent depression (Kim-Cohen, Caspi, & Moffitt, 2003). Although it is well established that both of these epidemiological shifts occur during adolescence, little research has examined the factors that underlie them. In the current chapter, we will examine both the emergence of sex differences in depression and the surge in depression rates in adolescence from the perspective of cognitive vulnerability-stress theories of depression.

Cognitive Theories of Depression

Cognitive theories of depression are concerned with the relationship between human mental activity and the experience of depressive symptoms and episodes (Ingram, Miranda, & Segal, 1998). Cognition is thought to encompass the mental processes of perceiving, recognizing, conceiving, judging, and reasoning. According to cognitive theorists, these cognitive variables have significant causal implications for the onset, maintenance, and remission of depression.

According to cognitive theories of depression, vulnerability is operationalized as an internal and stable feature of an individual that predisposes him or her to develop depression following negative events (Ingram et al., 1998). It is important to note that the majority of cognitive models are diathesis-stress models in that they posit that depression is produced by the *interaction* between an individual's cognitive vulnerability and certain environmental conditions that serve to trigger this diathesis into operation (for main-effect models, see Nolen-Hoeksema, 1991; Weisz, 1986; Weisz & Stipek, 1982). Under ordinary conditions, persons possessing cognitive vulnerability to depression are hypothesized to be no more likely than other individuals to report depressive symptoms. Only when vulnerable individuals are confronted with certain stressors are differences in symptom levels hypothesized to emerge (Ingram & Luxton, 2005; Monroe & Simons, 1991). For individuals who possess cognitive vulnerability factors, the occurrence of negative events is hypothesized to trigger a pattern of negative, biased, self-referent information processing that initiates a downward spiral into depression. Nonvulnerable individuals are hypothesized to react with an appropriate level of distress and depressive affect to the event but to not spiral into depression.

Cognitive theories of vulnerability to depression are titration models (Abramson, Alloy, & Metalsky, 1988; Alloy, Hartlage, & Abramson, 1988). In other words, such theories posit that cognitive vulnerability is best conceptualized along a continuum with some individuals exhibiting higher levels of cognitive vulnerability than others. Similarly, negative events are best conceptualized along a continuum with some negative events being more negative than others. According to such a perspective, the higher the level of cognitive vulnerability an individual possesses, the less stressful negative events must be to trigger the onset of depressive symptoms/episodes. Conversely, even youth possessing average or low levels of cognitive vulnerability may be at risk for developing depression following the occurrence of extreme stressors.

Cognitive theories of depression offer several hypotheses for why epidemiological shifts such as the sex difference and increases in rates of depression occur and why they begin during adolescence. These hypotheses center around two main approaches towards conceptualizing the mechanisms underlying sex and/or age differences in depression. The first approach is a *mediation* framework which posits that sex and/or age differences in depression rates are due, in part, to sex and/or age differences in levels of vulnerability and/or risk factors. From the perspective of cognitive vulnerability-stress theories, this approach would posit that sex and/or age differences in depression rates are due, in part, to girls reporting higher levels of cognitive vulnerability and/or stress than boys and older youth reporting higher levels of cognitive vulnerability and/or stress than younger youth. The second approach is a *moderation* framework which posits that sex and/or age differences exist in the strength of the association between risk and/or vulnerability factors and depressive symptoms. From the perspective of cognitive vulnerability-stress theories, this approach would posit that sex and/or age differences in depression rates are due, in part, to the strength of the association between cognitive vulnerability factors and increases in depressive symptoms following negative events being stronger in girls than in boys and/or in older youth than in younger youth. It is important to note that these two frameworks are not mutually exclusive. In other words, they are best viewed as complementary and the mechanisms underlying the emergence of sex and/or age differences in depression rates likely involve a combination of these two approaches.

One hypothesis concerning both the emergence of sex differences in depression and the surge in depression rates that has been researched and supported is that levels of stress increase in adolescence – particularly for girls (see Hankin & Abramson, 2001 for review). More specifically, the results from longitudinal studies suggest that both boys and girls, but especially girls, begin to encounter more stressors starting around age 13 (Ge, Lorenz, Conger, Elder, & Simons, 1994; Rudolph & Hammen, 1999), and that puberty, as a developmental transition, is associated with an increase in experienced negative life events (Caspi & Moffitt, 1991; Graber, Brooks-Gunn, & Petersen, 1996) especially for girls (Graber, Brooks-Gunn, & Warren, 1995). This trajectory of increasing levels of stressors closely parallels the emergence of the sex difference in depression throughout adolescence (Ge et al., 1994). Research has reported that girls encounter more interpersonal (e.g., peer, relationship) stressors, especially after puberty (Rudolph, 2002; Rudolph & Hammen, 1999), perhaps as a result of post-pubertal adolescent girls being more interpersonally oriented than boys and pre-pubertal girls (e.g., Cyranowski, Frank, Young, & Shear, 2000). Adolescent girls have also been found to experience higher levels of dependent stressors (e.g., stressors caused in part by their characteristics and/or behaviors) than boys, especially dependent stressors in interpersonal domains (Rudolph & Hammen, 1999).

The remainder of current chapter focuses on four alternative, yet complementary, hypotheses that have received little empirical investigation. More specifically, we will provide a review of the literature examining each of the following four hypotheses:

1) Do girls report higher levels of cognitive vulnerability factors than do boys?
2) Is the strength of the association between cognitive vulnerability factors and increases in depressive symptoms following negative events stronger for girls than for boys?
3) Do older youth report higher levels of cognitive vulnerability factors than do younger youth?
4) Is the strength of the association between cognitive vulnerability factors and increases in depressive symptoms following negative events stronger for older youth than for younger youth?

Although a multitude of cognitive vulnerability factors have been posited, we will focus our review on the following as they have been studied the most extensively across child, early adolescent, and adolescent populations: (1) depressogenic inferential styles about causes, consequences, and the self (Abramson, Seligman, & Teasdale, 1978; Abramson, Metalsky, & Alloy, 1989), (2) dysfunctional attitudes (Beck, 1967, 1983), (3) the tendency to ruminate in response to depressed mood (Nolen-Hoeksema, 1991), and (4) personality predispositions to depression (Beck, 1983; Blatt & Zuroff, 1992). In addition, we will focus our review on prospective studies, as they provide the most powerful tests of cognitive vulnerability theories.

Hopelessness Theory

The hopelessness theory is a cognitive diathesis-stress theory that posits a series of contributory causes that interact with one another to culminate in a proximal, sufficient cause of a specific subtype of depression: hopelessness depression (Abramson et al., 1989). The hopelessness theory postulates three distinct depressogenic inferential styles that serve as distal contributory causes of hopelessness depression: (1) the tendency to attribute negative events to global and stable causes; (2) the tendency to perceive negative events as having many disastrous consequences; and (3) the tendency to view the self as flawed or deficient following negative events. Each depressogenic inferential style predisposes individuals to the development of hopelessness depression by increasing the likelihood that they will make depressogenic inferences following negative events. Making such inferences increases the likelihood that hopelessness will develop. Once hopelessness develops, hopelessness depression is inevitable as the hopelessness theory views hopelessness as the proximal, sufficient cause of hopelessness depression.

As presented in Table 1, 27 studies have provided a prospective test of the hopelessness theory in child and/or adolescent samples (for a review of findings pertaining to the vulnerability-stress hypothesis of the hopelessness theory in youth, see Abela & Hankin, 2008). Of these studies, 20 have examined age and/or sex effects in levels of depressogenic inferential styles and/or the strength of the association between depressogenic inferential styles and increases in depressive symptoms following negative events.

Depressogenic Attributional Style

Thirteen studies have examined sex differences in levels of attributional style. Twelve of these studies reported no such sex difference (Abela, 2001; Abela & McGirr, 2007; Abela, Parkinson, Stolow, & Starrs, in press; Abela & Payne, 2003; Abela & Sarin, 2002; Abela, Skitch, Adams, & Hankin, 2006; Conley, Haines, Hilt, & Metalsky, 2001; Hankin, Abramson, & Siler, 2001; Joiner, 2000; Prinstein & Aikens, 2004; Southall & Roberts, 2002; Spence, Sheffield, & Donovan, 2002). In contrast, one of these studies reported that boys exhibited more depressogenic attributional styles then did girls (Lewinsohn, Joiner, & Rohde, 2001).

Table 1. Summary of prospective studies testing the Hopelessness Theory of Depression

Study	Sample	Follow-up	Measures	Sex Differences in Levels of Either Depressogenic Inferential or Attributional Styles	Age Differences in Levels of Either Depressogenic Inferential or Attributional Styles	Sex as a Moderator of the Prospective Association Between Either Depressogenic Inferential or Attributional Styles X Negative Events Interaction and Change in Depressive Symptoms Over Time	Age as a Moderator of the Prospective Association Between Either Depressogenic Inferential or Attributional Styles X Negative Events Interaction and Change in Depressive Symptoms Over Time	Sample Size
Abela (2001)	3rd and 7th graders	1.5 months	CCSQ, CLES, CDI	Girls reported higher levels of the DIS-Self than did boys. Girls and boys did not significantly differ in reported levels of the DIS-Causes and DIS-Consequences.	3rd graders reported higher levels of the DIS-Consequences and DIS-Self than did 7th graders. 3rd graders and 7th graders did not significantly differ in levels of the DIS-Causes.	The strength of the association between the DIS-Self × Stress interaction and change in depressive symptoms over time was stronger in girls than in boys. The strengths of the associations between both the DIS-Causes × Stress and the DIS-Consequences × Stress interactions and change in depressive symptoms over time were not moderated by sex.	The strengths of the associations between the DIS-Self × Stress, and DIS-Consequences × Stress interactions and change in depressive symptoms over time were not moderated by grade. The strength of the association between the DIS-Causes × Stress interaction and change in depressive symptoms over time was stronger among 7th graders than among 3rd graders.	382
Abela (2002)	12th graders	2.5 months	CSQ, CPQ, SEQ, MAACL	Not Examined	NA	The strengths of the associations between the DIS-Causes × Stress, DIS-Consequences × Stress, and DIS-Self × Stress interactions and change in depressive symptoms over time were not moderated by sex.	NA	136

Table 1. (Continued)

Abela & McGirr (2007)	6 – 14 year olds with an affectively ill parent	Every 6 weeks for 12 months	CCSQ, CHAS, CDI	Girls reported higher levels of the DIS-Self than did boys. Girls and boys did not differ in levels of the DIS-Causes, DIS-Consequences, or Weakest Link composite scores.	Age was not associated with levels of either the DIS-Self, DIS-Consequences, DIS-Causes, or Weakest Link composite scores.	The strength of the association between the Weakest Link × Stress interaction and change in depressive symptoms over time was stronger in girls than in boys. The strengths of the associations between the DIS-Causes × Stress, DIS-Consequences × Stress, and DIS-Self × Stress interactions and change in depressive symptoms over time were not moderated by sex.	The strengths of the associations between the Weakest Link × Stress, DIS-Causes × Stress, DIS-Consequences × Stress, and DIS-Self × Stress interactions and change in depressive symptoms over time were not moderated by grade.	140
Abela, McGirr, & Skitch (2007)	3rd and 7th graders	Every week, for 6 weeks	CASQ, CCSQ, CLES, CDI	Not Examined	Not Examined	The strengths of the associations between the Weakest Link × Stress, DIS-Causes × Stress, DIS-Consequences × Stress, and DIS-Self × Stress interactions and change in depressive symptoms over time were not moderated by sex.	The strengths of the associations between the Weakest Link × Stress, DIS-Causes × Stress, DIS-Consequences × Stress, and DIS-Self × Stress interactions and change in depressive symptoms over time were not moderated by grade.	382
Abela, Parkinson, Stolow, & Starrs (in press)	9th graders	1.5 months	CASQ, CLES, CDI	Girls and boys did not differ in levels of the DIS-Causes.	NA	The strength of the association between the DIS-Causes × Stress interaction and change in depressive symptoms over time was not moderated by sex.	NA	319

Study	Sample	Time	Measures	Sex differences	Age differences	Moderation by sex	Moderation by grade	N
Abela & Payne (2003)	3rd and 7th graders	1.5 months	CASQ, CCSQ, CHAS, CDI	Girls reported higher levels of the DIS-Self than did boys. Girls and boys did not differ in levels of either the DIS-Consequences, DIS-Causes, or Weakest Link composite scores.	3rd graders reported higher levels of the DIS-Self, DIS-Consequences, and Weakest Link composite scores than did 7th graders. Age was not associated with levels of the DIS-Causes.	The strength of the association between the Weakest Link × Stress interaction and change in depressive symptoms over time was not moderated by sex.	The strength of the association between the Weakest Link × Stress interaction and change in depressive symptoms over time was not moderated by grade.	314
Abela & Sarin (2002)	7th graders	2.5 months	CASQ, CCSQ, CLES, CDI	Girls and boys did not differ in levels of either the DIS-Consequences, DIS-Self, DIS-Causes, or Weakest Link composite scores.	NA	The strengths of the associations between the DIS-Consequences × Stress, DIS-Self × Stress, DIS-Causes × Stress, and the Weakest-Link × Stress interactions and change in depressive symptoms over time were not moderated by sex.	NA	79
Abela & Seligman (2000) Study 1	12th graders	2 months	EASQ, CSQ, AAQ, MAACL	Not Examined	NA	The strengths of the associations between the DIS-Consequences × Stress, DIS-Self × Stress, and DIS-Causes × Stress interactions and change in depressive symptoms over time were not moderated by sex.	NA	149

Table 1. (Continued)

Study	Sample	Time	Measures				N
Abela & Seligman (2000) Study 2	College undergraduates	2 weeks	EASQ, CSQ, AAQ, MAACL	Not Examined	NA	NA	The strengths of the associations between the DIS-Consequences × Stress, DIS-Self × Stress, and DIS-Causes × Stress interactions and change in depressive symptoms over time were not moderated by sex.	77
Abela, Skitch, Adams, & Hankin (2006)	6 – 14 year olds with an affectively ill parent	Every 6 weeks, for 12 months	CASQ, CCSQ, BDI, CDI	Girls reported higher levels of the DIS-Self than did boys. Girls and boys did not differ in levels of either the DIS-Consequences, DIS-Causes, or Weakest Link composite scores.	Age was not associated with levels of either the DIS-Self, DIS-Consequences, DIS-Causes, or Weakest Link composite scores.	The strength of the association between the Weakest Link × Stress interaction and change in depressive symptoms over time was stronger among girls than boys.	The strength of the association between the Weakest Link × Stress interaction and change in depressive symptoms over time was not moderated by age.	140
Bennett & Bates (1995)	11 – 13 year olds	6 months	CASQ-R CHS, LES, NRI CDI, CDIM, YSR, CBCL	Not Examined	Not Examined	Not Examined	Not Examined	95

Study	Age	Time	Measures				N
Brozina & Abela (2006)	8 – 13 year olds	1.5 months	CASQ, CCSQ, CHAS, CDI	Not Examined	Not Examined	The strengths of the associations between the DIS-Consequences × Stress, DIS-Self × Stress, and DIS-Causes × Stress interactions and change in depressive symptoms over time were not moderated by sex.	The strengths of the associations between the DIS-Consequences × Stress, DIS-Self × Stress, and DIS-Causes × Stress interactions and change in depressive symptoms over time were not moderated by age.	418
Conley, Haines, Hilt, & Metalsky (2001)	5 – 10 year olds	3 weeks	CASI, CASQ-R, Daily Hassles Questionnaire, Self Perception Profile, CDI	Not Examined	Younger children reported higher levels of the DIS-Causes on the CASQ-R. Older children reported higher levels of the DIS-Causes on the CASI.	Not Examined	The strength of the association between the DIS-Causes × Stress × Self-Esteem interaction and change in depressive symptoms over time was moderated by age. Younger children with Low Self-Esteem reported a stronger association than older children with Low Self-Esteem.	147
Dixon & Ahrens (1992)	9 – 12 year olds	1 month	KASTAN-R, CDCEQ, CDI	Not Examined	Not Examined	Not Examined	Not Examined	84
Gibb & Alloy (2006)	4th and 5th graders	6 months	CASQ-R, CTQ-VV, CDI	Not Examined	Not Examined	The strength of the association between the DIS-Causes × Stress interaction and change in depressive symptoms over time was not moderated by sex.	The strength of the association between the DIS-Causes × Stress interaction and change in depressive symptoms over time was stronger among 5th graders than among 4th graders.	415

Table 1. (Continued)

Author	Sample	Time	Measures					N
Hammen (1988)	8 – 16 year olds with either affectively ill, medically ill, or control mothers	6 months	Piers-Harris, CSLE, K-SADS, CDI	Not Examined	Not Examined	Not Examined	Not Examined	79
Hankin, Abramson, & Siler (2001)	9th – 12th graders	1.25 months	CASQ, APES, BDI, HDSQ-R, HS	Girls and boys did not differ in levels of the DIS-Causes.	Not Examined	The strength of the association between the DIS-Causes × Stress interaction and change in depressive symptoms over time was moderated by sex. The association was stronger for boys than for girls.	Not Examined	270
Hilsman & Garber (1995)	5th – 6th graders	0.25 months	CASQ, Perception of Control Questionnaire CES-DC, Depressive Adjective Questionnaire	Not Examined	Not Examined	Not Examined	Not Examined	439

Study	Sample	Interval	Measures	Sex differences	Age effects	Sex moderation	Age/time moderation	N
Joiner (2000)	9 – 17 year olds, inpatients	2 months	CASQ, CHS, CDI	Girls and boys did not differ in levels of the DIS-Causes.	Age was not associated with levels of the DIS-Causes.	Not Examined	Not Examined	34
Lewinsohn, Joiner, & Rohde (2001)	9th and 12th graders	12 months	CASQ, LES, CES-D	Boys reported higher levels of the DIS-Causes than did girls.	Not Examined	Not Examined	Not Examined	1,507
Nolen-Hoeksema, Girgus, & Seligman (1986)	8 – 11 year olds	Every 3 months, for 12 months	CASQ, LEQ, CDI	Not Examined	Not Examined	Not Examined	Not Examined	168
Nolen-Hoeksema, Girgus, & Seligman (1992)	3rd graders	Every 6 months, for 60 months	CASQ, LEQ, SBC, CDI	Not Examined	Not Examined	Not Examined	The interaction between the DIS-Causes × Stress emerged as a significant predictor of change in depressive symptoms over time, as children grew older.	432
Panak & Garber, (1992)	3rd – 5th graders	At 8 and 12 months	CASQ, P-REJ, SR-REJ, PAQ DEP, CDI, CBCL	Not Examined	Not Examined.	Not Examined.	Not Examined	521
Prinstein & Aikins (2004)	15 – 17 year olds	17 months	CASQ, Peer Importance, Peer Acceptance/ Rejection, CDI	Girls and boys did not differ in levels of the DIS-Causes.	Not Examined	The strength of the association between the DIS-Causes × Stress interaction and depressive symptoms over time was moderated by sex. The association was stronger for girls than for boys.	Not Examined	158

Table 1. (Continued)

Robinson, Garber, & Hilsman (1995)	6th graders	5 and 11 months	CASQ, Harter's Scale. Hassles Questionnaires. CDI	Not Examined	NA	Not Examined	NA	371
Southall & Roberts (2002)	14 – 19 year olds	14 weeks	CASQ, RSE, LES, BDI	Girls and boys did not differ in levels of the DIS-Causes.	Age was not significantly associated with levels of the DIS-Causes.	Not Examined	Not Examined	115
Spence, Sheffield, & Donovan (2002)	12 – 14 year olds	months	CASQ-R, NLE, SPSI-R, BDI	Girls and boys did not significantly differ in levels of the DIS-Causes.	Not Examined	The strength of the association between DIS-Causes × Stress interaction and depressive symptoms over time was not moderated by sex.	Not Examined	773

Note: CCSQ = Children's Cognitive Style Questionnaire; CLES = The Children's Life Events Scale; CDI = Child Depression Inventory; CSQ = Cognitive Style Questionnaire; CPQ = Cognitive Priming Questionnaire; SEQ = Self-Esteem Questionnaire; MAACL = Multiple Affect Adjective Checklist; CHAS = Children's Hassles Scale; CASQ = Children's Attributional Style Questionnaire; BDI = Beck Depression Inventory; EASQ = Extended Attributional Style Questionnaire; AAQ = Admission Aspiration Questionnaire; CASQ-R = Children's Attributional Style Questionnaire – Revised; CHS = Children's Hassles Scale; LES = Life Events Scale; NRI = Network of Relationships Inventory; CDIM = Children's Depression Inventory (Mother version); YSR = Youth Self-Report; CBCL = Child Behavior Checklist; CASI = Children's Attributional Style Interview; Daily Hassles Questionnaire; Self Perception Profile; KASTAN-R = KASTAN Children's Attributional Style Questionnaire – Revised; CDCEQ = Child Daily Camp Event Questionnaire; CTQ-VV = Childhood Trauma Questionnaire Verbal Victimization; Piers-Harris = Piers-Harris Children's Self-Concept Scale; CSLE = Children's Stressful Life Events; K-SADS = Kiddie Schedule for Affective Disorders; APES = Adolescent Perceived; HDSQ-R = Hopelessness Depression Symptoms Questionnaire-Revised; HS = Hopelessness Scale; Perception of Control Questionnaire = Student Perceptions of Control Questionnaire; CES-DC = Center for Epidemiological Studies Depression Scale for Children; Depressive Adjective Questionnaire; CES-D = Center for Epidemiological Studies Depression Scale; LEQ = Life Events Questionnaire; SBC = Student Behavior Checklist; P-REJ = Peer Rejection; SR-REJ = Self-report of Peer Rejection; PAQ = Particular Attributions for Problems with peers; DEP (CDI) = Self-report of Depressive Symptoms based on the CDI; Peer Importance, Peer Acceptance/Rejection = Peer Nomination Sociometric Procedure; Harter's Scale = Harter's Perceived Self-Competence Scale; Hassles Questionnaires = School-related Hassles Questionnaire (associated with 7th grade transition); RSE = Rosenberg Self-Esteem Scale; LES = Life Events Schedule; NLE = Modified version of the Life Events Record for Junior High School Students; SPSI-R = Social Problem-Solving Inventory – Revised, Short Form.

Thirteen studies have examined whether sex serves as a significant moderator of the association between a depressogenic attributional style and increases in depressive symptoms following negative events. Eleven of these studies have reported that sex is not a significant moderator of this association (Abela, 2001; Abela, 2002; Abela & McGirr, 2007; Abela, McGirr, et al., 2007; Abela et al., in press; Abela & Sarin, 2002; Abela & Seligman, 2001, Studies 1 and 2; Brozina & Abela, 2006; Gibb & Alloy, 2006; Spence et al., 2002). In contrast, one study reported that the strength of this association is greater in girls than boys (Prinstein & Aikens, 2004) whereas another study reported that the strength of this association is greater in boys than girls (Hankin et al., 2001).

Seven studies have examined age differences in levels of attributional style. Six of these studies found no age differences (Abela, 2001; Abela & McGirr, 2007; Abela & Payne, 2003; Abela et al., 2006; Joiner, 2000; Southall & Roberts, 2002). One of these studies reported that older children exhibited more depressogenic attributional styles than did younger children when attributional style was assessed using a semi-structured interview (Conley et al., 2001). In contrast, the same study reported that younger children exhibited more depressogenic attributional styles than did older children when attributional style was assessed using a self-report questionnaire (Conley et al., 2001).

Six studies have examined whether age serves as a moderator of the association between a depressogenic attributional styles and increases in depressive symptoms following negative events. Three of these studies have reported that age is not a significant moderator of this association (Abela & McGirr, 2007; Abela, McGirr, et al., 2007; Brozina & Abela, 2006). Two of these studies reported that the strength of this association is greater in older children than in younger children (Abela, 2001; Gibb & Alloy, 2006) whereas another study reported that the strength of this association is greater in younger children than in older children (Conley et al., 2001).

Depressogenic Inferential Style about Consequences

Five studies have examined sex differences in levels of the inferential style about consequences (Abela, 2001; Abela & McGirr, 2007; Abela & Payne, 2003; Abela & Sarin, 2002; Abela et al., 2006). None of these studies reported such a sex difference.

Eight studies have examined whether sex serves as a moderator of the association between a depressogenic inferential style about consequences and increases in depressive symptoms following negative events. None of these studies have found sex to be a significant moderator of this association (Abela, 2001; Abela, 2002; Abela & McGirr, 2007; Abela, McGirr, et al., 2007; Abela & Sarin, 2002; Abela & Seligman, 2001, Studies 1 and 2; Brozina & Abela, 2006).

Four studies have examined age differences in levels of the inferential style about consequences. Two of these studies have reported that younger children exhibit more depressogenic inferential styles about consequences than do older children (Abela, 2001; Abela & Payne, 2003). In contrast, the other two of these studies reported no such age difference (Abela & McGirr, 2007; Abela et al., 2006).

Four studies have examined whether age serves as a moderator of the association between a depressogenic inferential style about consequences and increases in depressive symptoms following negative events. None of these studies have found age to be a significant moderator of this association (Abela, 2001; Abela & McGirr, 2007; Abela, McGirr, et al., 2007; Brozina & Abela, 2006).

Depressogenic Inferential Style about the Self

Five studies have examined sex differences in levels of the inferential style about the self. Four of these studies reported that girls exhibited more depressogenic inferential styles about the self than did boys (Abela, 2001; Abela & McGirr, 2007; Abela & Payne, 2003; Abela et. al., 2006). In contrast, one of these studies reported no such sex difference (Abela & Sarin, 2002).

Eight studies have examined whether sex serves as a moderator of the association between a depressogenic inferential style about the self and increases in depressive symptoms following negative events. Seven of these studies have found sex not to be a significant moderator of this association (Abela, 2002; Abela & McGirr, 2007; Abela, McGirr, et al., 2007; Abela & Sarin, 2002; Abela & Seligman, 2001, Studies 1 and 2; Brozina & Abela, 2006). In contrast, one study reported that the strength of this association was greater in girls than in boys (Abela, 2001).

Four studies have examined age differences in levels of the inferential style about the self. Two of these studies have reported that younger children exhibit more depressogenic inferential styles about the self than do older children (Abela, 2001; Abela & Payne, 2003). In contrast, the other two of these studies reported no such age difference (Abela & McGirr, 2007; Abela et al., 2006).

Four studies have examined whether age serves as a moderator of the aassociation between a depressogenic inferential style about the self and increases in depressive symptoms following negative events. None of these studies have found age to be a significant moderator of this association (Abela, 2001; Abela & McGirr, 2007; Abela, McGirr, et al., 2007; Brozina & Abela, 2006).

Weakest Link Composite Scores

Four studies have examined sex differences in levels of weakest link composite scores. None of these studies have obtained such a sex difference (Abela & McGirr, 2007; Abela & Payne, 2003; Abela & Sarin, 2002; Abela et al., 2006).

Five studies have examined whether sex serves as a significant moderator of the strength of the association between weakest link composite scores and increases in depressive symptoms following negative events. Two studies have reported that the strength of this association is greater in girls than in boys (Abela & McGirr, 2007; Abela et al., 2006) whereas three studies have reported no such sex difference (Abela, McGirr, et al., 2007; Abela & Payne, 2003; Abela & Sarin, 2002).

Three studies have examined age differences in levels of weakest link composite scores. One of these studies reported that younger children exhibited more depressogenic weakest link composite scores than did older children. The other two of these studies have obtained no such age difference (Abela & McGirr, 2007; Abela et al., 2006).

Four studies have examined whether age serves as a moderator of the association between weakest link composite scores and increases in depressive symptoms following negative events. None of these studies have found age to be a significant moderator of this association (Abela & McGirr, 2007; Abela, McGirr, et al., 2007; Abela & Payne, 2002; Abela et al., 2006).

Beck's Cognitive Theory

Similar to hopelessness theory, Beck's cognitive theory is a diathesis-stress theory that posits a series of contributory causes that interact with one another to culminate in depression (Beck, 1967, 1983). Central to Beck's theory is the construct of schemata. Beck defines schemata as stored bodies of knowledge (i.e., mental representations of the self and prior experience) that are relatively enduring characteristics of a person's cognitive organization. When an individual is confronted with a situation, the schema most relevant to the situation is activated. Schema activation subsequently influences how the person perceives, encodes, and retrieves information regarding the situation.

Beck (1967, 1983) proposes that certain individuals possess depressogenic schema that confer vulnerability to depression. Beck hypothesizes that depressogenic schemata are typically organized as sets of dysfunctional attitudes such as "I am nothing if a person I love doesn't like me" or "If I fail at my work then I am a failure as a person." Such schemata are activated following the occurrence of negative life events. Once activated, depressogenic schemata trigger a pattern of negatively biased, self-referent information processing characterized by negative errors in thinking (e.g., negatively skewed interpretations of negative life events such as overgeneralization and catastrophizing). Negative errors in thinking increase the likelihood that an individual will develop the negative cognitive triad. Beck defines the negative cognitive triad as containing three distinct, depressogenic cognitive patterns: negative views of the self (e.g., the belief that one is deficient, inadequate or unworthy), the world (e.g., construing life experiences in terms of themes of defeat or disparagement), and the future (e.g., the expectation that one's difficulties will persist in the future and there is nothing one can do to change this). As Beck views the negative cognitive triad as a proximal, sufficient cause of depressive symptoms, once an individual develops the negative cognitive triad, he or she will develop depressive symptoms.

As presented in Table 2, six studies have provided a prospective test of Beck's (1967, 1983) cognitive theory of depression in child and/or adolescent samples (for a review of findings pertaining to the vulnerability-stress hypothesis of Beck's cognitive theory in youth, see Abela & Hankin, 2008). Of these studies, five have examined age and/or sex effects in levels of dysfunctional attitudes and/or the strength of the association between dysfunctional attitudes and increases in depressive symptoms following negative events.

Table 2. Summary of prospective studies testing Beck's Cognitive Theory of Depression

Study	Sample	Follow-up	Measures	Sex Differences in Levels of Dysfunctional Attitudes	Age Differences in Levels of Dysfunctional Attitudes	Sex as a Moderator of the Prospective Association Between the Dysfunctional Attitudes × Negative Events Interaction and Change in Depressive Symptoms Over Time	Age as a Moderator of the Prospective Association Between the Dysfunctional Attitudes × Negative Events Interaction and Change in Depressive Symptoms Over Time	Sample Size
Abela & D'Alessandro (2002)	12th graders	0.25 - 2 months	DAS, MAACL, CPQ	Not Examined	NA	The strength of the association between the Dysfunctional Attitudes × Stress × Stress interaction and change in depressive symptoms over time was not moderated by sex.	NA	136
Abela & Skitch (2007)	6 – 14 year olds with an affectively-ill parent	12 months multi-wave	CDAS, CDI, HASC	Girls and boys did not significantly differ in level of dysfunctional attitudes.	Age was negatively associated with levels of dysfunctional attitudes. Younger children reported higher levels of dysfunctional attitudes than did older children.	The strength of the association between the Dysfunctional Attitudes × Stress interaction and change in depressive symptoms over time was not moderated by sex.	The strength of the association between the Dysfunctional Attitudes × Stress interaction and change in depressive symptoms over time was not moderated by age.	140
Abela & Sullivan (2003)	7th graders	1.5 months	CDAS, CDI, CHAS	Girls and boys did not significantly differ in levels of dysfunctional attitudes.	NA	The strength of the association between the Dysfunctional Attitudes × Stress interaction and change in depressive symptoms over time was not moderated by sex.	NA	184

Table 2. (Continued)

Study	Sample	Follow-up	Measures	Sex Differences in Levels of Dysfunctional Attitudes	Age Differences in Levels of Dysfunctional Attitudes	Sex as a Moderator of the Prospective Association Between the Dysfunctional Attitudes × Negative Events Interaction and Change in Depressive Symptoms Over Time	Age as a Moderator of the Prospective Association Between the Dysfunctional Attitudes × Negative Events Interaction and Change in Depressive Symptoms Over Time	Sample Size
D'Alessandro & Burton (2006) Study 2	7-14 year olds	0.5 months	DAS-C, CDI, PRQ	Not Examined	Not Examined	The strength of the association between the Dysfunctional Attitudes × Parental Reaction interaction and change in depressive symptoms over time was not moderated by sex.	The strength of the association between the Dysfunctional Attitudes × Parental Reaction interaction and change in depressive symptoms over time was moderated by age at Time 3. This association was significantly stronger among the older adolescents (11-14 years of age).	241
Garber & Flynn (2001)	6th graders, with a mother (affectively-ill and non-affectively-ill mothers)	36 months	CASQ, CHS	Not Examined	NA	Not Examined	NA	240 (185 with affectively-ill mothers; 55 with non-affectively-ill mothers

Lewinsohn. Joiner, & Rohde (2001)	9th – 12th graders	12 months	DAS, CES-D, Negative Life Events	Girls and boys did not significantly differ in levels of dysfunctional attitudes.	Not Examined	Not Examined	1,507

Note: DAS = Dysfunctional Attitudes Scale; MAACL = Multiple Adjective Affect Checklist, CDAS = Children's Dysfunctional Attitudes Scale; CDI= Children's Depression Inventory, DAS-C = Dysfunctional Attitudes Scale for Children; CASQ = Children's Attributional Style Questionnaire; CHS = Children's Hopelessness Scale;

RSQ = Response Styles Questionnaire; CDI= Child Depression Inventory; PRQ = Parental Reaction Questionnaire; CES-D = Center for Epidemiological Studies Depression

Scale for Children; CHAS = Children's Hassles Scale, also referred to as HASC = Hassles Scale for Children; CPQ = Cognitive Priming Questionnaire.

Table 3. Summary of prospective studies testing the Response Styles Theory of Depression

Study	Sample	Follow-Up	Measures	Sex Differences in Levels of Rumination	Age Differences in Levels of Rumination	Sex as a Moderator of the Prospective Association Between Rumination × Negative Events and Change in Depressive Symptoms Over Time	Age as a Moderator of the Prospective Association Between Rumination × Negative Events and Change in Depressive Symptoms Over Time	Sample Size
Abela, Aydin, & Auerbach (2007) Study 1	7-13 year olds from 3rd and 7th grade	None	CRSQ	Girls and boys did not significantly differ in levels of rumination.	Not Examined	NA	NA	287
Abela, Aydin. & Auerbach (2007) Study 2	6 – 14 year olds with an affectively-ill parent	1.5 months	CRSQ, CDI	Girls and boys did not significantly differ in levels of rumination.	Age was not significantly associated with rumination.	The strength of the association between Rumination × Stress interaction and change in depressive symptoms over time was not moderated by sex.	The strength of the association between Rumination × Stress interaction and change in depressive symptoms over time was not moderated by age.	140
Abela, Brozina, & Haigh (2002)	3rd and 7th graders	1.5 months	CRSQ, CDI	Girls and boys did not significantly differ in levels of rumination.	3rd and 7th graders did not significantly differ in levels of rumination.	The strength of the association between Rumination × Stress interaction and change in depressive symptoms over time was not moderated by sex.	The strength of the association between rumination and change in depressive symptoms was not moderated by age.	314
Abela, Parkinson, Stolow, & Starrs (in press)	9th graders	1.5 months	CRSQ, CDI	Girls reported significantly higher levels of rumination than did boys.	NA	The strength of the association between Rumination × Stress interaction and change in depressive symptoms over	NA	319

Abela, Vanderbilt, & Rochon (2004)	3rd and 7th graders	None	CRSQ	Girls and boys did not significantly differ in levels of rumination.	3rd and 7th graders did not significantly differ in levels of rumination.	NA	[...] time was not moderated by sex.	260
Broderick & Korteland (2004)	4th – 6th graders	36 months	RSQ, CDI	Girls and boys did not significantly differ in levels of rumination at either Time 1 or Time 2. Boys reported significantly higher levels of rumination than did girls at Time 3.	Not Examined	Not Examined	Not Examined	79
Nolen-Hoeksema, Stice, Wade & Bohon (2007)	11 – 15 year old female adolescents	Annually at 3, 4, 5, and 6 years	RSQ, K-SADS	NA	Not Examined	NA	Not Examined	496
Schwartz & Koenig (1996)	9th – 12th graders	1.5 months	RSQ, BDI	Girls reported significantly higher levels of rumination than did boys.	Not Examined	Not Examined	The strength of the association between Rumination × Stress interaction and change in depressive symptoms over time was stronger among girls than among boys.	397

Table 3. (Continued)

Study	Sample	Follow-Up	Measures	Sex Differences in Levels of Rumination	Age Differences in Levels of Rumination	Sex as a Moderator of the Prospective Association Between Rumination × Negative Events and Change in Depressive Symptoms Over Time	Age as a Moderator of the Prospective Association Between Rumination × Negative Events and Change in Depressive Symptoms Over Time	Sample Size
Ziegert & Kistner (2002)	4th and 5th graders	None	CRSS, CDI	Girls reported significantly higher levels of rumination than did boys.	Not Examined	NA	NA	201

Note: CRSQ = Children's Response Styles Questionnaire, CDI= Children's Depression Inventory, RSQ = Response Styles Questionnaire, K-SADS= Kiddie Schedule for
Affective Disorders, BDI = Beck Depression Inventory, CRSS = Children's Response Style Scale.

Table 4. Summary of prospective studies testing Theories of Personality Diatheses to Depression

Study	Sample	Follow-up	Measures	Sex Differences in levels of either Interpersonal or Achievement Personality Vulnerabilities	Age Differences in levels of either Interpersonal or Achievement Personality Vulnerabilities	Sex as a Moderator of the Prospective Association between Interpersonal or Achievement Personality Vulnerabilities × Negative Events Interaction and Change in Depressive Symptoms Over Time	Age as a Moderator of the Prospective Association Between Interpersonal or Achievement Personality Vulnerabilities × Negative Events Interaction and Change in Depressive Symptoms Over Time	Sample Size
Abela, Sakellaropoulo, & Taxel (2007)	7th graders	2.5 months	CDEQ, CLES. CDI	Girls reported higher levels of Dependency than did boys. Girls and boys did not differ in levels of Self-Criticism.	NA	The strength of the association between either Self-criticism or Dependency × Stress interaction and change in depressive symptoms over time was not moderated by sex.	NA	79
Abela & Taylor (2003)	3rd and 7th graders	1.5 months	CDEQ, CHAS, CMAACL	Not Examined	Not Examined	The strength of the association between Self-Criticism × Achievement Hassles interaction and change in depressive symptoms over time was moderated by sex and grade. The association was significant among 3rd graders, and among 7th grade boys but not among 7th grade girls. The strength of the association between Dependency × Achievement Hassles interaction and change in depressive symptoms over time was not moderated by either sex or grade.	The strength of the association between Self-Criticism × Interpersonal Hassles interaction and change in depressive symptoms over time was not moderated by sex, but was moderated by grade. The association was stronger among 3rd graders than 7th graders. The strength of the association between Dependency × Interpersonal Hassles interaction and change in depressive symptoms over time was not moderated by either sex or grade.	303

Table 4. (Contionued)

Study	Sample	Follow-up	Measures	Sex Differences in levels of either Interpersonal or Achievement Personality Vulnerabilities	Age Differences in levels of either Interpersonal or Achievement Personality Vulnerabilities	Sex as a Moderator of the Prospective Association between Interpersonal or Achievement Personality Vulnerabilities × Negative Events Interaction and Change in Depressive Symptoms Over Time	Age as a Moderator of the Prospective Association Between Interpersonal or Achievement Personality Vulnerabilities × Negative Events Interaction and Change in Depressive Symptoms Over Time	Sample Size
Adams, Abela, Auerbach, & Skitch (2006)	7 – 14 year olds with an affectively-ill parent (experienced sample modeling)	Every week. for 6 weeks	CDEQ, CHAS, CDI	Girls and boys did not differ in levels of Self-Criticism or Dependency.	Age was not associated with levels of either Self-Criticism or Dependency.	Not Examined	Not Examined	49
Hammen & Goodman-Brown (1990)	8 – 16 year olds with affectively-ill, medically-ill, or control mothers	6 months	Self-Schema Assessment, Life Event Assessment, K-SADS	Not Examined	Not Examined	Not Examined	Not Examined	64

Study	Sample	Time	Measures	Sex differences in vulnerabilities		Sex differences in stress-vulnerability associations		N
Little & Garber (2000)	5th – 6th graders	3 months	SASC, Composite life-events and hassles scores, CDI	Girls reported higher levels of Connectedness than did boys. Girls and boys did not differ in levels of Neediness, Self-Criticism, or Individualistic-Achievement.	Not Examined	The strength of the association between Connectedness × Stress interaction and change in depressive symptoms over time was moderated by sex. The association was stronger among boys. The strengths of the associations between Neediness × Stress, Self-Criticism × Stress, and I-Achievement × Stress interactions and change in depressive symptoms over time were not moderated by sex.	Not Examined	486
Little & Garber (2004)	8th graders, with affectively-ill or control mothers	12 months	CAS, DEQ-A, School Hassles Questionnaire, CDI	Girls and boys did not differ in levels of Interpersonal or Achievement vulnerabilities.	NA	The strength of the association between the DEQ-A-Interpersonal × Peer Stressors interaction and change in depressive symptoms over time was moderated by sex. The association was stronger among girls. The strengths of the associations between the DEQ-A-Interpersonal × Academic Stressors, CAS-Achievement × Academic Stressors, and CAS-Achievement × Interpersonal Stressors interactions and change in depressive symptoms over time were not moderated by sex.	NA	129

Table 4. (Continued)

Study	Sample	Follow-up	Measures	Sex Differences in levels of either Interpersonal or Achievement Personality Vulnerabilities	Age Differences in levels of either Interpersonal or Achievement Personality Vulnerabilities	Sex as a Moderator of the Prospective Association between Interpersonal or Achievement Personality Vulnerabilities × Negative Events Interaction and Change in Depressive Symptoms Over Time	Age as a Moderator of the Prospective Association Between Interpersonal or Achievement Personality Vulnerabilities × Negative Events Interaction and Change in Depressive Symptoms Over Time	Sample Size
Little & Garber (2005)	6th graders with affective-ly-ill mothers	12 months	DEQ-A, LEIA, Composite Score (CDI, P-CDI, CDRS-R)	Girls and boys did not differ in levels of Neediness or Connectedness.	NA	Not Examined	NA	185
Shahar, Blatt, Zuroff, Kuperminc, & Leadbeater (2004)	6th and 7th graders	12 months	DEQ-A, APES, BDI	Not Examined	Not Examined	The strength of the association between DEQ-A × APES interaction and change in depressive symptoms over time was not moderated by sex.	Not Examined	452

| Shahar & Priel (2003) | 9th graders | 4 months | DEQ-A, DAS, PSI, LEC, CHS/CUS, CSLES, CES-CD | Girls and boys did not differ in levels of Self-Criticism or Dependency. | NA | Not Examined | NA | 603 |

Note: CDEQ = Children's Depressive Experiences Questionnaire; CLES = Children's Life Events Scale; CDI = Children's Depression Inventory; CHAS = Children's Hassles Scale; CMAACL = Children's Multiple Adjective Affect Checklist; Self-Schema Assessment = Interpersonal and Achievement Domains Measure; Life Event Assessment = Stressors Measure; K-SADS = Kiddie Schedule for Affective Disorders; SASC = Sociotropy-Achievement Scale for Children; Composite life-events and hassles scores = Life Events and two hassles questionnaires; CAS = Commitment to Achievement Scale; DEQ-A = Depressive Experiences Questionnaire for Adolescents; LEIA = Life Events Interview for Adolescents; Composite Score (CDI = Children's Depression Inventory, P-CDI = Parental report of the Children's Depression Inventory; CDRS-R = Children's Depression Rating Scale – Revised); APES = Adolescent Perceived Event Scale; BDI = Beck Depression Inventory; DAS = Dysfunctional Attitudes Scale; PSI = Personality Style Inventory; LEC = Life Events Checklist, CHS/CUS = Children's Hassles/Uplifts Scale, CSLES = College Student Life Events Scale; CES-D = Center for Epidemiological Studies Depression Scale for Children.

Three studies have examined sex differences in levels of dysfunctional attitudes (Abela & Skitch, 2007; Abela & Sullivan, 2003; Lewinsohn et al., 2001). All three of these studies reported no such sex difference. Four studies have examined whether sex serves as a moderator of the association between dysfunctional attitudes and increases in depressive symptoms following negative events (Abela & D'Alessandro, 2002; Abela & Skitch, 2007; Abela & Sullivan, 2003; D'Alessandro & Burton, 2006, Study 2). None of these studies have found sex to be a significant moderator of this association.

Only one study has examined age differences in levels of dysfunctional attitudes (Abela & Skitch, 2007). This study reported that age was negatively associated with levels of dysfunctional attitudes, with younger youth reporting higher levels of dysfunctional attitudes than older youth (Abela & Skitch, 2007). Two studies have examined whether age serves as a moderator of the association between dysfunctional attitudes and increases in depressive symptoms following negative events. Neither of these studies have found age to be a significant moderator of this association (Abela & Skitch, 2007; D'Alessandro & Burton, 2006, Study 2).

Response Styles Theory

The response styles theory posits that the way in which individuals respond to their symptoms of depression determines both the severity and duration of such symptoms (Nolen-Hoeksema, 1991). Two such responses are proposed: rumination and distraction. Nolen-Hoeksema argues that individuals who engage in ruminative responses to depressed mood are likely to experience increased severity and duration of symptoms whereas those who engage in distracting responses are likely to experience relief. The response styles theory was originally proposed to explain the finding that prevalence rates of depression are higher among women than men. Nolen-Hoeksema (1991) proposed that this difference could be accounted for, at least in part, by the differential response styles of the sexes. More specifically, she hypothesizes that women are more likely to ruminate in response to depressed mood whereas men are more likely to distract.

As presented in Table 3, nine studies have provided a prospective test of the response styles theory of depression in child and/or adolescent samples (for a review of findings pertaining to the vulnerability-stress hypothesis of the response styles theory in youth, see Abela & Hankin, 2008). Of these studies, eight have examined age and/or sex effects in levels of rumination and/or the strength of the association between rumination and increases in depressive symptoms.

Eight studies examined whether sex differences exist in levels of rumination. The majority of the studies that have utilized child and/or early adolescent samples have failed to find significant sex differences in levels of rumination (Abela, Aydin, & Auerbach, 2007, Study 1 and Study 2; Abela, Brozina, & Haigh, 2002; Abela, Vanderbilt, & Rochon, 2004). Of the two studies that have reported sex differences in child samples, one reported that girls exhibited higher rumination than boys (Zeigert & Kistner, 2004), whereas the other reported the reverse (Broderick & Korteland 2004). At the same time, studies that have utilized middle to late adolescent samples, have consistently obtained a sex difference with girls reporting higher rumination than boys (Abela, et al., in press; Schwartz & Koenig, 1996). Four of the nine studies examined whether sex moderates the prospective association between rumination and change in depressive symptoms over time. Three of these studies failed to report any moderation effects, (Abela, Aydin, et al., 2007, Study 2; Abela et al., 2002; Abela, et al., in press). In contrast, one study reported that the association between rumination and change in depressive symptoms over time was stronger in girls than boys (Schwartz & Koenig, 1996).

Of the nine studies, only three have examined age differences in levels of rumination, and none have reported age effects (Abela, Aydin, et al., 2007, Study 2; Abela, et al., 2002; Abela et al., 2004). Only two studies have examined whether age serves as a moderator of the prospective association between rumination and change in depressive symptoms over time and neither study reported significant age moderating effects (Abela, Aydin, et al., 2007, Study 2; Abela et al., 2002).

Personality Diatheses Theories

Researchers from diverse theoretical orientations have proposed that certain personality traits, also referred to as cognitive-affective styles, serve as vulnerability factors to depression (Beck, 1983; Blatt & Zuroff, 1992). Although differences exist in conceptualizations, each theory proposes a personality predisposition focused on interpersonal issues and another focused on achievement issues. These personality predispositions are labeled as dependency and self-criticism by psychodynamic theorists (Blatt & Zuroff, 1992) and as sociotropy and autonomy by cognitive theorists (Beck, 1983). Individuals high in dependency/sociotropy are concerned with interpersonal issues; they need the approval of others to maintain a sense of well-being. Dependent/sociotropic individuals are hypothesized to be at risk for developing depression when they perceive disruptions in their relationships with others, interpersonal loss, and/or social rejection. Individuals high in self-criticism/autonomy, on the other hand, are concerned with achievement issues; they need to meet their own and/or others' standards to maintain a sense of well-being. Self-critical/autonomous individuals are hypothesized to be at risk for developing depression when they perceive that they are not meeting such standards.

As presented in Table 4, nine studies have provided a prospective test of theories of personality predispositions to depression in child and/or adolescent samples (for a review of findings pertaining to the vulnerability-stress hypothesis of theories of personality predispositions to depression in youth, see Abela & Hankin, 2008). Of these studies, eight have examined age and/or sex effects in levels of cognitive vulnerability and/or the strength of the association between cognitive vulnerability and increases in depressive symptoms following negative events.

Achievement Domain

Five studies have examined sex differences in levels of personality predispositions in the achievement domain. All five of these studies reported that boys and girls do not significantly differ in levels of self-criticism and/or individualistic achievement orientation (Abela, Sakellaropoulo, & Taxel, 2007; Adams, Abela, Auerbach, & Skitch, 2008; Little & Garber, 2000; Little & Garber, 2004; Little & Garber, 2005; Shahar & Priel, 2003). Five studies have examined whether sex serves as a moderator of the association between personality predispositions in the achievement domain and increases in depressive symptoms following negative events. Four of these studies have found sex not to be a significant moderator of this association (Abela, Sakellaropoulo, et al., 2007; Little & Garber, 2000; Little & Garber, 2004; Shahar, Blatt, Zuroff, Kuperminc, & Leadbeater, 2004). In contrast, one study reported that the strength of the association between self-criticism and increases in depressive symptoms following negative achievement events was greater in early adolescent boys than early adolescent girls (Abela & Taylor, 2003).

Only one study has examined age differences in levels of personality predispositions in the achievement domain and this study reported no such difference (Adams et al., 2008). Similarly, only one study has examined age as a moderator of the association between personality predispositions in the achievement domain and increases in depressive symptoms following negative events and this study found the association was stronger in younger than in older youth (Abela & Taylor, 2003).

Interpersonal Domain

Six studies have examined sex differences in levels of personality predispositions in the interpersonal domain. Four of these studies reported that boys and girls do not significantly differ in levels of dependency, neediness, and/or connectedness (Adams et al., 2008; Little & Garber, 2000; Little & Garber, 2004; Little & Garber, 2005; Shahar & Priel, 2003). In contrast, two studies reported that girls exhibited higher levels of personality vulnerability in the interpersonal domain (Abela, Sakellaropoulo, et al., 2007; Little & Garber, 2000). Five studies have examined whether sex serves as a moderator of the association between personality predispositions in the interpersonal domain and increases in depressive symptoms following negative events. Three of these studies have found sex not to be a significant moderator of this association (Abela, Sakellaropoulo, et al., 2007; Abela & Taylor, 2003; Shahar et al., 2004). In contrast, one study reported that the strength of the association between personality predispositions in the interpersonal domain and increases in depressive symptoms following negative events was greater in boys than girls (Little & Garber, 2000) whereas a second study reported it was greater in girls than boys (Little & Garber, 2004).

Only one study has examined age differences in levels of personality predispositions in the interpersonal domain and this study reported no such difference (Adams et al., 2008). Similarly, only one study has examined age as a moderator of the association between personality predispositions in the interpersonal domain and this study reported no such difference (Abela & Taylor, 2003).

Conclusion

This chapter provides a review of prospective studies examining vulnerability to depression in children and adolescents. Research examining four cognitive vulnerability-stress theories was included in this review in order to examine the following four questions: (1) Do girls report higher levels of cognitive vulnerability factors than do boys?; (2) Is the strength of the association between cognitive vulnerability factors and increases in depressive symptoms following negative events stronger for girls than for boys?; (3) Do older youth report higher levels of cognitive vulnerability factors than do younger youth?; (4) Is the strength of the association between cognitive vulnerability factors and increases in depressive symptoms following negative events stronger for older youth than for younger youth?

Irrespective of which theory of cognitive vulnerability was examined, there is weak evidence at best supporting each of the four hypotheses regarding mechanisms underlying the emergence of the sex differences and the surge in depression rates in adolescence. More specifically, although 9 studies reported that girls exhibited higher levels of cognitive vulnerability than did boys, 19 studies reported no such sex difference and 1 study reported that boys exhibited higher levels of cognitive vulnerability than did girls. Similarly, although 6 studies reported that the strength of the association between cognitive vulnerability factors and increases in depressive symptoms over time was greater in girls than in boys, 18 studies reported that the strength of this association did not vary as a function of sex and 3 studies reported that the strength of this association was greater in boys than in girls. Regarding age effects, although 1 study reported that older youth exhibited higher levels of cognitive vulnerability than did younger youth, 8 studies reported no association between age and levels of cognitive vulnerability and 4 studies reported that younger youth exhibited higher levels of cognitive vulnerability than did older youth. Last, although 2 studies reported that the strength of the association between cognitive vulnerabilities and increases in depressive symptoms following negative events was stronger in older youth than in younger youth, 8 studies reported that the strength of this association did not vary as a function of age and 2 studies reported that the strength of this association was greater in younger youth than in older youth.

Some cognitive vulnerability factors appeared to be more likely to exhibit sex effects than did other cognitive vulnerability factors. More specifically, whereas sex differences in levels of attributional style, inferential style about consequences, dysfunctional attitudes, and self-criticism were rarely, if ever, observed, multiple studies reported sex differences in levels of inferential style about the self (four out of five studies), rumination (three out of eight studies), and personality predispositions in the interpersonal domain (two out of six studies). It is unclear, however, why sex differences in such vulnerabilities were observed in some studies but not in others. It is possible that the likelihood of observing sex differences in levels of such cognitive vulnerabilities varies as a function of age of sample, risk status of sample, and measure used to assess the particular cognitive vulnerability factor (i.e., different measures of the same construct may vary in their sensitivity to sex effects). For example, sex differences in levels of rumination were more reliably observed in studies using middle adolescent samples than in studies using early adolescent and child samples suggesting that sex differences in rumination may emerge in conjunction with sex differences in depression rather than prior to the emergence of such sex differences.

With respect to sex as a moderator of the association between cognitive vulnerabilities and increases in depressive symptoms following negative events, although the effect of no particular cognitive vulnerability factor on depressive symptoms appeared to be more likely to vary as a function of sex than the effect of other cognitive vulnerabilities, sex moderation effects, when such effects occurred, were more likely to occur in favor of the effect being stronger in girls. At the same time, it is unclear why such effects emerged in some studies but not others. Once again, it is likely the result of differences between studies in terms of age of sample, risk status of sample, type of stressors examined (i.e., interpersonal versus non-interpersonal), and measure of cognitive vulnerability used. As no specific patterns were observed in the current analysis with respect to sample composition or measurement approach and sex moderation effect, future research is needed aimed at identifying factors accounting for the emergence of such effects in studies of cognitive vulnerability to depression in youth.

Age differences in levels of cognitive vulnerability, when such differences occurred, tended to be in the opposite direction than predicted. More specifically, younger children appeared to exhibit higher levels of cognitive vulnerability than did older children. It is unclear whether such differences reflect actual age-related differences in levels of cognitive vulnerability or whether they are the result of age-related reporting biases. For example, younger children may be more likely than older children to choose extreme responses (i.e., always or never as opposed to once in a while or many times). Such age-related response biases may be more likely to be observed with some measures of cognitive vulnerability than with others. Consistent with such a possibility, one study reported younger children to exhibit higher levels of cognitive vulnerability than older children when using a self-report measure of vulnerability, but older children to exhibit higher levels of cognitive vulnerability when using a semi-structured interview to assess vulnerability (Conley et al., 2001). Future research is needed examining whether measures of cognitive vulnerability such as those reported on in the current chapter exhibit measurement invariance across developmental stages (i.e., childhood, early adolescence, adolescence, etc.,) before any firm conclusions regarding age differences in levels of such constructs can be drawn.

With respect to age as a moderator of the association between cognitive vulnerability factors and increases in depressive symptoms following negative events, the majority of studies failed to find age as a significant moderator of this association despite the commonly held view that cognitive vulnerability factors emerge during the transition from childhood to early adolescence (Gibb & Coles, 2005; Nolen-Hoeksema, Girgus, & Seligman, 1992; Turner & Cole, 1994). Interestingly, three out of the four studies that reported age as a moderator of the association between cognitive vulnerability factors and increases in depressive symptoms following negative events were studies examining attributional style. Thus, certain cognitive vulnerability constructs may be more likely than other cognitive vulnerability constructs to exhibit age moderating effects perhaps due to the types of cognitive processes that they draw upon. At the same time, it is also possible that some cognitive vulnerability factors are more likely to exhibit age moderating effects because of the measures used to assess them rather than the construct itself. In line with this possibility, two studies reported the strength of the association between a depressogenic attributional style and increases in depressive symptoms following negative events to be stronger in older children than younger children whereas a third study reported the reverse. The two studies that found the strength of this association to be greater in older as opposed to younger children used a self-report measure of attributional style. In contrast, the study that reported that the strength of this association to be greater in younger as opposed to older children used a semi-structured interview assessing attributional style. Thus, age moderating effects may be more likely to occur with specific cognitive constructs as a consequence of the measure used to assess the construct.

Limitations and Future Directions

This current chapter focused on examining sex and age differences in levels of cognitive vulnerability factors as well as sex and age differences in the strength of the association between cognitive vulnerability factors and increases in depressive symptoms following negative events. The review provided weak evidence at best supporting each of our four hypotheses regarding the role of cognitive vulnerability factors in the emergence of sex differences in depression and the surge in depression rates in adolescence. Although the current chapter provides a preliminary synthesis of findings obtained to date examining this topic, substantial work remains to be done before firm conclusions can be drawn. In the remainder of the chapter, we outline directions for future research aimed at uncovering the role of cognitive vulnerability factors in the emergence of the sex difference in depression and the surge in depression rates during adolescence.

First, the current chapter focused on examining sex and age differences pertaining to cognitive vulnerability factors featured in the following four cognitive theories of depression: the hopelessness theory (Abramson et al., 1989), Beck's (1967, 1983) cognitive theory, the response styles theory (Nolen-Hoeksema, 1991), and theories of personality predispositions to depression (Blatt & Zuroff, 1992; Beck, 1983). Thus, we can not infer that the findings of the current review will extend to the cognitive vulnerability constructs proposed by other cognitive vulnerability-stress theories of depression including Weisz and colleagues' (Weisz, 1986; Weisz & Stipek, 1982) contingency-competence-control model of depression, Cole's (1991) competency-based model of depression, Bandura and colleagues' (Bandura, Pastorelli, Barbaranelli, & Caprara, 1999) self-efficacy model of depression, Higgins and colleagues' (Higgins, 1987, 1999; Higgins, Klein, & Strauman, 1985) self-discrepancy theory, and Linville's (1985, 1987) self-complexity theory. Additional work is needed from the perspective of these theories examining whether sex and age differences exist in levels of cognitive vulnerability and/or in the strength of the association between cognitive vulnerability factors and increases in depressive symptoms following negative events.

Second, research on sex differences in depression has suggested that girls may be more vulnerable to depression than boys specifically in the interpersonal domain (Bandura et al., 1999; Leadbeater, Blatt, & Quinlan, 1995; Leadbeater, Kuperminc, Blatt, & Hertzog, 1999). Thus, sex differences in vulnerability factors may be more pronounced with cognitive factors that are more interpersonal in nature than those reviewed in the current chapter such as negative attachment cognitions (Hammen, Burge, & Daley, 1995), the cognitive scripts hypothesized to underlie excessive reassurance seeking tendencies (Joiner & Metalsky, 2001; Van Orden, Wingate, Gordon, & Joiner, 2005), and perceived social support (Furman, 1998). On a related note, sex moderating effects may be more apt to occur when examining the interaction of cognitive vulnerability factors with the occurrence of interpersonal stressors specifically rather than with the occurrence of stressors in general.

Third, it is possible that the strength of the association between cognitive vulnerability factors and increases in depression following negative events varies as a function of third variables in which girls differ from boys and/or older youth differ from younger youth. For example, a depressogenic attributional style has been found to predict greater increases in depressive symptoms following negative events in individuals possessing low, as opposed to high, levels of self-esteem (Abela & Payne, 2003; Conley et al., 2001). Girls have been found to possess lower levels of self-esteem than boys (Abela, Morrison, & Starrs, 2007). Thus, as a consequence of possessing lower levels of self-esteem, the deleterious impact of a pessimistic attributional style on depression following negative events may be greater in girls. Other third variables which may moderate the strength of the association between cognitive vulnerability factors and increases in depression following negative events on which girls and boys have been found to differ include negative affectivity (Chorpita, Plummer, & Moffitt, 2000; Jacques & Mash, 2004; Lonigan, Hooe, David, Kistner, 1999; Lonigan, Phillips, & Hooe, 2003), a history of emotional, physical, and/or sexual abuse (Cutler & Nolen-Hoeksema, 1991; Levitan, Parikh, Lesage, Hegadoren, Adams, Kennedy, et al., 1998; Rind, Tromovitch, & Bauserman, 1998), and genetic vulnerability (Silberg, Rutter, & Eaves, 2001; Silberg, Pickles, Rutter, Hewitt, Simonoff, Maes, et al., 1999). With respect to age, third variables which may moderate the strength of the association between cognitive vulnerability factors and increases in depression following negative events on which older youth and younger youth have been found to differ include self-consciousness (Elkind, 1967, 1978; Garber, Weiss, & Shanley, 1993), egocentrism (Elkind, 1967, 1978; Garber et al., 1993), and abstract reasoning/formal operational thought (Turner & Cole, 1994).

Fourth, the bulk of research examining age and/or sex differences in levels of cognitive vulnerability factors has used cross-sectional designs in which scores on measures of cognitive vulnerability are compared across age (i.e., children versus adolescents), sex (boys versus girls), and/or age by sex combinations (i.e., pre- and post-pubescent boys versus girls). The bulk of research examining age and/or sex differences in the strength of the association between cognitive vulnerability factors and increases in depression following negative events has conducted between-group comparisons of association obtained using short-term longitudinal designs. Thus, little is known about within-youth changes in levels of cognitive vulnerability over time and whether such within-youth changes play a role in either the emergence of the sex differences in depression or the surge in depression rates. Similarly, little is known about whether the strength of the association between cognitive vulnerability and increases in depression following negative events changes within youth over time and whether such within-youth changes play a role in either the emergence of the sex differences in depression or the surge in depression rates. In order to be able to examine from a developmental psychopathology perspective whether cognitive vulnerability factors play a role in the epidemiological shifts in depression rates observed during adolescence, such longitudinal studies using within-subject approaches to analyses such as those outlined above will ultimately be needed.

Fifth, an important area of research that has been relatively neglected to date is examinations of whether measures commonly used to assess cognitive vulnerability to depression in youth exhibit measurement invariance across girls and boys and across youth at different developmental stages. A demonstration that such measures exhibit at least partial measurement invariance is needed before truly meaningful comparisons can be made between the sexes and between age groups. Otherwise, it is not possible to determine whether observed differences (or lack of differences) between the sexes and between age groups reflect true differences in levels of the construct of interest or whether they are simply the result of age- or sex-biases in measurement.

Last, as with any review or meta-analysis, the methodological differences between the studies reviewed were many and it is important to acknowledge some of these differences as they may play an important role in patterns of findings observed across studies. More specifically, although all the studies included in this review were prospective in nature, they varied in study duration (e.g., one week to five years), frequency of assessments (e.g., two time points versus nine time points), measures used to assess constructs of interest, sample size and resulting statistical power (e.g., 35 participants to 1,500 participants), sample characteristics (e.g., age and risk status), and statistical analyses employed (e.g., hierarchical multiple regression versus hierarchical linear modeling). In addition, although there is a certain amount of stability that exists among theoretical concepts and research examining them, it is possible that over a larger span of time studies become less compatible for comparison. Finally, for those studies that did not examine sex or age differences as part of their analyses, it is unclear what results would have been obtained.

It is therefore imperative to continuously explore the theoretical explanations via methodologically rigorous research designs, in order to understand the factors and processes underlying the emergence of the sex difference in depression and the surge in depression rates during adolescence It will prove both interesting and important for future research to examinee a wider range of cognitive-vulnerability theories – particularly those that are social or interpersonal in nature. Examinations of additional third-variable moderators such as neuroticism, self-esteem, genetic vulnerabilities, temperament, and/or their intricate combinations with specific types of stressors (i.e., only achievement vs. only interpersonal stressors) may add important insights to mechanisms and/or processes underlying these epidemiological shifts. Finally drawing from developmental psychology literature, more research should be conducted with an emphasis on certain either age or maturity-phase transitions (e.g., physical growth, grade transitions) and how these transitions may explain the rapid changes in rates of depression throughout this period of development.

References

Abela, J.R.Z. (2001). The hopelessness theory of depression: A test of the diathesis-stress and causal mediation components in third and seventh grade children. *Journal of Abnormal Child Psychology, 29,* 241-254.

Abela, J.R.Z. (2002). Depressive mood reactions to failure in the achievement domain: A test of the integration of the hopelessness and self-esteem theories of depression. *Cognitive Therapy and Research, 26,* 531-552.

Abela, J.R.Z., Aydin, C., & Auerbach, R.P. (2007). Responses to depression in children: Reconceptualizing the relation among response styles. *Journal of Abnormal Child Psychology, 35,* 913-927.

Abela, J.R.Z., Brozina, K. & Haigh, E.P. (2002). An examination of the response styles theory of depression in third and seventh grade children: A short-term longitudinal study. *Journal of Abnormal Child Psychology, 30,* 513-525.

Abela, J.R.Z. & D'Alessandro, D.U. (2002). Beck's cognitive theory of depression: A test of the diathesis-stress and causal mediation components. *British Journal of Clinical Psychology, 41,* 111-128.

Abela, J.R.Z. & Hankin, B.L. (2008). Cognitive vulnerability to depression in children and adolescents: A developmental psychopathology perspective. In J.R.Z. Abela and B.L. Hankin (Eds.), Handbook of Depression in Children and Adolescents. (pp. 35-78). New York, New York: The Guilford Press.

Abela, J.R.Z., Morrison, E., & Starrs, C. (2007). Excessive *r*eassurance *s*eeking, self–esteem, and depressive symptoms in children of affectively ill parents: An experience sampling analysis. *Journal of Social and Clinical Psychology, 26*(7), *849-869.*

Abela, J.R.Z. & McGirr, A. (2007). Operationalizing "cognitive vulnerability" and "stress" from the perspective of the hopelessness theory: A multi-wave longitudinal study of children of affectively-ill parents. *British Journal of Clinical Psychology, 46,* 377-395.

Abela, J.R.Z., McGirr, A., & Skitch, S.A. (2007). Depressogenic inferential styles, negative events, and depressive symptoms in youth: An attempt to reconcile past inconsistent findings. *Behaviour Research and Therapy, 45,* 2397-2406.

Abela, J.R.Z., Parkinson, C., Stolow, D., & Starrs, C. (in press). A test of the integration of the hopelessness and response styles theories of depression in middle adolescence.

Abela, J.R.Z. & Payne, A.V.L. (2003). A test of the integration of the hopelessness and self-esteem theories of depression in schoolchildren. Cognitive Therapy & Research, 27, 519-535.

Abela, J.R.Z., Sakellaropoulo, M., & Taxel, E. (2007). Integrating two subtypes of depression: Psychodynamic theory and its relation to hopelessness depression in schoolchildren. *Journal of Early Adolescence.*

Abela, J.R.Z. & Sarin, S. (2002). Cognitive vulnerability to hopelessness depression: A chain is only as strong as its weakest link. *Cognitive Therapy and Research, 26,* 811-829.

Abela, J.R.Z. & Seligman, M.E.P. (2000). The hopelessness theory of depression: A test of the diathesis-stress component in the interpersonal and achievement domains. *Cognitive Therapy and Research, 24,* 361-378.

Abela, J.R.Z. & Skitch, S.A. (2007). Dysfunctional attitudes as a cognitive vulnerability factor for depression in children of affectively-ill parents: A multi-wave longitudinal study. *Behaviour Research and Therapy.*

Abela, J.R.Z., Skitch, S.A., Adams, P., & Hankin, B.L. (2006). The timing of parent and child depression: A hopelessness theory perspective. *Journal of Clinical Child and Adolescent Psychology, 35,* 253-263.

Abela, J.R.Z. & Sullivan, C. (2003). A test of Beck's cognitive diathesis-stress theory of depression in early adolescents. *Journal of Early Adolescence, 23*, 384-404.

Abela, J.R.Z. & Taylor, G. (2003). Specific vulnerability to depressive mood reactions in children: The moderating role of self-esteem. *Journal of Clinical Child and Adolescents Psychology, 32,* 408-418.

Abela, J.R.Z., Vanderbilt, E. & Rochon, A. (2004). A test of the integration of the response styles and social support theories of depression in third and seventh grade children. *Journal of Social and Clinical Psychology, 5*, 653-674.

Abramson, L.Y., Alloy, L.B., Hankin, B.L., Haeffel, J.G., MacCoon D.G., & Gibb, B.E. (2002). Cognitive vulnerability-stress models of depression in a self-regulatory and psychobiological context. In I.H. Gotlib & C.L. Hammen (Eds.), *Handbook of depression* (pp. 268-294). New York: Guilford.

Abramson, L.Y., Alloy, L.B., & Metalsky, G.I. (1988). The cognitive diathesis-stress theories of depression: Toward an adequate evaluation of the theories' validities. In L.B. Alloy (Ed.), *Cognitive processes in depression* (pp. 3-30). New York: Guilford.

Abramson, L.Y., Metalsky, G.I., & Alloy, L.B. (1989). Hopelessness depression: A theory-based subtype of depression. *Psychological Review, 96,* 358-372.

Abramson, L.Y., Seligman, M.E.P., & Teasdale, J. (1978). Learned helplessness in humans: Critique and reformulation. *Journal of Abnormal Psychology, 87*, 49-74.

Adams, P., Abela, J.R.Z., Auerbach, R. P., & Skitch, S.A. (2008). Self-criticism, dependency, and stress reactivity: An experience sampling approach to testing Blatt and Zuroff's (1992) theory of personality predispositions to depression in high-risk youth. Manuscript submitted for publication.

Alloy, L.B., Hartlage, S., & Abramson, L.Y. (1988). Testing the cognitive diathesis-stress theories of depression: Issues of research design, conceptualization, and assessment. In L.B. Alloy (Ed.), *Cognitive processes in depression* (pp. 31-73). New York: Guilford.

Angold, A., Erkanli, A., Silberg, J., Eaves, L., & Costello, E. J. (2002). Depression scale scores in 8-17-year-olds: Effects of age and gender. *Journal of Child Psychology & Psychiatry & Allied Disciplines, 43*, 1052-1063.

Avenevoli, S., Knight, E., Kessler, R. C. & Merikangas, K.R. (2008). Epidemiology of depression in children and adolescents. In J.R.Z. Abela and B.L. Hankin (Eds.), Handbook of Depression in Children and Adolescents. (pp. 6-32). New York, New York: The Guilford Presss.

Bandura, A., Pastorelli, C., Barbaranelli, C., & Caprara, G.V. (1999). Self-efficacy pathways to childhood depression. *Journal of Personality and Social Psychology, 76,* 258-269.

Beck, A.T. (1967). *Depression: Clinical, experimental, and theoretical aspects.* New York: Harper & Row.

Beck, A.T. (1983). Cognitive therapy of depression: New perspectives. In P.J. Clayton & J.E. Barrett (Eds.), *Treatment of depression: Old controversies and new approaches.* New York: Raven Press.

Bennett, D.S. & Bates, J.E. (1995). Prospective models of depressive symptoms in early adolescence: Attributional style, stress, and support. *Journal of Early Adolescence, 15,* 299–315.

Blatt, S.J. & Zuroff, D.C. (1992). Interpersonal relatedness and self-definition: Two prototypes for depression. *Clinical Psychology Review, 12,* 527-562.

Broderick, P.C. & Korteland, C. (2004). A prospective study of rumination and depression in early adolescence. *Clinical Child Psychology and Psychiatry, 9,* 383-394.

Brozina, K. & Abela, J.R.Z. (2006). Symptoms of Depression and Anxiety in Children: Specificity of the Hopelessness Theory. *Journal of Clinical Child and Adolescent Psychology, 35(4),* 515-527.

Caspi, A. & Moffitt, T.E. (1991). Individual differences are accentuated during periods of social change: The sample case of girls at puberty. *Journal of Personality and Social Psychology, 61,* 157-168.

Chorpita, B. F., Plummer, C. M. & Moffitt, C. E. (2000). Relations of tripartite dimensions of emotion to childhood anxiety and mood disorders. Journal of Abnormal Child Psychology, 28, 299-310.

Clark, D.A. & Beck, A. T. (1999). Scientific foundations of cognitive theory and therapy of depression. New York: John Wiley & Sons.

Cole, D. A. (1991). Preliminary Support for a Competency-Based Model of Depression in Children. *Journal of Abnormal Psychology, 100,* 181-190.

Conley, C.S., Haines, B.A., Hilt, L.M., & Metalsky, G.I. (2001). The children's attributional style interview: Developmental tests of cognitive diathesis-stress theories of depression. *Journal of Abnormal Child Psychology, 29,* 445-463.

Costello, E.J., Mustillo, S., Erkanli, A., Keeler, G., & Angold, A. (2003). Prevalence and development of psychiatric disorders in childhood and adolescence. *Archives of General Psychiatry, 60,* 837-844.

Cutler, S. E. & Nolen-Hoeksema, S. (1991). Accounting for sex differences in depression through female victimization: Childhood sexual abuse. *Sex Roles, 24,* 425-438.

Cyranowski, J.M., Frank, E., Young, E., & Shear, K. (2000). Adolescent onset of the gender difference in lifetime rates of major depression: a theoretical model. *Archives of General Psychiatry, 57,* 21-27.

D'Alesasandro, D. U. & Burton, K. D. (2006). Development and validation of the dysfunctional attitudes scale for children: Tests of Beck's cognitive diathesis-stress theory of depression, of its causal mediation component, and of developmental effects. *Cognitive Theory and Research, 30,* 335-353.

Dixon, J. F. & Ahrens, A.H. (1992). Stress and attributional styles as predictors of self-reported depression in children. *Cognitive Therapy and Research, 16,* 623-634.

Elkind, D. (1967). Egocentrism in adolescence. *Child Development, 38,* 1025-1034.

Elkind, D. (1978). Understanding the young adolescent. *Adolescence, 49,* 127-134.

Furman, W. (1998).The measurement of friendship perceptions: Conceptual and methodological issues. In W.M. Bukowski & A.F. Newcomb (Eds.), *Company they keep: Friendship in childhood and adolescence.* New York, NY: Cambridge University Press.

Garber, J. & Flynn, C. (2001). Predictors of depressive cognitions in young adolescents. *Cognitive Therapy and Research, 25,* 353-376.

Garber, J., Weiss, B. & Shanley, N. (1993). Cognitions, Depressive Symptoms, and Development in Adolescents. *Journal of Abnormal Psychology, 102,* 47-57.

Ge, X., Lorenz, F.O., Conger, R.D., Elder, G.H., Simons, R.L. (1994). Trajectories of stressful life events and depressive symptoms during adolescence. *Developmental Psychology, 30,* 467-483.

Gibb, B.E. & Alloy, L.B. (2006). A prospective test of the hopelessness theory of depression in children. *Journal of Clinical Child and Adolescent Psychology, 35,* 264-274.

Gibb, B.E. & Coles, M.E. (2005). Cognitive vulnerability models of psychopathology: A developmental perspective. In B.L. Hankin and J.R.Z. Abela (Eds.), Development of Psychopathology: A Vulnerability-Stress Perspective. (pp. 104-135). Thousand Oaks, California: Sage Publications.

Gotlib, I.H. & Hammen, C.L. (Eds.). (2002). *Handbook of depression.* New York: Guilford Press.

Graber, J.A., Brooks-Gunn, J., & Petersen, A. C. (1996). *Transitions through adolescence: Interpersonal domains and context.* Hillsdale, NJ: Lawrence Erlbaum Associates, Inc.

Graber, J.A., Brooks-Gunn, J., & Warren, M.P. (1995). The antecedents of menarcheal age: Heredity, family environment, and stressful life events. *Child Development, 66,* 346-359.

Hammen, C.L., Adrian, C., & Hiroto, D. (1988). A longitudinal test of the attributional vulnerability model of depression in children at risk for depression. *British Journal of Clinical Psychology, 27,* 37-46.

Hammen, C. L., Burge, D. & Daley, S. E. (1995). Interpersonal attachment cognitions and prediction of symptomatic responses to interpersonal stress. *Journal of Abnormal Psychology, 104(3),* 436-443.

Hammen, C.L. & Goodman-Brown, T. (1990). Self-schemas and vulnerability to specific life stress in children at risk for depression. *Cognitive Therapy and Research, 14,* 215-227

Hankin, B.L. (2005). Childhood maltreatment and psychopathology: Prospective tests of attachment, cognitive vulnerability, and stress as mediating processes. *Cognitive Therapy and Research, 29,* 645-671.

Hankin, B.L. & Abela, J.R.Z. (2005). Depression from childhood through adolescence and adulthood: A developmental vulnerability-stress perspective. In B.L. Hankin and J.R.Z. Abela (Eds.), *Development of Psychopathology: A Vulnerability-Stress Perspective.* (pp. 245-288). Thousand Oaks, California: Sage Publications.

Hankin, B. L. & Abramson, L. Y. (2001). Development of sex differences in depression: An elaborated cognitive vulnerability-transactional stress theory. *Psychological Bulletin, 127,* 773-796.

Hankin, B.L. & Abramson, L.Y. (2002). Measuring cognitive vulnerability to depression in adolescence: Reliability, validity, and gender differences. *Journal of Child and Adolescent Clinical Psychology, 31,* 491-504.

Hankin, B.L., Abramson, L.Y., Miller, N., & Haeffel, G. (2004). Cognitive vulnerability-stress theories of depression: Examining affective specificity in the prediction of depression versus anxiety in three prospective studies. *Cognitive Therapy and Research, 28,* 309-345.

Hankin, B.L., Abramson, L.Y., Moffitt, T.E., Silva, P.A., McGee, R., & Angell, K.A. (1998). Development of depression from preadolescence to young adulthood: Emerging gender differences in a 10 year longitudinal study. *Journal of Abnormal Psychology, 107,* 128-141.

Hankin, B.L., Abramson, L.Y. & Siler, M. (2001). A prospective test of the hopelessness theory of depression in adolescence. *Cognitive Therapy and Research, 25,* 607-632

Hankin, B.L., Lakdawalla, Z., Lee, A., Grace, D., & Roesch, L. (November, 2004). *Cognitive vulnerabilities for emotional distress in adolescence: Disentangling the comorbidity of depression and anxiety in a multi-wave prospective study.* Paper presented at the symposium, "Depression and Anxiety: Issues of Specificity and Comorbidity." Benjamin L. Hankin, and John R.Z. Abela Co-Chairs. 38th Annual Meeting of the Association for Advancement of Behavior Therapy, New Orleans.

Hankin, B.L., Mermelstein, R., & Roesch, L. (in press). Sex differences in adolescent depression: Stress exposure and reactivity models. *Child Development.*

Hankin, B.L., Wetter, E., & Cheely, C. (2008). Sex differences in child and adolescent depression: A developmental psychopathological approach. In Abela, J.R.Z. and Hankin, B.L. (Eds). *Handbook of depression in children and adolescents.* (pp. 377-414). New York, USA: Guilford Press.

Higgins, E. T. (1987). Self-discrepancy: A theory relating self and affect. *Psychological Review*, *94*, 319-340.

Higgins, E. T. (1999). When do self-discrepancies have specific relations to emotions? *Journal of Personality and Social Psychology*, *77*, 1313-1317.

Higgins, E. T., Klein, R. & Strauman, T. (1985). Self-concept discrepancy theory: A psychological model for distinguishing among different aspects of depression and anxiety. *Social Cognition*, *3*, 51-76.

Hilsman, R. & Garber, J. (1995). A test of the cognitive diathesis-stress model of depression in children: Academic stressors, attributional style, perceived competence, and control. *Journal of Personality and Social Psychology, 69,* 370-380.

Ingram, R.E. & Luxton, D.D. (2005). Vulnerability-stress models. In B.L. Hankin & J.R.Z. Abela (Eds.), *Development of psychopathology: A vulnerability-stress perspective* (pp. 32-46). Thousand Oaks, CA: Sage.

Ingram, R.E., Miranda, J., & Segal, Z.V. (1998). *Cognitive Vulnerability to Depression.* New York, NY. Guilford Press.

Jacques, H. A. K. & Mash, E. J. (2004). A test of the tripartite model of anxiety and depression in elementary and high school boys and girls. *Journal of Abnormal Child Psychology, 32(1),* 13-25.

Joiner, T.E., Jr. (2000). A test of the hopelessness theory of depression in youth psychiatric inpatients. *Journal of Clinical Child Psychology*, *29*, 167-176.

Joiner, T.E., Jr. & Metalsky, G.I. (2001). Excessive reassurance seeking: Delineating a risk factor involved in the development of depressive symptoms. *Psychological Science, 12,* 371-378.

Kessler, R. C., McGonagle, K. A., Swartz, M., Blazer, D. G. & Nelson, C. B. (1993). Sex and depression in the National Comorbidity Survey I: Lifetime prevalence, chronicity and recurrence. *Journal of Affective Disorders, 29(2-3),* 85-96.

Kim-Cohen, J., Caspi, A. & Moffitt, T. E. (2003). Prior juvenile diagnoses in adults with mental disorder: Developmental follow-back of a prospective-longitudinal cohort. *Archives of General Psychiatry, 60,* 709-717.

Leadbeater, B.J., Blatt, S.J. & Quinlan, D.M. (1995). Gender-linked vulnerabilities to depressive symptoms, stress, and problem behaviors in adolescents. *Journal of Research on Adolescence, 5,* 1-29.

Leadbeater, B. J., Kuperminc, G. P., Blatt, S. J., & Hertzog, C. (1999). A multivariate model of gender differences in adolescents' internalizing and externalizing disorders. *Developmental Psychology, 35,* 1268-1282.

Levitan, R. D., Parikh, S. V., Lesage, A. D., Hegadoren, K. M., Adams, M., Kennedy, S. H., & Goering, P. N. (1998). Major depression in individuals with a history of childhood physical or sexual abuse: Relationship to neurovegetative features, mania, and gender. *American Journal of Psychiatry, 155(12),* 1746-1752.

Lewinsohn, P.M., Joiner, T.E., & Rohde, P. (2001). Evaluation of cognitive diathesis-stress models in predicting major depressive disorder in adolescents. *Journal of Abnormal Psychology, 110,* 203-215.

Linville, P. (1985). Self-complexity and affective extremity: Don't put all of your eggs in one cognitive basket. *Social Cognition, 3,* 94-120.

Linville, P. W. (1987). Self-complexity as a cognitive buffer against stress-related illness and depression. *Journal of Personality and Social Psychology, 52,* 663-676.

Little, S.A. & Garber, J. (2000). Interpersonal and achievement orientations and specific stressors predicting depressive and aggressive symptoms in children. *Cognitive Therapy & Research, 24,* 651-670.

Little, S.A. & Garber, J. (2004). Interpersonal and achievement orientations and specific stressors predict depressive and aggressive symptoms. *Journal of Adolescent Research, 19,* 63-84.

Little, S.A. & Garber, J. (2005). The role of social stressors and interpersonal orientation in explaining the longitudinal relation between externalizing and depressive symptoms. *Journal of Abnormal Psychology, 114* 432-443.

Lonigan, C. J., Hooe, E. S., David, C. F., & Kistner, J. A. (1999). Positive and negative affectivity in children: Confirmatory factor analysis of a two-factor model and its relation to symptoms of anxiety and depression. *Journal of Consulting and Clinical Psychology, 67,* 374-386.

Lonigan, C. J., Phillips, B. M., & Hooe, E. S. (2003). Relations of positive and negative affectivity to anxiety and depression in children: Evidence from a latent variable longitudinal study. *Journal of Consulting and Clinical Psychology, 71,* 465-481.

Metalsky, G.I. & Joiner, T.E., Jr. (1992). Vulnerability to depressive symptomatology: A prospective test of the diathesis-stress and causal mediation components of the hopelessness theory of depression. *Journal of Personality and Social Psychology,* 63, 667-675.

Moffitt, T.E. (2005). The new look of behavioral genetics in developmental psychopathology: Gene-environment interplay in antisocial behaviors. Psychological Bulletin, 131, 533-554

Monroe, S.M. & Harkness, K. L. (2005). Life stress, the "kindling" hypothesis, and the recurrence of depression: Considerations from a life stress perspective. *Psychological Review, 112,* 417-445.

Monroe, S.M. & Simons, A.D. (1991). Diathesis-stress theories in the context of life stress research: Implications for the depressive disorders. *Psychological Bulletin, 110*, 406-425.

Nolen-Hoeksema, S. (1991). Responses to depression and their effects on the duration of depressive episodes. *Journal of Abnormal Psychology, 100*, 569-582.

Nolen-Hoeksema, S. & Corte, C. (2004). Gender and self-regulation. In R.F. Baumeister & K.D. Vohs (Eds.) *Handbook of self-regulation: Research, theory, and applications* (pp. 411-421). New York: Guilford.

Nolen-Hoeksema, S., Girgus, J.S,. & Seligman, M.E.P. (1986). Learned helplessness in children: A longitudinal study of depression, achievement, and attributional style. *Journal of Personality and Social Psychology, 51*, 435-442.

Nolen-Hoeksema, S., Girgus, J.S., & Seligman, M.E.P. (1992). Predictors and consequences of childhood depressive symptoms: A five-year longitudinal study. *Journal of Abnormal Psychology, 101,* 405-422.

Nolen-Hoeksema, S., Stice, E., Wade, E., & Bohon, C. (2007). Reciprocal relations between rumination and bulimic, substance abuse, and depressive symptoms in female adolescents. *Journal of Abnormal Psychology, 116*, 198-207.

Panak, W.F. & Garber, J. (1992). Role of aggression, rejection, and attributions in the prediction of depression in children. *Development and Psychopathology, 4*, 145-165.

Prinstein, M.J., & Aikens, J.W. (2004). Cognitive moderators of the longitudinal association between peer rejection and adolescent depressive symptoms. *Journal of Abnormal Child Psychology, 32*, 147-158.

Rind, B., Tromovitch, P. & Bauserman, R. (1998). A meta-analytic examination of assumed properties of child sexual abuse using college samples. *Psychological Bulletin, 124,* 22-53.

Robinson, N.S., Garber, J., & Hilsman, R. (1995). Cognitions and stress: direct and moderating effects on depressive versus externalizing symptoms during the junior high school transition. *Journal of Abnormal Psychology, 104*, 453-463.

Rohde, P., Lewinsohn, P.M., Seeley, J.R. (1994). Are adolescents changed by an episode of major depression? *Journal of the American Academy of Child and Adolescent Psychiatry, 33*, 1289-1298.

Rudolph, K.D. (2002). Gender differences in emotional responses to interpersonal stress during adolescence. *Journal of Adolescent Health, 30*, 3-13.

Rudolph, K.D. & Hammen, C. (1999). Age and gender as determinants of stress exposure, generation, and reactions in youngsters: A transactional perspective. *Child Development, 70*, 660-677.

Shahar, G., Blatt, S.J., Zuroff, D.C., Kuperminc, G., & Leadbeater, B.J. (2004). Reciprocal relations between depressive symptoms and self-criticism (but not dependency) among early adolescent girls (but not boys). *Cognitive Therapy and Research, 28*, 85-103.

Shahar, G. & Priel, B. (2003). Active vulnerability, adolescent distress, and the mediating/suppressing role of life events. *Personality and Individual Differences, 35*, 199-218.

Silberg, J. L., Pickles, A., Rutter, M., Hewitt, J., Simonoff, E., Maes, H., et al. (1999). The influence of genetic factors and life stress on depression among adolescent girls. *Archives of General Psychiatry, 56(3),* 225-232.

Silberg, J., Rutter, M., & Eaves, L. (2001). Genetic and environmental influences on the temporal association between earlier anxiety and later depression in girls. *Biological Psychiatry , 49(12),* 1040-1049.

Southall, D. & Roberts, J.E. (2002). Attributional style and self-esteem in vulnerability to adolescent depressive symptoms following life stress: A 14-week prospective study. *Cognitive Therapy and Research, 26,* 563-579.

Spence, S.H., Sheffield, J., & Donovan, C. (2002). Problem–solving orientation and attributional style: Moderators of the impact of negative life events on the development of depressives in adolescence? *Journal of Clinical Child Psychology, 31,* 219–229.

Schwartz, J.A.J. & Koenig, L.J. (1996). Response styles and negative affect among adolescents. *Cognitive Therapy and Research,* 20, 13-36.

Turner, J.E. & Cole, D.A. (1994). Developmental differences in cognitive diatheses for child depression. *Journal of Abnormal Child Psychology, 22(1),* 15-32.

Twenge, J. M., & Nolen-Hoeksema, S. (2002). Age, gender, race, socioeconomic status, and birth cohort difference on the children's depression inventory: A meta-analysis. *Journal of Abnormal Psychology, 111,* 578-588.

Van Orden, K., Wingate, L.R., Gordon, K.H., & Joiner, T.E. (2005). Interpersonal factors as vulnerability to psychopathology over the lifecourse. In B. L. Hankin and J. R. Z. Abela (Eds.), *Development of Psychopathology: A Vulnerability-Stress Perspective.* (pp. 136-160). Thousand Oaks, California: Sage Publications.

Weisz, J. R. (1986). Understanding the developing understanding of control. In M. Perlmutter (Ed.), *Cognitive perspectives on children's social and behavioral development: The Minnesota Symposia on Child Psychology* (pp. 219-285). Hillsdale, NJ: Erlbaum.

Weisz, J. R., & Stipek, D. J. (1982). Competence, contingency, and the development of perceived control. *Human Development, 25,* 250-281.

Ziegert, D.I., & Kistner, J.A. (2002). Response styles theory: Downward extension to children. *Journal of Clinical Child and Adolescent Psychology, 31,* 325-334.

Zuroff, D.C., Santor, D.A., & Mongrain, M. (2004). Dependency, self-criticism, and maladjustment. In J.S. Auerbach, K.J. Levy, & C.E. Schaffer (Eds.), *Relatedness, self-definition and mental representation: Essays in honor of Sidney J. Blatt* (pp. 75-90). Brunner-Routledge: London.

In: Women and Depression
Editors: Paula Hernandez and Sara Alonso

ISBN 978-1-60456-647-5
© 2009 Nova Science Publishers, Inc.

Chapter 4

Differential Risk for Emotion Processing Difficulties by Gender and Age in Major Depressive Disorder

Sara L. Wright[3][1,2] *and Scott A. Langenecker*[1,3]
[1]University of Michigan Medical School, Department of Psychiatry
[2]Ann Arbor Veterans Affairs Medical Center, Geriatric, Research, Education, and Clinical Center (GRECC), Ann Arbor, MI, USA
[3] Depression Center, Molecular and Behavioral Neuroscience Institute, University of Michigan, MI USA

Abstract

Background: Differences in emotion processing during Major Depressive Disorder (MDD) have not been well explored as a potential explanation for age and gender disparities in rates of depression and depressive symptoms. Early studies by our group demonstrated that those with MDD underperform in emotion processing of faces, although recently we showed a selective decrement in younger women with MDD. We now extend this study of gender differences in facial emotion processing during MDD to the full age spectrum. We assessed emotion processing performance using posed facial emotional expressions in those with early (age 18- 35) and middle/ late (age 36-73) MDD as well as in women and men to determine if there was differential impact of MDD in these four groups. We hypothesized that knowledge about gender, age, and emotion processing performance differences might increase understanding of risk for and expression of MDD in women and in those with later onset MDD.

Methods: Participants included 161 individuals in younger age groups (YA; 123 women, 38 men) and 150 individuals in middle/ elder age groups (MEA; 100 women, 50 men) diagnosed with MDD, as well as 97 healthy control YAs (60 women, 37 men) and 35 healthy controls MEAs (24 women, 11 men). A conservative age classification ≤ age

---

[3] Correspondence to: Sara L. Wright, Ph.D. Department of Psychiatry, University of Michigan Medical Center, 2101 Commonwealth Blvd., Suite C. Ann Arbor, MI 48105, Telephone 734-936-3180, Fax 734-936-9262. Electronic mail: sarawrig@med.umich.edu.

35 was used to separate YAs from MEAs in order to be to be confident that potential causes of middle-late onset MDD (e.g., cardiovascular) were less likely to be present in the younger MDD groups.

Results: There was an interaction between age, gender, and MDD status for response time, with slower response times in YA MDD patients compared to their age-matched control groups. This effect of slower response time was not detected in the comparisons between MEAs with and without MDD. MEA women, YA women, and MEA men with MDD made significantly more errors than did their same-age, same-gender control counterparts ($ps < .05$), whereas YA men with MDD performed similarly to same-age control men ($p > .26$). Further, although MEA women and men with MDD performed more poorly in facial perception relative to same age control cohorts, MEA men with late onset MDD performed worse than MEA men with early onset MDD, in contrast to no difference between performance of MEA women with late and early onset MDD.

Conclusions: These findings suggest that YA men with MDD may have a different neurobiological etiology of depression compared to YA women. In contrast, MEA men and all women with MDD appear to have similar difficulties with emotion processing, suggesting overlap in brain regions affected, albeit likely through different mechanisms. Notably, MEA men with late onset MDD appear to have a greater burden of emotion processing decrement compared to other depressed groups.

Keywords: *psychiatric disorders, affect perception, gender differences*

Introduction

Women are nearly twice as likely as men to be diagnosed with Major Depressive Disorder (MDD; American Psychiatric Association, 2000). These gender differences persist into middle and older adulthood (Weissman, Bruce, Leaf, Florio, and Holzer, 1991), despite that the mechanisms underlying depression during older age likely broaden to include medical illness, cerebrovascular and cardiovascular events, dementia, hypercortisolemia, and loss of a spouse relationship through death (Blazer and Hybels, 2005; Goldstein and Gruenberg, 2007; Holley and Mast, 2007; Wright and Persad, 2007). While rates of MDD during middle and old age are similar to those observed in younger samples, and even decline in the oldest age groups, prevalence of clinically significant depressive symptoms increases (Weissman et al, 1991). These numbers are often difficult to capture due to increased primary and secondary morbidity in older adults with MDD, yet it does appear that a gender bias in the prevalence of depression is continuous throughout the lifespan. Various biological, cognitive, and interpersonal hypotheses have been offered and tested to explain gender (Geerts and Bouhuys, 1998; Grigoriadis and Robinson, 2007; Joiner, 2000; Lara and Klein, 1999) and age (Blazer and Hybels, 2005) differences in prevalence rates and characteristics of depressive symptoms. This article will explore facial emotion processing ability as a possible variable underlying age and gender differences in depression.

Emotion Processing Construct and Neuroanatomical Correlates

Emotion processing and categorization are necessary for successful communication and adaptive social behavior. Indeed, those with the most adaptive social behavior are often the most interpersonally successful, and attempts to integrate the concept of emotional intelligence into cognitive and affective neuroscience predate these terms themselves (Thorndike, 1920). In a recent formulation, Phillips, Drevets, Rauch, and Lane (2003a) contend that emotion processing entails a three-step process, including 1) identifying and appraising the emotional implication of the stimulus; 2) producing autonomic, neuroendocrine, somatomotor, and affective responses to the stimuli; and 3) regulating the affective response, which can involve inhibitory and modification processes. We add that the individual can make adaptive social and behavioral responses only with accurate emotion perception. Behaving in accord with accurate perceptions can help ameliorate any potential social discord. For example, those with higher non-verbal decoding ability in communication are more likely to be successful in their professions, particularly those that rely on social interaction for success (e.g., foreign service workers, teachers, and therapists, Rosenthal, Hall, DiMatteo, Rogers, & Archer, 1979). As such, it is reasonable to conclude that an interpersonal basis for depression could be the end result of poor emotion perception, poor control of one's emotional responses, or inability to execute corrective behaviors and strategies in social relationships. We have focused largely on emotion perception accuracy as a critical mediating factor in the etiology of depression, and have, along with others, repeatedly demonstrated emotion processing decrements in individuals with depression, described in greater detail below.

Cognitive and affective neuroscience studies exploring the neurophysiology of facial emotion perception and processing have burgeoned in the last decade. Indeed, early work with tumor and lesion patients demonstrated a right hemisphere bias in the processing of facial characteristics, particularly the emotional aspects of faces (Bowers, Bauer, Coslett, & Heilman, 1985; Ley and Bryden, 1979). More, specifically, the fusiform face area (FFA) has been specifically linked to face recognition and identification (Grill-Spector, Knouf, and Kanwisher, 2004), and the amygdala and ventral striatal regions have been implicated in the processing of specific types of emotions (Adolphs, Tranel, Damasio, and Damasio, 1994; Gur, Skolnick, and Gur, 1994). Emotion discrimination is a complex cognitive process that involves multiple cortical and limbic areas. Phillips and colleagues (2003a) propose that a ventral system (i.e., amygdala, insula, ventral striatum, ventral anterior cingulate gyrus, ventral prefrontal cortex) is responsible for identifying and generating an emotional response and a dorsal system (i.e., hippocampus, dorsal anterior cingulate cortex, dorsal prefrontal cortex) is accountable for planning an appropriate behavioral response and regulating affect.

The early research into the laterality of facial emotion processing suggested a more critical role for the right hemisphere in emotion processing (e.g., Borod, Koff, Lorch, and Nicholas, 1986; Bowers et al., 1985; DeKosky, Heilman, Bowers, and Valenstein, 1980). More recent functional imaging studies, however, have also shown activation of the left hemisphere, especially during processing of sad and fearful faces (e.g., Blair, Morris, Frith, Perrett, and Dolan, 1999; Iidaka et al., 2001). It has been suggested that the left hemisphere is involved in the analytic tasks associated with facial emotion processing, while the right hemisphere may be responsible for holistic processing (Sergent and Bindra, 1981). Further, as most of the emotion processing task literature studies facial emotion processing, one might suspect that the right hemisphere dominance for emotion may be in part mediated by this factor. Even so, there is one study that controlled for visual spatial acuity that still showed a relative, greater deficit in those with right hemisphere damage (Bowers et al., 1985). Further, a recent study by our group demonstrated no difficulty on visual perception and categorization of animals by patients with left or right hemisphere damage, whereas the left hemisphere damage group performed worse than published norms, and the right hemisphere damage group performed worse than the left hemisphere damage group on categorization of faces (Paradee et al., 2008).

Depression and Emotion Processing

The present line of research follows from the premise that the etiology of depression in at least some individuals shares a common pathway with deficient emotion processing skills. Interest in this line of inquiry has expanded greatly in recent years, including behavioral and functional imaging studies. Individuals with MDD tend to remember events more negatively than controls (see Matt, Vazquez, and Campbell, 1992 for review). Further, those with depression generally perceive environmental stimuli as more negative than do individuals who are not depressed (Hollon and Kendall, 1980). One study reported that subjects with MDD recognized angry facial expressions better than happy expressions (Gilboa-Schechtman, Erhard-Weiss, and Jeczemien, 2002), although we have shown a bias in younger women with depression to overendorse anger as the emotion expressed (Wright et al., in press). This is in the context of decreased accuracy in categorizing sad and fearful expressions; an effect that was not present in younger men with depression.

Inaccuracies in classification of emotional facial expressions are also more frequent among depressed than non-depressed individuals, both during their categorization (e.g., Deldin, Keller, Gergen, and Miller, 2001; Gotlib and Hammen, 1992; Gur et al., 1992; Langenecker et al., 2005; Langenecker et al., 2007a; Mikhailova, Vladimirova, Iznak, Tsusulkovskaya, & Sushko, et al., 1996; Rubinow and Post, 1992; Surguladze et al., 2004) and when self-simulated (Jaeger, Borod, and Peselow, 1986). However, the kinds of errors reported as characteristic of depressed patients vary across the literature. For example, Gur and colleagues (1992) found that depressed patients made more false negative categorizations for positive stimuli, more true positive categorizations for negative stimuli, and more frequently interpreted neutral faces as sad than did controls. The bias toward over-interpretation of neutral faces as sad has been replicated and was related to risk of relapse in one study (Bouhuys, Geerts and Gordjin, 1999). In contrast, other studies have found that depressed patients are more likely than controls to classify sad faces incorrectly and are no different from controls in identifying neutrally posed expressions (Mikhailova et al.,1996; Rubinow and Post, 1992), or that controls make more errors in classifying happy expressions (Langenecker et al., 2005; Surguladze et al., 2004). Still others have found no evidence that depressed patients perform more poorly in recognizing any particular types of emotional expressions (Persad and Polivy, 1993).

Inconsistencies in the reported literature about the error patterns of participants with MDD may be explained in part by sample differences (e.g., inpatient as opposed to outpatient samples), differing diagnostic criteria, inclusion/exclusion of comorbid illness, and methodological variability across studies. For example, some studies have presented facial expressions for very brief periods of time (80-300 ms) using a computer (Langenecker et al., 2005, Mikhailova et al., 1996), whereas others have asked participants to match expressions with key photographs that most closely resemble the posed expressions (Rubinow and Post, 1992). The one study that detected no differences between groups (Persad and Polivy, 1993) gave no categorization time limit to participants, which may account for the null findings. It is critically important to attempt to simulate as much as possible the real-time demands of processing emotions in experiments with depression, as these studies are more likely to reflect the real-life challenges of those who suffer from depression (Langenecker et al., 2005).

Few studies of facial emotion processing deficits among patients with MDD have specifically examined differences in reaction time to faces among individuals with and without MDD, and those that have asked this question have yielded equivocal findings. Langenecker and colleagues (2005) found no differences between depressed and non-depressed individuals in reaction time to faces in one study, but found the opposite pattern in a larger study (Langenecker et al., 2007a). Surguladze and colleagues (2004) showed that individuals with MDD were slower than controls to respond to sad, but not happy faces. Participants in the latter study were somewhat older (M age = 46.9) than participants in the former study (M age = 32.2), possibly explaining disparate findings.

Neurophysiological Correlates of Emotion Processing Abnormalities in MDD

In their seminal review of emotion processing abnormalities among patients with psychiatric disorders, Phillips, Drevets, Rauch, and Lane (2003b) provide a convincing argument for disruptions in both dorsal and ventral emotion processing systems among patients with MDD. Within the ventral system, important for identifying and responding to emotional stimuli, volume reductions have been shown in the amygdala, ventral striatum, and subgenual cingulate gyrus. Within the dorsal system, crucial to planning and regulating responses to emotional stimuli, volumetric reductions have been shown in the prefrontal cortical regions and hippocampus. Functional studies, too, support increased activation in regions important for identifying and responding to emotional stimuli and partially reciprocal deactivations in areas crucial for regulating affective states, with increased activation found in the subgenual cingulate gyrus, ventrolateral prefrontal cortex, amygdala, anterior insula, ventral striatum, and thalamus (Keedwell, Andrew, Williams, Bramner, and Phillips, 2005; Siegle, Steinhauer, Thase, Stenger, and Carter, 2002). There are mixed reports of decreased activity in the dorsomedial and dorsolateral prefrontal cortices depending upon whether there is equivalent or enhanced performance on cognitive tasks (higher activation in MDD, Harvey et al., 2005; Holmes et al., 2005; Langenecker et al., 2007b; Wagner et al., 2006) decreased performance (decreased frontal and increased limbic, Siegle, Thompson, Carter, Steinhauer, and Thase, 2007), or no performance required (decreased frontal and increased limbic,

Mayberg, Liotti, Brannan, McGinnis, and Mahurin,1999). Further decreased activation, blood flow, and electrical activity in medial frontal regions is linked to a decreased probability of successful treatment response (Langenecker et al., 2007b; Mayberg et al., 1997; Pizzagalli et al., 2001; Siegle, Carter, and Thase, 2006).

Age and Emotion Processing

Studies have rather consistently found that as people age, they become less adept at recognizing negative facial expressions, such as anger, sadness, and fear. At the same time, the ability to recognize relatively more positive emotions displayed in facial expressions, including happiness and surprise, has been found to be similar in younger and older adults (Calder et al., 2003; Keightley, Winocur, Burianova, Hongwanishkul, and Grady, 2006; MacPherson, Phillips, and Sala, 2002; Malatesta, Izard, Culver, and Nicolich, 1987; McDowell, Harrison, and Demaree, 1994; Phillips, MacLean, and Allen, 2002; Sullivan and Ruffman, 2004). This could be due to the relatively few positive emotion expressions available compared to the complexity of more possible negative emotion expressions available. For example, of the eight primary emotions reported by Ekman, happiness is the only positive emotion that is readily distinguished across cultures, and there is some difficulty in distinguishing surprise from fear (Ekman and Friesen, 1976; Ekman, 1984). In comparison, disgust, fear, sadness, and anger are equally well recognized across cultures. Selection of a negative emotion is inherently more difficult as a result of having more potential choices.

A recent exception highlighting this potential bias in complexity for positive emotions was conducted by Isaacowitz and colleagues (2007), who found that older adults (aged 60-85) were less accurate than younger (18-39) and middle-aged (40-59) adults in recognizing posed facial expressions of happiness and less accurate than younger adults in recognizing anger, but equivalent in recognizing neutral expressions and expressions of disgust, fear, sadness, and surprise. They contend that previous studies finding no age differences in the detection of happiness may have been confounded by ceiling effects or emotion specific response biases. To test the latter hypothesis, scores were adjusted for the number of correct responses for a specific type of expression that would be expected by chance, and this was incorporated into a formula that included the number of correct responses and the total number of items per task. The resultant value for this equation for each participant was then used as the dependent variable for all analyses. Results demonstrated that younger adults were significantly better than middle-aged but not older adults at recognizing expressions of disgust and happiness. Older adults performed more poorly than the other two groups in recognizing facial expressions of fear. There were also age differences for anger, but none of the pairwise-comparisons reached significance. Recognition of expressions of sadness and surprise were equivalent among the three groups.

Very few studies that have examined age-effects of facial emotion processing have assessed reaction time group differences. Those that have analyzed such data have found that older adults are also slower than younger adults, overall, in identifying emotions in posed facial expressions, and this is especially true for negatively-valenced expressions (Keightley et al., 2006; Sullivan and Ruffman, 2004). Some portion of the differences in processing speed between older and younger adults is likely explained by known age-related declines in general processing speed (Salthouse, 1996), although this does not explain the relatively greater declines in processing negatively-valenced expressions. Socioemotional Selectivity Theory may provide some insight into this finding. This theory postulates that during older age, emotional information becomes more salient and emotion regulation increases (Carstensen and Turk-Charles, 1994; Kliegel, Jäger, and Phillips, 2007). The latter may be explained by older adults' tendency to selectively inhibit negative stimuli (e.g., Charles, Mather, and Carstensen, 2003), and this would be consistent with findings of changes during older age in the ability to process negative emotions. However, this has been an equivocal finding across studies (see Mather, 2004 for review).

Neurophysiological Changes with Age

Changes in emotion processing with age might also be related to age-related changes in brain structure and function. Normal aging has been associated with overall reduction in brain volume (Raz, 2000; Resnick, Pham, Kraut, Zonderman, and Davatzikos, 2003), though different subregions demonstrate disparate rates of decreasing volume. The lateral prefrontal cortex shows the greatest reduction in volume with age (Raz, 2000, 2004; Tisserand et al., 2002), with corresponding decreases in regional cerebral blood flow (De Leon et al., 1987; Garraux et al., 1999). Likewise, cognitive functions mediated by the prefrontal cortex, especially ventrolateral and dorsolateral regions, are especially likely to decline during old age. Hippocampal, amygdala, and neostriatal volume also demonstrate a moderate negative relationship to aging (Raz and Rodrigue, 2006; Langenecker, Briceno, Hamid, and Nielson, 2007) and these are known to be involved in processing and categorizing emotion. Findings of increases in white matter lesions are also generally unequivocal across studies, particularly in periventricular and frontal areas (for review, see Raz and Rodrigue, 2006). That age-related regional structural and functional changes occur in some of the same regions as are important for emotion processing, including the amygdala, ventral prefrontal cortex, hippocampus, and medial and dorsal prefrontal cortex may provide an explanation for age-related emotion processing changes reported in the literature.

Functional neuroimaging studies may also illuminate the etiology of the age differences found in the ability to detect emotions in facial expressions. A study by Gunning-Dixon and colleagues (2003) found that during a facial emotion discrimination task involving displays of happiness, sadness, anger, fear, disgust, and neutrality, younger adults (M age = 25.8) activated limbic regions, including the amygdala and temporo-limbic areas, to a greater extent than did older adults (M age = 72.3), who were more likely than younger adults to activate left-frontal regions. These findings are consistent with those of Iidaka and colleagues (2002) who found greater bilateral amygdala activation among younger adults (M age = 25.1), as compared to older adults (M age = 65.2) during sex discrimination of angry and disgusted faces. Finally, a study by Fischer and colleagues (2005) sought to separate possible age-related emotion processing differences from age-related cognitive-processing differences by constructing a task that involved only passive viewing of blocks of angry and neutral faces. They found that while viewing angry faces, older adults (M age = 74.1) activated right anterior-ventral insula cortex to a greater extent than did younger adults (M age = 24.7), while younger adults demonstrated greater activation in the right amygdala/ hippocampus region. Unlike the other aforementioned functional imaging studies, this study did not find differences in frontal activation between younger and older adults, potentially because the emotion processing task did not require emotion discrimination. Although age differences in the ability to classify facial emotion expressions may help in explaining increased prevalence of depressive symptoms during middle- and old age, no study thus far has examined whether age contributes to facial emotion processing ability independently of MDD status.

Gender and Emotion Processing

Gender is also an important area of inquiry in understanding the experience and sequela of MDD. Of note, we use the term gender here as opposed to sex. While sex refers to the biological differentiation of man from woman, gender encompasses the sociocultural implications of being a woman or a man. We can make no assumptions about the etiology of the relationships between brain and behavior differences in emotional processing between women and men, and thus choose the broader term, gender, for use throughout this chapter. Differences in treatment-seeking behavior do not account for the large discrepancies observed in the prevalence of MDD among women and men (Kornstein, 1997). A multitude of explanations have been offered to explain this gap in prevalence of MDD, including gender differences in perceived self-efficacy (Nolen-Hoeksema and Jackson, 2001), general life stress (Hammen, 2005), poverty (Brown and Moran, 1997), rumination (Nolen-Hoeksema, Parker, and Larson, 1994), and biological (Robert et al., 2006) and hormonal (Kravitz, Janssen, Lotrich, Kado, and Bromberger, 2006) factors.

Differences in how emotions are processed and relative experience with emotion processing might help to explain some of the disparities in the prevalence of MDD between women and men. Gender may also be an important moderating variable in emotion processing and categorization during MDD. Gender differences in facial emotion processing of a wide variety of emotions have consistently favored healthy women when compared to healthy men, both in terms of speed of processing and accuracy in qualifying emotional information (Hall and Matsumoto, 2004; Montagne, Kessels, Frigerio, de Haan, and Perrett, 2005; Mufson and Nowicki, 1991; Thayer and Johnsen, 2000). Men tend to be less emotionally expressive in relation to women overall, and women demonstrate stronger physiological responses to emotional stimuli (Kring and Gordon, 1998).

Neuroimaging studies of gender differences, in both anatomical structure and functional activation, have been marshaled to help explain differences in emotion processing. Gender differences have been found in the volume of structures related to emotion processing, as well as in functional activation patterns in response to emotion stimuli, although the significance of these differences is still unclear. Women have larger orbital frontal cortices (Gur, Gunning-Dixon, Bilker, and Gur, 2002), an area important for cross-hemispheric integration in emotion processing. Women also show greater overall activation in the basal ganglia (Wager, Phan, Liberzon, and Taylor, 2003) and more bilateral activation during emotion processing than men (Kline, Allen, and Schwartz, 1998; Sutton and Davidson, 2000; Wager et al., 2003). Others have demonstrated lateralization of amygdala activation differences between women (left) and men (right) in response to recognizing previously presented aversive stimuli, although the region of interest analysis did not allow for comparisons of limbic and cortical regions by gender (Mackiewicz, Sarinopoulos, Clevan, and Nitschke, 2007). Schneider, Habel, Kessler, Salloum, and Posse (2000) showed a relationship between level of sad mood induction and blood flow in the right amygdala for men but not women.

Gender differences in emotion processing have not been specifically addressed in a uniform fashion with a large enough sample and behavioral correlates to understand functional and structural relationships with emotion processing. Nonetheless, the presence of these anatomic and functional findings in the context of differential emotion processing ability can certainly generate reasonable hypotheses about how they may be related. Increased activation and a more bilateral activation pattern may suggest greater resource availability or utilization in emotion processing for women, although other hypotheses may be equally valid. Emotion processing skills may develop and mature differently in women and men, supported by the behavioral, as well as brain volumetric and functional activation findings available at present. In addition, the impact of differences in social expectations and learning as they affect brain development can not be ignored. Given our inability to retrospectively tease apart neurobiological, social learning, and interactive developmental processes, we can not distinguish among these mechanisms. This may explain, in part, why it is unclear whether and how emotion processing differences between women and men are relevant to the increased prevalence of MDD in women.

With the exception of one recent study (Wright, et al., in press), we are not aware of any research to date exploring gender as potentially moderating the relationship between depression and facial emotion processing, and some studies have been composed primarily or exclusively of women (Gur et al., 1992; Langenecker et al., 2005; Persad and Polivy, 1993; Rubinow and Post, 1992) or only of men (Jaeger et al., 1986; Mikhailova et al., 1996). The recent study by our group (Wright et al., in press) found that gender and MDD status in younger adults (< 35) interact in predicting facial emotion processing errors. Specifically, women with MDD made substantially more errors and had significantly slower reaction times than did non-depressed women; especially to negative stimuli. Men with MDD, on the other hand, performed similarly to their non-depressed men counterparts. These results suggest that depression in younger adults differentially affects emotion processing symptoms in women as compared to men. Reasons for these findings are not entirely clear at this time, although we discuss these results in the context of gender differences in neurobiological, socioemotional, and social cognitive processing. Concomitant studies of functional activation among young women and men with and without MDD will help to provide some clarification between these hypotheses.

Few studies have explored the interaction of age and gender in predicting facial emotion processing accuracy. Calder and colleagues (2003) asked participants falling into five different age groups to identify six different morphed facial expressions, primarily expressing surprise, happiness, fear, sadness, anger, or disgust. Results suggest that men performed more poorly than women in classifying fear, but the same linear reduction with age was shown for both genders.

The Present Study

The present study was designed to address the effects of age, gender, and MDD status in predicting facial emotion processing accuracy and speed. First, we hypothesized that 1) individuals in middle/ elder age (MEA) groups would perform more poorly than individuals in younger age groups (YA); 2) that individuals with MDD would perform more poorly than non-depressed controls; and 3) that men would perform more poorly than women on a task of facial emotion processing. Second, we were interested in learning whether the women-specific emotion processing decrement that we have observed in YA adults with MDD is also present in MEA adults with MDD. We hypothesized that the interaction of MDD status and gender would persist into middle and older adulthood, such that women with MDD would exhibit emotion processing deficits when compared to their same-age counterparts, but that men with MDD would not be similarly affected. As we knew there was an interaction between gender and MDD status, we collected additional information that we believed might be pertinent to explaining this interaction, including depression chronicity, severity, and age-of-onset.

Methods

One-hundred-, thirty-two healthy control (HC) subjects were recruited in three separate studies. Seventy-one participants were formally screened by licensed and trained clinicians with the Structured Clinical Interview for DSM-IV (SCID-IV; First, Spitzer, Gibbon, and Williams, 1995) or the Diagnostic Interview for Genetic Studies (Nurnberger et al., 1994) and 61 participants were screened with a semi-structured psychiatric and neurologic interview (Langenecker et al., 2005; Langenecker and Nielson., 2003). The semi-structured interview (by SAL) includes rule out diagnoses for neurologic conditions, psychosis, and substance abuse as taken from the DSM-IV/SCID-IV.

Three hundred-eleven patients with MDD were recruited through three separate mechanisms, two prospective studies and retrospective collection of patients from inpatient psychiatry (IP) clinics at the University of Michigan Comprehensive Depression Center. Twenty-eight completed the SCID-IV and 251 completed interviews by a licensed psychologist and/or licensed psychiatrist, with diagnosis and exclusion criteria confirmed by chart review. Those patients retrospectively collected also had diagnoses achieved by consensus group discussion after the clinical interview, by more than one member of the outpatient psychiatry teams. Thirty-two completed the semi-structured interview (by SAL). Those with MDD alone ($n = 211$) as well as comorbid MDD and anxiety disorder ($n = 70$) or MDD and dysthymia ($n = 30$) were included in the study.

Prospective participants had documented informed consent, and informed consent was waived for retrospectively included participants (between the years of 2001-2007), each as approved by the IRB of the University of Michigan and consistent with the Declaration of

Helsinki. Some data was retrospectively collected from the University of Michigan Comprehensive Depression Center clinics, again with IRB approved waiver of informed consent. General exclusion criteria included past or current psychotic symptoms, bipolar disorder, dementia, head injury, schizophrenia, history of ECT, or conditions that might affect cognitive functioning (e.g., epilepsy).

Facial Emotion Perception Test

The Facial Emotion Perception test was designed by our group using the Ekman faces (Ekman and Friesen 1976; Langenecker et al 2005; Rapport, Friedman, Tzelepis, and VanVoorhis, 2002). Participants were asked to categorize faces into one of four possible categories (happy, sad, fearful, angry) and animals from each of four categories (dogs, cats, primates, and birds). Each event began with a briefly presented orienting cross (500 ms), followed by a brief presentation of the stimulus (300 ms), a visual mask (100 ms), and a response window (2600 ms). Index through pinky fingers were used to respond to the choices presented (e.g., types of facial expressions and animal categories). Choices were always presented and did not need to be remembered. The task took seven minutes to complete. There were four primary dependent variables: animal accuracy, faces accuracy, response time for animals, and response time for faces. There were also secondary measures of the number of errors for each of the stimulus types, and also the types of error choices made by participants (including the four emotions and no responses).

Depression Measures and Diagnosis

As participants were selected from several clinical and research samples, measures to assess depression were not similar across clinical (Patient Health Questionnaire, Kroenke, Spitzer, and Williams, 1997) and research (Hamilton Rating Scale for Depression, Hamilton, 1960) settings. Minimum severity of depression symptoms was not used for inclusion in the study. Means and standard deviations for both measures are listed in Table 1.

Age of Onset and Chronicity

Age of onset was derived from the semi-structured clinical interview, SCID-IV, or from clinical records when available. This information was available for 281 patients. Age of onset was used in posthoc analyses to assess differential gender by age effects based upon early or late age of onset. To conservatively capture late age of onset, we used those having first onset after age 36 or later as late onset MDD subjects. Chronicity was measured as number of years of illness. Age of onset and chronicity are presented in Table 1. Total number and duration of MDD episodes was not available for enough participants to conduct adequately powered analyses.

Medications

Some participants with MDD were taking psychotropic medications at the time of the evaluation. As there are reports of psychotropic effects on cognitive functioning, we ran analyses to ascertain the nature of these effects, if present. To this end, we classified medication effects as SSRI or SSRI-like ($n = 112$) medications, as well as Wellbutrin ($n = 33$), into one group we call SSRI-like. We also combined those taking SSRI-like medication or Wellbutrin plus combinations of Neurontin ($n = 7$), mood stabilizers ($n = 10$), opiates ($n = 14$), stimulants ($n = 5$), tranquilizers ($n = 12$), and/or anxiolytics ($n = 27$) as well as a primary SSRI-like medication ($n = 41$), we call SSRI plus. Those in the SSRI plus group were on average four years older ($F(2, 296) = 3.68$, $p = .03$, $M = 39.1$ $SD = 12.0$) than the non-medicated ($M = 35.0$ $SD = 12.0$) and SSRI-like groups ($M = 34.5$ $SD = 11.9$). In addition, as might be expected, those with comorbid MDD and anxiety were more likely to be in the SSRI-plus group (22/64) compared to the MDD alone (40/199) and comorbid MDD and dysthymia (4/30) groups (X^2 (2, N = 293) $= 9.46$, $p = .05$). The effects of medication class and MDD comorbidity are explored in specific posthoc analyses, as we can not tease apart potential medication by diagnosis and age interactions in a naturalistic study.

Statistical Analyses

Two repeated measures multivariate analyses of variance (rmANOVA) were computed with depression status (yes or no), age group (<36 or >35), and gender as factors. The first rmANOVA was conducted with response time for animal categorizations and emotion choices, while the second analysis was conducted with accuracy for animal categorizations and emotion choices. Planned posthoc analyses addressed our previous findings of emotion perception decrements that are specific to younger women, but not men participants with MDD, but were expanded to include middle and elder aged adults. Further, posthoc analyses also explored effects of age of onset, chronicity, symptom severity, and medication group on dependent variables of interest.

Results

Demographic Analyses

Analysis of demographic variables indicate a significant interaction between age group, MDD status, and gender for years of formal education (F (1, 435) $= 4.46$, $p = .035$), with the YA HC men having fewer years of formal education relative to the MEA groups and the YA women with MDD. The MEA groups also had significantly more years of formal education compared to the YA groups ($F(1, 435) = 5.51$, $p = .019$). When comparing the groups on age, the interaction between age group and MDD status was significant ($F(1, 435) = 21.58$, $p = .0001$), as was the interaction between age group and gender ($F(1, 435) = 13.83$, $p = .0001$). The YA MDD group was on average four years older than the corresponding HC group, whereas the MEA MDD group was on average two years younger than the corresponding HC group. Whereas there was no difference between men and women in the YA group, the MEA men were on average four years older than the MEA women. Men were 1.7 years older than women ($F(1, 433) = 5.1$, $p = .02$) and MDD patients were one year older than HCs ($F(1, 433) = 2.66$, $p = .10$). Although these modest differences would be expected to have no impact on cognitive function, we ran the analyses with education as a covariate throughout. Age was not entered as a covariate, as it would undermine the age group comparisons planned for the study.

Table 1. Demographic and Clinical Information for Groups by Age Group, Gender, and MDD status

	Men		Women	
Control	<=35, $n = 37$	>35, $n = 11$	<=35, $n = 60$	>35, $n = 24$
Age [a]	20.7 (3.4)	51.5 (9.1)	23.3 (4.4)	46.1 (7.8)
Education [b]	14.2 (2.4)	16.6 (2.1)	15.2 (2.5)	15.3 (2.4)
HDRS [c]	0.8 (1.8)	0.9 (1.2)	1.2 (2.3)	1.2 (1.7)
	Men		Women	
MDD	<=35, $n = 38$	>35, $n = 50$	<=35, $n = 123$	>35, $n = 100$
Age [a]	26.8 (5.0)	48.3 (7.9)	26.3 (4.8)	44.9 (6.9)
Education [b]	15.5 (2.7)	15.6 (3.0)	15.2 (2.4)	15.5 (2.7)
HDRS [c]	20.3 (0.6), $n = 3$	18.1 (1.6), $n = 7$	13.7 (5.4), $n = 18$	15.8 (5.0), $n = 28$
Age of Onset [d]	18.1 (7.3)	28.2 (14.0)	18.9 (6.0)	27.5 (13.0)
Chronicity [e]	8.9 (7.3)	19.7 (15.3)	7.5 (6.0)	16.8 (11.9)
PHQ-8	13.3 (6.4), $n = 28$	16.7 (5.3), $n = 38$	13.4 (5.9), $n = 87$	15.9 (5.6), $n = 57$
Medications				
none	$n = 16$	$n = 18$	$n = 53$	$n = 34$
SSRI-Like	$n = 14$	$n = 15$	$n = 47$	$n - 36$
SSRI-plus	$n = 6$	$n = 13$	$n = 21$	$n = 26$
Comorbidity [f]				
MDD alone	$n = 21$	$n = 32$	$n = 89$	$n = 64$
MDD and Anxiety	$n = 13$	$n = 11$	$n = 19$	$n = 26$
MDD and Dysthymia	$n = 4$	$n = 7$	$n = 14$	$n = 5$

[a] YA MDD subjects were older than YA HC subjects ($F(1, 433) = 14.6$, $p = .0001$), and MEA men were older than MEA women ($F(1, 433) = 8.2$ $p = .004$). [b] The YA HC subjects had fewer years of formal education compared to the MDD subjects ($ps < .036$) and the MEA men HC group ($p = .007$). [c] MDD subjects had higher HDRS (Hamilton Rating Scale for Depression) scores compared to the healthy controls ($p < .0001$). [d] MEA MDD subjects had later age of onset compared to YA MDD subjects ($F(1, 277) = 45.9$, $p = .0001$). [e] MEA MDD subjects had more years of illness (chronicity) compared to YA MDD subjects ($F(1, 277) = 54.7$, $p = .0001$). [f] YA men with MDD were less likely to be diagnosed with MDD alone and more likely to be diagnosed with MDD and anxiety ($X^2(2, N = 160) = 6.4$, $p = .04$) compared to YA women. No gender effect by MDD interaction was present in diagnoses for the MEA groups ($X^2(1, N = 145) = 3.5$, $p = .18$).

Assessment of Interaction between Age Group, Gender, and MDD Status on Emotion and Animal Processing

The first analysis was a rmANOVA assessing the factors of age group, gender, and MDD status with response time in either facial emotion perception or animal categorization as the dependent variables. Here, education was a significant covariate ($F(1, 430) = 4.23$, $p = .04$) and there was a significant effect of age group ($F(1, 430) = 44.91$, $p = .0001$), with slower response time with increasing age. There was also a main effect of gender, with faster response times observed in women ($F(1, 430) = 7.52$, $p = .006$). The interaction between MDD status, gender, and age group was significant ($F(1, 430) = 5.14$, $p = .02$). Furthermore, there was a significant interaction between MDD status, gender, age group, and response time ($F(1, 430) = 5.18$, $p = .02$). This interaction is displayed in Figure 1. Reaction time was generally slower in MDD groups compared to HC groups, including both younger groups ($t(73) = -2.73$, $p = .004$), one tailed for men, and ($t(181) = -2.20$, $p = .015$), one tailed for women). The difference was in the same direction, but not significant in MEA women ($t(122) = -0.85$, $p = .20$), one tailed), and non-significant in the opposite direction in the MEA men ($t(59) = 0.53$, $p = .30$), one tailed).

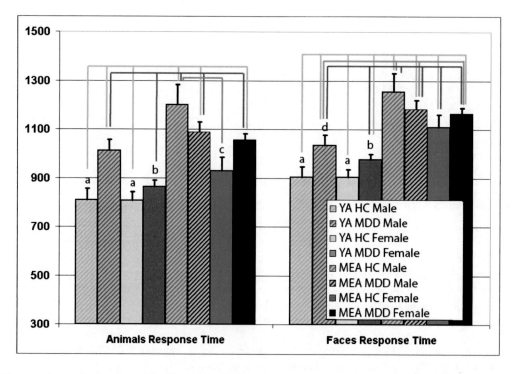

Figure 1. Interaction between Stimulus Category, Response Time, Gender, Age Group, and Depression Status. [a] YA men and women HCs were significantly faster than the YA men MDD, MEA men HC, MEA men MDD, and MEA women MDD groups in faces and animal response time and compared to YA women MDD and MEA women HC in faces response time. [b] YA women MDD group was significantly faster than the YA men MDD, MEA men HC, MEA men MDD, and MEA women MDD groups in animals and faces response time and faster than the MEA women HC in faces response time. [c] The MEA women HC group was faster than the MEA men group in animals response time. [d] YA men MDD were significantly faster than the MEA men HC, MEA men MDD, and MEA women MDD groups in faces response time.

The second analysis was a rmANOVA assessing the relationship of age group, gender, and MDD status to accuracy in either facial emotion perception or animal categorization as the dependent variables. The effect of MDD status was significant ($F(1, 434) = 16.57$, $p = .0001$), with poorer performance in MDD groups relative to the other groups. MEA groups also performed more poorly than the YA groups ($F(1, 434) = 7.44$, $p = .007$). The interaction between MDD status, gender, age group, and accuracy was not significant ($F(1, 434) = 0.78$, $p = .38$), but is displayed in Figure 2 for comparison with Figure 1.

The critical hypotheses of interest were related to whether the women-specific emotion processing accuracy decrement that we have observed in younger adults with MDD is also present in middle-aged and elder adults with MDD. As expected, there was better performance among HC women as compared to women with MDD in both YA ($t(181) = 2.41$, $p = .008$, one tailed) and MEA cohorts ($t(122) = 3.01$, $p = .002$, one tailed). Contrary to expectation, MEA men with MDD exhibited significantly worse performance relative to MEA HC men for face perception ($t(59) = 1.74$, $p = .043$, one tailed), whereas we extended our previous finding of no difference in emotion processing in YA men with MDD in comparison to the HC cohort ($t(73) = 0.65$, $p = .265$, one tailed).

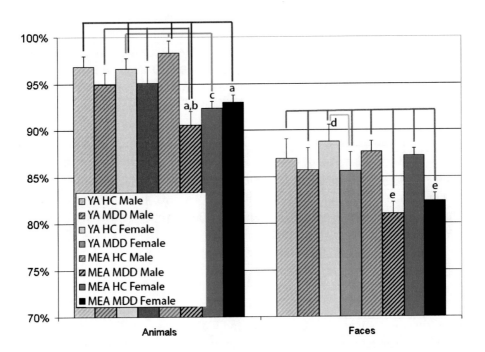

Figure 2. Interaction between Stimulus Category, Accuracy, Gender, Age Group, and Depression Status. The MEA MDD groups were worse in animals accuracy compared to the YA HC group, and the MEA men HC group. [b] The MEA men MDD group was worse in animals accuracy compared to the YA MDD groups. [c] The MEA women HC group had significantly worse animals accuracy compared to the YA women HC and MEA men HC groups. [d] The YA women HC group was significantly better in faces accuracy compared to the YA women MDD group. [e] The MEA MDD groups were worse than all other groups for faces accuracy.

We explored this gender by age disparity in further analyses, taking into consideration the stimulus properties of the faces (e.g, happy, sad, angry, fearful), the specific choices the participants made during errors (happy, sad, angry, fearful, no response) and finally in posthoc analyses examining the relationship of age of onset, chronicity, depression severity, and medication class to performance. First, we wished to replicate our findings of specific types of difficulty in emotion processing of emotional stimuli. For example, we previously demonstrated that YA women with MDD had difficulty in categorizing facial expressions of sadness and fear, and that they were more likely to erroneously indicate that these facial expressions were angry (Wright et al., in press). We suspected that this pattern would hold in a larger YA cohort of MDD patients, and we were interested to see what patterns might be evident in MEAs with MDD. We also hypothesized that in the absence of preserved emotion perception, as noted in the YA men cohorts, MEA men with MDD may have dysfunction in emotion processing through as yet undetermined secondary mechanisms (e.g., vascular).

Posthoc Exploration of Stimulus Properties, Response Biases, and Clinical Variables that Might Explain Differential Performance by Gender, Age Group, and MDD Status

Facial Stimulus Characteristics. To assess the potential difficulty of processing certain types of stimuli in MDD, we ran a posthoc rmANOVA with specific types of emotional stimuli (happy, sad, anger, fear) as the dependent variable, and MDD status, age group, and gender as independent variables. The interaction between MDD status, age group, and gender was significant ($F(1, 344) = 5.30$, $p = .02$). The interaction between stimulus type and age group was also significant ($F(3, 1032) = 2.61$, $p = .05$). Further posthoc analysis indicated that MEA men with MDD had significantly more errors than their MEA men HC counterparts in the number of errors for fearful stimuli ($t(45) = -2.23$, $p = .015$, one tailed), but not angry ($t(45) = -1.23$, $p = .011$, one tailed), happy ($t(45) = -0.31$, $p = .33$, one tailed), or sad (t($45) = -1.43$, $p = .08$, one tailed) stimuli. Consistent with our prior study, YA women with MDD made more errors for fearful stimuli ($t(136) = -1.81$, $p = .036$, one tailed), but not for sad stimuli ($t(136) = -1.36$, p $= .088$, one tailed). There were also no differences in errors between YA women with and without MDD for happy ($t(136) = -0.79$, $p = .215$, one tailed) or angry ($t(136) = -0.04$, $p = .485$, one tailed) stimuli. There were no differences between MEA women with and without MDD for any specific stimulus type ($ts(98) < |0.66|$, $ps > .255$, one tailed).

Error Response Choices to Facial Stimuli. As we had done previously, we further explored the specific choices (e.g., biases) that individuals were making with a MDD status, by age group, and gender rmANOVA with choices of fear, anger, happiness, sadness, or no response as the dependent variables. The interaction between MDD status, age group, gender, and response choice was significant ($F(4, 1376) = 2.37$, $p = .05$). In posthoc t-tests, there were no differences in response choices in comparing YA men with and without MDD ($ts(66) < |0.49|$, $ps > .285$, one tailed). MEA men with MDD were more likely to choose happy when making an error in comparison to MEA men without MDD ($t(45) = -3.00$, $p = .0025$, one tailed), whereas there were no difference in choices of anger ($t(45) = -1.41$, $p = .084$, one tailed), fear ($t(45) = -1.29$, $p = .103$, one tailed), sadness ($t(45) = 0.24$, $p = .406$, one tailed), or no response ($t(45) = -1.08$, $p = .143$, one tailed). As we had shown in the previous study (Wright et al, in press), YA women with MDD were more likely to choose anger erroneously compared to YA HC women (t(136) = -2.23, p = .014, one tailed), but not fear (t(136) = -0.65, p = .263, one tailed), happiness (t(136) = -0.46, p = .325, one tailed), sadness (t(136) = 0.89, p = .183, one tailed), or no response (t(136) = -0.73, p = .235, one tailed). In contrast, MEA women with MDD were more likely to make no response compared to MEA HC women (t(98) = -1.90, p = .03, one tailed), but not happiness (t(98) = -1.57, p = .06, one tailed), or the other choices (ts(98) < |0.79|, ps > 215, one tailed).

Age of Onset. To assess age of onset effects in explaining the gender by age group and MDD status interaction, a posthoc rmANOVA was computed for the effects of gender and (categorical) age of onset on face and animal processing, this time only in MEAs with MDD. Age was used as a covariate given because age of onset and age were significantly correlated (r = .50 p = .0001). The effect of age of onset was not significant (F(1, 124) = 3.24, p = .074), although the interaction between gender and age of onset was significant (F(1, 124) = 5.05, p = .03).

Specifically, the MEA men with later age of onset (n = 15) showed specific decreased performance in face perception accuracy relative to MEA adults with MDD from the three other groups (MEA men early onset n = 28 (t(41) = 1.78, p = .041, one tailed), MEA women early onset n = 62 (t(75) = 1.93, p = .028, one tailed), and MEA women late onset n = 28, (t(41) = 1.79, p = .04, one tailed),). MEA men with later age of onset also demonstrated slowed response time for faces relative to the two early onset groups (t(41) = 2.78, p = .006, one tailed) and (t(41) = -2.54, p = .007, one tailed), for men and women with early onset MDD, respectively, (Figure 3), but not compared to the late onset women with MDD. (t(41) = -1.59, p = .06, one tailed). There was a similar pattern for animal response time compared to faces response time for these groups, but not for accuracy in animal perception. Due to space limitations, these effects are not reported here.

Chronicity (Years of Illness). To assess for chronicity effects, we used the entire MDD sample where age of onset was available (n = 281) in another rmANOVA posthoc analysis, here again with MEA adults with MDD only. We conducted a median split of chronicity (*md* = 9.0, *M* = 12.5, *SD* = 11.3) and created high and low burden chronicity groups. Subsequently, we conducted another rmANOVA with the four dependent variables, with gender and chronicity status as the independent variables. Age was used as a covariate, as it is strongly correlated with chronicity (r = .51, p = .0001) and age of onset (r = -.49, p = .0001). The effect of chronicity was not significant (F(1, 272) = 2.18, p = .141), nor was the interaction between gender and chronicity (F(1, 272) = 3.12, p = .079).

To rule out more general effects of age of onset and chronicity on performance, we ran partial correlations with these two variables and the four dependent variables, covarying age, as age was significantly correlated with both MDD severity variables. Only one correlation was significant, that of chronicity with face response time (r (148) = -.15, p = .015), whereas none of the other seven correlations was significant (|rs| < .09, ps > .13).

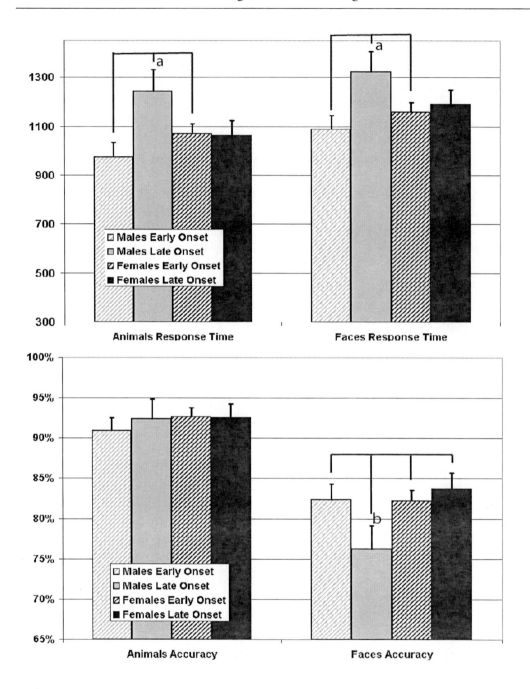

Figure 3. Interaction between Age of Onset and Gender for Accuracy and Response Time. MEA men, late onset, performed slower than MEA men and women, early onset, in response time for faces and animals. [b] MEA men, late onset performed more poorly in faces accuracy compared to all other MEA groups, including women, late onset.

Symptom Severity. We also assessed whether the interaction between age, gender, and MDD status might be explained by symptoms of depression severity. As we had both HDRS and PHQ-8, we could not rerun a rmANOVA with severity as a covariate. Thus, we split the MDD group into high and low symptoms by median split for each variable (*md* HDRS = 16.0, *SD* = 4.9, *md* PHQ-8 = 14.6, *SD* = 5.9). There was no significant effect of symptom severity ($F(1, 254) = 1.28, p = .26$), nor were any of the interactions significant ($Fs(1, 254) < 1.90, ps > .169$). We then ran correlations of these measures with the four dependent variables (accuracy and response time for faces and animals), again covarying the effects of age. The HDRS ($n = 56$) was significantly correlated with response time for faces ($r = .28, p = .036$), but not with the other three variables ($|rs| < .21, ps > .12$). The PHQ-8 ($n = 88$) was significantly correlated with animals accuracy ($r = .25, p = .013$), but not with the other three variables ($|rs| < .09, ps > .38$).

Medication Effects. We also completed posthoc evaluations to analyze any potential effects of medication upon the interaction of age and gender within the MDD group. This rmANOVA used age group, gender, and medication class as independent variables and the four dependent variables of interest. The effect of medication class was significant, with slower performance in the unmedicated and SSRI-plus groups compared to the SSRI-like group ($F(2, 283) = 4.46, p = .012$). Posthoc analyses suggest that the non-medicated group was slower compared to the SSRI-like group for animal categorization response time ($t(229) = 2.18, p = .03$), but not for faces response time ($t(229) = 1.44, p = .15$). The SSRI-plus group was slower than the SSRI-like group in faces ($t(173) = -3.00, p = .003$) and animals ($t(173) = -2.76, p = .006$) response time. There were no significant effects of medication class on performance accuracy ($F(2, 287) = 0.02, p = .98$).

Comorbid Illness. Finally, we completed a similar rmANOVA with the MDD group, this time investigating effects of comorbidity upon performance. This rmANOVA used age group, gender, and MDD diagnostic class (MDD alone, MDD plus anxiety, or MDD plus dysthymia) as independent variables and the four dependent variables. The interaction between gender and MDD diagnostic class was significant ($F(2, 289) = 6.29, p = .002$) for both faces and animals response time. Posthoc analyses indicated slower response time for animals in men with either comorbid condition relative to MDD alone ($t(72) = -2.14, p = .006$ and ($t(60) = -2.11, p = .04$ for MDD plus anxiety and MDD plus dysthymia, respectively). Women with comorbid MDD and dysthymia responded more rapidly to faces ($t(173) = 3.43, p = .002$) and animals (t($173) = 3.79, p = .001$), as compared to the women with MDD only. The interaction between accuracy for faces and animals with MDD diagnostic class, gender, and age group was significant ($F(2, 293) = 3.39, p = .035$). MEA women with MDD and dysthymia performed significantly better for faces ($t(69) = -2.27, p = .026$) and animals ($t(69) = -3.09, p = .014$) accuracy as compared to women with MDD alone.

Discussion

In this large study across the age spectrum, we examined whether previous findings of an interaction between gender and presence of MDD could be extended to those above the age of 35. We expanded the YA HC and MDD samples and added MEA HC and MDD samples for a total of over 400 participants. To our knowledge, this is the largest study to address the complex interplay among gender, MDD, and age on facial emotion processing. We replicated findings of women-specific emotion processing decrements in YA MDD subjects. More specifically, in this larger sample of younger adults with and without MDD, we again showed relatively equivalent performance in depressed and non-depressed YA men and in YA women with MDD. Yet, the healthy YA women outperformed their same-gender MDD group in accuracy. We failed to extend findings of a women specific emotion processing deficit in MDD participants under the age of 35 to those in the age spectrum over age 35. In fact, we illustrated that men with MDD over age 35 are equally poor in emotion processing accuracy of faces when compared to women with MDD over age 35. Both groups were worse than respective HC groups of similar age.

Consistent with our prior study, YA women with MDD were more likely to make incorrect responses choices for fearful stimuli and were more likely to incorrectly choose anger, when compared to their same-gender and age counterparts. MEA women with MDD did not show these emotion specific processing deficits, however, and in fact, were more likely not to respond to stimuli, as compared to their same-gender and age counterparts. Similar to our previous work, YA men did not demonstrate specific stimulus or response biases, however, MEA men with MDD made more errors for fearful stimuli and were, interestingly, more likely to choose happy when making an error as compared to their same gender and age counterparts.

In an attempt to explain the lack of a gender by MDD status interaction in the MEA group, we explored clinical variables in posthoc analyses that might contribute to this finding. The most robust of the clinical variables in explaining decrements in MEA men with MDD was age of onset. Those men with later age of onset (after age 35) demonstrated poorer performance than men with early age of onset and than MEA women with MDD, including those with early and late onset. Chronicity of MDD, severity of MDD symptoms, and category of psychotropic medications prescribed did not contribute to the differences found between YA and MEA women and men with MDD in emotion processing accuracy of faces. Intriguingly, and with admittedly smaller numbers, we demonstrated that comorbidity of MDD with anxiety and dysthymia may have different emotion processing sequela for women and men. For example, YA men with comorbid MDD and anxiety performed worse than YA men with MDD alone, whereas MEA women with comorbid MDD and dysthymia performed better than MEA women with MDD alone.

Mechanisms for Early Disruption of Emotion Processing Circuits in Women but not Men

A number of explanations, including neurobiological, socioemotional, and sociocultural may account for the disparate findings of emotion processing skills in YA women and men with MDD. We will briefly summarize these mechanisms here, and also refer the reader to Wright and colleagues (in press). First, with regard to neurobiological explanations, it is feasible that women's and men's ability to process emotions relies on different neurodevelopmental circuits. Research on gender differences in functional activation during emotion processing suggests that women rely on limbic and paralimbic circuits to a greater degree than do men during both euthymic and sad states (George, Ketter, Parekh,

Herscovitch, and Post, 1996; Hall, Wittelson, Szechtman, and Nahmias, 2004), while men are more likely to activate unilateral frontal regions (Hall et al., 2004) associated with inhibitory control (Langenecker et al., 2007b). While women rely less on inhibitory emotional repair strategies than do men (Bjorklund and Kipp, 1996), during depressed states, increased limbic activation (Frodl et al., 2007) may abate emotional repair strategies in women, resulting in greater emotion processing inaccuracy. At the same time, given that men already rely heavily on frontal regions to process emotions (Hall et al., 2004), decreased modulation of limbic signals during depressed states in response to emotional stimuli might sustain their ability to sufficiently process emotions.

Second, socioemotional development is known to differ between women and men from very early in life. Interpersonal relations are accorded greater value for women than for men, while men are taught to strive for individualism (Jack, 1991; Miller, 1976). As a consequence, interpersonal skill is strongly related to self-esteem in women (Nolen-Hoeksema and Girgus, 1994; Stein, Newcomb, and Bentler, 1992), and when self-esteem is degraded, risk of developing MDD is heightened (Kendler, Gardner, and Prescott, 2002; Kernis et al., 1998; Roberts and Kassel, 1997). These findings of competence in interpersonal relationships suggest that decrements in emotion processing, which is an essential component of interpersonal skills, place women, but perhaps not men, at greater risk for MDD.

Finally, women and men are known to process emotions differently during non-depressed states, suggesting that social cognitive mechanisms might also be important in explaining the emotion processing difficulties detected in women, but not in men with MDD. Non-depressed women have consistently shown superiority over men in recognizing, expressing, and interpreting emotional stimuli (Barrett, Lane, Sechrest, and Schwartz, 2000; Johnsen, Thayer, and Hugdall, 1995; Kring and Gordon, 1998; Thayer and Johnsen, 2000). During depressed states, however, women and men are known to engage in different cognitive strategies that may affect emotion processing skills in disparate ways. Specifically, during depressed states, women are more likely to engage in rumination, whereas men are more likely to distract themselves (Nolen-Hoeksema, Larson, and Grayson, 1999). Given that rumination has been shown to affect appraisal of the past, present, and future (Lyubormirsky, Caldwell, and Nolen-Hoeksema, 1998; Lyubormirsky and Nolen-Hoeksema, 1995), it is likely to lead to result in distorted perceptions of events, including those that are emotionally arousing. Rumination has also been shown to disrupt problem solving (Nolen-Hoeksema, 1991, 2001), and processing emotional stimuli such as facial expressions might be considered to engage problem-solving resources.

Mechanisms for Equal Disruption of Emotion Processing Circuits in MEA Men and Women with MDD

Neurobiological explanations may help to account for the finding that during middle and older age, both women and men with MDD demonstrate decrements in facial emotion processing relative to their same age and gender counterparts. This finding runs counter to the finding that in younger adults there are gender specific decrements in facial emotion processing skills among only women with MDD. The neurobiological circuits disrupted during MDD and during normal aging overlap, and both are involved with emotion processing skills. Specifically, prefrontal and medial temporal regions are known to be affected during both aging and MDD (De Leon et al., 1987; Garraux et al., 1999; Phillips et al., 2003b; Raz, 2004; Tisserand et al., 2002). It is possible that in younger adulthood, men's tendency to activate frontal, but less so limbic regions (George et al., 1996; Hall et al., 2004), allows them to compensate for the increased limbic activation seen during depressed states (Frodl et al., 2007).

At the same time, the lateral prefrontal cortex demonstrates the greatest volumetric reduction during older age (Raz, 2000, 2004; Tisserand et al., 2002), with corresponding decreases in regional cerebral blood flow (De Leon et al., 1992). Given that HC women and men did not demonstrate a change in facial emotion processing accuracy with age, these data would suggest that age-related neurobiological changes alone do not lead to emotion processing deficits. Instead, it is possible that a "double burden" of MDD and age impedes the ability of these men to successfully perceive emotional expressions in faces. The neurobiological disruptions that are evident in women with MDD at a younger age are now apparent in middle and elder aged men with MDD, likely resulting in increased risk for MDD.

Despite that MEA women and men with MDD demonstrate similar difficulties with facial emotion processing, they make errors on different types of stimuli and display different response biases. While MEA women showed no tendency to respond incorrectly to any specific types of stimuli, MEA men were more likely to respond incorrectly to fearful stimuli. MEA men also demonstrated a proclivity to erroneously perceive faces as expressing happiness, while MEA women were more likely to make no response. These findings are different from the specific kinds of errors found in younger MDD groups, whereby YA women were found to be likely to respond erroneously to fearful stimuli and to incorrectly choose anger when compared to YA women controls. These age and gender differences in the types of errors made for specific kinds of facial expressions suggest that disparate processing biases or skill deficits are present in YA and MEA women and MEA men with MDD. Further research might explore mechanisms behind such age and gender specific differences in emotion processing during MDD. For example, it may be that older adults' superiority in emotion regulation (Carstensen and Turk-Charles, 1994; Kliegel et al., 2007) translates to their misperceptions of facial emotions during MDD, such that they either ignore the emotion altogether, and thus make no response, as was shown for MEA women with MDD or misperceive the emotion as happy, as was found in MEA men with MDD. Further, MDD in middle and elder aged adults, and the accompanying underlying neurological disruption, may also circumvent emotion regulation skills.

Age of Onset as a Mechanism for Disproportionate Disruption in Emotion Processing Circuits in MEA Men with MDD

Age of MDD onset is an important variable to consider in exploring the emotion processing decrements detected in MEA adults with MDD. Specifically, why is this significant in MEA men with MDD, but not in MEA women? In the present study, MEA men with later age of onset were less accurate and slower to process emotional stimuli than were MEA men with early age of onset and MEA women with early age of onset, suggesting a "triple burden" in men with late onset MDD. Late onset MDD has been hypothesized to stem from cerebrovascular changes in frontostriatal circuits, and has even been termed vascular depression, by some authors (Alexopoulis et al., 1997). Individuals with late-onset MDD are also known to exhibit cognitive difficulties mediated by frontostriatal circuits, including in the domains of executive functioning and processing speed (Herrmann, Goodwin, and Ebmeier, 2007). While we did not assess executive functioning skills in this study, findings of slowed reaction time in MEA men with late onset MDD to both face and animal stimuli suggest that these men might be experiencing the consequences of cerebrovascular pathology, possibly explaining the "triple burden" hypothesis.

It is interesting that age of onset was a significant finding for MEA men, but not MEA women. That MEA women with MDD show emotion processing difficulties regardless of age of onset is consistent with a finding of early age decrements, and late onset difficulties of a potentially different etiology. At the same time, it is not altogether surprising that men with later age of onset show far greater decrements, given that men are known to show higher rates of most cardiovascular risk factors than are MEA women, although this sex difference becomes smaller with age (Jousilahti, Vartiainen, Tuomilehto, and Puska, 1999). Our findings here suggest that emotion processing skills might be an important domain to assess in middle and elder aged adults with MDD that may have a vascular or heretofore unknown origin. This incidental finding deserves further investigation in a study that can specifically assess and relate white matter hyperintensities in these regions to emotion processing deficits.

Other Incidental yet Pertinent Findings in the Study of Emotion Processing in MDD

In post-hoc analyses, we found that MDD severity, as measured by the Hamilton Rating Scale for Depression (Hamilton, 1960) is predictive of speed of face recognition processing for all depressed groups studied. Thus, no matter the age or gender of the depressed individual, as depression symptoms worsen, facial emotion processing is slowed. This is consistent with previous findings of slowed reaction time to faces during depression (Surguladze et al., 2004), but not Langenecker and colleagues (2005). That MDD severity was correlated with face, but not animal processing speed suggests a selective processing speed deficit for faces with increasing depression severity, inferring that the processing speed decrement found in facial emotion processing during MDD is not fully explained by general slowed processing.

We also found medication effects for face and animal processing speed, with slower performance exhibited by unmedicated and SSRI-plus groups as compared to the SSRI-like group. This finding might be explained in a number of ways. First, patients taking SSRIs in addition to other psychotropic medications, such as benzodiazepines or mood stabilizers, may be more likely to experience cognitive slowing as a result of medication side effects and/ or interactions including increased somnolence (Gray, Lai, and Larson, 1999). This group was older and had significantly greater symptoms of depression compare to the SSRI-like groups, which may also explain the medication effect. This would not explain the slower processing exhibited by unmedicated patients, however. Instead, depression severity might account for slowing in both groups, as it is feasible that unmedicated patients are untreated by choice or due to economic hardship, which may be a corollary to depression severity. Further, patients taking more than one medication for depression might experience a more severe form of depression. Future studies specifically designed to examine the consequences of these factors on processing speed of faces and animals might be helpful in parsing out these discrepancies.

Finally, we found significant effects of comorbidity for processing speed of faces and animals. Men with comorbid diagnoses exhibited slower performance for faces and animals than did men with MDD alone. In contrast, women with comorbid MDD and dysthymia processed visual information faster than those with MDD alone. There were no differences detected in diagnostic subgroups of women. We have not performed analyses that could assist us in directly understanding the reason for this discrepancy between women and men with MDD because of the relatively small sample sizes, particularly in the comorbid MDD and dysthymia group.

Importantly, it is possible that the biological and socioemotional development of men and women interact with diagnostic subtypes in such a way that would explain these discrepancies. As this was a posthoc analysis, we suggest that future studies with planned subgroup analyses can fruitfully exploit these findings. One potential hypothesis to explore is actual symptoms of anxiety as they relate to emotion perception skill. It is possible that those with higher anxiety have hyper-alertness to stimuli, and thus faster processing speed. This would be consistent with research demonstrating a positive relationship between anxiety and higher alertness to faces (Dennis and Chen, 2007). In addition, we did not assess for the presence of melancholic subtype of MDD, which in turn might be more common in the men in this sample, resulting in greater psychomotor retardation (Naismith et al., 2003; Parker, 2000).

Conclusion

This is a complex study with a number of variables addressed toward understanding biological, social, and cultural explanations for increased prevalence of depression in women compared to men. Whereas we attempted to be comprehensive in the analyses that we performed toward this end, it is inevitable that some were overlooked. There are a number of limitations that restrain the conclusions that might be drawn from this study.

First, the use of age 35 as a cut-off for middle/ elder versus younger adults is not ideal. This was necessitated in part by the small number of healthy adults recruited to date over the age of 35. This was beneficial in some respects, as it converged with evidence that late 30s and early 40s would be the upper extreme of a "traditional" onset for MDD (American Psychiatric Association, 2000). Thus, those studied under age 35 are very likely to have a developmental form of MDD, while those over age 35 were roughly evenly split between those who could recall onset of depression and episodes of MDD prior to age 36 and those who denied any such illness until after age 36. Ideally, middle and elder age groups would be compared to one another and to a younger age group to better gauge the effect of age of onset and chronicity, and we encourage future studies with this goal.

The relatively small size of the MEA healthy adult groups does limit confidence in the age-related findings. In fact, we showed general age effects of slowing for both face emotion and animal categorization response time, and of decreasing accuracy for animal categorization. This could be a reflection of the limited power of the small sample sizes in the MEA adults, or it may suggest that facial emotion perception of emotion is a relatively preserved skill set for middle and elder aged adults. Of course, the rigorous screening criteria that individuals in the healthy MEA group must meet in order to be eligible for this study may by itself render these "control" subjects non-representative of the general population of middle and elder aged adults. Planned studies of the cumulative effects of depression in elders are underway by our group and others and we encourage the exploration of gender effects in this age group.

Another weakness of the present study that must be considered is the use of retrospective clinical data in the diagnosis of some patients with MDD. While this is clearly not ideal in a prospective study, it is a common limitation of a retrospective study. On a positive note, many of these patients were followed clinically for a number of visits, and we confirmed the initial diagnosis with later clinical records. We were able to exclude some patients with psychotic symptoms and/ or bipolar illness who at first reported symptoms of and were diagnosed with MDD or MDD and a comorbid illness. There were no marked differences in MDD comparisons between those who had clinical data used when compared to those collected in prospective research studies, so this concern may only be modest in nature. The differential diagnostic tools render the MDD comorbidity analyses weaker, however. We did not take great lengths to explore or interpret these findings, particularly as the comorbid dysthymia group was small and the reliability of our clinical diagnostic procedures is not described in the scientific literature. Heartening to these findings, though, was the relative severity of MDD symptoms in our clinical and research samples, with depression on average in the moderate range.

In summary, the present study extends our previous findings suggestive of an underlying neurobiology for increased incidence of MDD in women that can be measured with a six minute test of facial emotion perception accuracy. We accentuate this finding with now a substantially larger sample in the younger age group. Furthermore, we show that with age, particularly in those MEA men with a late age of onset, there are significant decrements in emotion processing accuracy among depressed individuals. MEA women with MDD continue to have emotion processing difficulties, though they misperceive facial emotional stimuli differently from YA women with MDD. Neurobiological changes are thought to strongly contribute to the presence of late onset MDD (e.g., Alexopoulos et al., 1997) and our findings suggest that these disruptions in neurological function are not additive for women. This suggests that the neural circuitry disrupted in late onset MDD is the same as that involved in poorer emotion processing accuracy in younger women with early onset MDD and in those middle and elder aged women with late and early onset MDD. Younger men with early onset MDD do not appear to have disruptions in this circuitry, or are able to compensate for it in some fashion. MEA men with early onset MDD do show decrements in emotion processing accuracy equivalent to that seen in MEA women with MDD regardless of age of onset. In contrast, MEA men with late onset MDD, appear to have a similar neural network that is disrupted to a far greater degree than the other MEA depressed groups. These stimulating findings may lead to better understanding of the different risk for depression by gender and by age and toward more effective and efficacious treatments of the underlying neurobiological disruptions.

Acknowledgements

This research was supported in part by Rachel Upjohn Clinical Scholars Awards (to SAL and SLW), K-12 Mentored Career Development Award (to SAL), NIH grant P01 MH 42251 (to Elizabeth Young, M.D. and Jon-Kar Zubieta, M.D., Ph.D.), internal support from the Depression and Neuropsychology Sections of the Department of Psychiatry, University of Michigan Medical Center, and the Department of Psychology, Marquette University (to Kristy A. Nielson, Ph.D.) and we thank these sources for support in completing this project. The present study is a further exploration of findings reported previously with a larger sample and there is some overlap ($n = 124$) in participants across both studies (Langenecker et al., 2007a). In addition, all subjects in a separate study in this edition (Langenecker et al., 2008) are also reported in this article. A subset of these data ($n = 151$) was presented at the annual meeting of the Cognitive Neuroscience Society, 2007. The aid of a number of students and assistants was invaluable in completing this project: Ami S. Antonucci, Ph.D., Erich Avery, Andrew Benway, Emily M. Briceno, Rachel Burns, Korey Cantrell, Luis Casenas, Stephen Crocker, Ph.D., Karla Felske, Caroline Freitag, Kristen Grabar, Leslie M. Guidotti, Najat M. Hamid, Melissa R. Hill, Thomas A. Hooven, Nicole Huby, Psy.D., Allison M. Kade, Jessica Layne, Hadia Leon, Benjamin D. Long, Justin B. Miller, Rebecca Reiten, Michael-Paul Schallmo, Maureen Schrock, Megan Shaheen, Simrat Singh, Karendeep Singh, Clare Tyson, Naalti Vats, Lesley Weitekamp, Yahong Yang, and Naomi Yodkovik. We thank Michael Ransom, Ph.D. for his review of this chapter and helpful comments.

References

Adolphs, R., Tranel, D., Damasio, H., Damasio, A. R. (1994). Impaired recognition of emotion in facial expressions following bilateral damage to the human amygdala. *Nature, 372,* 669-672.

Alexopoulos, G. S., Meyers, B. S., Young, R. C., Campbell, S., Silbersweig, D., and Charlson, M. (1997). 'Vascular depression' hypothesis. *Archives of General Psychiatry, 9,* 844-845.

American Psychiatric Association. (2000). *Diagnostic and statistical manual of mental disorders* (4th ed.-Text Revision). Washington, DC, American Psychiatric Association.

Barrett, L. F., Lane, R. D., Sechrest, L., and Schwartz, G. E. (2000). Sex differences in emotional awareness. *Journal of Personality and Social Psychology, 26,* 1027-1035.

Bjorklund, D. F., and Kipp, K. (1996). Parental investment theory and gender differences in the evolution of inhibition mechanisms. *Psychological Bulletin, 120,* 163-188.

Blair, R. J., Morris, J. S., Frith, C. D., Perrett, D. I., and Dolan, R. J. (1999). Dissociable neural responses to facial expressions of sadness and anger. *Brain, 122,* 883-893.

Blazer, D.G., and Hybels, C. F. (2005). Origins of depression in later life. *Psychological Medicine, 35,* 1241-1252.

Borod, J. C., Koff, E., Lorch M. P., and Nicholas, M. (1986). The expression and perception of facial emotion in brain-damaged patients. *Neuropsychologia, 24,* 169-180.

Bouhuys, A. L., Geerts, E., and Gordjin, M. C. M. (1999). Depressed patients' perceptions of facial emotions in depressed and remitted states are associated with relapse: A longitudinal study. *Journal of Nervous and Mental Disease, 187,* 595-602.

Bowers, D., Bauer, R. M., Coslett, H. B., and Heilman, K. M. (1985). Processing of faces by patients with unilateral hemisphere lesions: I. Dissociation between judgments of facial affect and facial identity. *Brain and Cognition, 4,* 258-272.

Brown, G. W., and Moran, P. M. (1997). Single mothers, poverty and depression. *Psychological Medicine, 27,* 21-33.

Calder, A. J., Keane, J., Manly, T., Sprengelmeyer, R., Scott, S., Nimmno-Smith, I., and Young, A. W. (2003). Facial expression recognition across the adult life span. *Neuropsychologia, 41,* 195-202.

Carstensen, L. L., and Turk-Charles, S. (1994). The salience of emotion across the adult life span. *Psychology and Aging, 9,* 259-264.

Charles, S. T., Mather, M., and Carstensen, L. L. (2003). Aging and emotional memory: The forgettable nature of negative images for older adults. *Journal of Experimental Psychology: General, 132,* 310-324.

DeKosky, S., Heilman, K. M., Bowers, D., and Valenstein, E. (1980). Recognition and discrimination of emotional faces and pictures. *Brain and Language, 9,* 206-214.

Deldin, P. J., Keller, J., Gergen, J. A., and Miller, G. A. (2001). Cognitive bias and emotion in neuropsychological models of depression. *Cognition and Emotion, 15,* 787-802.

DeLeon, M. J., George, A. E., Tomanelli, J., Christman, D., Kluger, A., Miller, J., et al. (1987). Positron emission tomography studies of normal aging: A replication of PET III and 18-FDG using PET VI and 11-CDG. *Neurobiology of Aging, 8,* 319-323.

Dennis, T. A., and Chen C. C. (2007). Neurophysiological mechanisms in the emotional modulation of attention: The interplay between threat sensitivity and attentional control. *Biological Psychiatry, 76,* 1-10.

Ekman, P. (1984). Expression and the nature of emotion. In K. Scherer and P. Ekman (Eds.), *Approaches to emotion* (pp. 319-344). Hillsdale, N.J.: Erlbaum.

Ekman P., and Friesen W. (1976). *Pictures of facial affect.* California: Consulting Psychologists Press.

First, M. B., Spitzer, R. L., and Gibbon, M., and Williams, J. B. W. (1995). *Structured Clinical Interview for DSM-IV Axis 1 Disorder.* New York: Biometrics Research Department, New York State Psychiatric Institute.

Fischer, H., Sandblom, J., Gavazzeno, J., Fransson, P., Wright, C. I., Bachman, L. (2005). Age-differential patterns of brain activation during perception of angry faces. *Neuroscience Letters, 386,* 99-104.

Frodl, T., Scheuerecker, J., Albrecht, J., Kleemann, A. M., Muller-Schunk, S., Koutsouleris, N. et al. (2007). Neuronal correlates of emotional processing in patients with major depression. *World Journal of Biological Psychiatry, epub ahead of print,* 1-7.

Garraux, G., Salmon, E., Degueldre C., Lemaire, C. Laureys, S., and Frank, G. (1999). Comparison of impaired subcortico-frontal metabolic networks in normal aging, subcortico-frontal dementia, and cortical frontal dementia. *Neuroimage, 10,* 149-162.

Geerts, E., and Bouhuys, N. (1998). Multi-level prediction of short-term outcome of depression: non-verbal interpersonal processes, cognitions and personality traits. *Psychiatry Research, 79,* 59-72.

George, M. S., Ketter, T. A., Parekh, P. I., Herscovitch, P., and Post R. M. (1996). Gender differences in regional cerebral blood flow during transient self-induced sadness or happiness. *Biological Psychiatry, 40,* 859-871.

Gilboa-Schechtman, E., Erhard-Weiss, D., and Jeczemien, P. (2002). Interpersonal deficits meet cognitive biases: Memory for facial expressions in depressed and anxious men and women. *Psychiatry Research, 113,* 279-293.

Goldstein, R. D., and Gruenberg, A. M. (2007). Major Depressive Disorder in the older adult: Implications for women. *Journal of Women and Aging, 19,* 63-78.

Gotlib I. H., and Hammen, C. L. (1992). *Psychological aspects of depression: Toward a cognitive-interpersonal integration.* England: John Wiley and Sons, Inc.

Gray, S. L., Lai, K. V., and Larson, E. B. (1999). Drug-induced cognition disorders in the elderly: Incidence, prevention, and management. *Drug Safety, 21,* 101-122.

Grigoriadis, S., and Robinson, G. E. (2007). Gender issues in depression. *Annals of Clinical Psychiatry, 19,* 247-255.

Grill-Spector, K., Knouf, N., and Kanwisher, N. (2004). The fusiform face area subserves face perception, not generic within-category identification. *Nature and Neuroscience, 7*(5), 555-562.

Gunning-Dixon, F. M., Gur, R. C., Perkins, A. C., Schroeder, L., Turner, T., Turetsky, B. I., et al. (2003). Age-related differences in brain activation during emotional face processing. *Neurobiology of Aging, 24,* 285-295.

Gur, R. C., Erwin, R. J., Gur, R. E., Zwil, A. S., Heimberg, C., and Kraemer, H. C. (1992). Facial emotion discrimination: II. Behavioral findings in depression. *Psychiatry Research, 42,* 241-251.

Gur, R. C., Gunning-Dixon, F., Bilker, W. B., and Gur, R. E. (2002). Sex differences in temporo-limbic and frontal brain volumes of healthy adults. *Cerebral Cortex, 12,* 998-1003.

Gur, R. C., Skolnick, B. E., and Gur, R. E. (1994). Effects of emotional discrimination tasks on cerebral blood flow: regional activation and it's relation to performance. *Brain and Cognition, 25,* 271-286.

Hall, G. B., Witelson, S. F., Szechtman, H., and Nahmias, C. (2004). Sex differences in functional activation patterns revealed by increased emotion processing demands. *Neuroreport, 15,* 219-223.

Hall, J. A., and Matsumoto, D. (2004). Gender differences in judgments of multiple emotions from facial expressions. *Emotion, 4,* 201-206.

Hamilton, M. (1960). A rating scale for depression. *Journal of Neurology, Neurosurgery and Psychiatry, 23*, 56-62.

Hammen, C. (2005). Stress and depression. *Annual Review of Clinical Psychology, 1,* 293-319.

Harvey, P. O., Fossati, P., Pochon, J. B., Levy, R., LeBastard, G., Leheriey, S. et al. (2005). Cognitive control and brain resources in major depression: An fMRI study using the n-back task. *NeuroImage, 26*, 860-869.

Herrmann, L. L., Goodwin, G. M., and Ehmeier, K. P. (2007). The cognitive neuropsychology of depression in the elderly. *Psychological Medicine, 37*, 1963-1972.

Holley, C. K., and Mast, B. T. (2007). The effects of widowhood and vascular risk factors on later-life depression. *American Journal of Geriatric Psychiatry, 15*, 690-698.

Hollon, S. D., and Kendal, P. C. (1980). Cognitive self-statements in depression: Development of an automatic thoughts questionnaire. *Cognitive Therapy and Research, 4*, 383-395.

Holmes, A. J., Macdonald, A., Carter, C. S., Barch, D. M., Stenger, V. A., and Cohen, J. D. (2005). Prefrontal functioning during context processing in schizophrenia and major depression: An event-related fMRI study. *Schizophrenia Research, 76*, 199-206.

Iidaka, T., Omori, M., Murata, T., Kosaka, H., Yonekura, Y., Okada, T., et al. (2001). Neural interaction of the amygdala with the prefrontal and temporal cortices in the processing of facial expressions as revealed by fMRI. *Journal of Cognitive Neuroscience, 13*, 1035-1047.

Iidaka, T., Okada, T., Murata, T., Omori, M., Kosaka, H., Sadato, N., et al. (2002). Age-related differences in the medial temporal lobe responses to emotional faces as revealed by fMRI. *Hippocampus, 12,* 352-362.

Isaacowitz, D. M., Lockenhoff, C. E., Lane, R. D., Wright, R., Sechrest, L., Riedel, R., et al. (2007). Age differences in recognition of emotion in lexical stimuli and facial expressions. *Psychology and Aging, 22,* 147-159.

Jack D. C. (1991). *Silencing the self: Women and depression.* Massachusetts: Harvard University Press.

Jaeger, J., Borod, J. C., and Peselow, E. (1986). Facial expression of positive and negative emotions in patients with unipolar depression. *Journal of Affective Disorders, 11,* 43-50.

Johnson, B. H., Thayer, J. F., and Hugdahl, K. (1995). Affective judgment of the Ekman faces: A dimensional approach. *Journal of Psychophysiology, 9,* 193-202.

Joiner, T. E. (2000). Depression's vicious scree: Self-propagating and erosive processes in depression chronicity. *Clinical Psychology: Science and Practice, 7,* 203-218.

Jousilahti, P., Vartiainen, E., Tuomilehto, J., and Puska, P. (1999). Sex, age, cardiovascular risk factors, and coronary heart disease: A prospective follow-up study of 14,786 middle-aged men and women in Finland. *Circulation, 99,* 1165-1172.

Keedwell, P., Andrew C., Williams, S. C. R., Bramner, M. J., and Phillips, M. L. (2005). A double dissociation of ventromedial prefrontal cortical responses to sad and happy stimuli in depressed and healthy individuals. *Biological Psychiatry, 58,* 495-503.

Keightley, M. L., Winocur, G., Burianova, H., Hongwanishkul, D., and Grady, C. L. (2006). Age effects on social cognition: Faces tell a different story. *Psychology and Aging, 21,* 558-572.

Kendler, K. S., Gardner, C.O., and Prescott, C. A. (2002). Toward a comprehensive developmental model for major depression in women. *American Journal of Psychiatry, 159,* 1133-1145.

Kernis, M. H., Whisenhunt, C. R., Waschull, S. B., Greenier, K. D., Berry, A., Herlocker, C. E., et al. (1998). Multiple facets of self-esteem and their relations to depressive symptoms. *Personality and Social Psychology Bulletin, 24,* 657-668.

Kliegel, M., Jäger, T., and Phillips, L. H. (2007). Emotional development across adulthood: Differential age-related emotional reactivity and emotion regulation in a negative mood induction procedure. *International Journal of Aging and Human Development, 64,* 217-244.

Kline, J. P., Allen, J. J. B., and Schwartz, G. E. (1998). Is left frontal brain activation in defensiveness gender specific? *Journal of Abnormal Psychology, 107,* 149-153.

Kornstein, S.G. (1997). Gender differences in depression: Implications for treatment. *Journal of Clinical Psychiatry 58,* 12-18.

Kravitz, H. M., Janssen, I., Lotrich, F. E., Kado D. M., and Bromberger, J. T. (2006). Sex steroid hormone gene polymorphisms and depressive symptoms in women at midlife. *American Journal of Medicine, 119,* S87-93.

Kring, A. M., and Gordon, A. H. (1998). Sex differences in emotion: Expression, experience, and physiology. *Journal of Personality and Social Psychology, 74,* 686-703.

Kroenke K., Spitzer R. L., and Williams J. B. (2001). The PHQ-9: validity of a brief depression severity measure. *Journal of General Internal Medicine, 16,* 606-613.

Langenecker, S. A., Bieliauskas, L. A., Rapport, L. J., Zubieta, J-K., Wilde, E. A., and Berent, S. (2005). Face emotion perception and executive functioning deficits in depression. *Journal of Clinical and Experimental Neuropsychology, 27,* 320-333.

Langenecker S. A., Briceno E. M., Hamid N. M., Nielson K. A. (2007). Contributions of functional and volumetric MRI to understanding response control in elders. *Brain Research, 1135,* 58-68.

Langenecker, S. A., Caveney, A. F., Giordani, B., Young E. A., Nielson K. A., Rapport L. J., et al. (2007a). The sensitivity and psychometric properties of a brief computer-based cognitive screening battery in a depression clinic. *Psychiatry Research; 152:* 143-154.

Langenecker, S. A., Kennedy, S. E., Guidotti, L. M., Briceno, E. M., Own, L., Hooven, T., Young, E. A., Akil, H., Noll, D. C., Zubieta, J-K. (2007b). Frontal and limbic activation during inhibitory control predicts treatment response in Major Depressive Disorder. *Biological Psychiatry, 62* (11): 1272-1280.

Langenecker, S. A., and Nielson K. (2003). Frontal recruitment during response inhibition in older adults replicated with fMRI. *Neuroimage, 20,* 1384-1392.

Lara, M. E., and Klein, D. N. (1999). Psychosocial processes underlying the maintenance and persistence of depression: Implications for understanding chronic depression. *Clinical Psychology Review, 19,* 553-570.

Ley, R. G., and Bryden, M. P. (1979). Hemispheric differences in processing emotion and faces. *Brain and Language, 7,* 127-138.

Lyubormirsky, S., Caldwell, N. D., and Nolen-Hoeksema, S. (1998). Effects of ruminative and distracting responses to depressed mood on retrieval of autobiographical memories. *Journal of Personality and Social Psychology, 75,* 166-177.

Lyubormirsky, S., and Nolen-Hoeksema, S. (1995). Effects of self-focused rumination on negative thinking and interpersonal problem solving. *Journal of Personality and Social Psychology, 69,* 176-190.

Mackiewicz, K. L., Sarinopoulos, I., Cleven, K. L., and Nitschke J. B. (2006). The effect of anticipation and the specificity of sex differences for amygdala and hippocampus function in emotional memory. *Proceedings of the National Academy of Sciences, 103,* 14200-14205.

MacPherson, S. E., Phillips, L. H., and Sala, S. D., (2002). Age, executive function, and social decision making: A dorsolateral prefrontal theory of cognitive aging. *Psychology and Aging, 17,* 598-609.

Malatesta, C. Z., Izard, C. E., Culver, C., and Nicolich, M. (1987). Emotion communication skills in young, middle-aged, and older women. *Psychology of Aging, 2,* 193-203.

Mather, M. (2004). Aging and emotional memory. In D. Reisberg and P. Hertel (Eds.), *Memory and emotion* (pp. 272-307). New York: Oxford University Press.

Matt, G. E., Vazquez, C., and Campbell, W. K. (1992). Mood-congruent recall of affectively toned stimuli: A meta-analytic review. *Clinical Psychology Review, 12,* 227-255.

Mayberg, H. S., Brannan, S., Mahurin, R., Jerabek, P., Brickman, J., Tekell, J. et al. (1997). Cingulate function in depression: a potential predictor of treatment response. *NeuroReport, 8,* 1057-1061.

Mayberg, H. S., Liotti, M., Brannan, S., McGinnis, S., and Mahurin, R. (1999). Reciprocal limbic-cortical function and negative mood: Converging PET findings in depression and normal sadness. *American Journal of Psychiatry, 156,* 675-82.

McDowell, C. L., Harrison, D. W., and Demaree, H. A. (1994). Is right hemisphere decline in the perception of emotion a function of aging? *International Journal of Neuroscience. 79,* 1-11.

Mikhailova, E. S., Vladimirova, T. V., Iznak, A. F., Tsusulkovskaya, E. J., and Sushko, N. V. (1996). Abnormal recognition of facial expression of emotions in depressed patients with Major Depressive Disorder and Schizotypal Personality Disorder. *Biological Psychiatry, 40,* 697-705.

Miller, J.B. (1976). *Towards a new psychology of women.* Massachusetts: Beacon Press.

Montagne, B., Kessels, R. P. C., Frigerio, E., de Haan, E. H. F., and Perrett, D. I. (2005). Sex differences in the perception of affective facial expressions: Do men really lack emotional sensitivity? *Cognitive Processing, 6,* 136-141.

Mufson, L., and Nowicki, S. (1991). Factors affecting the accuracy of facial affect recognition. *Journal of Social Psychology, 131,* 815-822.

Naismith, S., Hickie, I., Turner, K., Little, C., Winter, V., Ward, P. et al. (2003). Neuropsychological performance in patients with depression is associated with clinical, etiological and genetic risk factors. *Journal of Clinical and Experimental Neuropsychology, 25,* 866-877.

Nolen-Hoeksema, S. (1991). Responses to depression and their effects on the duration of depressive episodes. *Journal of Abnormal Psychology, 100,* 509-582.

Nolen-Hoeksema, S. (2001). Gender differences in depression. *Current Directions in Psychological Science, 10,* 173-176.

Nolen-Hoeksema, S., and Girgus, J. S. (1994). The emergence of gender differences in depression during adolescence. *Psychological Bulletin, 115*, 424-443.

Nolen-Hoeksema, S., and Jackson, B. (2001). Mediators of the gender difference in rumination. *Psychology of Women Quarterly, 25,* 37-47.

Nolen-Hoeksema, S., Larson, J., and Grayson, C. (1999). Explaining the gender difference in depressive symptoms. *Journal of Personality and Social Psychology, 77,* 1061-1072.

Nolen-Hoeksema, S., Parker, L. E., and Larson, J. (1994). Ruminative coping with depressed mood following loss. *Journal of Personality and Social Psychology, 67,* 92-104.

Nurnberger J. I., Jr., Blehar M. C., Kaufmann C. A., York-Cooler, C., Simpson S. G., Harkavy-Friedman, J., et al. (1994). Diagnostic interview for genetic studies. Rationale, unique features, and training. NIMH Genetics Initiative. *Archives of General Psychiatry 51*, 849-859.

Paradee, C. V., Rapport, L. J., Lumley, M. A., Langenecker, S. A., Hanks, R. A., and Whitman, D. (2007). Circadian preference and facial emotion recognition among rehabilitation inpatients. *Journal of Head Trauma Research, 53*, 46-53.

Parker, G. (2000). Classifying depression: Should paradigms lost be regained. *American Journal or Psychiatry, 157*, 1195-1203.

Persad, S., and Polivy, J. (1993). Differences between depressed and nondepressed individuals in the recognition of and response to facial emotional cues. *Journal of Abnormal Psychology, 102,* 358-368.

Phillips, L. H., MacLean, R. D., and Allen, R. (2002). Age and the understanding of emotions: Neuropsychological and sociocognitive perspectives. *Journal of Gerontology B Psychological Science, Social Sciences, 57,* 526-530.

Phillips, M. L., Drevets, W. C., Rauch, S. L., and Lane, R. (2003a). Neurobiology of emotion perception I: The neural basis of normal emotion perception. *Biological Psychiatry, 54,* 504-528.

Phillips, M., Drevets, W., Rauch, S., and Lane, R. (2003b). Neurobiology of emotion perception II: Implications for major psychiatric disorders. *Biological Psychiatry, 54,* 515-528.

Pizzigalli, D., Pascual-Marqui, R. D., Nitschke, J., Oakes, T. R., Larson, C. L., Abercrombie, H. et al. (2001). Anterior cingulate activity as a predictor of degree of treatment response in major depression: Evidence from brain Electrical Tomography Analysis. *American Journal of Psychiatry, 158*, 405-415.

Rapport, L. J., Friedman, S., Tzelepis, A., and VanVoorhis, A. (2002). Experienced emotion and affect recognition in adult attention-deficits hyperactivity disorder. *Neuropsychology, 16,* 102-110.

Raz, N. (2000). Aging of the brain and its impact on cognitive performance: Integration of structural and functional findings. In F. I. M. Craik and T. A. Salthouse (Eds)., *Handbook of Aging and Cognition-II.* Erlbaum, Mahwah, NJ, pp. 1-90.

Raz, N. (2004). The aging brain observed in vivo: differential changes and their modifiers. In R. Cabeza, L. Nyberg, and D. C. Park (Eds.), *Cognitive Neuroscience of Aging: Linking Cognitive and Cerebral Aging.* Oxford University Press, New York, pp. 17-55.

Raz, N., and Rodrigue, K. M. (2006). Differential aging of the brain: Patterns, cognitive correlates and modifiers. *Neuroscience and Biobehavioral Reviews, 30,* 730-748.

Resnick, S. M., Pham, D. L., Kraut, M. A., Zonderman, A. B., Davatzikos, C. (2003). Longitudinal magnetic resonance imaging studies of older adults: A shrinking brain. *Journal of Neuroscience, 23*, 3295-3301.

Robert, J. J. T., Hoffmann R. F., Emslie, G. J., Hughes C., Rintelmann, J., Moore J., and Armitage R. (2006). Sex and age differences in sleep macroarchitecture in childhood and adolescent depression. *Sleep, 29*, 351-358.

Roberts, J. E., and Kassel, J. D. (1997). Labile self-esteem, life stress, and depressive symptoms: Prospective data testing a model of vulnerability. *Cognitive Therapy Research, 21,* 569-589.

Rosenthal, R., Hall, J. A., DiMatteo, M. R., Rogers, P. L., and Archer, D. (1979). *Sensitivity to nonverbal communication: The PONS test.* Baltimore, MD: Johns Hopkins University Press.

Rubinow, D. R., and Post, R. M. (1992). Impaired recognition of affect in facial expression in depressed patients. *Biological Psychiatry, 31,* 947-953.

Salthouse, T. A. (1996). The processing-speed theory of adult age differences in cognition. *Psychological Review, 103,* 403-428.

Schneider, F., Habel, U., Kessler, C., Salloum, J. B., and Posse, S. (2000). Gender differences in regional cerebral activity during sadness. *Human Brain Mapping, 9,* 226-238.

Sergent, J., and Bindra, D. (1981). Differential hemispheric processing of faces: Methodological considerations and reinterpretation. *Psychological Bulletin, 89,* 541-554.

Siegle, G. J., Carter, C. S., and Thase, M. E. (2006). Use of fMRI to predict recovery from unipolar depression with cognitive behavior therapy. *American Journal of Psychiatry, 163,* 735-7U1.

Siegle, G. J., Steinhauer, S. R., Thase, M. E., Stenger, A., and Carter, C. S. (2002). Can't shake that feeling: Event-Related fMRI assessment of sustained amygdala activity in response to emotional information in depressed individuals. *Biological Psychiatry, 51,* 693-707.

Siegle, G. J., Thompson, W., Carter, C. S., Steinhauer, S. R., and Thase, M. E. (2007). Increased amygdala and decreased dorsolateral prefrontal BOLD responses in unipolar depression: related and independent features. *Biological Psychiatry, 61,* 198-209.

Stein, J. A., Newcomb, M. D., and Bentler, P. M. (1992). The effect of agency and communality on self-esteem: Gender differences in longitudinal data. *Sex Roles, 26,* 465-483.

Sullivan, S., and Ruffman, T. (2004). Emotion recognition deficits in the elderly. *International Journal of Neuroscience, 114,* 403, 432.

Surguladze, S. A., Young, A.W., Senior, C., Brebion, G., Travis, M. J., and Phillips, M. L. (2004). Recognition accuracy and response bias to happy and sad facial expressions in patients with major depression. *Neuropsychology, 18,* 212-218.

Sutton, S. K., and Davidson, R. J. (2000). Prefrontal brain electrical asymmetry predicts the evaluation of affective stimuli. *Neuropsychologia, 38,* 1723-1733.

Thayer, J. F., and Johnsen, B. H. (2000). Sex differences in judgment of facial affect: A multivariate analysis of recognition errors. *Scandinavian Journal of Psychology, 41,* 243-246.

Thorndike, R. K. (January 1920). Intelligence and Its Uses, *Harper's Magazine, 140,* 227-335.

Tisserand, D. J., Pruessner, J. C., Sanz Arigita, E. J, van Boxtel, M. P., Evans, A. C., Jolles, J., et al. (2002). Regional frontal cortical volumes decrease differentially in aging: An MRI study to compare volumetric approaches and voxel-based morphometry. *Neuroimage, 17,* 657-659.

Wager, T. D., Phan, K. L., Liberzon, I., and Taylor, S. F. (2003). Valence, gender, and lateralization of functional brain anatomy in emotion: a meta-analysis of findings from neuroimaging. *Neuroimage, 19,* 513-531.

Wagner, G., Sinsel, E., Sobanski, T., Kohler, S., Marinou, V., Mentzel, H. J. et al. (2006). Cortical inefficiency in patients with unipolar depression: An event-related MRI study with the Stroop task. *Biological Psychiatry, 59,* 958-965.

Weissman, M. M., Bruce, M. L., Leaf, P. I., Florio, L. P., and Holzer, C., III. (1992). Affective disorders in psychiatric disorders in America: The Epidemiologic Catchment Area Study. In L. N. Robins and D. A. Regier (Eds.), *Psychiatric disorders in America: The Epidemiologic Catchment Area Study* (pp. 53-80). New York: Free Press.

Wright, S. L., Langenecker, S. A., Deldin, P, Rapport, L., Nielson, K., Kade A., et al. (In Press). Gender specific changes in emotion processing in young adults with depression. *Depression and Anxiety.*

Wright, S. L., and Persad, C. (2007). Distinguishing between depression and dementia in older persons: Neuropsychological and neuropathological correlates. *Journal of Geriatric Psychiatry and Neurology, 20,* 189-198.

In: Women and Depression
Editors: Paula Hernandez and Sara Alonso

ISBN 978-1-60456-647-5
© 2009 Nova Science Publishers, Inc.

Chapter 5

Gender Differences in Depression in Patients with Neurological Diseases

S. Paolucci, F.R. Fusco, L. Pratesi, M. Bragoni, P. Coiro, D. De Angelis, D. Morelli, and V. Venturiero

Fondazione I.R.C.C.S. Santa Lucia, Via Ardeatina 306, 00179 - Rome, Italy

Abstract

Literature on psychiatric comorbidities in neurologic diseases (including stroke, multiple sclerosis, Parkinson disease, Alzheimer dementia) are generally consistent about the prevalence of female gender in depression in most of these illnesses. These data are in agreement with those of functional depression, in which female preponderance in depression rates appears to be a consistent finding. In the literature, several possible explanations have been suggested and investigated, such as biological, social and psychological factors. However, existing data on the role of gender in depression in neurological comorbidities is, to our knowledge, only exhaustive for post-stroke depression (PSD) and less exhaustive for other diseases.

Mood depression is a common and serious complication during neurological diseases, as stroke, multiple sclerosis, Parkinson's and Alzheimer's disease, with a prevalence ranging between 30-50% [1,2]. Literature on psychiatric comorbidities in such neurologic diseases are consistent on the prevalence of female gender in depression in most of these illnesses [3]. These data are in agreement with those of functional depression, in which female preponderances in depression rates appears to be a consistent finding [4]. Today, the prevalence of depression in women is almost twice as high as in men [5], which is similar to that of nearly twenty years ago, when ratio female/male for major depression was quantified in 2.4:1 [6]. In the literature, several possible explanations such as biological, social and psychological factors have been suggested and investigated. However, it has recently been observed that, in late-life depression, when age and competing risk factors were taken into account, the relative risks for females were considerably reduced, and most likely due to greater exposure to risk factors, as presence of chronic illnesses, functional limitations, lower education and lower income [5].

Today, the longer life-expectancy of females and the direct relationship between most common neurological diseases, such as stroke, Parkinson's or Alzheimer's disease, and advanced age suggest that the problem of depression in such diseases is most likely estimated to increase, and especially in females, due to their increasing longevity. It is safe to make the statement that aging is female. Indeed, at present, in most of the western countries there are more older women than older men: in 2001, in Italy, for example, women were 58.81% of the population age ≥ 65 and 63.64% of the population age ≥ 75 [7], and projections indicate that life expectancy will increase even more in women than in men. Thus, the Italian Statistical Institute (ISTAT) recently reported an increase of mean life span of females from 83.3 yrs of 2005 to 86.6 yrs of 2030, in comparison with 77.4 yrs of males of 2005 and 81.0 of 2030 [8].

Thus, it is necessary to increase our knowledge about the prevalence and impact of gender in depression during neurological diseases. However, literature data on the role of gender in depression in these neurological illnesses are exhaustive only for post-stroke depression (PSD) and less meticulous for other diseases.

Post-Stroke Depression (PSD)

Mood depression is a common and serious complication after stroke. According to epidemiological studies, nearly one third of stroke patients develop depression, either early or late after stroke [9]. In most of studies, being female was a clear prognostic factor for development of PSD.

In 1987, Wade and colleagues evaluated 379 patients on the third week after stroke, and reported depression in 26% of females in comparison with 19% of males (p0 0.09). Moreover, these authors observed an association of female gender with a more severe depression (assessed by the Wakefield Assessment Depression Inventory) [10].

In 1993, Angeleri and co-workers studied 180 consecutive patients in central Italy, reporting greater severity of depression (assessed with the Beck Depression Inventory) in females [11].

In 1994, Sharpe and co-workers found a trend toward a significant prevalence of PSD in females (depressed 30.4% of females vs. 10.8% of males), but this difference failed to reach statistical significance. However, in a multivariate analysis, female gender (together with functional dependence and lesion volume) was associated with high probability of depression after controlling for all other variables (OR= 8; 95% CI 1.1-56) [12].

In the same year, Andersen and co-workers, evaluating an unselected cohort of 285 stroke patients, studied the correlations between potential risk factors and the 1-year incidence of PSD. In this series, 60% of patients with depression were women (51 out of 85), and female gender explained 2% of observed variance in development of PSD [13]. Similarly, in a study on multiethnic sample performed in Singapore, females were 62.1% (18 out of 29) of depressed patients [14].

In the following year, in the Perth Community Stroke Study (PCSS), a population-based study evaluating 294 out of 492 patients, there was a nearly equal prevalence of depression in men (23%) and women (24%) [15]. However, a significant (p<0.001) difference between sexes was found evaluating the psychiatric history of patients: 39% of females in comparison with 16% of males had had a depression before stroke [15].

In 1998, Paradiso and Robinson, evaluating 301 consecutive stroke patients, found that females were twice as frequently diagnosed with major depression as males on one hand, and that there was no significant difference in depression severity scores as measured by the Hamilton Rating Scale for Depression [16], on the other. In particular, 21 of 170 males (12.3%) and 31 of 131 females (23.6%) had major depression (P=0.01). Also in this series, an association was reported between more severe depression and prior psychiatric history.

In the same year other three important studies on PSD were published, and in two of them female gender played a significant role. In the first one, the FINNSTROKE Study, on 594 first-ever strokes, female sex was associated with a high risk (OR 1.71, 95% CI 1.10-2.66) of development of depression in an univariate analysis [17]. In the second study, namely, the Sunnybrook Stroke Study, with 436 patients recorded at entry, depressed patients were more likely to be female (p<0.05), even if gender did not enter multivariate models [18]. Conversely, in the third study, that evaluated a consecutive series of 486 patients with ischemic stroke, Pohjasvaara and colleagues found no statistically significant difference in genders between depressed and nondepressed patients [19].

In the following year, a study was published on nearly 500 consecutive patients admitted to a rehabilitation hospital for sequelae of their first stroke. In multivariate analysis, women had nearly twice the probability of developing PSD of men (OR= 1.94, 95% CI 1.27- 2.96). In this series, PSD was observed in 129 patients, with a higher percentage of females in the depressed group (females 80 out 129 [62.0%] vs. males 49 out of 129 [38.0%], p=0.01) [20].

Recently, the Italian Multicenter study DeSTRO (Depression in Stroke), with a total of 1064 patients evaluated, and periodically assessed in the first 9 months after the event, reported a higher frequency of PSD in women (43.56% vs. 30.93%) [21]. Moreover, DeSTRO confirmed that female gender was *per se* a risk factor for the development of PSD. In particular, female sex alone seems to raise the risk by 7-10%; a male with a first-ever cerebrovascular event, no history of depression, and no severe disability, has an approximately 25% risk of developing PSD, compared with 32.41% for a woman with all the same features [22]. Combinations of other relevant factors, as prior strokes, marked disability and depression before stroke, raised the risk of PSD exponentially. This sex difference remained virtually constant as other variables were analyzed. The greatest likelihood (89.1%) was for women with previous stroke, previous depressive episodes, and moderate or moderate-severe disability [22].

Parkinson's Disease (PD)

Depression is the most common neuropsychiatric disturbance in Parkinson's disease (PD) and has been shown to be more common in PD than in other chronic and disabling disorders.

The reported prevalence of depression in PD has been reported to be as high as 40%, even if widely variable (4-70%) [23].

Today, there is no consensus as to whether female gender is a risk factor for depression in PD [24]. A depression-female gender relationship has been previously reported [25,26], but more recent data have not resolved this issue. In fact, while some studies found no difference between sexes on one hand [27,28], other papers found a female preponderance, on the other [29,30].

In fact, Kuopio and colleagues, evaluating quality of life in 282 patients with Parkinson Disease in the south-western part of Finland, found depression in 41% of males and in 63% of females [31]. Rojo et al., evaluating 353 PD patients, found a gender-related difference (p<0.001) in the prevalence of depressive symptoms (68.6% in women and 40.64% in men) [32]. Evaluating the subgroup with patients with mild–moderate depressive symptoms (MD, Geriatric Depression Scale –GDS - score 11–20), these authors found that females were 69% out 142 case of this group, whereas in the subgroup with moderate–severe depressive symptoms (GDS score >20) females were nearly 75% (F 74.5% vs. M 25.5%) [33]. In a recent study of on more than 24 000 nursing home residents with PD in five US states, symptoms of depression were reported to be slightly more common among women than men (24% versus 21%). Another important observation of this study was that men were more likely to receive an antipsychotic agent and the women an antidepressant [34].

Nilsson and coworkers estimated that female patients with PD have a likelihood of depression of 3.29 (95% CI: 2.00–5.40) compared with male patients with PD, and observed that, for female patients with PD, it is more elevated in comparison with female patients with diabetes (1.90, 95% CI: 1.52–2.37) or with osteoarthritis (1.77, 95% CI: 1.44–2.16) [35]. These data are in disagreement with those of Leentjens and colleagues who, performing a two-step logistic regression to predict depression in 161 consecutively PD patients, found that positive family history of depression was the only individual variable (among age, sex, prior history of depression, a positive family history of depression and the presence of comorbid somatic disorders) whose contribution to the multivariate model was statistically significant. Moreover, in the bivariate analysis, not only a positive family history of depression, but also all other variables became significant or showed a trend towards significance, with the exception of sex [36].

Lastly, Scott and coworkers studied gender-related symptom differences in 948 subjects with PD, and found that a significant difference (P<0.001) in the prevalence of anxiety disorder (F 42.2 vs. M 37.8) [37]. Although depression is not one of primary reported symptoms (36%), a majority of female subjects found this symptom as constantly distressing.

Alzheimer's Disease (AD)

Depression is one of the most frequent psychiatric complications of AD, affecting up to 50% of patients [38]. As in other neurological disorders, there is no consensus on the role of female gender as risk factor for depression in AD. In fact, while a relationship with female gender was previously reported [39,40], most of more recent studies did not evaluate gender differences .

In 1995, Migliorelli and colleagues found depression in 51% of a consecutive series of 103 patients with probable Alzheimer's disease (28% with dysthymia and 23% with major depression), and observed that females had a significantly higher prevalence of both major depression and dysthymia than males [41].

In the following year, Lyketsos and co-workers found a gender difference in the likelihood of developing depression, with a significantly increased risk for major depression in women with family history of mood disorders (OR= 2.82, 95% CI 1.19- 6.69) [42]. It has been hypothesized that depression in women with AD might be associated with apolipoprotein E epsilon 4 allele frequency, significantly increased in depressed women but not in men [43].

Lastly, it is important to note that a gender-related difference was observed in the relative hazard of premorbid depressive symptomatology for development of dementia and AD. In fact, sufficient data are available today to hypothesize the possibility that depression is a risk factor for dementia and cognitive decline [44]. However, the risk of dementia, especially AD, was significantly increased with premorbid depressive symptoms, although only in men [45].

Multiple Sclerosis (MS)

A mood disorder is common in Multiple Sclerosis (MS). In a recent review, Siegert and Abernethy reported a lifetime prevalence of major depression of nearly 50% [46], and higher in patients than in the general population [47].

An evaluation of gender-related differences on depression in MS should be interpreted with caution due to higher prevalence of MS in females. Indeed, a female:male ratio around 2.0 [48] has recently been reported in Europe. Thus, the correlation of depression with female gender has given variable results. In fact, while some studies described an association with female gender [49-51], others did not [52-58].

In 1998, Schiffer and colleagues, evaluated 56 MS patients and observed in a whole sample a correct female:male ratio (40 F and 16 M, 2.5:1). However, this ratio increased to 6.75 in 31 MS patients with major affective disorder (27 females and four males) [59].

In 2000, Patten and colleagues evaluated136 SM patients, and reported that 22.8% of them had lifetime major depressive episodes and that a higher prevalence was found in women, in patients under 35 years of age, and in those with a family history of major depression, with high levels of stress and with heavy ingestion of caffeine [60]. However, the same authors, evaluating 163 MS patients treated with beta interferon or glatiramer acetate, found that female sex did not enter as significant variable in logistic regression analysis predicting depression [61].

More recently, Galeazzi et al., evaluating 50 consecutive patients with clinical Relapsing Remitting MS, observed that risk factors for depression were female sex and severity of disability, but not therapy with interferon beta or longer duration of illness. In particular, females had a probability nearly four times higher than males to develop a depression (OR= 3.89, 95% CI 1.19–12.68) [62].

A critical problem in MS is suicide. Data available from two studies are consistent with a slightly increased risk of suicide for females, probably related to depression [63,64], although none of the these studies specifically addressed the etiology [65]. However, in the Danish study a significant gender-related difference was observed in suicide rate in patients with MS, with a higher rate of suicide in men, associated to (but not only) previous suicidal behavior and previous mental disorder [66,67].

Conclusion

The importance of diagnosis and treatment of depression associated with neurological disease is gaining momentum. Indeed, it is crucial for physicians to be able to address this issue, also for the efficacy of treatment of the underlying disorder.

References

[1] Fann JR,Tucker GJ: Mood disorders with general medical conditions. *Curr. Opin. Psychiatry* 1995; 8: 13-18

[2] Rickards H: Depression in neurological disorders: Parkinson's disease, multiple sclerosis, and stroke. *J. Neurol. Neurosurg Psychiatry* 2005; 76 Suppl 1: i48-i52

[3] Okiishi CG, Paradiso S, Robinson RG: Gender differences in depression associated with neurologic illness: clinical correlates and pharmacologic response. *J. Gend Specif. Me*d. 2001; 4: 65-72

[4] Takkinen S, Gold C, Pedersen NL, Malmberg B, Nilsson S, Rovine M: Gender differences in depression: a study of older unlike-sex twins. *Aging Ment. Health* 2004; 8: 187-195

[5] Sonnenberg CM, Beekman AT, Deeg DJ, van Tilburg W: Sex differences in late-life depression. Acta Psychiatrica *Scandinavica* 2000; 101: 286-292

[6] Weissman MM, Leaf PJ, Holzer CE, III, Myers JK, Tischler GL: The epidemiology of depression. An update on sex differences in rates. *J. Affect. Disord.* 1984; 7: 179-188

[7] ISTAT: Censimento 2001, 14° censimento generale della popolazione e delle abitazioni. http://dawinci istat it/pop/ 2005;

[8] ISTAT: Previsioni demografiche nazionali: 1° gennaio 2005 - 1° gennaio 2050. htpp://demo istat it 2006;

[9] Hackett ML, Yapa C, Parag V, Anderson CS: Frequency of depression after stroke: a systematic review of observational studies. *Stroke* 2005; 36: 1330-1340

[10] Wade DT, Legh-Smith J, Hewer RA: Depressed mood after stroke. A community study of its frequency. *Br. J. Psychiatry* 1987; 151: 200-205

[11] Angeleri F, Angeleri VA, Foschi N, Giaquinto S, Nolfe G: The influence of depression, social activity, and family stress on functional outcome after stroke. *Stroke* 1993; 24: 1478-1483

[12] Sharpe M, Hawton K, Seagroatt V, Bamford J, House A, Molyneux A, Sandercock P, Warlow C: Depressive disorders in long-term survivors of stroke. Associations with

demographic and social factors, functional status, and brain lesion volume. *Br. J. Psychiatry* 1994; 164: 380-386

[13]   Andersen G, Vestergaard K, Ingemann-Nielsen M, Lauritzen L: Risk factors for post-stroke depression. *Acta Psychiatr. Scand.* 1995; 92: 193-198

[14]   Ng KC, Chan KL, Straughan PT: A study of post-stroke depression in a rehabilitative center. *Acta Psychiatrica Scandinavica* 1995; 92: 75-79

[15]   Burvill PW, Johnson GA, Jamrozik KD, Anderson CS, Stewart-Wynne EG, Chakera TM: Prevalence of depression after stroke: the Perth Community Stroke Study. *Br. J. Psychiatry* 1995; 166: 320-327

[16]   Paradiso S,Robinson RG: Gender differences in poststroke depression. *J. Neuropsychiatry Clin. Neurosci.* 1998; 10: 41-47

[17]   Kotila M, Numminen H, Waltimo O, Kaste M: Depression after stroke: results of the FINNSTROKE Study. *Stroke* 1998; 29: 368-372

[18]   Herrmann N, Black SE, Lawrence J, Szekely C, Szalai JP: The Sunnybrook Stroke Study: a prospective study of depressive symptoms and functional outcome. *Stroke* 1998; 29: 618-624

[19]   Pohjasvaara T, Leppavuori A, Siira I, Vataja R, Kaste M, Erkinjuntti T: Frequency and clinical determinants of poststroke depression. *Stroke* 1998; 29: 2311-2317

[20]   Paolucci S, Antonucci G, Pratesi L, Traballesi M, Grasso MG, Lubich S: Poststroke depression and its role in rehabilitation of inpatients. *Arch. Phys. Med. Rehabil.* 1999; 80: 985-990

[21]   Paolucci S, Gandolfo C, Provinciali L, Torta R, Toso V, on behalf of DESTRO Study Group: The Italian multicenter observational study on post-stroke depression (DESTRO). *J. Neurol.* 2006; 253: 556-562

[22]   Paolucci S, Gandolfo C, Provinciali L, Torta R, Sommacal S, (on behalf of DESTRO Study Group), Toso V: Quantification of the risk of post stroke depression: the Italian multicenter observational study DESTRO. *Acta Psychiatrica Scandinavica* 2005; 112: 272-278

[23]   Cummings JL,Masterman DL: Depression in patients with Parkinson's disease. *Int. J. Geriatr. Psychiatry* 1999; 14: 711-718

[24]   Burn DJ: Depression in Parkinson's disease. *Eur .J .Neurol .2002;* 9 Suppl 3: 44-54

[25]   Gotham AM, Brown RG, Marsden CD: Depression in Parkinson's disease: a quantitative and qualitative analysis. *J. Neurol. Neurosurg Psychiatry* 1986; 49: 381-389

[26]   Brown RG,MacCarthy B: Psychiatric morbidity in patients with Parkinson's disease. *Psychol. Med .1990;* 20: 77-87

[27]   Tandberg E, Larsen JP, Aarsland D, Cummings JL: The occurrence of depression in Parkinson's disease. A community-based study. *Arch. Neurol .1996;* 53: 175-179

[28]   Meara J, Mitchelmore E, Hobson P: Use of the GDS-15 geriatric depression scale as a screening instrument for depressive symptomatology in patients with Parkinson's disease and their carers in the community. *Age Ageing* 1999; 28: 35-38

[29]   Kuopio AM, Marttila RJ, Helenius H, Toivonen M, Rinne UK: The quality of life in Parkinson's disease. *Mov. Disord.* 2000; 15: 216-223

[30] Rojo A, Aguilar M, Garolera MT, Cubo E, Navas I, Quintana S: Depression in Parkinson's disease: clinical correlates and outcome. *Parkinsonism Relat. Disord.* 2003; 10: 23-28

[31] Kuopio AM, Marttila RJ, Helenius H, Toivonen M, Rinne UK: The quality of life in Parkinson's disease. *Mov.Disord* .2000; 15: 216-223

[32] Rojo A, Aguilar M, Garolera MT, Cubo E, Navas I, Quintana S: Depression in Parkinson's disease: clinical correlates and outcome. *Parkinsonism Relat. Disord.* 2003; 10: 23-28

[33] Rojo A, Aguilar M, Garolera MT, Cubo E, Navas I, Quintana S: Depression in Parkinson's disease: clinical correlates and outcome. *Parkinsonism Relat. Disord.* 2003; 10: 23-28

[34] Fernandez HH, Lapane KL, Ott BR, Friedman JH: Gender differences in the frequency and treatment of behavior problems in Parkinson's disease. SAGE Study Group. Systematic Assessment and Geriatric drug use via Epidemiology. *Mov. Disord.* 2000; 15: 490-496

[35] Nilsson FM, Kessing LV, Sorensen TM, Andersen PK, Bolwig TG: Major depressive disorder in Parkinson's disease: a register-based study. *Acta Psychiatr. Scand.* 2002; 106: 202-211

[36] Leentjens AF, Lousberg R, Verhey FR: Markers for depression in Parkinson's disease. *Acta Psychiatr. Scand.* 2002; 106: 196-201

[37] Scott B, Borgman A, Engler H, Johnels B, Aquilonius SM: Gender differences in Parkinson's disease symptom profile. *Acta Neurol. Scand.* 2000; 102: 37-43

[38] Lyketsos CG,Olin J: Depression in Alzheimer's disease: overview and treatment. *Biol. Psychiatry* 2002; 52: 243-252

[39] Reifler BV, Larson E, Teri L, Poulsen M: Dementia of the Alzheimer's type and depression. *J. Am. Geriatr. Soc.* 1986; 34: 855-859

[40] Lazarus LW, Newton N, Cohler B, Lesser J, Schweon C: Frequency and presentation of depressive symptoms in patients with primary degenerative dementia. *Am. J. Psychiatry* 1987; 144: 41-45

[41] Migliorelli R, Teson A, Sabe L, Petracchi M, Leiguarda R, Starkstein SE: Prevalence and correlates of dysthymia and major depression among patients with Alzheimer's disease. *Am. J. Psychiatry* 1995; 152: 37-44

[42] Lyketsos CG, Tune LE, Pearlson G, Steele C: Major depression in Alzheimer's disease. An interaction between gender and family history. *Psychosomatics* 1996; 37: 380-384

[43] Muller-Thomsen T, Arlt S, Ganzer S, Mann U, Mass R, Naber D, Beisiegel U: Depression in Alzheimer's disease might be associated with apolipoprotein E epsilon 4 allele frequency in women but not in men. *Dement. Geriatr. Cogn. Disord.* 2002; 14: 59-63

[44] Jorm AF: Is depression a risk factor for dementia or cognitive decline? A review. *Gerontology* 2000; 46: 219-227

[45] Dal Forno G, Palermo MT, Donohue JE, Karagiozis H, Zonderman AB, Kawas CH: Depressive symptoms, sex, and risk for Alzheimer's disease. *Ann. Neurol* .2005; 57: 381-387

[46] Siegert RJ,Abernethy DA: Depression in multiple sclerosis: a review. *J. Neurol. Neurosurg Psychiatry* 2005; 76: 469-475

[47] Schubert DS,Foliart RH: Increased depression in multiple sclerosis patients. A meta-analysis. *Psychosomatics* 1993; 34: 124-130

[48] Pugliatti M, Rosati G, Carton H, Riise T, Drulovic J, Vecsei L, Milanov I: The epidemiology of multiple sclerosis in Europe. *Eur. J. Neurol.* 2006; 13: 700-722

[49] Schiffer RB, Weitkamp LR, Wineman NM, Guttormsen S: Multiple sclerosis and affective disorder. Family history, sex, and HLA-DR antigens. *Arch. Neurol.* 1988; 45: 1345-1348

[50] Patten SB, Metz LM, Reimer MA: Biopsychosocial correlates of lifetime major depression in a multiple sclerosis population. *Mult. Scler.* 2000; 6: 115-120

[51] Galeazzi GM, Ferrari S, Giaroli G, Mackinnon A, Merelli E, Motti L, Rigatelli M: Psychiatric disorders and depression in multiple sclerosis outpatients: impact of disability and interferon beta therapy. *Neurol. Sci.* 2005; 26: 255-262

[52] Moller A, Wiedemann G, Rohde U, Backmund H, Sonntag A: Correlates of cognitive impairment and depressive mood disorder in multiple sclerosis. *Acta Psychiatr. Scand.* .1994; 89: 117-121

[53] Arnett PA, Higginson CI, Voss WD, Wright B, Bender WI, Wurst JM, Tippin JM: Depressed mood in multiple sclerosis: relationship to capacity- demanding memory and attentional functioning. *Neuropsychology* 1999; 13: 434-446

[54] Zorzon M, de Masi R, Nasuelli D, Ukmar M, Mucelli RP, Cazzato G, Bratina A, Zivadinov R: Depression and anxiety in multiple sclerosis. A clinical and MRI study in 95 subjects. *J. Neurol.* 2001; 248: 416-421

[55] Chwastiak L, Ehde DM, Gibbons LE, Sullivan M, Bowen JD, Kraft GH: Depressive symptoms and severity of illness in multiple sclerosis: epidemiologic study of a large community sample. *Am. J. Psychiatry* 2002; 159: 1862-1868

[56] Zephir H, de Seze J, Stojkovic T, Delisse B, Ferriby D, Cabaret M, Vermersch P: Multiple sclerosis and depression: influence of interferon beta therapy. *Mult. Scler.* 2003; 9: 284-288

[57] Mohr DC, Hart SL, Fonareva I, Tasch ES: Treatment of depression for patients with multiple sclerosis in neurology clinics. *Mult. Scler.* 2006; 12: 204-208

[58] Beal CC, Stuifbergen AK, Brown A: Depression in multiple sclerosis: a longitudinal analysis. *Arch. Psychiatr. Nurs.* 2007; 21: 181-191

[59] Schiffer RB, Weitkamp LR, Wineman NM, Guttormsen S: Multiple sclerosis and affective disorder. Family history, sex, and HLA-DR antigens. *Arch. Neurol.* 1988; 45: 1345-1348

[60] Patten SB, Metz LM, Reimer MA: Biopsychosocial correlates of lifetime major depression in a multiple sclerosis population. *Mult. Scler.* 2000; 6: 115-120

[61] Patten SB, Fridhandler S, Beck CA, Metz LM: Depressive symptoms in a treated multiple sclerosis cohort. *Mult. Scler.* 2003; 9: 616-620

[62] Galeazzi GM, Ferrari S, Giaroli G, Mackinnon A, Merelli E, Motti L, Rigatelli M: Psychiatric disorders and depression in multiple sclerosis outpatients: impact of disability and interferon beta therapy. *Neurol. Sci.* 2005; 26: 255-262

[63] Sadovnick AD, Eisen K, Ebers GC, Paty DW: Cause of death in patients attending multiple sclerosis clinics. *Neurology* 1991; 41: 1193-1196

[64] Stenager EN, Stenager E, Koch-Henriksen N, Bronnum-Hansen H, Hyllested K, Jensen K, Bille-Brahe U: Suicide and multiple sclerosis: an epidemiological investigation. *J. Neurol. Neurosurg. Psychiatry* 1992; 55: 542-545

[65] Feinstein A: Multiple sclerosis, depression, and suicide. *BMJ* 1997; 315: 691-692

[66] Stenager EN, Stenager E, Koch-Henriksen N, Bronnum-Hansen H, Hyllested K, Jensen K, Bille-Brahe U: Suicide and multiple sclerosis: an epidemiological investigation. J *Neurol. Neurosurg. Psychiatry* 1992; 55: 542-545

[67] Stenager EN, Koch-Henriksen N, Stenager E: Risk factors for suicide in multiple sclerosis. *Psychother. Psychosom.* 1996; 65: 86-90

In: Women and Depression
Editors: Paula Hernandez and Sara Alonso

ISBN 978-1-60456-647-5
© 2009 Nova Science Publishers, Inc.

Chapter 6

The Phenomena of Depression in Latino/Hispanic Women: Some Issues to Understand a Complex Relationship

José R. Rodriguez. and Carmen C. Salas-Serrano
University of Puerto Rico

Introduction

The Latino/Hispanic population is the fastest growing ethnic group in the United States. The proportion of Latino/Hispanics in the population grew by 14.2% in fourteen years, from 6.4% in 1980 (14.6 million) to an estimated 12.5% (35.5 million) in 2001(with a 58% increase during the 90's) (Asomoa, Rodriguez, Gines, Varela, Dominguez et al., 2004). This numbers does not include illegal migrants, a number that is difficult to establish. It is well known that most of the migrating populations that arrive in the USA are of Latino/Hispanic origin, being Mexican Americans the largest subgroup, Puerto Ricans the second, and Cuban Americans the third largest subgroup (Lewis-Fernandez, Das, Alfonso, Weissman and Olfson, 2005). Some of them leave their country of origin to pursue the "American dream", which for many of them is synonymous to having freedom, better educational and economic opportunities, and prosperity. Others have to do so because of threats or political issues.

A recent trend is the fact that more women have been entering the migration stream, which had been primarily male (Forbes Martin, 2004). Latino/Hispanic women, especially migrants, have been identified to be at a higher risk for mental health problems due to the myriad of acculturation issues and economic hardships they may suffer with the migration process. Frequently, Latino/Hispanics are identified as a high-risk group for serious physical and mental health conditions, particularly depression, anxiety, substance abuse, cardiovascular disease and diabetes (Polednak, 2007; Mikolajczyk, Khelaifat, Maier, and Maxwell, 2007; National Alliance for Latino/Hispanic Health, 2001). These problems tend to be more prevalent among women. Furthermore, research has demonstrated that Latino/Hispanic ethnicity emerged as a risk factor for depressive symptoms, mainly among disadvantaged subgroups experiencing serious hardship (i.e., higher poverty) in the context of their historical, political, and societal reality (Bandiera, Pereira, Arif, Dodge, and Asal, 2008). Given that by 2020 depression is expected to be the second largest health care problem after heart disease worldwide, (5-A), the scope of this problem will be enormous among Latino/Hispanic women.

As mentioned before, Latino/Hispanic women suffer serious mental health pathologies, especially depression, because of the adaptation processes to the host society. However, current research indicates that recently arrived Latino immigrants, presumably most affected by acculturative stress, have better health outcomes than those who have spent greater time in the United States (5). The famous "Latino/Hispanic Paradox", which refers to the phenomenon that Latino/Hispanic groups that are characterized by low socioeconomic positions have better than expected health and mortality outcomes (Franzini, Ribble, and Keddie, 2001) is an extraordinary reality that needs to be studied more profoundly. Nevertheless, it is important to consider that Latino/Hispanics, especially Latino/Hispanic women, are different and that their multidiversity is explained by their diverse points of origin, subjective evaluations of the migration experience, immigration history, and social-class background. It is crucial to understand the aforementioned characteristic if we want to have a comprehensive view of the mental health phenomena in Latino/Hispanic women, especially depression within this population.

Triggering Factors

Acculturation and Social Support

Acculturation is defined as a sociocultural process through which the continuous contact between two or more different societies generates a cultural change. This necessarily implies a complex bilateral effect within the society or culture that serves as host (mainstream culture) and the immigrant culture (ethnic culture). Acculturation is classically used by many authors to explain ethnic differences in many mental and physical health research projects and their outcomes (Hunt, Scheider, and Comer, 2004; Dressler, 1993). Acculturation presumes that cultural foundations and practices such as traditions, beliefs, attitudes, knowledge, perceptions, among others, can cause people to act in a certain manner and make specific health decisions that can affect their quality of life.

For some individuals the migration process can be exciting and can be experienced as an adventure. After a while, it can evolve into a very stressful situation, when individuals begin facing loneliness, grief for the ones they left behind, fear of the unknown and frustration for not being able to fulfill their dreams. These factors can create chronic stress and contribute to the development of emotional difficulties, depressive symptoms, anxiety, and somatic problems (Achótegui, 2004).

The literature in mental health describes that acculturation stress may act as a trigger to develop depressive symptomatology (Crockett, Iturbide, Torres Stone, McGinley, Raffaelli, and Carlo, 2007). However, research has demonstrate that after adjusting for economic and social support variables the differences between groups begin to disappear (Mikolajczyk,

Bredehorst, Khelaifat, Maier, and Maxwell, 2007). This finding is relevant to explain how Latino/Hispanic women are vulnerable to develop depressive symptomatology, especially when they have some identified protective factors (i.e., adequate economic subsistence and support networks) that may diminish the probability of developing depression. Thus, the development of depression is not necessarily associated to migration as a process, but with the social support that the woman receives once she is inserted in the host society. Specifically, if Latino/Hispanic women have difficulty in identifying or receiving social support to facilitate and guarantee her basic physical, health and emotional needs, and those of her family, the possibility of developing depression is higher (Rodriguez, 1993).

While some Latino/Hispanic women migrate with their family or join them in the host country, a significant number of them migrate alone. Alone or with their family, it is a fact that they face multiple challenges when entering a foreign culture. These challenges are related to culture and language, as well as to gender roles. Migrant Latino/Hispanic women are exposed to different types of stressors, mainly those generated by cultural changes in gender roles and family structure (Ritsner, Ponizovsky, Nechamkin, and Modai, 2001).

Gender roles

Gender relations within the family, as well as hierarchies, are affected by migration because it is usually within the family that these systemic factors have their influence. For some women, this may mean acquiring relative independence and autonomy. For others, it may mean increased dependence and ostracism.

Traditionally, Latino/Hispanic men are characterized by "machismo", a social phenomenon composed by set of attitudes and behaviors in which men and women form two unequal groups, and in which men have the power and women are subordinated. Within this construct, men are expected to fulfill familial obligations associated with their gender and provide for the needs of the family (Sobralske, 2006). This leads to an increase in women's dependence and can limit their access to education, work opportunities and social integration, thus increasing the probability of developing depressive symptoms. Furthermore, many of these women are preoccupied with avoiding abandonment because of their dependence on their husband's earnings. Even under the threat of physical abuse, they keep their place and men continue to carry out the standards of machismo and associated dominance. Many women who migrate find themselves at risk of gender-based violence and exploitation.

Language Barriers

Language barriers may be an additional factor that can trigger mental health problems. The US Census 2000 states that more than 46 million people in the United States do not speak English as their primary language, and more than 21 million speak English less than "very well" (Jacobs, Chen, Karliner, Agger-Gupta and Mutha, 2006). Moreover, nearly half of the Latinos who primarily speak Spanish in their residences report difficulties speaking English (Lewis-Fernandez et al., 2005). An individual who enters a new country without knowing the language, or with serious problems to communicate using it, will face many structural barriers, as for instance, finding a job, obtaining access to basic governmental services, primary medical attention and various other major areas of need.

This problem is more critical when a Latino/Hispanic woman seeks assistance during or after an emergency, especially the ones related to mental health or an act of violence. Research findings indicate that a higher rate of violent act reports come from Latinas (Murdaugh, Hunt, Sowell and Santana, 2004). These women not only have difficulty in calling for assistance but also in coping with the violent event. The investigators found that that the major reasons for not telling were feeling ashamed or embarrassed (59%), not being able to speak English and not having a translator (41%).

Poverty

Poverty is not just the absence of income and physical resources, but it is also exclusion from participation in society, lack of power, and unequal distribution of resources. All of these factors may be playing a role in the lives of Latino/Hispanic immigrant women. Furthermore, the effects of discrimination that immigrant women face can create additional obstacles that hinder the escape from poverty. This is partly because of overt racism, but also institutional racism that does not give recognition to foreign credentials and experience.

Diversity can lead to a high degree of discrimination and exclusion from participation in society and can significantly increase the risk of poverty for certain groups of women. Migrant women who are often refugees or foreign domestic workers are particularly at risk of poverty and exploitation, as they are often forced to work in unregulated or clandestine employment. They are paid low wages, and despite the fact that they contribute significantly to the economy, they are not entitled to many of the public benefits.

Belle and Doucet (2003) demonstrated that the causes of depression in women in the United States seemed to be poverty, discrimination and lack of power. Poverty is one of the factors that consistently correlates with depression in women, because even when they are at a high risk, they rarely receive the treatment they need (Poleshuck, Giles, and Tu, 2006) . Poverty may result from migration, both for the migrant and for the family left behind, often mostly affecting women and children.

Substance Use and Abuse

Latino/Hispanic women have distinctive cultural factors that can put them at risk for the use of illicit drug and alcohol dependence. These may included the stress of recent immigration or illegal migratory status, having jobs in which being alert or even working double shifts is required. The additional stressors to which immigrant women are exposed, and the possibility of experiencing traumatic events such as domestic violence, can further compromise their psychological adjustment and trigger illegal substance use, which places them at a greater risk for depression. Moreover, researchers have demonstrated that drugs and alcohol may be used to reduce the effect of the absence of support in everyday life. This diminishes the possibility to understand reality, and may act as a compensatory factor to the overwhelming and constant negative affect that otherwise may causes extreme levels of emotional pain and stress (Khantzian, 1997; Krystal, 1997). If such levels of emotional distress cannot be diminished, depression may arise.

Alcohol dependence may also serve as a factor that can further compromise the psychological adjustment and well-being of Latino/Hispanic women. It is important to notice that Latino/Hispanic women have reported significantly greater occurrence of heavy drinking, positive attitudes about drinking, and perception that most of their friends use alcoholic beverages (Safer and Piane, 2007). Furthermore, the literature also indicates that Latino/Hispanic women drink more and may develop more alcohol-related problems as they acculturate (Polednak, 1997). It is important for mental health professional to be aware of this in order to be more efficient in their health interventions with Latino/Hispanic women (Caetano, Ramisetty-Mikler, Wallisch, McGrath and Spence, 2008).

Conclusion

There is a need for continued research of the various factors associated with the depression phenomena in Latino/Hispanic women. Given that Latino/Hispanic women are not a homogenous group, the design and development of linguistically and culturally sensitive and effective interventions that may serve for the prevention of depression in that group needs to be considered in a more specific manner.

It is crucial to pay attention to the significant differences between the Latino/Hispanic subpopulations. Programs intended to reduce feelings of isolation, lack of support, power, language barriers and economic hardship need to be developed by private and public agencies. This can include activities to enhance assertiveness and communication skills, empowerment, and financial independence in order to diminish risk factors for the development of depression in Latino/Hispanic women.

For being effective, interventions need to have a grassroots origin. Interventions that address issues in a more sensitive way, taking into consideration cultural factors, will be more readily accepted by Latino/Hispanic women and will reduce the resistance these women may have and will give them a higher probability of improving their quality of life and adaptation to the host society.

References

Achótegui, J. (2004). Emigrar en situación extrema: El Síndrome del inmigrante con estrés crónico y múltiple. *Norte de Salud Mental, 6*(21): 39-50.

Asamoa, K., Rodríguez, M., Ginés, V., Varela, R., Dominguez, K., Mills, C., Sotomayor, G., and Beck-Sagué, C. (2004). Report from the CDC. Use of preventive health services by Hispanic/Latino women in two urban communities: Atlanta, Georgia and Miami, Florida, 2000 and 2001. *Journal of Women's Health, 13*(6):654-61

Bandiera, F.C, Pereira, D.B, Arif, A.A, Dodge, B, and Asal, N. (2008). Race/ethnicity, income, chronic asthma, and mental health: a cross-sectional study using the behavioral risk factor surveillance system. *Psychosomatic Medicine, 70*(1):77-84.

Belle, D., Doucet, J., Harris, J., Miller, J., and Tan, E. (2000) Who is rich? Who is happy?*American Psychologist, 55*(10):1160-1161.

Caetano, R., Ramisetty-Mikler, S., Wallishc, L.S., MacGrath, C. and Spence, R.T. (2008). Acculturation, drinking and alcohol abuse and dependence among Latino/Hispanics in the Texas Mexico border. *Alcoholism: Clinical and Experimental Research, 32*(2): 314-321.

Crockett, L.J., Iturbide, M.I., Torres Stone, R.A., McGinley, M., Raffaelli, M., and Carlo, G. (2007). Acculturative stress, social support, and coping: relations to psychological adjustment among Mexican American college students. *Cultural Diversity and Ethnic Minority Psychology. 13*(4):347-55.

Dressler, W. (1993) Health in the African American community: accounting for health inequalities. *Medical Anthropology Quarterly, 7*:325–345.

Forbes Martin, S. (2-4 December, 2004). Women and Migration. Consultative Meeting on Migration and Mobility and How This Movement Affects Women. United Nations. Malmö, Sweden

Hunt, L.M., Schneider, S., and Comer, B. (2004) "Acculturation" be a variable in health research? A critical review of research on U.S. Latino/Hispanics. *Soc Sci Med.,* 59:973–86.

Jacobs, E., Chen, A.H., Karliner, L.S., Agger-Gupta, N., and Mutha, S. (2006). The need for more research on language barriers in health care: a proposed research agenda. *Milbank Quarterly. 84*(1):111-33.

Khantzian, E.J. (1997). The self-medication hypothesis of substance use disorders: A reconsideration and recent applications. *Harvard Review of Psychiatry,* 4: 231–244.

Krystal, H. (1997). Self representation and the capacity for self care. In: Yalisove, D.L. (Ed). *Essential papers on addiction.* New York: New York University Press; pp. 87–108.

Lewis-Fernández R, Das AK, Alfonso C, Weissman MM, and Olfson M. (2005). Depression in US Hispanics: diagnostic and management considerations in family practice. *Journal of the American Board Family Practice; 18*(4):282-96.

Mikolajczyk, R.T., Bredehorst, M., Khelaifat, N., Maier, C. and Maxwell, A.E. (2007) Correlates of depressive symptoms among Latino and Non-Latino White adolescents: findings from the 2003California Health Interview Survey. *BMC Public Health, 21*, 7-21

Murdaugh,C., Salena H., Sowell, R., and Irma Santana, I. (2004). Domestic Violence in Hispanics in the SoutheasternUnited States: A Survey and Needs Analysis. *Journal of Family Violence, 19* (2): 108-115

National Alliance for Latino/Hispanic Health (2001) Quality Health Services for Latino/Hispanics: The Cultural Competency Component.

Nguyen, H.T., Clark, M., and Ruiz, R.J. (2007). Effects of acculturation on the reporting of depressive symptoms among Hispanic pregnant women. *Nursing Research, 56*(3):217-23.

Polednak, A.P. (1997). Gender and acculturation in relation to alcohol use among Latino/Hispanic adults in two areas of the northeastern United States. *Substance Abuse and Misuse, 32*(11): 1513-1524

Polednak, A.P. (2007) Prevalence and predictors of comorbid diabetes among newly diagnosed Latino/Hispanic cancer patients in Connecticut. *Cancer Detect Prev. 31*(6):453-6.

Poleshuck, E.L., Giles, D.E., and Tu, X. (2006). Pain and depressive symptoms among financially disadvantaged women's health patients. Women's Health, 15(2):182-93.

Ramisetty-Mikler S, Caetano R, and McGrath C. (2007). Sexual aggression among White, Black, and Hispanic couples in the U.S.: alcohol use, physical assault and psychological aggression as its correlates. *American Journal Drug Alcohol Abuse. 33*(1):31-43.

Rodríguez, J. (1993). Family structure and depression: a study of Puerto Rican women in New York. Fordham University, Unpublished doctoral dissertation, Graduate School of Social Sciences and Arts. New York.

Ritsner, M., Ponizovsky, A., Nechamkin, Y., and Modai, I. (2001). Gender differences in psychosocial risk factors for psychological distress among immigrants. *Comprehensive Psychiatry,. 42*(2):151-60.

Safer, A.M., and Piane, G. (2007). Analysis of acculturation, sex, and heavy alcohol use in Latino college students. *Psychological Reports, 101*(2): 565-573

Sobralske, M. (2006). Machismo sustains health and illness beliefs of Mexican American men.*Journal American Academy of Nurse Practitioners, 18*(8):348-50.

In: Women and Depression
Editors: Paula Hernandez and Sara Alonso

ISBN 978-1-60456-647-5
© 2009 Nova Science Publishers, Inc.

Chapter 7

Networking rCBF Gender Differences in Major Depression

Dario Salmaso[1], Marco Pagani[1,2] and Ann Gardner[3]

[1]Institute of Cognitive Sciences and Technologies (ISTC), CNR, Rome and Padua, Italy
[2]Department of Nuclear Medicine, Karolinska Hospital, Stockholm, Sweden
[3]Karolinska Institutet, Department of Clinical Neuroscience, Stockholm, Sweden

Abstract

Background: There is large evidence that major depressive disorder (MDD) has prevalence rates almost twice as high in females as in men. However, few studies have investigated in MDD the regional cerebral blood flow (rCBF) differences between genders. The aim of the study was to identify the influence of gender on the rCBF distribution in a group of depressed patients. This was performed by means of Volume of Interest (VOI) analysis and Principal Component Analysis (PCA), this latter exploring functional brain connectivity and transforming a number of correlated variables by clustering them into functionally uncorrelated factors

Methods: A group of 76 major depressed patients (36 males and 40 females) were investigated by ^{99m}Tc-HMPAO and SPECT. Analysis of covariance (ANCOVA) and PCA were performed on 54 VOIs. Neuropsychiatric tests (MADRS, SCID, CFQ, KSP) were also carried out to assess disease severity without finding any gender differences.

Results: VOIs analysis identified in females as compared to males a significantly higher rCBF distribution ($F(1,73)=10.875$; $p=0.002$). A significant VOI*Gender interaction was also found ($F(26,1898)=2.180$; $p=0.001$) revealing that 10 regions belonging to the frontal, temporal, parietal and occipital cortex were particularly involved in gender differences. An overall effect of gender was also found for PCA ($F(1,73)=8.814$; $p=0.004$). The significant PCs*Gender interaction ($F(12,876)=3.258$; $p<0.000$) revealed lower rCBF distribution in males as compared to females in 6 PCs. Such PCs, grouped brain regions belonging to parietal-limbic cortex (PC3; $p=0.033$), parieto-temporo-occipital cortex (PCs 8 and 9; $p=0.001$), fronto-parietal cortex (PC10; $p=0.017$), fronto-temporal cortex (PC12; $p=0.001$) and hippocampi (PC 13; $p=0.017$). Age related hippocampal differences were found in PC13 in female only.

Conclusion: PC8 grouped two areas involved in linguistic processing, the angular and the supramarginal gyrus of the left hemispheres for which gender differences are widely accepted. PC9 with the right angular gyrus was also likely to show rCBF differences since females are known to be more bilaterally organized. Gender differences in hippocampi confirmed previous findings. However, medial prefrontal cortex (anterior cingulate) bilaterally and right dorsolateral prefrontal cortex, regions known from the existing literature to be implicated in MDD, were grouped by PCA into different PCs (PC1 and PC4, respectively) but did not show any sex difference speaking against specific gender related rCBF changes in major depression.

PCA grouping functionally connected brain regions increased the depth of the analysis yielding more information on the processes underlying perfusion distribution measurements in MDD.

Depression, Neuroimaging and Related Methodology

Background

Major Depressive Disorder (MDD) is a primary idiopathic condition (i.e. arising spontaneously, or from an unknown cause) characterized by the occurrence of depressive episodes (Unipolar Depression). The symptoms ought to be present for at least two weeks and cause significant distress in important areas of brain functioning. It has been suggested that MDD episodes are the most severe state of illness representing only the tip of the iceberg in a common, chronic and disabling disease with alternating symptom severity [1].

The lifetime prevalence of MDD has been reported to be as high as 26% [2]. MDD is now included among the ten leading disorders for global disease burden and in the next years will become one of the dominant neuro-psychiatric and social issues.

The concept of neuronal activity may refer to spiking activity or local synaptic activity, and is associated with several physiological variables such as energy and oxygen consumption, glucose utilization and regional cerebral blood flow (rCBF). In neuroimaging studies using Single Photon Emission Computed Tomography (SPECT) and Positron Emission Tomography (PET) the measured signals are indirectly related to the neuronal activity reflecting, to various extents, the above mentioned variables. Increases of brain energy demands have for more than a century been believed to increase brain blood flow, but the precise nature of the relationship remains unknown even if wide experimental evidence provides support for direct coupling between glucose metabolism and neuronal activity. However cerebral blood flow is easier to measure than glucose metabolism, and measurements of blood flow have a better temporal resolution. Positive correlations exist between capillary density, metabolic rate and blood flow and interpreting the magnitude of rCBF changes as changes in synaptic and neuronal activity may be reasonable foremost during normal circumstances.

Increased SPECT tracer distribution in various regions, including frontal regions, was reported in depression studies [3]. However, reviewing functional imaging studies in depression it was found that the decreased tracer distribution in frontal regions compared to control subjects was the most common finding [4-22]. It is yet not clear if alterations of tracer distribution reflect 'trait' phenomena that are present prior to onset of overt depression, or 'state' phenomena. It is also unknown if abnormalities of tracer distribution are patho-physiologically involved in the evolution of depression, or are an additional expression of an as yet unknown etiological factor of the disease. For all these above mentioned reasons the deeper investigation level allowed by multivariate analysis might help in clarifying in MDD the fine and hidden relationships between regions not detectable with conventional statistical analysis [23].

In a meta-study, the trend for reductions in all cortical and subcortical regions remained for remitted depressed patients [24]. Increased tracer retention in the left frontal and anterior cingulate gyrus has been reported after electro-convulsive treatment [25], and decreased retention was found in the orbitofrontal and/or anterior cingulate after treatment with repetitive transcranial stimulation [26].

In Alzheimer's Disease and Parkinson Disease, decreased radiopharmaceutical retention has been linked to regional cell loss. The decrease retention that has been reported in depression may, hypothetically, reflect the spine loss indicated by the decreases of synaptic "products" [27], the decrease of inhibitory local circuit neurons [28], and/or the reduced cortical glial cell numbers [29]. Decreased activity in a few of the functional circuits is another possibility.

Conversely, increased retention in depression may reflect increased activity in some functional units as well as other phenomena such as increased intracellular GSH levels. This phenomenon has been described in the early stages of mitochondrial disease and is considered to be due to increased oxidative stress secondary to reduced respiratory chain enzyme activity [30].

Single Photon Emission Computed Tomography (SPECT)

Modern gamma camera, operating on-line to a computer system for additional signal and image processing, image display and tomographic reconstruction, are designed with more than one camera head, typically three. Tomographic examination is a pre-requisite for rCBF SPECT, due to the complex brain anatomy with superimposed anatomo-functional structures. The resulting contrast-enhancing effect of the tomographic registration technique is of great importance since the differences between normal and pathological uptake in various brain regions may be rather small.

The studies of rCBF using SPECT are based on depicting the distribution of ^{99m}Tc - d,l – hexamethylpropylene amine oxime (^{99m}Tc-HMPAO), ^{99m}Tc – ethyl cysteinate dimer (^{99m}Tc-ECD) or [^{123}I]-Iodoamphetamine, which are imaged in the brain after intravenous administration. Despite that [^{123}I]-Iodoamphetamine may best represent rCBF, this tracer is rarely used due to a high cost and restricted availability. In this paper we have reviewed only studies performed with ^{99m}Tc-HMPAO.

The intracellular retention of ^{99m}Tc-HMPAO in the central nervous system is the effect of a rapid conversion from the lipophilic into the hydrophilic form at the exposure to endogenous intracellular glutathione, which is a powerful reducing agent. Trapped in the cell, ^{99m}Tc-HMPAO remains practically unchanged being its detection limited by decay of [99m]Tc (t½=6.02 h). This specific property allows for scans performed several hours later to still depict the rCBF at the moment of administration and is of paramount importance when examining physically and mentally impaired patients allowing for the administration to be made in a quite environment and the scan postponed according to patients physical and psychological status.

Standardization Software

In the recent past standardization software and novel statistical methodologies have been implemented by several groups in both neurodegenerative and psychiatric research in order to improve the diagnostic accuracy of functional neuroimaging.

The assessment of CBF patterns in various brain disorders by SPECT or PET have in the past mainly been carried out either by visual evaluation or by outlining the regions of interest (ROIs) in a manual or semiautomatic mode. Such methods might suffer from excessive operator's influence in the choice of the ROIs and, due to the variable shape of human brains, lack of spatial normalization, resulting in anatomical in-homogeneous brain samples among subjects.

Recently, semi-automatic approaches to assess regional CBF changes in group comparison have been developed opening up the conditions for a new approach in research and allowing an easier and earlier diagnosis. By carefully spatially standardizing each scan is possible, by means of subtractions images and/or statistical comparisons, to precisely identify regions with abnormal flow. The advantage of this techniques is the possibility to exploit the knowledge of rCBF patterns as assessed in normative or pathological scans identifying regional difference on a group to group basis.

In 3D analysis, the inclusion of the white matter makes the sample more representative for global neurodegenerative changes and volumes of interest (VOIs) can be positioned on both anatomical and functional regions improving the physiological significance of the analysis. White matter is an important part of the neuronal system and it is affected by neurodegenerative, cerebrovascular and psychiatric disorders to the same extent as grey matter. Grey matter perfusion is 2.0-3.5 times higher than white matter perfusion. When 3D analysis is performed on extensive data the resulting rCBF is then calculated by averaging, in a certain volume, a variable number of counts detected in both grey and white matter kernels.

The most currently available 3D standardization software share similar principles and can be classified into two categories: the voxel-based ones (i.e. SPM) and the ones based on neuroanatomy (i.e. CBA). We briefly describe these two different approaches.

Statistical Parametrical Mapping (SPM) [31], is the worldwide mostly used voxel-based standardization software in brain imaging for between- and within-subject group comparisons. Images are spatially standardized into a common space, and smoothed. Parametric statistical models are summed, at each voxel, using the General Linear Model to describe the variability in the data. Hypotheses expressed in terms of the model parameters are assessed at each voxel with univariate statistics. This results in an image whose voxel values are statistics, producing t-statistical maps of significant changes in distribution and basing the output on the analyses of clusters of voxels. Such analysis should take into account the statistical threshold as well as the size of the cluster in relationship to the implemented methodology: the higher the spatial resolution of the camera the smaller the size of cluster of voxels for statistically significance.

The Computerized Brain Atlas (CBA) is a software tool originally developed by Greitz et al. [32], and applicable to any brain imaging modality. It is based on data from one cryosectioned brain in combination with information from the literature. It contains 3D surface descriptions, or volumes of interest (VOIs) of approximately 400 brain structures including the brain surface, the ventricular system, the cortical gyri and sulci, as well as the cortical cytoarchitectonic areas (Brodmann areas, BAs). The major basal ganglia and the brain stem nuclei are also included.

All image sets are spatially normalized into the stereotactic space of the atlas by using global polynomial transformation [33]. It consists of translations, rotations and linear scaling along and around each of the three image axes. It also contains 18 non-linear shape-deforming parameters, which makes it possible to individualize the shape of the brain. CBA identifies the brain surface, the ventricular system and some central nuclei and fits to the aforementioned structures by minimizing the difference in voxel intensity. Subsequently, it deforms and stretches these structures, maximizing a simple similarity measure, to fit them to a previously defined reference SPECT scan. A major advantage of the technique is that it creates an almost fully automatic tool able to decrease the analysis time and to standardize subjects' brains providing additional anatomic information. The segmentation of the brain in VOIs reduces the number of variables to an amount that is possible, in a second step, to submit to multivariate analysis.

Statistical Approach

Univariate Analysis

In univariate analysis there is only one variable under consideration. It can be independent, as in the case of CBF data or dependent as in the case of the same subject measured at two different times. In both cases it is possible to describe the data in terms of mean and variance (the two parameters of the normal distribution). After testing the two means, possible significant differences need to be explained. The standard approach is to assume that the difference is due to an experimental effect and sources of variance are under control. However, this is not so obvious in neuro-functional studies in which many sources of variance are present. Hence, if we want to study the relationships among those sources, multivariate analysis has to be implemented.

The t-test for dependent samples is the most commonly used method to evaluate the differences in means between two groups of observation made on the same sample of subjects who were tested twice. When group of observation are made on different subjects a t-test for independent samples is used. One-way Analysis of Variance (ANOVA) is performed when groups are three or more. In such cases nothing can be done about the variation due to individual differences since it is not possible to identify, or subtract, such differences. This is why the t-test for independent samples is always less sensitive.

Multivariate Analysis

Multivariate statistic provides a simultaneous analysis of multiple independent (i.e. gender, disease) and dependent (i.e. hemispheres, VOI) variables in order to determine the differences within them and their relationship. Such statistical approach also introduces regional analyses based on the assumption that correlated patterns exist among different brain regions and such relationships affect reciprocally the investigated variable. Variables may be correlated with each other, and their statistical dependence is often taken into account when analyzing such data. In fact, the consideration of statistical dependence and intercorrelations between variables make multivariate analysis somewhat different in approach and considerably more complex than the corresponding univariate analysis, in which there is only one variable under consideration. In the multivariate perspective each voxel is considered conjointly with explicit reference to the interactions among brain regions rendering it particularly appropriate for brain studies and providing a complementary characterization of CBF patterns.

Multivariate analysis requires the number of observations (scans) to be greater than the number of components of the multivariate observation (variables, i.e. voxels). In neuroimaging techniques (in which the raw images contain and extremely high number of voxels) the number of variables needs therefore to be reduced, by using VOIs or factorial groupings.

Multivariate analysis takes also into account the statistical inference about the response of the entire brain, without regional specificity. If interactions are present one can move from an "omnibus" effect to regional changes with the limitation of the sample size (ROI/VOI/factor).

Principal Component Analysis (PCA)

Principal Component Analysis (PCA) is a data driven technique (i.e., there is no a-priori model or hypothesis) that transforms a number of (possibly) correlated variables into a (smaller) number of not-correlated factors, called principal components. PCA is totally data-led and is independent by any model or a-priori hypothesis. It does not create effects that are not present in the data, nor does lose information. The first principal component accounts for the highest percentage of the variability in the data and each of the following component accounts for a portion of the remaining variability in a descending scale. Variables are summarized in fewer dimensions while retaining most of the information. Each factor, or PC, explains a different part of the total variance of data set. This statistical approach introduces regional analyses based on the assumption that correlated patterns exist among different brain regions and such relationships affect reciprocally the rCBF or the metabolism. It sorts subject-region interaction and it guarantees that regional coupling has been accounted for. In PCA each component is orthogonal and functionally not correlated to the remaining ones.

An advantage with a neuroanatomic atlas-VOI-based approach is that it allows for the investigation of the rCBF relationships between anatomically distributed but physiologically correlated brain regions using PCA. Applying PCA to the VOIs permits for a reduction of the number of variables through the grouping of VOIs into PCs. This latter characteristic of PCA might be of utmost importance in analyzing pathological conditions, as in the case of psychiatric disorders, in which functionally integrated pathways are involved in the disease process.

Functional Connectivity

Functional connectivity implies that pool activities of brain areas "go up and down" together and regions share a significant number of neurons whose dynamic interactions occur at the same time. Correlated areas will have correlated perfusion and neuronal activity. Functional connectivity is simply a statement about the observed correlations and characterizes distributed brain systems.

The functional role played by any component (neuron) of a connected system (brain) is largely defined by its connections. Extrinsic connections between cortical areas are not continuous but occur in patches or clusters (functional segregation, in which cells with common functional properties are thought to be grouped together).

On the other hand functional integration is mediated by the interactions between functionally segregated areas resulting in a general functional connectivity effect on the brain. Functional connectivity characterizes distributed brain systems and implies "model-free" temporal correlations between neurophysiological events: correlated areas will have correlated perfusion and neuronal activity.

The issues related to functional segregation are generally investigated by means of univariate analysis while functional integration is better analyzed by multivariate analysis.

SPM is typically predicated by functional segregation and analyses regionally specific aspects of functional organization. PCA and multivariate analysis are inspired by functional integration mediated by anatomical, functional and effective connections that form the basis for characterizing patterns of correlations and describe distributed changes in terms of systems.

Networking rCBF Gender Differences in Major Depression

Introduction

In a recent article Halbreich and Kahn reviewed the gender differences in various form of depression [34]. They reported that women as compared to men have a higher probability to suffer from MDD, have a two-fold greater risk for recurrent MDD and an higher lifetime

MDD estimates having been these variability mainly due to biological vulnerabilities and environmental provoking experiences [35]. Chronicity of depression appears to affect more women that men [36] but in a MDD study Lacerda et al. [37] found a significant reduced left lateral orbito-frontal cortex volume in males but not in female.

However, brain functional studies have reported few and sparse findings about gender differences in MDD and no conclusive results about an established rCBF pattern common to the most of MDD patients have reached a wide consensus within the neuroimaging community.

The aim of present investigation was to contribute to the understanding of sex differences in a group of MDD patients as assessed by SPECT and multivariate analysis.

Materials and Methods

Patients and Neuropsychiatric Testing

Seventy-six subjects representing a selected group of MDD patients were included in the study. Thirty-six patients were males (mean age±SD 51.4±8.7 yrs) and forty females (mean age±SD 46.0±8.6 yrs). Thirty-six percent of males (n=13) and twenty-eight percent of females (n=11) were taking psychotropic medications at the time of the SPECT. No patient was taking any neuroleptic agent.

The remaining patients were either drug naive (n=52) or had previously been treated with antidepressant or psychotherapy without any effect. In some of them antidepressant treatment was interrupted due to side effects. Patients were mainly right-handed (88 percent for males and 90 percent for females). The patients were recruited from a hospital-affiliated psychiatric outpatient clinic accepting patients with concomitant physical symptoms (audiological, pain and/or intestinal motility symptoms), i.e. symptoms that have been found to be commonly associated with mood disorders [38-43]. All patients had had at least one MDD episode according to DSM-IV criteria and had a chronic depressive disorder with pronounced physical symptoms and significant impairment in social functioning. For ethical and practical reasons SPECT was performed during the chronic depressive state rather than during spikes with exacerbated mood symptoms. All subjects were outpatients and had to travel to the SPECT examination without any assistance.

Neuropsychiatric tests were administered few days before SPECT. Patients were administered the Karolinska Scales of Personality (KSP), a self-report questionnaire conceived to quantify of some crucial personality or temperament dimensions representing qualities of the information processing and arousal systems of the individual [44]. The scores of the patients were compared with normative data transformed to t-scores (50 ± 10) which have been obtained from 400 subjects randomly sampled from the Stockholm population and standardized for age and sex. In patients with ongoing MDD as well as in patients who have recovered from mood symptoms, high scores have been reported on the Psychasthenia, Muscular Tension, Somatic Anxiety, and Psychic Anxiety scales, and low scores on the Socialization scale [45-46]. The self-rating 9-items version of the Montgomery Aasberg Depression Rating Scale with a 6-point response format (MADRS-S; 9), was used to assess current mood. The Structured Clinical Interview for DSM-IV (SCID), a 100-item semi-structured diagnostic interview, was used to evaluate personality disorders and the Cognitive Failures Questionnaire (CFQ), a 25-item test to assess the frequency of everyday slips and errors, investigated the cognitive domain and the everyday memory.

The study was approved by the local ethical committee and all patients provided written informed consent.

Radiopharmaceutical and SPECT

After 30 min rest at a tranquil place with dimmed light, 1000 MBq (27.0 mCi) of ^{99m}Tc-HMPAO, (Ceretec®, Amersham International plc, Little Chalfont, UK) was injected i.v. within 15 min from reconstitution. The radiopharmaceutical was prepared strictly according to the manufacturer's instructions. SPECT brain imaging was performed using a three-headed gamma camera (TRIAD XLT 20, Trionix Research Laboratory Inc., Twinsburg, OH, USA) equipped with low-energy ultra-high resolution collimators. The projection data were acquired for 15 seconds per projection at 90 equal angles of a complete revolution (0-360°).

Before reconstruction, the projection data were pre-processed using a 2D Hamming filter with a cut-off frequency of 2.25 cycles/cm. Sectional images were reconstructed by filtered back projection using a Ramp filter with a cut-off frequency of 0.6 cycles/cm. During pre-processing correction for attenuation was made using the uniform Chang method [47]. No scatter correction was applied. Both acquisition and reconstruction were performed in 128x128 matrices with a pixel size of 2.22 x 2.22 mm^2.

Standardization Software

CBA was implemented for anatomo-functional standardization and for image analysis.

For evaluation and statistical analysis of the reformatted data sets, 27 VOIs, bilaterally, were selected. These regions corresponded to Brodmann Areas and numeration, in prefrontal (BA9, BA10, BA46), frontal (BA4, BA6, BA8, BA44, BA45), parietal (BA1-2-3 (SE), BA5, BA7, BA39, BA40) and temporal (BA21, BA37, BA38) cortex. Four regions, representing primary and associative auditory cortex (BA22, BA41, BA42, BA52) were merged into one single VOI (AUD). The remaining regions corresponded to cingulate (BA24, BA31, BA32) and occipital (BA17, BA18, BA19) cortex as well as putamen, nucleus caudatus, thalamus and hippocampus. In order to obtain a set of normalized relative flow data, a scaling factor was computed by averaging the brain voxels data and setting the global brain average to a pre-defined value. Before averaging the voxel data, a fixed counts/voxel threshold was selected to include in the normalization process the 30% of all brain voxels with the highest counts. The normalized value was set to 50 "uptake-units" and all rCBF values of this work were related to this value.

Statistical Analysis

After adaptation and definitions of VOIs using CBA, the ^{99m}Tc-HMPAO uptake data of all subjects were exported to a statistical package (Systat 10, 2000) for subsequent statistical analysis.

Principal Component Analysis was performed on all 76 patients and was based on all 54 VOIs (27 for each hemisphere). PCA transformed a number of correlated variables by clustering them into common factors (PCs), such that variables with higher loadings within each factor were highly correlated, but factors were uncorrelated to one another.

PCs may be treated as new variables and their values can be computed for individual cases. These values are known as factor scores, or component scores (CS), and are a linear combination of each variable included in the analysis. They should be used both to re-evaluate group differences and as predictor variables in diagnostic research. However, in the latter case, it is preferable not to use CS, but an imperfect estimate (coarse component scores, CCS) generated by summing all the VOIs with higher loading in a given factor. An advantage to using CCS is that they can more easily be computed and interpreted than CS and can also be compared between studies. The number of factors was determined by the number of eigenvalues greater than one. We considered as representative of a factor the variables with an absolute factor loadings greater than 0.5. This is an arbitrary value, but it is commonly used since it explains a moderate part of the variance of the factor. By increasing the value further, some variables should be eliminated from the calculation of CCS reducing the variance explained by these scores. Furthermore, CCS are computed only from VOIs with higher loadings on each PC and each VOI enters only one time in PC calculation. CCS were standardized to a 0-1 scale.

ANCOVA (age as covariate) was applied to VOIs values and then to the CCS of PCs to test rCBF differences for statistical significance, considering gender as a between subject variable. As for VOIs analysis, a third within-factor was considered, i.e. the hemisphere. Significance level for all analyses was set to $p \leq 0.05$.

Results

Demographic data of males and females are shown in Table 1. Males were older than females (t-test (df=74)=2.72; p=0.008). Therefore, all subsequent ANOVA were covaried for age. Values for the various neuropsychiatric scales are reported in Table 1. No differences were detected between males and females.

The ANCOVA performed on the 54 VOIs showed a main effect for gender (F(1,73)=10.875, p=0.002) and a significant interaction hemisphere*gender (F(26,1898)=2.180, p<0.001). We therefore performed 27 ANCOVA at single VOI level, considering only gender as factor. Gender differences were found in 10 VOIs belonging to prefrontal, temporal, parietal and occipital cortex (see Table 2). In all VOIs rCBF in females was higher than in males (44.8 vs. 44.3). Statistical analysis did not show any effect of medication on CBF.

Table 1. Demographic data relative to gender

	Male			Female		
	N	MEAN	SD	N	MEAN	SD
AGE *	36	51.4	8.7	40	46.0	8.6
MADRS	27	22.93	9.92	32	22.09	9.18
CFQ	31	57.74	18.76	32	56.75	19.04
SCIDTOTAL	20	34.75	19.27	28	37.39	17.25
KSP Somatic anxiety	22	70.36	17.3	34	65.06	10.68
KSP Psychasthenia	22	59.36	11.67	34	56.29	11.34
KSP Muscular tension	22	75.55	16.96	34	70.32	10.78
KSP Social desirability	22	49.05	9.13	34	51.03	10.21
KSP Detachment	22	48.14	14.07	34	50.06	10.21
KSP Psychasthenia	22	72.14	12.98	34	69.91	10.42
KSP Socialization	22	34.64	11.83	34	35.82	14.35
KSP Verbal aggression	22	51.32	9.13	34	47.18	9.97
KSP Irritability	22	55.55	10.45	34	55.71	11.45
KSP Suspicion	22	57.45	14.4	34	55.88	13.52
KSP Guilt	22	54.55	10.39	34	50.65	8.81
Handedness	34	88%		38	90%	
Medication free	23	63%		29	73%	

* Significant at t-test: $p<0.01$.

Table 2. Relative mean rCBF and relative SD values for males and females. F and p values are relative to the single ANCOVA (with age as covariate) analyses in which gender was considered

VOIs	Female (n=40)		Male (n=36)		Main effect: Gender	
	Mean	SD	Mean	SD	F(1,73)	p=
AUD	44.7	1.50	43.5	1.54	11.364	0.001
BA07	46.2	1.47	45.3	1.66	4.077	0.047
BA18	41.2	1.60	40.6	1.62	5.979	0.017
BA19	41.4	1.14	40.4	1.06	22.188	0.000
BA21	41.7	1.61	40.3	1.56	15.301	0.000
BA37	43.0	1.36	41.9	1.36	10.168	0.002
BA39	41.7	1.37	40.8	1.36	10.037	0.002
BA40	43.2	1.31	42.1	1.53	9.553	0.003
BA44	45.6	1.35	44.6	1.69	4.262	0.043
SE	42.6	1.23	41.7	1.08	9.981	0.002

Mean CBF values are normalized to 50. BA=Brodmann area; SE=1+2+3; AUD=22+41+42+52;

Table 3. Factorial grouping of volumes of interest (VOIs) following principal component analysis on depressed patients. F and p values are relative to gender differences

PC	VOIs with high loading on the PC	CCS VALUES				
		Female (n=40)		Male (n=36)		Main effect: Gender
		Mean	SD	Mean	SD	F(1,73)=	p=
PC1	BA24R BA24L BA32R BA32L BA44L	0.58	0.16	0.49	0.21		
PC2	BA21L BA38R BA38L	0.61	0.22	0.54	0.22		
PC3	BA05R BA05L BA07R BA07L BA31L	0.56	0.18	0.44	0.21	4.708	0.033
PC4	BA08R BA09R BA10R BA45R BA46R	0.41	0.20	0.43	0.25		
PC5	BA17R BA17L BA18R BA18L	0.47	0.19	0.50	0.26		
PC6	BA04L BA06R BA06L BA08L	0.48	0.18	0.54	0.26		
PC7	PUTR PUTL THALL	0.46	0.20	0.49	0.28		
PC8	BA19L BA39L BA40L	0.56	0.20	0.41	0.21	13.152	0.001
PC9	BA19R BA37R BA39R	0.60	0.18	0.44	0.17	15.505	0.000
PC10	BA04R BA40R SER	0.49	0.23	0.37	0.20	5.985	0.017
PC11	CAUDR CAUDL THALR	0.63	0.21	0.60	0.17		
PC12	AUDR AUDL BA21R BA44R	0.58	0.20	0.41	0.19	12.511	0.001
PC13	BA37L HIPPR HIPPL	0.47	0.22	0.33	0.21	4.513	0.037
OVERALL MEANS		0.53	0.20	0.46	0.22		

The 13 PCs explain the 81.5% of total variance. CCS= Coarse Component Scores; CAUD= caudate nucleus; PUT= putamen; THAL= thalamus; HIPP= hippocampus; AUD= Auditory cortex (22+41+42+52); BA= Brodmann area; L= left; R= right. The PCA excluded from the final solution BA09L BA10L BA45L BA46L SEL in the left hemisphere, and BA31R in the right hemisphere. The CCS values were standardized to a 0-1 scale.

PCA, performed on the 54 VOIs, resulted in 13 factors (PCs). These orthogonal and un-correlated factors explained the 81.5% of the total data variance. Only 6 out of 54 VOIs were excluded from the final solutions. The structure of PCA is reported in Table 3 together with ANCOVA results. Overall analysis showed both a main effect for gender (F(1,73)=8.814; p=0.004; Figure 1) and a gender*factor interaction (F(12, 876)=3.258, p<0.001).

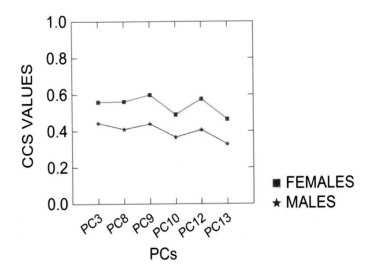

Figure 1. Overall gender effect on CCS values of significantly different PCs.

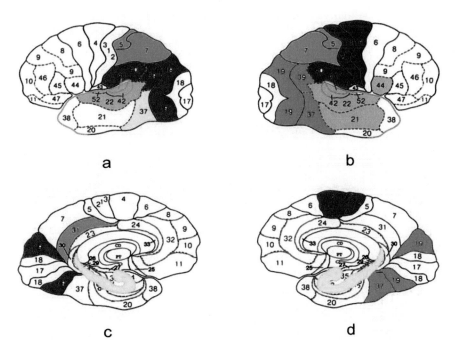

a

b

c

d

Figure 2. Representation of lateral and medial aspects of hemispheres depicting the 6 PCs for which there was a significant gender effect in 76 MDD patients. a = Left lateral aspect; b = Right lateral aspect; c = Left medial aspect; d = Right medial aspect. VOIs grouped into each PC are depicted with the same color.

As compared to males, females rCBF was relatively higher in 6 out of 13 PC (see Table 3 and Figure 2). Such PCs, grouped brain regions belonging to parietal-limbic cortex (PC3), parieto-temporo-occipital cortex (PCs 8 and 9), right fronto-parietal cortex (PC10), fronto-temporal cortex (PC12) and hippocampi (PC13).

At the end we conducted age-related regression analyses for both males and females and for each of the significant PC. Results showed a significant effect of age in females for PC13 ($F(1,38)=6.98$, $p=0.01$, Figure 3) but not in males. Linear regression was: PC13=0.93-0.01*AGE.

Conclusion

Previous investigations on rCBF in depressed patients have often been conflicting, showing either increased or decreased rCBF tracer distribution in various regions These regions and/or clusters of voxels have almost always been analyzed as variables independent from each other.

The functional role of neurons is strictly dependent on their connections. In this respect it is important to take anatomo-functional connectivity into account, highlighting the correlated patterns existing among the variables [23]. It has been argued in favor of methods able to determine possible networking within brain regions [48] considering brain regions not as single units (univariate analysis) but taking into account their mutual relationships (factor analysis). Functional connectivity in major depression has recently been explored by investigating pairs of structures belonging to the limbic system and connected by a simple bivariate linear mode [49]. By implementing a multivariate model we were able to correlate cortical and subcortical interactions at a higher level.

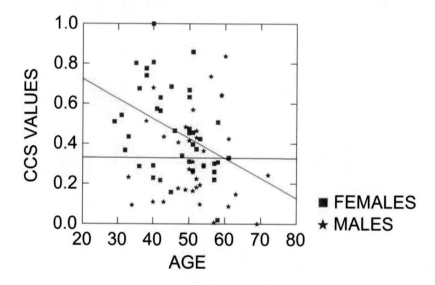

Figure 3. Regression analysis depicting the variations of PC13 CCS with age.

Compared with male MDD patients, we found a significantly higher rCBF in female patients in large regions (as defined by PCA) in frontal, temporal, parietal and occipital cortex. In our study regions showing significant group differences were larger when changes were analyzed by PCs as compared to single VOI analysis (see Tables 2 and 3) and gender differences in the hippocampi were highlighted by PCA only. In PCA, VOIs were considered as independent variables and grouped into factors either containing or not containing the homologous contralateral Brodmann areas. This is an interesting aspect of the analysis with important neurophysiological implications in the lateralization of most of the VOIs showing statistically significant difference between genders. This effect was not present at single VOI analysis in which an hemispheric effect was not present and might have an impact on the different contribution of right and left hemisphere to emotional feelings.

The VOIs shown by single analysis to differ significantly between genders were mostly grouped by multivariate analysis in PCs containing adjacent and functionally correlated BAs (PCs 8, 9, 10, 12), reinforcing the biological significance of the analysis.

Medial prefrontal cortex (including anterior cingulate cortex bilaterally, PC1) and right dorsolateral prefrontal cortex (PC4), regions previously reported to be implicated in MDD, did not show any difference speaking against specific gender related rCBF changes in major depression. However in our specific group of patient the finding of a statistically significant increased rCBF tracer distribution in six PCs in females as compared to male deserves attention.

The majority of patients participating in the present study have been previously investigated by the same methodology [50] and a significantly higher ^{99m}Tc-HMPAO distribution was found in several cortical regions in the whole group of patients (males and females as taken together). They suffered long-standing depression with concomitant physical symptoms and represent a subpopulation of depressed patients with chronic physical problems rather than depressed patients in the general population. The vast majority of patients exhibited flight of ideas and difficulties in keeping to the topic of conversation, suggesting increased thought processes. Hence during the SPECT scan, even if performed at rest, some form of thought rumination was possible and may have locally increased the rCBF as an exaggerated or maladaptive compensatory process.

The finding of increased ^{99m}Tc-HMPAO distribution in MDD confirmed previous studies in which relative hypermetabolism in distinct regions of the brain was reported [51-56]. However, the most of the functional neuroimaging studies about major depression described reduced rCBF in medial prefrontal cortex and central structures. Such different and sometimes contradictory findings may be explained by a variety of heterogeneous factors such as group size, the age of subjects and the gender ratio. Furthermore, the methods of data analysis (including the use of CBA and VOIs/PCA), the selection of healthy controls (specifically recruited to serve as normal subjects) and patients (selected group of outpatients with physical symptoms), the timing of SPECT (performed during the chronic depressive state in the resting state with the eyes closed), the radiopharmaceutical used and patients medication might account for the discrepancies between the present study and some of the previous investigations.

Independently of MDD, females have a significantly higher relative CBF as compared to men, as previously reported [57-62], possibly due to the higher relative percentage of grey matter in women than in men [63]. Although the performed neuropsychiatric test did not show any difference in the disease severity between males and females, the increased flow distribution in this latter group might represent the neurobiological substrate of a trend towards a more accentuated brain involvement in the disorder. This has been extensively described by epidemiological studies reporting findings of higher lifetime prevalence of MDD for women than men [64, 65] or by the higher prevalence of comorbidity disorders in women [64].

The rCBF changes between genders were found predominantly in the right temporo-parietal cortex and such findings are in accordance with the differential role of the right hemisphere in negative emotions [66, 67] and with the different lateralization between genders, being women more bilaterally organized. It has also been hypothesized a gender difference between anterior and posterior area of the brain, particularly in those processing language. However, neuroimaging studies to date have only provided support for differences in the anterior language areas and Kansaku et al [68] have shown some differences between men and women in posterior temporal lobes. Our results seems to support a higher rCBF distribution in both the whole right hemisphere and in temporo-parietal cortex in women. Moreover PCA clearly separated the angular and the supramarginal gyri of the left hemisphere (PC8) from those of the right hemisphere (PC9 and PC10) showing significant perfusion differences between males and females in these regions.

A further important difference between gender is in PC13 including hippocampi and the left posterior temporal cortex. A significant age effect was found in female with a rCBF reduction in adulthood (Fig 3) but not in males. This finding suggests, as previously reported, that ageing had no effect on males rCBF but had a significant effect on females rCBF [62]. Moreover hippocampus is a structure in which differences have been found in both MDD and gender. For example Murphy et al. [69] showed a greater age related volumetric decrease in frontal and temporal lobes in males, and in hippocampus and parietal lobes in females. Additionally, some authors found hyperactivity of amygdala, hippocampus and parts of the temporal lobes in the depressed state [70]. Patients with depression have been found to have volume reductions or other abnormalities in the prefrontal cortex and hippocampus, areas connected to the regulation of mood [71, 72].

In conclusion, our study showed in a group of 76 MDD patients regional cerebral blood flow differences related to gender but not to the disease. PCA networked brain regions increasing the depth and the significance of the analysis and contributing to better clarify the processes underlying perfusion distribution measurements.

References

[1] Judd, LL; Akiskal, HS; Maser, JD; Zeller, PJ; Endicott, J; Coryell, W; Paulus, MP; Kunovac, JL; Leon, AC; Mueller, TI; Rice, JA; Keller, MB. A prospective 12-year study of subsyndromal and syndromal depressive symptoms in unipolar major depressive disorders. *Arch Gen Psychiatry* 1998;55:694-700.

[2]   Levitt, AB; Boyle, MH; Joffe, RT; Baumal, Z. Estimated prevalence of the seasonal subtype of major depression in a Canadian community sample. *Can J. Psychiatry* 2000;45:650-654.

[3]   Tutus, A; Kibar, M; Sofuoglu, S; Basturk, M; Gönül, AS. A technetium-99m hexamethylpropylene amine oxime brain single-photon emission tomography study in adolescent patients with major depressive disorder. *Eur J Nucl Med* 1998;25:601-606.

[4]   Baxter, LR; Schwartz, JM; Phelps, ME; Mazziotta, JC; Guze, BH; Selin, CE; Gerner, RH; Sumida, RM. Reduction of prefrontal cortex glucose metabolism common to three types of depression. *Arch Gen Psychiatry* 1989;46:243-250.

[5]   Bench, CJ; Friston, KJ; Brown, RG; Scott, LC; Frackowiak, RS; Dolan, RJ. The anatomy of melancholia – focal abnormalities of cerebral blood flow in major depression. *Psychol Med* 1992;22:607-615.

[6]   Dolan, RJ; Bench, CJ; Brown, RG; Scott, LC; Friston, KJ; Frackowiak, RS. Regional cerebral blood flow abnormalities in depressed patients with cognitive impairment. *J Neurol Neurosurg Psychiatry* 1992;55:768-773.

[7]   Bench, CJ; Friston, KJ; Brown, RG; Frackowiak, RS; Dolan, RJ. Regional cerebral blood flow in depression measured by positron emission tomography: the relationship with clinical dimensions. *Psychol Med* 1993;23:579-590.

[8]   Drevets, WC; Videen, TO; Price, JL; Preskorn, SH; Carmichael, ST; Raichle, ME. A functional anatomical study of unipolar depression. *J Neurosci* 1992;12:3628-3641.

[9]   Mentis, MH; Krasuski, J; Pietrini, P. Cerebral glucose metabolism in late onset depression without cognitive impairment. *Soc Neurosci* 1995;21:1736 (Abs).

[10]   Ebert, D; Ebmeier, KP. The role of the cingulate gyrus in depression: from functional anatomy to neurochemistry. *Biol Psychiatry* 1996;39:1044-1050.

[11]   Drevets, WC. Functional neuroimaging studies of depression: the anatomy of melancholia. *Annu Rev Med* 1998;49:341-361.

[12]   Gardner, A; Pagani, M. A review of SPECT in neuropsychiatric disorders: neurobiological background, methodology, findings and future perspectives. *Alasbimn Journal* 2003;5:1-41.

[13]   Yazici, KM; Kapucu, O; Erbas, B; Varoglu, E; Gülec, C; Bekdik, CF. Assessment of changes in regional cerebral blood flow in patients with major depression using the ^{99m}Tc-HMPAO single photon emission tomography method. *Eur J Nucl Med* 1992;19:1038-1043.

[14]   Lesser, IM; Mena, I; Boone, KB; Miller, BL; Mehringer, CM; Wohl, M. Reduction of cerebral blood flow in older depressed patients. *Arch Gen Psychiatry* 1994;51:677-686.

[15]   Fischler, B; D'Haenen, H; Cluydts, R; Michiels, V; Demets, K; Bossuyt, A; Kaufman, L; De Meirleir, K. Comparison of ^{99m}Tc HMPAO SPECT scan between chronic fatigue syndrome, major depression and healthy controls: an exploratory study of clinical correlates of regional cerebral blood flow. *Neuropsychobiology* 1996;34:175-183.

[16]   Navarro, V; Gasto, C; Lomena, F; Mateos, JJ; Marcos, T. Frontal cerebral perfusion dysfunction in elderly late-onset major depression assessed by [99m]TC-HMPAO SPECT. *Neuroimage* 2001;4:202-205.

[17]   Kowatch, RA; Devous, MD; Harvey, DC; Mayes, TL; Trivedi, MH; Emslie, GJ; Weinberg, WA. A SPECT HMPAO study of regional cerebral blood flow in depressed

adolescents and normal controls. *Prog Neuropsychopharmacol Biol Psychiatry* 1999;23:643-656.

[18] Milo, TJ, Kaufman, GE; Barnes, WE. Changes in regional cerebral blood flow after electroconvulsive therapy for depression. *J ECT* 2001;17:15-21.

[19] Bonne, O; Louzoun, Y; Aharon, I; Krausz, Y; Karger, H; Lerer, B; Bocher, M; Freedman, N; Chisin, R. Cerebral blood flow in depressed patients: a methodological comparison of statistical parametric mapping and region of interest analyses. *Psychiatry Res* 2003;122:49-57.

[20] Fountoulakis, KN; Iacovides, A; Gerasimou, G; Fotiou, F; Ioannidou, C; Bascialla, F; Grammaticos, P; Kaprinis, G. The relationship of regional cerebral blood flow with subtypes of major depression. *Prog Neuropsychopharmacol Biol Psychiatry* 2004;28:537-546.

[21] Krausz, Y; Freedman, N; Lester, H; Barkai, G; Levin, T; Bocher, M; Chisin, R; Lerer, B; Bonne, O. Brain SPECT study of common ground between hypothyroidism and depression. *Int J Neuropsychopharmacol* 2007;10:99-106.

[22] Pagani, M; Salmaso, D; Nardo, D; Jonsson, C; Jacobsson, H; Larsson, SA; Gardner, A. Imaging the neurobiological substrate of atypical depression by SPECT. *Eur J Nucl Med Mol Imaging* 2007;34:110-120.

[23] Pagani, M; Salmaso, D; Borbely, K. Optimisation of statistical methodologies for a better diagnosis of neurological and psychiatric disorders by means of SPECT. *Nuc Med Review* 2005;8:140-149.

[24] Nikolaus, S; Larisch, R; Beu, M; Vosberg, H; Müller-Gärtner, HW. Diffuse cortical reduction of neuronal activity in unipolar major depression: a retrospective analysis of 337 patients and 321 controls. *Nucl Med Commun* 2000;21:1119-1125.

[25] Vangu, MD; Esser, JD; Boyd, IH; Berk, M. Effects of electroconvulsive therapy on regional cerebral blood flow measured by ^{99m}Technetium HMPAO SPECT. *Prog Neuropsychopharmacol Biol Psychiatry* 2003;27:15-9.

[26] Nadeau, SE; McCoy, KJ; Crucian, GP; Greer, RA; Rossi, F; Bowers, D; Goodman, WK; Heilman, KM; Triggs, WJ. Cerebral blood flow changes in depressed patients after treatment with repetitive transcranial magnetic stimulation: evidence of individual variability. *Neuropsychiatry Neuropsychol Behav Neurol* 2002;15:159-175.

[27] Eastwood, SL; Harrison, PJ. Synaptic pathology in the anterior cingulate cortex in schizophrenia and mood disorders. A review and a Western blot study of synaptophysin, GAP-43 and the complexins. *Brain Res Bull* 2001;55:569-578.

[28] Rajkowska, G. Postmortem studies in mood disorders indicate altered numbers of neurons and glial cells. *Biol Psychiatry* 2000;48:766-777.

[29] Cotter, DR; Pariante, CM; Everall, IP. Glial cell abnormalities in major psychiatric disorders: the evidence and implications. *Brain Res Bull* 2001;55:585-595.

[30] Filosto, M; Tonin, P; Vattemi, G; Savio, C; Rizzuto, N; Tomelleri, G. Antioxidant agents have a different expression pattern in muscle fibers of patients with mitochondrial diseases. *Acta Neuropathol (Berl)* 2002;103:215-220.

[31] Friston, K; Holmes, A; Worlsey, K; Poline, J; Frith, C; Frackowiak, R. Statistical parametric maps in functional imaging: a general linear approach. *Human Brain Mapping* 1995;2:189-210.

[32] Greitz, T; Bohm, C; Holte, S; Eriksson, L. A computerized brain atlas: construction, anatomical content, and some applications. *J Comput Assist Tomogr* 1991;15:26-38.

[33] Thurfjell, L; Bohm, C; Bengtsson, E. CBA – an atlas based software tool used to facilitate the interpretation of neuroimaging data. *Comput. Methods Programs Biom* 1995;4:51-71.

[34] Halbreich, U; Kahn, LS. Atypical depression somatic depression and anxious depression in women: Are they gender-preferred phenotypes? *J Affective Disorder* 2007;102:245-258.

[35] Kessler, RC. Epidemiology of women and depression. *J Affective Disorders* 2003: 74:5-13.

[36] Kornstein, SG; Schatzberg, AF; Thase ME; Yonkers, KA; McCullough, JP; Keitner, GI; Gelenberg, AJ; Ryan, CE; Hess, AL; Harrison, W; Davis, SM; Keller, MB. Gender differences in chronic major and double depression. *J Affect Disord* 2000;60:1-11.

[37] Lacerda, AL; Keshavan, MS; Hardan, AY; Yorbik, O; Brambilla, P; Sassi, RB; Nicoletti, M; Mallinger, AG; Frank, E; Kupfer, DJ; Soares, JC. Anatomic evaluation of the orbitofrontal cortex in major depressive disorder. *Biol Psychiatry* 2004;55:353-358.

[38] Mathew, RJ; Weinman, ML; Mirabi, M. Physical symptoms of depression. *Br J Psychiatry* 1981; 13:293-296.

[39] Corruble, E; Guelfi, JD. Pain complaints in depressed inpatients. *Psychopathology* 2000;33:307-309.

[40] Coulehan, JL; Schulberg, HC; Block, MR; Zettler-Segal, M. Symptom patterns of depression in ambulatory medical and psychiatric patients. *J Nerv Ment Dis* 1988;176:284-288.

[41] Dewsnap, P; Gomborone, J; Libby, G; Farthing, M. The prevalence of symptoms of irritable bowel syndrome among acute psychiatric inpatients with an affective diagnosis. *Psychosomatics* 1996;37:385-389.

[42] Yovell, Y; Sackeim, HA; Epstein, DG; Prudic, J; Devanand, DP; McElhiney, MC; Settembrino;,JM; Bruder, GE. Hearing loss and asymmetry in major depression. *J Neuropsychiatr Clin Neurosci* 1995;7:82-89.

[43] Moldin, SO; Scheftner, WA; Rice, JP; Nelson, E; Knesevich, MA; Akiskal, H. Association between major depressive disorder and physical illness. *Psychol. Med* 1993;23:755-761.

[44] Gardner, A; Hallstrom, T. High somatic distress with high long-term stability in selected patients with chronic depression: a 3-year follow-up of ratings with Karolinska Scales of Personality (KSP). *Nord J Psychiatry* 2004;58:415-420.

[45] Pendse, B; Westrin, Å; Engström, G. Temperament traits in seasonal affective disorder, suicide attempters with non-seasonal major depression and healthy controls. *J Affect Disord* 1999;54:55-65.

[46] Ekselius, L; von Knorring, L. Changes in personality traits during treatment with sertraline or citalopram. *Br J Psychiatry* 1999;174:444-448.

[47] Chang, L-T. A method for attenuation correction in radionuclide computed tomography. *IEEE Trans Nucl Sci* 1978;25:638-643.

[48] Sackeim, HA. Functional brain circuits in major depression and remission. *Arch Gen Psychiatry* 2001;58:649-650.

[49] Shajahan, PM; Glabus, MF; Steele, JD; Doris, AB; Anderson, K; Jenkins, JA; Gooding, PA; Ebmeier, KP. Left dorso-lateral repetitive transcranial magnetic stimulation affects cortical excitability and functional connectivity, but does not impair cognition in major depression. *Prog Neuropsychopharmacol Biol Psychiatry* 2002;26:945-954.

[50] Pagani, M; Gardner, A; Salmaso, D; Sánchez-Crespo, A; Jonsson, C; Jacobsson, H; Lindberg, G; Wägner, A; Hällström, T; Larsson, SA. Principal Component and Volumes of Interest Analyses in Depressed Patients by 99m-Tc-HMPAO SPET - A Methodological Comparison. *Eur J Nuc Med Mol Imaging* 2004;31:995-1004.

[51] Kennedy, SH; Javanmard, M; Vaccarino, FJ. A review of functional neuroimaging in mood disorders: positron emission tomography and depression. *Can J Psychiatry* 1997;42:467-475.

[52] Parsey, RV; Mann, JJ: Applications of positron emission tomography in psychiatry. *Semin Nucl Med* 2003;33:129-135.

[53] Soares, JC; Mann, JJ. The functional neuroanatomy of mood disorders. *J Psychiatr Res* 1997;31:393-432.

[54] Mayberg, HS. Positron emission tomography imaging in depression: a neural systems perspective. *Neuroimaging Clin N Am* 2003;13:805-815.

[55] Ketter, TA; Kimbrell, TA; George, MS; Willis, MW; Benson, BE; Danielson, A; Frye, MA; Herscovitch, P; Post, RM. Baseline cerebral hypermetabolism associated with carbamazepine response, and hypometabolism with nimodipine response in mood disorders. *Biol Psychiatry* 1999;46:1364-1374.

[56] Drevets, WC. Prefrontal cortical-amygdalar metabolism in major depression. *Ann N Y Acad Sci* 1999;877:614-637.

[57] Rodriguez, G; Warkentin, S; Risberg, J; Rosadini, G. Sex differences in regional cerebral blood flow. *J Cereb Blood Flow Metab* 1988;8:783-789.

[58] Van Laere, K; Versijpt, J; Audenaert, K; Koole, M; Goethals, I; Achten, E; Dierckx, R. ^{99m}Tc-ECD brain perfusion SPET: variability, asymmetry and effect of age and gender in healthy adults. *Eur J Nucl Med* 2001;28:873-887.

[59] Ragland, JD; Coleman, AR; Gur, RC; Glahn, DC; Gur, RE. Sex differences in brain-behavior relationships between verbal episodic memory and resting regional cerebral blood flow. *Neuropsychologia* 2000;38:451-461.

[60] Pagani, M; Gardner, A; Salmaso, D; Sánchez-Crespo, A; Jonsson, C; Jacobsson, H; Hällström, T; Larsson, SA. Effect of gender on cerebral hemispheres and lobes uptake in 183 subjects examined at rest by ^{99m}Tc-HMPAO SPET. *Eur J Nuc Med* 2003;30:S198.

[61] Videbech, P; Ravnkilde, B; Pedersen, AR; Egander, A; Landbo, B; Rasmussen, NA; Andersen, F; Stodkilde-Jorgensen, H; Gjedde, A; Rosenberg, R. The Danish PET/depression project: PET findings in patients with major depression. *Psychol Med* 2001;31:1147-1158.

[62] Pagani, M; Salmaso, D; Jonsson, C; Hatherly, R; Jacobsson, H; Larsson. SA; Wägner, A. Brain regional blood flow as assessed by principal component analysis and ^{99m}Tc-HMPAO SPET in healthy subjects at rest – normal distribution and effect of age and gender. *Eur J Nuc Med* 2002;29:67-75.

[63] Gur, RC; Turetsky, BI; Matsui, M; Yan, M; Bilker, W; Hughett, P; Gur, RE. Sex differences in brain gray and white matter in healthy young adults: correlations with cognitive performance. *J Neurosci* 1999;19:4065-4072.

[64] Kessler, RC; McGonagle, KA; Nelson, CB; Hughes, M; Swartz, MS; Blazer, DG; 1994. Sex and depression in the National Comorbidity Survey II: Cohort effects. *J Affect Disord* 1994;30:15-26.

[65] Wilhelm, K; Roy, K; Mitchell, P; Brownhill, S; Parker, G. Gender differences in depression risk and coping factors in a clinical sample. *Acta Psychiatr Scand* 2002;106:45-53.

[66] Hellige, J. Hemispheric asymmetry. Cambridge, MA: Harvard University Press. 1993.

[67] Ayan, SJ. Right Brain May Be Wrong. *Scientific American Mind* 2005;16:82-83.

[68] Kansaku, K; Yamaura, A; Kitazawa, S. Sex differences in lateralization revealed in the posterior language areas. *Cereb Cortex* 2000;10:866-872.

[69] Murphy, DG;, DeCarli, C; McIntosh, AR; Daly, E; Mentis, MJ; Pietrini, P; Szczepanik, J; Schapiro, MB; Grady, CL; Horwitz, B; Rapoport, SI. Sex differences in human brain morphometry and metabolism: an in vivo quantitative magnetic resonance imaging and positron emission tomography study on the effect of aging. *Arch Gen Psychiatry* 1996;53:585-594.

[70] Doris, A; Ebmeier, K; Shajahan, P. Depressive illness. *Lancet* 1999;354:1369-1375.

[71] Campbell, S; Marriott, M; Nahmias, C; MacQueen, GM. Lower hippocampal volume in patients suffering from depression: A metaanalysis. *Am J Psychiatry* 2004;161:598-607.

[72] Grigoriadis, S; Robinson, GE. Gender Issues in Depression. *Annals of Clinical Psychiatry* 2007;19:247-255.

In: Women and Depression
Editors: Paula Hernandez and Sara Alonso

ISBN 978-1-60456-647-5
© 2009 Nova Science Publishers, Inc.

Chapter 8

Gender Differences and Pharmacogenomics with Antidepressants in Depression

Eugene Lin[41] and Sen-Yen Hsu[2]

[1]Vita Genomics, Inc., 7 Fl., No. 6, Sec. 1, Jung-Shing Road, Wugu Shiang,
Taipei, Taiwan
[2]Department of Psychiatry, Chi Mei Medical Center, Liouying,
Tainan, Taiwan

Abstract

Depression is the most common psychiatric disorder worldwide. No single antidepressant has been shown to be more effective than any other in lifting depression, and the effectiveness of any particular antidepressant in an individual is difficult to predict. Thus, doctors must prescribe antidepressants based on trial and error. Single nucleotide polymorphisms (SNPs) can be used in clinical association studies to determine the contribution of genes to drug efficacy. In addition, some findings suggest that women respond differently to antidepressant treatment than men. In this chapter, we review gender differences, pharmacogenomics, and gene-gender interactions with the drug efficacy of antidepressants in depression. First, we survey the SNPs and genes identified as genetic markers that are correlated and associated with the drug efficacy of antidepressants. Evidence is accumulating to suggest that the efficacy of antidepressants results from the combined effects of a number of genetic variants, such as SNPs. Although there are not enough data currently available to prove this hypothesis, more and more genetic variants associated with antidepressant response are being discovered. Secondly, we investigate the recent reports that antidepressants may work somewhat differently in men and women. Some theoretical reasons have been suggested for suspecting that gender differences in antidepressant response exist. Thirdly, we study gender-specific SNP and gene contributions to antidepressant treatment response and

4 Corresponding author: Eugene Lin, E-mail addresses: eugene.lin@vitagenomics.com.Phone: (+ 886) 2-8976-9123 ext 7751, Fax: (+ 886) 2-8976-9523.

demonstrate pattern recognition approaches to evaluate the epistasis among genes and gender. These techniques may provide tools for clinical association studies and help find genes and SNPs involved in responses to therapeutic drugs or adverse drug reactions.

Keywords: *antidepressants, artificial neural network algorithms, depression, gender differences, gene-gender interactions, pattern recognition, pharmacogenomics, single nucleotide polymorphisms.*

Introduction

Depression is the most common mental disorder worldwide [Lin et al. 2006b]. No single antidepressant has ever been shown to be more effective than any other in lifting depression [Lin et al. 2006b]. The effectiveness of antidepressant treatment is unknown so that doctors can only prescribe antidepressants based on a trial and error approach [Lin et al. 2006b]. Single nucleotide polymorphisms (SNPs) can be used in clinical association studies to determine the contribution of genes to drug efficacy [Lin et al. 2006b]. The drug efficacy of antidepressants could usually result from the combined effects of genetic variants such as SNPs [Serretti and Artioli 2004; Lin et al. 2006b; Lin and Chen 2008a]. Furthermore, recent reports indicate that antidepressants may work somewhat differently in men and women [Gorman 2006; Grigoriadis and Robinson 2007]. In this chapter, we review gender differences, pharmacogenomics, and gene-gender interactions with the drug efficacy of antidepressants in depression.

First, we survey the SNPs and genes identified as genetic markers that are correlated and associated with the drug efficacy of antidepressants. Evidence is accumulating to suggest that the efficacy of antidepressants results from the combined effects of a number of genetic variants, such as SNPs [Serretti and Artioli 2004; Lin et al. 2006b; Lin and Chen 2008a]. Although there are not enough data currently available to prove this hypothesis, more and more genetic variants associated with antidepressant response are being discovered [Serretti and Artioli 2004; Lin et al. 2006b; Lin and Chen 2008a].

Secondly, we investigate some findings that women respond differently to antidepressant treatment than men. A number of studies have suggested potential gender differences in the efficacy of antidepressant medications [Gorman 2006; Grigoriadis and Robinson 2007]. Future research is needed to determine how gender influences response to treatment of depression [Gorman 2006; Grigoriadis and Robinson 2007].

Thirdly, we study gender-specific SNP and gene contributions to antidepressant treatment response and demonstrate pattern recognition approaches to evaluate the epistasis among genes and gender. These techniques may provide tools for clinical association studies and assist in finding genes and SNPs involved in responses to therapeutic drugs or adverse drug reactions [Lin et al. 2007a]. It is highly desirable, clinically and economically, to establish tools based on genetic markers to distinguish responders from non-responders and to predict the possible outcomes of antidepressant treatment [Lin and Chen 2008a]. Future research using pattern recognition approaches [Lin et al. 2007a] is needed in order to model associations between gene variants and antidepressant response, as well as to evaluate the epistasis among genes and clinical factors [Lin and Chen 2008a].

Pharmacogenomics in Antidepressants

Based on the findings in the literature, we focus on candidate genes and their corresponding candidate SNPs that were found to be strongly associated with the drug efficacy of antidepressants such as selective serotonin reuptake inhibitor (SSRI), serotonin and norepinephrine reuptake inhibitor (SNRI), and tricyclic antidepressants (TCAs). These candidate genes include ATP-binding cassette, sub-family B, member 1 (ABCB1), brain-derived neurotrophic factor (BDNF), catechol-O-methyltransferase (COMT), corticotropin-releasing hormone receptor1 (CRHR1), guanine nucleotide binding protein beta polypeptide 3 (GNB3), glutamate receptor, ionotropic, kainate 4 (GRIK4), 5-hydroxytryptamine 2A receptor (HTR2A), 5-hydroxytryptamine 3B receptor (HTR3B), interleukin-1 beta (IL1B), phosphodiesterase (PDE), solute carrier family 6, member 2 (SLC6A2; noradrenalin neurotransmitter transporter), solute carrier family 6, member 4 (SLC6A4; serotonin neurotransmitter transporter), and tryptophan hydroxylase 1 (TPH1).

We address the following discussion in terms of specific antidepressants such as citalopram, fluoxetine, fluvoxamine, paroxetine, milnacipran, and nortriptyline. Due to the results based on various antidepressants, we skip some genes including p75 neurotrophin receptor (p75(NTR)) [Gau et al. 2007], dystrobrevin-binding-protein 1 (DTNBP1) [Pae et al. 2007a], heat-shock protein-70 (HSP-70) [Pae et al. 2007b], and solute carrier family 6, member 3 (SLC6A3; dopamine neurotransmitter transporter) [Kirchheiner et al. 2007].

Citalopram

In the Sequenced Treatment Alternatives for Depression (STAR*D) study, McMahon and colleagues [2006] collected DNA from 1,953 patients with major depressive disorder (MDD) who were treated with the antidepressant citalopram. A significant and reproducible association was detected between citalopram treatment response and the SNP rs7997012 in the HTR2A gene [McMahon et al. 2006]. An interesting finding was that the association between HTR2A and antidepressant citalopram outcome was mainly confined to the white subjects instead of black subjects in the STAR*D sample [McMahon et al. 2006].

Similarly, from the STAR*D cohort, Paddock and colleagues [2007] demonstrated that the SNP rs1954787 in the GRIK4 gene was reproducibly associated with response to the antidepressant citalopram in addition to the previously identified SNP in the HTR2A gene. Moreover, a nominal association between the SNP rs1880916 of the PDE11A gene and citalopram response was detected in an African-American population from the STAR*D cohort [Teranishi et al. 2007].

Furthermore, it was observed that the long and short variants of the SLC6A4 gene were associated with citalopram adverse effects in the STAR*D sample [Hu et al. 2007]. To control for bias from population stratification, a white American subsample was analyzed. A lesser adverse effect burden was found to be associated with long/long genotype frequency or long allele frequency [Hu et al. 2007].

In a Korean population, Ham and colleagues [2007] investigated the polymorphism A218C of the TPH1 gene and found that the remission rate to citalopram treatment was better in MDD subjects with the TPH1 C/C genotype than in those with the TPH1 A/A and A/C genotypes. The TPH1 gene codes for the rate-limiting enzyme in serotonin biosynthesis [Serretti and Artioli 2004].

Similarly, in a Korean population with MDD, Choi and colleagues [2006] studied the polymorphism Val66Met in the BNDF gene and suggested that the BDNF Val66Met polymorphism was associated with citalopram efficacy, with M-allele carriers responding better to citalopram treatment. Based on various antidepressants, other studies in different populations have also indicated BDNF involvement in antidepressant treatment outcome [Tsai et al. 2003; Yoshida et al. 2007; Gratacòs et al. 2007]. The BDNF gene encodes a protein of the nerve growth factor family and may underlie the effects of antidepressants [Nibuya et al. 1995].

In the depressive patients of Italian and Spanish origin, Arias and colleagues [2006] analyzed the functional polymorphism Val158Met of the COMT gene and suggested that the COMT gene could have a small and indirect effect on clinical response in citalopram treatment.

Fluoxetine

In a study of Taiwanese patients with moderate-to-severe depression, the SLC6A4 gene was associated with the antidepressant response to fluoxetine [Yu et al. 2002]. It was shown that patients with the long/lonng genotype had a significantly better response than those of short-allele carriers [Yu et al. 2002]. A recent meta-analysis observed a significant association of short and long variants of SLC6A4 with remission rate and response rate [Serretti et al. 2007].

Similarly, in a Taiwanese population with MDD, it has been tested the hypothesis that the IL1B gene polymorphism was associated with fluoxetine antidepressant response [Yu et al. 2003]. Their finding suggests that patients with homozygous for the -511T allele of the IL1B gene had more favorable fluoxetine response than ones with the -511C allele [Yu et al. 2003].

In another study, it was shown that three SNPs in the TPH1 gene and one SNP in the SLC6A4 gene were associated with fluoxetine responses after a 12-week trial [Peters et al. 2004]. Their clinical sample consisted of subjects with MDD treated with fluoxetine. The subjects included Caucasian, African-American, Hispanic, Asian, and other.

In a sample of depressed Mexican Americans, Wong and colleagues [2006] investigated an association between the PDE genes and antidepressant response and found significant associations with remission in response to fluoxetine treatment with SNPs in the PDE genes (rs1549870 in PDE1A, rs2544934 in PDE6A, rs884162 in PDE8B, rs1880916 in PDE11A, and rs3770018 in PDE11A).

In Han Chinese patients with MDD, it was shown that the G/G genotype of the SNP rs242941 and the homozygous GAG haplotype of the three SNPs (rs1876828, rs242939, and rs242941) in the CRHR1 gene were associated with fluoxetine antidepressant response [Liu et al. 2007].

Fluvoxamine

The polymorphism A218C of the TPH1 gene was investigated for the possible association with the antidepressant activity of fluvoxamine in a sample of inpatients affected by MDD [Serretti et al. 2001a]. That study found that the polymorphism A218C of the TPH1 gene was associated with fluvoxamine antidepressant treatment [Serretti et al. 2001a]. TPH1 A/A was associated with a slower response to fluvoxamine antidepressant treatment than the subjects with TPH1 C/C and TPH1 A/C variants [Serretti et al. 2001a].

Similarly, Serretti and colleagues [2003] tested a possible effect of the GNB3 C825T gene variant on the antidepressant activity in a sample of MDD patients treated with fluvoxamine. Subjects with GNB3 T/T variants showed better response to treatment than the ones with T/C and C/C variants [Serretti et al. 2003]. Other studies have also revealed that the GNB3 C825T allele may significantly influence antidepressant response based on various antidepressants [Lee et al. 2004; Wilkie et al. 2007].

Moreover, it was suggested that the long and short variants of the SLC6A4 gene influence the antidepressant response to fluvoxamine [Smeraldi et al. 1998; Zanardi et al. 2001]. The short variant of the SLC6A4 gene was found to be associated with a poor response to fluvoxamine treatment [Smeraldi et al. 1998; Zanardi et al. 2001].

Paroxetine

The polymorphism A218C of the TPH1 gene was investigated for the possible association with the antidepressant activity of paroxetine in a sample of inpatients affected by MDD [Serretti et al. 2001b]. In that study, it was demonstrated that the subjects with TPH1 A/A and TPH1 A/C variants were associated with a poorer response to paroxetine treatment than the ones with TPH1 C/C variant [Serretti et al. 2001b].

In addition, it was reported that the long and short variants of the SLC6A4 gene were linked with the antidepressant response to paroxetine [Pollock et al. 2000; Zanardi et al. 2000]. Subjects with the long/long and long/short genotypes showed better clinical responses that the ones with short/short genotype [Pollock et al. 2000; Zanardi et al. 2000]. Another study suggested that the SLC6A4 variants had a dramatic effect on adverse events among paroxetine-treated subjects, with short allele carriers experienced more severe adverse events [Murphy et al. 2004].

In a Japanese MDD sample, Kato and colleagues [2007] examined three functional polymorphisms (rs1045642, rs2032582, and rs1128503) of the ABCB1 gene and reported a significant association of the SNP rs2032582 with treatment response to paroxetine.

Furthermore, it was shown that paroxetine-induced side effects were strongly associated with the HTR2A C/C genotype in elderly patients with MDD [Murphy et al. 2003]. Similarly, the polymorphism Tyr129Ser of the HTR3B gene had a significant effect on the incidence of nausea induced by paroxetine in Japanese psychiatric patients [Sugai et al. 2006].

Milnacipran

Based on a sample of Japanese patients with MDD, it was found that a polymorphism of SLC6A2 gene was associated with the antidepressant response to milnacipran (an SNRI) [Yoshida et al. 2004]. The presence of the T allele of the SLC6A2 T-182C polymorphism was found to be associated with a superior antidepressant response [Yoshida et al. 2004]. In addition, the A/A genotype of the SLC6A2 G1287A polymorphism was found to be associated with a slower onset of therapeutic response [Yoshida et al. 2004].

Nortriptyline

In Korean patients with MDD, Kim and colleagues [2006] tested whether antidepressant responses are associated with the genetic polymorphisms of the corresponding monoamine transporters, such as the short/long polymorphisms in the SLC6A4 gene and the G1287A variation in the SLC6A2 gene. In that study, the G/G genotype of SLC6A2 G1287A was found to be associated with better response to nortriptyline, a TCA [Kim et al. 2006]. In addition, the short variant of the SLC6A4 gene was found to be associated with nortriptyline response [Kim et al. 2006].

Gender Differences in Antidepressants

Preliminary evidence suggests that different pharmacodynamic responses are observed between women and men [Gorman 2006; Grigoriadis and Robinson 2007]. Some theoretical reasons have been suggested for suspecting that gender differences in antidepressant response exist. Large prospective clinical trials are necessary in order to answer whether men and women respond equally well to antidepressant medications [Grigoriadis and Robinson 2007].

Kornstein and colleagues [2000] examined gender differences in treatment response to sertraline (an SSRI) and to imipramine (a TCA) in chronic depression. Women showed a significantly higher response rate to sertraline than to imipramine, while men showed a favorable response to imipramine than to sertraline [Kornstein et al. 2000]. In terms of time to response, women responded significantly more slowly than men to treatment with imipramine [Kornstein et al. 2000].

A report compared the efficacy of venlafaxine, an SNRI, with that of SSRIs by gender [Entsuah et al. 2001]. In women, the response rate with venlafaxine was found to be significantly greater than the one with SSRIs [Entsuah et al. 2001]. In that study, a gender difference in time to response was also observed. Response was found to occur earlier with venlafaxine than with SSRIs in women [Entsuah et al. 2001]. In contrast, the time to response was observed to be similar with both antidepressants in men [Entsuah et al. 2001].

Another large retrospective analysis of 1,746 patients reported that women had a statistically superior response to monoamine oxidase inhibitor (MAOI) antidepressants than men [Quitkin et al. 2002]. However, no gender differences were found in response to TCAs or fluoxetine in that report [Quitkin et al. 2002].

Recent data indicate that the efficacy of SSRIs may be influenced by gender differences [Khan et al. 2005; Pinto-Meza et al. 2006; Berlanga and Flores-Ramos 2006; Naito et al. 2007]. In the Khan and colleagues study [2005], women had a significantly greater response to SSRI antidepressants than men. Interestingly, Pinto-Meza and colleagues [2006] found that menopause is related to a worse treatment response. SSRI treatment response in women seems to be negatively effective by menopause [Pinto-Meza et al. 2006]. Similarly, it was reported that fluvoxamine, an SSRI, was more effective in younger female patients than older female patients and male patients [Naito et al. 2007]. In another study, females treated with citalopram (an SSRI) were found to show a significantly greater response than females treated with reboxetine (a selective noradrenaline reuptake inhibitor), whereas no differences were observed for both antidepressants in men [Berlanga and Flores-Ramos 2006].

Some findings suggest that a similar trend was seen for those assigned to an SNRI antidepressant, although not to the same extent as with SSRI antidepressants [Khan et al. 2005; Kornstein et al. 2006; Naito et al. 2007]. In an analysis of pooled data, there was a trend for female patients to show a more robust response to duloxetine, an SNRI, than male patients [Kornstein et al. 2006]. However, it was reported that the efficacy of duloxetine did not differ significantly in male and female patients [Kornstein et al. 2006]. Similarly, the gender differences of antidepressant response were not observed in the patients treated with milnacipran, an SNRI [Naito et al. 2007].

Gender differences in TCA treatment response have not been found consistently. In a meta-analysis study, men were observed to respond better to TCAs than premenopausal women, but differences diminished after menopause [Bies et al. 2003]. However, another study found no gender difference in the efficacy of TCAs [Wohlfarth et al. 2004]. In that study, the estimated effect size was similar for women younger and older than age 50 and for men [Wohlfarth et al. 2004].

Gene-Gender Interactions in Antidepressants

Some findings are consistent with the hypothesis that major depression may be related to some distinct genes in male versus female patients [Kendler et al. 2006]. A recent study demonstrated that there were gender differences in depression-related behaviors in BDNF conditional knockout mice [Monteggia et al. 2007]. Treatment response may follow a similar division between men and women. In this section, we survey gender-specific SNP and gene contributions to antidepressant treatment response, review pattern recognition approaches to epistasis analysis, and demonstrate an artificial neural network (ANN) based method to evaluate the epistasis among genes and gender. To the best of our knowledge, this is the first study that proposes to use the ANN-based approach to assess gene-gender interactions in antidepressant therapy.

Gender-Specific SNP and Gene in Antidepressants

In a study of patients with MDD of Caucasian descent, antidepressant responsiveness was found to be correlated with the COMT gene [Baune et al. 2007]. Patients were treated with a variety of antidepressant medication (mirtazapine, citalopram/escitalopram, venlafaxine, TCA, MAOIs, lithium). Their results revealed the gender-specific effects of COMT gene variation such that poor outcome in the female subjects was observed to show an association with the COMT 158Val/Val genotype [Baune et al. 2007].

In the STAR*D study, Paddock and colleagues [2007] reported that the SNP rs6416623 of the glutamate receptor, ionotropic, N-methyl D-aspartate 2A (GRIN2A) gene and the SNP rs2178865 of the glutamate receptor, ionotropic, kainate 1 (GRIK1) gene were significantly associated with treatment response in female patients treated with citalopram.

For Germany MDD patients, Tadić and colleagues [2007a] investigated whether the monoamine oxidase A (MAOA) T941G polymorphism is involved in antidepressant treatment outcome. Their data suggested that female mirtazapine-treated patients homozygous for the T-allele had a significantly faster and better treatment response than T/G and G/G patients [Tadić et al. 2007a]. In male patients, no association was shown between the MAOA T941G polymorphism and mirtazapine response [Tadić et al. 2007a].

Similarly, for Germany MDD patients, Tadić and colleagues [2007b] analyzed a possible association of the polymorphism A644G in the monoamine oxidase B (MAOB) gene with mirtazapine or paroxetine antidepressant treatment response. Their data showed that female patients with homozygous for the A-allele had a significantly faster and more pronounced antidepressant treatment response than A/G and G/G carriers [Tadić et al. 2007b]. In male patients, no association was found between the MAOB A644G polymorphism and antidepressant treatment response [Tadić et al. 2007b].

In a Taiwanese population of MDD patients, Yu and colleagues [2005] studied a variable-number-tandem-repeat (VNTR) polymorphism in the promoter region of the MAOA gene. MDD female patients with 3-repeat homozygotes had a significantly better response to 4-week fluoxetine treatment when compared to 4-repeat allele carriers [Yu et al. 2005]. In contrast, there was no significant difference found in male patients [Yu et al. 2005].

Similarly, in Taiwanese MDD patients, Yu and colleagues [2006] tested whether the polymorphism C-1019G of the 5-hydroxytryptamine 1A receptor (HTR1A) gene is related to a 4-week fluoxetine antidepressant effect. A gender-specific association was identified such that female patients with -1019C/C genotype were found to have a better response than the carriers of the -1019G allele [Yu et al. 2006].

Pattern Recognition Approaches to Epistasis Analysis

Epistasis analysis for gene-gene and gene-environment interactions has been advocated for deciphering the complex mechanisms, particularly when each involved factor only demonstrates a minor marginal effect [Bell et al. 2006; Carlborg and Haley 2004]. Gene-gender interactions can be viewed as a portion of gene-environment interactions. It is essential to address gene-gene and gene-environment interactions for describing complex traits in pharmacogenomics [Lin et al. 2007a]. Association studies based on individual SNPs or haplotypes, using a locus-by-locus or region-by-region approach, may overlook the associations which can only be found when gene-gene and gene-environment interactions are investigated [Lin et al. 2007a].

Several pattern recognition techniques, such as logistic regression methods [Ma et al. 2005], the multifactor dimensionality reduction (MDR) method [Ritchie and Motsinger 2005], and the ANN-based method [Lin et al. 2007b] were proposed for detecting gene-gene and gene-environment interactions. The main issue confronted by conventional logistic regression methods is that it is insufficient in detecting high-order gene-gene interactions because of the sparseness of the data in high dimensions [Ma et al. 2005]. To improve the ability to identify the high-order gene-gene interactions with the use of relatively small sample sizes, the MDR method was used to detect gene-gene interactions in a tabular format in pharmacogenomics studies [Ritchie and Motsinger 2005]. However, the limitation is that MDR has difficulty in distinguishing true interactive effects from joint effects [Ma et al. 2005]. The ANN approach is based on ANN algorithms that have several advantages, including nonlinearity, fault tolerance, universality, and real-time operation, and are quite suitable for complex applications such as high-order gene-gene interactions [Kung and Hwang 1998; Erb 1993].

A study by Lin and colleagues [2006a] focused on assessing drug efficacy and illustrated that the ANN model should be considered as a good method to deal with the complex non-linear relationship between clinical factors and the responsiveness of interferon (IFN). Another study by Lin and colleagues [2007b] developed an ANN-based methodology to address gene-gene and gene-environment interactions in IFN therapy for CHC patients by using genetic and clinical factors such as twenty SNPs, viral genotype, viral load, age, and gender. The previous findings encouraged us to extend the research and conduct epistasis analyses for gene-gender interactions in antidepressant therapy based on ANN algorithms.

ANN algorithms, such as supervised feed-forward neural networks (FFNN) [Kung and Hwang 1998], are generally adopted for classification applications [Lin et al. 2006a]. From the structural point of view, an FFNN is a spatially iterative neural network with several layers of hidden neuron units between the input and output neuron layers [Lin et al. 2006a]. The basis function of each neuron is the linear basis function, and the activation is modeled by a non-decreasing and differentiable sigmoid function [Rumelhart et al. 1996]. From an algorithmic point of view, a simple gradient descent approach known as the back-propagation algorithm [Rumelhart et al. 1996] is used for the learning scheme. Furthermore, an adaptive momentum and learning rate is employed to improve the convergence rates of the back-propagation algorithm [Nestorov et al. 1999; Lin et al. 2006a]. The gradient descent method includes a term with a proportion of the last weight change [Lin et al. 2006a]. Hence, the determined learning rate is different for each epoch [Lin et al. 2006a].

In summary, the FFNN is trained first by repeatedly presenting input-output training pairs and performing the back-propagation learning algorithm [Lin et al. 2006a]. After this training, the FFNN is tested by presenting the inputs of testing pairs (i.e., clinical factors) to the network [Lin et al. 2006a]. The forward propagation of the FFNN provides the responsiveness of antidepressants for a particular patient, giving us a means of inference from cause to effect [Lin et al. 2006a].

Epistasis Analysis for Gene-Gender Interactions

To investigate gene-gender interactions, an ANN-based method is implemented for identifying significant interactions between genes and gender using the five-fold cross-validation method [Hastie et al. 2001; Bishop 1995] and permutation tests [Hirschhorn and Daly 2005; North et al. 2003]. First, the whole dataset is randomly divided into five distinct parts. Second, a set of N factors is selected from the list of all factors. Third, the ANN model is trained by four-fifths of the data and is tested by the remaining fifth of data to estimate the predictive performance. Our algorithm uses a feed-forward neural network for modeling the responsiveness of antidepressants. Inputs contain the information of clinical factors such as SNPs and gender for the depression patients. Outputs contain the information about the responsiveness of antidepressants. To measure the performance of prediction models, the accuracy is calculated as the proportion of true predicted subjects of all tested subjects [Lin et al. 2007b]. Then, the above procedure is repeated four more times by leaving out a different fifth of data as testing data and different four-fifths of the data as training data. With these five groups of data, the average values of performance measures are used to represent the abilities of diagnostic prediction for the prediction models. Finally, all possible combinations of N factors are sequentially evaluated with performance measures, and the best N-factor model is selected [Lin et al. 2007b].

In the present study, the criteria to determine whether the diagnostic prediction is true or false are as follows [Lin et al. 2007b]. The cut-off threshold is set at 0.5. If the teacher value is 0.9, and the predicted value is greater than 0.5, the prediction is true (true responder; TR); for lower than 0.5, the prediction is false (false non-responder; FN). If the teacher value is 0.1, and the predicted value is lower than 0.5, the prediction is true (true non-responder; TN); for greater than 0.5, the prediction is false (false responder; FR).

In this study, the input-output training data pairs are used to train a FFNN [Lin et al. 2007b]. Inputs are the genetic and clinical factors such as SNP markers and gender. Outputs are the drug responding status. For our approach, the SNP genotyping data is converted into two-numeral data with two inputs per SNP [Lin et al. 2007b]. Because there are three genotypes per locus, {0, 0} is provided for homozygote of the major allele, {0, 1} for heterozygote, and {1, 1} for homozygote of the minor allele, respectively. The gender data is further converted into numerical forms, that is, 1 for "male" and 0 for "female", respectively. In addition, the clinical diagnostic data is converted into numerical forms, that is, 1 for "responder" and 0 for "non-responder", respectively.

Finally, a permutation test is applied to measure the statistical significance of the association between clinical factors, such as SNPs and gender, and drug responses [Lin et al. 2007b]. The permutation test allows the whole dataset to be incorporated in both the training and testing of the model [North et al. 2003; Lin et al. 2007b]. A statistic is calculated to compare the difference between the outputs for responders and non-responders by a t-test. A large number, denoted N, of replicate data sets is generated from the original data by randomly permuting clinical factors with respect to responsiveness. For each of these replicate datasets, the dataset is trained and tested as before, and a statistic is then calculated for each dataset. The number, denoted R, of times is counted to represent any of these statistic values exceeds the statistic value of the real dataset. Then, the p-value is calculated in terms of $(R + 1)/(N + 1)$ that provides an unbiased estimate for the statistical significance of the association between clinical factors and responsiveness in the real dataset [North et al. 2003; Lin et al. 2007b].

The performance of predictive models is bound to be at risk of over-fitting and/or finding false positives by using numerous exploratory variables and so few subjects [Lin et al. 2007a]. It is essential to assess the out-of-sample performance of the predictive models using either a training set/test set paradigm (when the sample size allows) or a cross-validation method [Lin et al. 2007b]. However, the cross-validation method presents a disadvantage that it may lead to a loss of power if the training and testing data have different patterns of association between clinical factors and drug efficacy [Lin et al. 2007b]. In order to overcome this problem, the permutation test [North et al. 2003] is applied to derive an empirical p-value, showing the level of association between clinical factors and responsiveness. The permutation test incorporates the whole dataset in both the training and testing of the ANN model and requires a substantial increase in computing time because the procedure must be repeated thousands of times in order to obtain an appropriate number of replicates for providing an acceptable estimate of the statistical significance [North et al. 2003; Lin et al. 2007b].

In future work, we will investigate gene-gender interactions based on the Bayesian variable selection strategies. A Bayesian-based methodology treats the mapping of genetic markers as a problem of model determination and variable selection and may be suitable for modeling interactions [Lin and Huang 2008b].

Conclusion

Based on the findings as reported in the literature, we review pharmacogenomics, gender differences, gene-gender interactions, and pattern recognition techniques with the drug efficacy of antidepressants in depression. Our proposed ANN tool may provide a plausible way to detect gene-gender interactions in antidepressant therapy. Over the next few years, our proposed method could be utilized to develop molecular diagnostic and prognostic tools. However, there are a number of important challenges to overcome before the results of SNP-based studies can be integrated into routine clinical practice [Lin et al. 2007b]. The individualized therapy for depression will become a reality after a prospective clinical trial has been conducted to validate clinical factors and genetic markers.

Acknowledgements

The authors extend their sincere thanks to Vita Genomics, Inc. for funding this research. The authors would also like to thank Dr. Charles Wang of Interlake Psychiatric Associates, Bellevue, WA, USA for helpful suggestions.

References

Arias B, Serretti A, Lorenzi C, Gastó C, Catalán R, Fañanás L. Analysis of COMT gene (Val 158 Met polymorphism) in the clinical response to SSRIs in depressive patients of European origin. *J. Affect. Disord.*, 2006, 90(2-3), 251-6.

Baune BT, Hohoff C, Berger K, Neumann A, Mortensen S, Roehrs T, Deckert J, Arolt V, Domschke K. Association of the COMT val158met variant with antidepressant treatment response in major depression. *Neuropsychopharmacology*, 2008, 33 (4), 924-32.

Bell JT, Wallace C, Dobson R, Wiltshire S, Mein C, Pembroke J, Brown M, Clayton D, Samani N, Dominiczak A, Webster J, Lathrop GM, Connell J, Munroe P, Caulfield M, Farrall M. Two-dimensional genome-scan identifies novel epistatic loci for essential hypertension. *Hum. Mol. Genet*, 2006, 15, 1365-1374.

Berlanga C, Flores-Ramos M. Different gender response to serotonergic and noradrenergic antidepressants: A comparative study of the efficacy of citalopram and reboxetine. *J. Affect. Disord.*, 2006, 95(1-3), 119-23.

Bies RR, Bigos KL, Pollock BG. Gender differences in the pharmacokinetics and pharmacodynamics of antidepressants. *J. Gend. Specif .Med.*, 2003, 6(3), 12-20.

Bishop CM. Neural networks for pattern recognition. Oxford: Clarendon Press; 1995.

Carlborg O, Haley CS. Epistasis: too often neglected in complex trait studies. *Nature*, 2004, 5, 618-625.

Choi MJ, Kang RH, Lim SW, Oh KS, Lee MS. Brain-derived neurotrophic factor gene polymorphism (Val66Met) and citalopram response in major depressive disorder. *Brain Res,*. 2006, 1118(1), 176-82.

Entsuah R, Huang H, Thase ME. Response and remission rates in different subpopulations with major depressive disorder administered venlafaxine, selective serotonin reuptake inhibitors, or placebo. *J. Clin. Psychiatry*, 2001, 62, 869-877.

Erb RJ. Introduction to backpropagation neural network computation. *Pharm. Res.*, 1993, 10, 165-170.

Gau YT, Liou YJ, Yu YW, Chen TJ, Lin MW, Tsai SJ, Hong CJ. Evidence for association between genetic variants of p75 neurotrophin receptor (p75(NTR)) gene and antidepressant treatment response in chinese major depressive disorder. *Am. J. Med. Genet. B Neuropsychiatr Genet*, Epub 2007 Dec 14.

Gorman JM. Gender differences in depression and response to psychotropic medication. *Gend Med*, 2006, 3(2), 93-109.

Gratacòs M, Soria V, Urretavizcaya M, González JR, Crespo JM, Bayés M, de Cid R, Menchón JM, Vallejo J, Estivill X. A brain-derived neurotrophic factor (BDNF) haplotype is associated with antidepressant treatment outcome in mood disorders. *Pharmacogenomics J.*, Epub 2007 May 15.

Grigoriadis S, Robinson GE. Gender issues in depression. *Ann. Clin. Psychiatry*, 2007, 19(4), 247-55.

Ham BJ, Lee BC, Paik JW, Kang RH, Choi MJ, Choi IG, Lee MS. Association between the tryptophan hydroxylase-1 gene A218C polymorphism and citalopram antidepressant response in a Korean population. *Prog. Neuropsychopharmacol. Biol. Psychiatry*, 2007, 31(1), 104-7.

Hastie T, Tibshirani R, Friedman JH. The elements of statistical learning. New York: Springer-Verlag; 2001.

Hirschhorn JN, Daly MI. Genome-wide association studies for common diseases and complex traits. *Nature Review Genet.*, 2005, 6, 95-108.

Hu XZ, Rush AJ, Charney D, Wilson AF, Sorant AJ, Papanicolaou GJ, Fava M, Trivedi MH, Wisniewski SR, Laje G, Paddock S, McMahon FJ, Manji H, Lipsky RH. Association between a functional serotonin transporter promoter polymorphism and citalopram treatment in adult outpatients with major depression. *Arch. Gen. Psychiatry*, 2007, 64(7), 783-92.

Kato M, Fukuda T, Serretti A, Wakeno M, Okugawa G, Ikenaga Y, Hosoi Y, Takekita Y, Mandelli L, Azuma J, Kinoshita T. ABCB1 (MDR1) gene polymorphisms are associated with the clinical response to paroxetine in patients with major depressive disorder. *Prog. Neuropsychopharmacol Biol. Psychiatry*, 2008, 32(2), 398-404.

Kendler KS, Gatz M, Gardner CO, Pedersen NL.A Swedish national twin study of lifetime major depression. *Am. J. Psychiatry*, 2006, 163(1), 109-14.

Khan A, Brodhead AE, Schwartz KA, Kolts RL, Brown WA. Sex differences in antidepressant response in recent antidepressant clinical trials. *J. Clin. Psychopharmacol.*, 2005, 25(4), 318-24.

Kim H, Lim SW, Kim S, Kim JW, Chang YH, Carroll BJ, Kim DK. Monoamine transporter gene polymorphisms and antidepressant response in koreans with late-life depression. *JAMA*, 2006, 296(13), 1609-18.

Kirchheiner J, Nickchen K, Sasse J, Bauer M, Roots I, Brockmöller J. A 40-basepair VNTR polymorphism in the dopamine transporter (DAT1) gene and the rapid response to antidepressant treatment. *Pharmacogenomics J.*, 2007, 7(1), 48-55.

Kornstein SG, Schatzberg AF, Thase ME, Yonkers KA, McCullough JP, Keitner GI, Gelenberg AJ, Davis SM, Harrison WM, Keller MB. Gender differences in treatment response to sertraline versus imipramine in chronic depression. *Am. J. Psychiatry*, 2000, 157(9), 1445-52.

Kornstein SG, Wohlreich MM, Mallinckrodt CH, Watkin JG, Stewart DE. Duloxetine efficacy for major depressive disorder in male vs. female patients: data from 7 randomized, double-blind, placebo-controlled trials. *J. Clin. Psychiatry*, 2006, 67(5), 761-70.

Kung SY, Hwang JN. Neural networks for intelligent multimedia processing. *Proceedings of the IEEE*, 1998, 86, 1244-1272.

Lee HJ, Cha JH, Ham BJ, Han CS, Kim YK, Lee SH, Ryu SH, Kang RH, Choi MJ, Lee MS. Association between a G-protein 3 subunit gene polymorphism and the symptomatology and treatment responses of major depressive disorders. *Pharmacogenomics J*, 2004, 4, 29–33.

Lin E, Hwang Y, Wang SC, Gu ZJ, Chen EY. An artificial neural network approach to the drug efficacy of interferon treatments. *Pharmacogenomics*, 2006a, 7 (7), 1017-1024.

Lin E, Hwang Y, Tzeng CM. A case study of the utility of the HapMap database for pharmacogenomic haplotype analysis in the Taiwanese population. *Mol. Diagn. Ther.*, 2006b, 10(6), 367-370.

Lin E, Hwang Y, Liang KH, Chen EY. Pattern-recognition techniques with haplotype analysis in pharmacogenomics. *Pharmacogenomics*, 2007a, 8(1), 75-83.

Lin E, Hwang Y, Chen EY. Gene-gene and gene-environment interactions in interferon therapy for chronic hepatitis C. *Pharmacogenomics*, 2007b, 8(10), 1327-1335.

Lin E, Chen PS. Pharmacogenomics with antidepressants in the STAR*D study. *Pharmacogenomics*, 2008a. In press.

Lin E, Huang LC. Identification of significant genes in genomics using Bayesian variable selection methods. *Computational Biology and Chemistry: Advances and Applications*, 2008b. In press.

Liu Z, Zhu F, Wang G, Xiao Z, Tang J, Liu W, Wang H, Liu H, Wang X, Wu Y, Cao Z, Li W. Association study of corticotropin-releasing hormone receptor1 gene polymorphisms and antidepressant response in major depressive disorders. *Neurosci Lett*, 2007, 414(2), 155-8.

Ma DQ, Whitehead PL, Menold MM, Martin ER, Ashley-Koch AE, Mei H, Ritchie MD, Delong GR, Abramson RK, Wright HH, Cuccaro ML, Hussman JP, Gilbert JR, Pericak-Vance MA. Identification of significant association and gene-gene interaction of GABA receptor subunit genes in autism. *Am. J. Hum. Genet.*, 2005, 77(3), 377-388.

McMahon FJ, Buervenich S, Charney D, Lipsky R, Rush AJ, Wilson AF, Sorant AJ, Papanicolaou GJ, Laje G, Fava M, Trivedi MH, Wisniewski SR, Manji H. Variation in the gene encoding the serotonin 2A receptor is associated with outcome of antidepressant treatment. *Am. J. Hum. Genet.*, 2006, 78(5), 804-14.

Monteggia LM, Luikart B, Barrot M, Theobold D, Malkovska I, Nef S, Parada LF, Nestler EJ. Brain-derived neurotrophic factor conditional knockouts show gender differences in depression-related behaviors. *Biol. Psychiatry*, 2007, 61(2), 187-97.

Murphy GM Jr, Kremer C, Rodrigues HE, Schatzberg AF. Pharmacogenetics of antidepressant medication intolerance. *Am. J .Psychiatry*, 2003, 160, 1830–1835.

Murphy GM Jr, Hollander SB, Rodrigues HE, Kremer C, Schatzberg AF. Effects of the serotonin transporter gene promoter polymorphism on mirtazapine and paroxetine efficacy and adverse events in geriatric major depression. *Arch. Gen. Psychiatry*, 2004, 61(11), 1163-9.

Naito S, Sato K, Yoshida K, Higuchi H, Takahashi H, Kamata M, Ito K, Ohkubo T, Shimizu T. Gender differences in the clinical effects of fluvoxamine and milnacipran in Japanese major depressive patients. *Psychiatry Clin. Neurosci.* 2007, 61(4), 421-7.

Nestorov I, Hadjitodorov ST, Petrov I, Rowland M. Empirical versus mechanistic modelling: comparison of an artificial neural network to a mechanistically based model for quantitative structure pharmacokinetic relationships of a homologous series of barbiturates. *AAPS PharmSci*, 1999, 1(4), Article 17.

Nibuya M, Morinobu S, Duman RS. Regulation of BDNF and trkB mRNA in rat brain by chronic electroconvulsive seizure and antidepressant drug treatments. *J. Neurosc.i*, 1995, 15(11), 7539-47.

North BV, Curtis D, Cassell PG, Hitman GA, Sham PC. Assessing optimal neural network architecture for identifying disease-associated multi-marker genotypes using a permutation test, and application to calpain 10 polymorphisms associated with diabetes. *Ann. of Human Genet.*, 2003, 67348-356.

Paddock S, Laje G, Charney D, Rush AJ, Wilson AF, Sorant AJ, Lipsky R, Wisniewski SR, Manji H, McMahon FJ. Association of GRIK4 with outcome of antidepressant treatment in the STAR*D cohort. *Am. J. Psychiatry*, 2007, 164(8), 1181-8.

Pae CU, Serretti A, Mandelli L, De Ronchi D, Patkar AA, Jun TY, Kim JJ, Lee CU, Lee SJ, Lee C, Paik IH. Dysbindin associated with selective serotonin reuptake inhibitor antidepressant efficacy. *Pharmacogenet Genomics*, 2007a, 17(1), 69-75.

Pae CU, Mandelli L, Serretti A, Patkar AA, Kim JJ, Lee CU, Lee SJ, Lee C, De Ronchi D, Paik IH. Heat-shock protein-70 genes and response to antidepressants in major depression. *Prog Neuropsychopharmacol Biol. Psychiatry*, 2007b, 31(5), 1006-11.

Peters EJ, Slager SL, McGrath PJ, Knowles JA, Hamilton SP. Investigation of serotonin-related genes in antidepressant response. *Molecular Psychiatry*, 2004, 9, 879-889.

Pinto-Meza A, Usall J, Serrano-Blanco A, Suárez D, Haro JM. Gender differences in response to antidepressant treatment prescribed in primary care. Does menopause make a difference? *J. Affect Disord.*, 2006, 93(1-3), 53-60.

Pollock BG, Ferrell RE, Mulsant BH, Mazumdar S, Miller M, Sweet RA, Davis S, Kirshner MA, Houck PR, Stack JA, Reynolds CF, Kupfer DJ. Allelic variation in the serotonin transporter promoter affects onset of paroxetine treatment response in late-life depression. *Neuropsychopharmacology*, 2000, 23, 587–590.

Quitkin FM, Stewart JW, McGrath PJ, Taylor BP, Tisminetzky MS, Petkova E, Chen Y, Ma G, Klein DF. Are there differences between women's and men's antidepressant responses? *Am. J .Psychiatry*, 2002, 159(11), 1848-54.

Rumelhart DE, Hinton GE, William RJ. Learning internal representation by error propagation. Parallel distributed processing: explorations. In: *The micro-structure of cognition, vol.1, Foundations.* Cambridge, MA: MIT Press; 1996.

Ritchie MD, Motsinger AA. Multifactor dimensionality reduction for detecting gene-gene and gene-environment interactions in pharmacogenomics studies. *Pharmacogenomics* 2005, 6(8), 823-34.

Serretti A, Zanardi R, Rossini D, Cusin C, Lilli R, Smeraldi E. Influence of tryptophan hydroxylase and serotonin transporter genes on fluvoxamine antidepressant activity. *Mol. Psychiatry*, 2001a, 6, 586–592.

Serretti A, Zanardi R, Cusin C, Rossini D, Lorenzi C, Smeraldi E. Tryptophan hydroxylase gene associated with paroxetine antidepressant activity. *Eur. Neuropsychopharmacol.*, 2001b, 11, 375–380.

Serretti A, Lorenzi C, Cusin C, Zanardi R, Lattuada E, Rossini D, Lilli R, Pirovano A, Catalano M, Smeraldi E. SSRIs antidepressant activity is influenced by Gbeta3 variants. *Eur. Neuropsychopharmacol.*, 2003, 13, 117–122.

Serretti A, Artioli P. The pharmacogenomics of selective serotonin reuptake inhibitors. *Pharmacogenomics*, 2004, 4, 233–244.

Serretti A, Kato M, De Ronchi D, Kinoshita T. Meta-analysis of serotonin transporter gene promoter polymorphism (5-HTTLPR) association with selective serotonin reuptake inhibitor efficacy in depressed patients. *Mol. Psychiatry*, 2007, 12(3), 247-57.

Smeraldi E, Zanardi R, Benedetti F, Dibella D, Perez J, Catalano M. Polymorphism within the promoter of the serotonin transporter gene and antidepressant efficacy of fluvoxamine. *Mol. Psychiatry*, 1998, 3, 508–511.

Sugai T, Suzuki Y, Sawamura K, Fukui N, Inoue Y, Someya T. The effect of 5-hydroxytryptamine 3A and 3B receptor genes on nausea induced by paroxetine. *Pharmacogenomics J.*, 2006, 6(5), 351-6.

Tadić A, Müller MJ, Rujescu D, Kohnen R, Stassen HH, Dahmen N, Szegedi A. The MAOA T941G polymorphism and short-term treatment response to mirtazapine and paroxetine in major depression. *Am. J. Med. Genet .B Neuropsychiatr. Genet.*, 2007a, 144(3), 325-31.

Tadić A, Rujescu D, Müller MJ, Kohnen R, Stassen HH, Dahmen N, Szegedi A. A monoamine oxidase B gene variant and short-term antidepressant treatment response. *Prog. Neuropsychopharmacol. Biol. Psychiatry*, 2007b, 31(7), 1370-7.

Tsai SJ, Cheng CY, Yu YW, Chen TJ, Hong CJ. Association study of a brain-derived neurotrophic-factor genetic polymorphism and major depressive disorders, symptomatology, and antidepressant response. *Am. J. Med. Genet B Neuropsychiatr. Gene.t*, 2003, 123(1), 19-22.

Teranishi KS, S L Slager, H Garriock, J B Kraft, E J Peters, M S Reinalda, G D Jenkins, P J McGrath and S P Hamilton. Variants in PDE11A and PDE1A are not associated with citalopram response. *Molecular Psychiatry*, 2007, 12, 1061–1063.

Wilkie MJ, Smith D, Reid IC, Day RK, Matthews K, Wolf CR, Blackwood D, Smith G. A splice site polymorphism in the G-protein beta subunit influences antidepressant efficacy in depression. *Pharmacogenet Genomics*, 2007, 17(3), 207-15.

Wohlfarth T, Storosum JG, Elferink AJ, van Zwieten BJ, Fouwels A, van den Brink W. Response to tricyclic antidepressants: independent of gender? *Am. J. Psychiatry*, 2004, 161(2), 370-2.

Wong ML, Whelan F, Deloukas P, Whittaker P, Delgado M, Cantor RM, McCann SM, Licinio J. Phosphodiesterase genes are associated with susceptibility to major depression and antidepressant treatment response. *Proc Natl Acad Sci U S A*, 2006, 103(41), 15124-9.

Yoshida K, Takahashi H, Higuchi H, Kamata M, Ito K, Sato K, Naito S, Shimizu T, Itoh K, Inoue K, Suzuki T, Nemeroff CB. Prediction of antidepressant response to milnacipran by norepinephrine transporter gene polymorphisms. *Am. J. Psychiatry*, 2004, 161(9), 1575-80.

Yoshida K, Higuchi H, Kamata M, Takahashi H, Inoue K, Suzuki T, Itoh K, Ozaki N. The G196A polymorphism of the brain-derived neurotrophic factor gene and the antidepressant effect of milnacipran and fluvoxamine. *J. Psychopharmacol.*, 2007, 21(6), 650-6.

Yu YWY, Tsai SJ, Chen TJ, Lin CH, Hong CJ. Association study of the serotonin transporter promoter polymorphism and symptomatology and antidepressant response in major depressive disorders. *Mol. Psychiatry*, 2002, 7, 1115-9.

Yu YW, Chen TJ, Hong CJ, Chen HM, Tsai SJ. Association Study of the interleukin-1beta (C-511T) genetic polymorphism with major depressive disorder, associated symptomatology, and antidepressant response. *Neuropsychopharmacology*, 2003, 28, 1182–1185.

Yu WY, Tsai SJ, Hong CJ, Chen TJ, Chen MC, Yang CW. Association study of a monoamine oxidase A gene promoter polymorphism with major depressive disorder and antidepressant response. *Neuropsychopharmacology*, 2005, 30(9), 1719-1723.

Yu YW, Tsai SJ, Liou YJ, Hong CJ, Chen TJ. Association study of two serotonin 1A receptor gene polymorphisms and fluoxetine treatment response in Chinese major depressive disorders. *Eur. Neuropsychopharmacol.*, 2006, 16(7), 498-503.

Zanardi R, Benedetti F, DiBella D, Catalano M, Smeraldi E. Efficacy of paroxetine in depression is influenced by a functional polymorphism within the promoter of serotonin transporter gene. *J. Clin. Psychopharmacol.*, 2000, 20, 105–107.

Zanardi R, Serretti A, Rossini D, Franchini L, Cusin C, Lattuada E, Dotoli D, Smeraldi E. Factors affecting fluvoxamine antidepressant activity: influence of pindolol and 5-HTTLPR in delusional and nondelusional depression. *Biol. Psychiatry*, 2001, 50, 323–330.

In: Women and Depression   ISBN 978-1-60456-647-5
Editors: Paula Hernandez and Sara Alonso   © 2009 Nova Science Publishers, Inc.

Chapter 9

Contributors to Depressive Symptoms in Older Women with HIV: Health and Psychosocial Stressors

Mark Brennan[5], Allison Applebaum[6], Marjorie Cantor, R. Andrew Shippy, and Stephen E. Karpiak

AIDS Community Research Initiative of America (ACRIA)
New York, NY, USA

Abstract

High rates of depression are often reported among women with HIV (Cook et al. 2002). Factors contributing to depression among persons with HIV have been identified as greater, age, physical symptoms, comorbid health conditions, loneliness, substance abuse, stigma, and other stressors (Jones et al., 2003; Heckman et al., 2001; Oursler et al, 2006; Rabkin et al., 2004; Riley et al., 2003; Vance, 2006). Factors mitigating depression in this population include effective coping strategies, social support, and spirituality (Coleman et al., 2006; Heckman et al., 2001; Heckman et al., 2002). However, despite the growing aging population living with HIV, the impact of depression on older women with HIV has received limited attention in the research literature. The success of antiretroviral therapy has moved HIV into the category of chronic disease. In New York City, the epicenter of HIV in the United States, 33% of the 100,000 people living with this virus are now over the age of 50 (New York City Department of Health and Mental Hygiene, 2007). This pattern is seen throughout the United States, where it is expected that one-half of those with HIV will be 50 years or older by 2015. This graying population of persons with HIV will confront the challenges of physical and mental health comorbidities, coupled with the panoply of psychosocial challenges that are associated with aging. The present study is one of the first to examine the effects of

---

5 Mark Brennan, PhD, Senior Research Scientist, AIDS Community Research Initiative of America, 230 West 38th Street, 17th Floor, New York, NY, 10018. (212) 924-3934 ext. 131; (212) 924-3936 [fax]; MBrennan@acria.org.
6 Boston University, Boston, MA.

stressors on depressive symptoms among a large sample of women 50 years and older living with HIV.

The sample consisted of 264 women, 50 to 76 years old (*M* age = 55 years). Approximately one-third had post-high school educations, 58% were Black, 34% were Hispanic, and 5% were White. To examine the impact of health-related and psychosocial stressors, the conceptual model employed for analysis was a modified Stress and Coping Model (Folkman and Lazarus, 1984). The multivariate model explained 48% of the variance in depressive symptoms. The number of comorbid conditions and the need for assistance as a result of HIV infection were positively related to greater depressive symptoms, as were both loneliness and stigma. Higher cognitive functioning and spirituality were significantly related to lower levels of depression. These findings support the need for interventions to address depression, health, and psychosocial stressors among older women with HIV. In addition, programs to increase access to spiritual resources for older women with HIV may help to ameliorate depression in this population.

Keywords: *HIV/AIDS, Older Women, Depression, Stress, Spirituality, Social Support*

Just over ten years ago, highly active antiretroviral therapy (HAART) became available for the treatment of HIV/AIDS. HAART has resulted in fundamental life-altering changes for persons living with HIV. HAART has shifted the perception of HIV/AIDS from that of an inevitably fatal disease to one that is chronic but still life-threatening, requiring vigilance and medical intervention (Karpiak, Shippy, and Cantor, 2006). In turn, concerns for those living with HIV have evolved from questions of survival to a focus on physical health, disease management, and life quality (McKelroy and Vosvick, 2006). Paralleling these shifts in HIV management have been changes in the characteristics of the population living with HIV. Today, those with HIV are mostly people of color (75% to 80%) and almost one-third are women, who are for the most part heterosexual (CDC, 2007). Rates of new HIV infections in the United States have remained relatively constant since 2000 at approximately 40,000 to 45,000 annually (CDC). Given these relatively stable rates of infection and the longer survival possible with HAART, the population living with HIV is graying.

Older adults with HIV, using the Centers for Disease Control and Prevention (CDC) criterion of 50 years and older (see Poindexter and Emlet, 2006), account for 24% of all persons living with HIV in the United States in the 33 states with confidential HIV name-based reporting (CDC, 2007). It is highly probable that the majority of persons living with HIV in the next decade will be over the age of 50 (Karpiak et al., 2006). The proportion of women infected with HIV/AIDS has more than tripled in the past decade (Catz, Gore-Felton, and McClure, 2002), and women currently account for nearly one-third (27%) of this population (CDC, 2007). When HIV affects a woman, the cascade of effects beyond her are largely due to the critical role she assumes within the family structure in many minority families as a provider and a caregiver to both children and grandchildren (Catz et al.; Dalmida, 2006). Many times, this involves caring for others with HIV, and these competing demands may mean that these women neglect their own care (Mayers and Svartberg, 2001).

However, little research has been conducted on older adults with HIV, and even less has considered older women with this condition. This chapter focuses on the experience of depression among this segment of the population living with HIV, a disorder with a critical impact on their physical well-being, psychosocial functioning, and quality of life (QOL). This chapter provides an overview of depression among older adults, and examines this condition among older women with HIV/AIDS. The review of the literature then examines factors that both augment and attenuate depression in this population.

Depression and Older Adults

Depression is a common mental health problem that affects upwards of 121 million individuals worldwide. It is defined by the World Health Organization (WHO) as involving symptoms of depressed mood, loss of interest or pleasure, feelings of guilt or low self-worth, changes in sleep or appetite, low energy, and poor concentration lasting 2 or more weeks (WHO, 2007). Depression, including both a diagnosis of a major depressive disorder or significant depressive symptomatology, has been identified as one of the major public health problems affecting older adults (Lyness, King, Cox, Yoediono, and Caine, 1999).

Among older adults, the prevalence of a clinically diagnosed major depressive disorder ranges from 1% to 4%, while significant levels of depressive symptoms affect an additional 8% to 10% of community-dwelling older persons (Blazer, 2002; 2003; U. S. Department of Health and Human Services, 1999). While the likelihood of major depressive disorder decreases with age, older adults are at greater risk for the development of significant depressive symptomatology (U. S. Department of Health and Human Services, 1999). These lower levels of depression, often termed "subsyndromal" or "subthreshold," have been linked to poorer functioning and lower QOL among adults (Horowitz, Reinhardt, and Kennedy, 2005; Rabkin, McElhiney, Rabkin, McGrath, and Ferrando, 2006). A prior diagnosis of major depression, as well as depressive symptoms, increases the likelihood of future depression (Harlow, Goldberg, and Comstock, 1991; Lyness et al., 1999; Mueller et al., 2004). Among older adults, there is growing evidence that women may be more likely to experience depression compared with their male peers. In the general population, the rate of depression in women is twice that of men (McGrath et al., 1990). Barry and colleagues found that among persons 70 years and older, women had a higher prevalence of depression, and these depressive symptoms were more likely to persist in women compared with men (Barry et al., 2008).

In representative samples of community-dwelling older adults, a consistent relationship has emerged between depressive symptoms and physical health, as measured by indices of chronic physical disease and functional disability (Cummings, Neff, and Husaini, 2003; Dent et al., 1999). This view is further supported by evidence that among older persons the presence of depressive symptoms is associated with both greater disability over time (Cummings et al.; Gitlin, Hauck, Dennis, and Schulz, 2007; Han and Jylha, 2006; Kempen, Ranchor, van Sonderen, van Jaarsveld, Cornelia, and Sanderman, 2006; Wolinsky et al., 2007) and greater utilization of health care services (Chen et al., 2007; Ghose, Williams, and Swindle, 2005; Smallbrugge et al., 2006). The physical effects of depression on health and immune function are particularly noteworthy for those with HIV who are aging. Several studies report that depression can suppress immune responses (e.g., Tiemeier, van Tuijl, Hofman, Kiliaan, and Breteler, 2003). Kiecolt-Glaser and Glaser (2002) found that depression is associated with an increased inflammatory response. Consequently, depression may aggravate health conditions associated with aging, such as cardiovascular disease, arthritis, cancer, and general functional decline, leading to greater risks for morbidity and mortality. Finally, there is evidence (e.g., Gibbie et al., 2006) that depression can contribute to neuropsychological impairment or exacerbate cognitive deterioration caused by normal aging in HIV-infected adults. These cognitive effects are manifested by decrements in one's quality of life and the ability to perform activities of daily living, including adherence to multiple treatment regimens of antiretroviral therapy as well as treatments for other chronic diseases associated with aging.

Depression among Women with HIV

Because depression is associated with physical disease and functional disability, it is not surprising that the topic of depression has received a great deal of attention in the HIV/AIDS literature. Depressive symptoms among persons with HIV are not likely to be caused by the disease *per se*, but rather they result from the consequences and concomitant sequelae of receiving a diagnosis of being HIV seropositive (Catz et al., 2002; Rabkin and Remien, 1995). In fact, depression has been recognized as the most commonly observed mental health problem for persons with HIV. Clinical depression may affect up to 20% of this group (New York State Department of Health AIDS Institute, 2005). However, few studies of depression have focused on women with HIV (Goggin, Engelson, Rabkin, and Kotler, 1998), and even fewer have considered older women in this population. Although there has been debate on the prevalence of depression among persons living with HIV due to the overlap between somatic symptoms of depression and HIV disease and treatment effects (e.g., weight loss, fatigue; Rabkin and Remien, 1995), it appears that HIV-infected women are particularly vulnerable to experiencing depressive symptomatology (Cook et al., 2002; Hader, Smith, Moore and Holmberg, 2001; Turrina et al., 2001). Some data indicate that the prevalence of depression among women with HIV (30% to 60%) markedly exceeds levels found in their male counterparts (20% or less; Ickovics et al., 2001; Tostes, Chalub, and Botega, 2004; Tryznka and Erlen, 2004). However, other research has failed to find differences in rates of depression based on gender among persons with HIV (Goggin et al., 1998).

Effects of Depression on Women with HIV

The significance of depression among persons with HIV stems not only from its negative impact on life quality, but also from the well-documented negative impact depression has on physical health. Most significant for this population are repeated reports that depression negatively influences adherence to HAART therapy (Chesney, 2000; Holzemer et al., 1999; Mehta, Moore, and Graham, 1997; Singh et al., 1996; Tryznka and Erlen, 2004; Wagner,

Kanouse, Koegel and Sullivan, 2003). Adherence to antiretroviral therapy is critical because failure to adhere to treatment results in failure to control the infection, allows the emergence of antiretroviral-resistant strains of the virus, and increases the risk of the transmission of HIV to others (Tryznka and Erlen). Research indicates that depression disproportionately affects adherence to HAART among women as compared with men (Turrina, Fiorazzo and Turano, 2001). In addition, HIV-infected depressed women are significantly less likely to be adherent to HAART compared with women with HIV who are not depressed (Cook et al., 2002).

Moreover, depression results in lower health-related quality of life QOL among persons with HIV (Tostes et al., 2004). Lower levels of QOL are reported in women than in men, regardless of HIV status (McGrath et al., 1990, Shor-Posner et al., 2000). This may be a result of the negative relation between QOL and depression coupled with the higher prevalence of depression among women living with HIV. Additionally, depression has been related to decreased immune function as indicated by CD4 counts among women with HIV (Boarts, Sledjeski, Bogart, and Delahanty, 2006; Ickovics et al., 2001). In one study, women with HIV who were depressed were twice as likely to die when compared with those with no depressive symptoms (Ickovics et al.).

Physical and Mental Health Comorbidity

Parallel to research in the general population, there is a strong relationship between physical health status (e.g., HIV symptoms, number of comorbid conditions, health-related functioning) and depression among persons with HIV (Tostes et al., 2004; Tsao, Dobalian, Moreau, and Dobalian, 2004). Furthermore, there is a greater likelihood of current depression if there is a prior history of either major depressive disorder or significant depressive symptomatology (Harlow, Goldberg, and Comstock, 1991; Lyness et al., 1999; Mueller et al., 2004). Rabkin and Remien (1995) have posited that the high rates of depression found among persons with HIV are largely explained by depressive disorders that predate their HIV diagnosis. In addition, there are considerable levels of comorbid psychiatric disorders among persons with HIV, including anxiety disorders, bipolar disorders, post-traumatic stress disorder (PTSD), and substance use (Pence, Miller, Whetten, Eron, and Gaynes, 2006; Rabkin, Ferrando, Lin, Sewell, and McElhiney, 2000; Leserman et al., 2005). Such psychiatric comorbidity was evidenced among women with HIV in Brazil; nearly two-fifths had received past treatment with psychiatric drugs (39.5%) and one-quarter had a history of mental health service utilization (Tostes et al., 2004). Substance use often characterizes this population, with reported prevalence of substance use approaching 50% in some studies (Commerford, Gular, Orr, Reznikoff, and O'Dowd, 1994; Pence et al.; Rabkin et al., 2000). Many research findings indicate that rates of depression in HIV-infected adults are associated with patterns of substance use (Brienza et al, 2000; Darke and Ross, 1997; Dodds et al., 2003; 2001; Goggin et al., 1998; Knowlton et al., 2001; Rabkin et al., 1997; Turrina et al., 2001; Tryznka and Erlen, 2004). Rates of depression are very high among HIV-infected female injection drug users (Moore et al., 1999; Powell-Cope, White, Henkelman and Turner, 2005).

Chronic Stress, Trauma and Depression

Chronic stress resulting from adverse life situations has been identified as one of the factors precipitating depression among women with HIV. In the United States, the prevalence of HIV/AIDS is greatest among non-Hispanic Blacks, Hispanics, and other ethnic minorities (Pence et al., 2006). The vast majority of women living with HIV are women of color, and the vast majority of these are at the lower end of the socioeconomic spectrum (Catz et al., 2002; Gurung, Taylor, Kemeny, and Myers, 2004). These women must cope with a variety of chronic stressors related to their race/ethnicity and gender status that are further exacerbated by persistent challenges in the management of finances, employment, housing, caregiving responsibilities, and health care access, as well as exposure to crime and endemic substance use (Gurung et al.; (Jones et al., 2003). Chronic stress is also fostered by receiving the diagnosis of a chronic life-threatening illness, such as HIV, which may result in considerable psychological distress (Catz et al.). In one study of stress and depression among women with HIV, chronic stressors were associated with greater depressive symptoms, even when controlling for socioeconomic status among African American, European American, and Latina women (Gurung et al.).

In addition to chronic stress, women with HIV have a greater likelihood of having experienced traumatic life events, including being the victims of abuse, which is strongly correlated with depression (Jones et al., 2003; Gurung et al., 2004). In a sample of both men and women with HIV, Leserman et al. (2005) found that nearly three-quarters reported at least two substantial traumatic events in their lifetimes, including 34% with a history of sexual abuse, 38% with a history of physical abuse, 54% with both sexual and physical abuse, 26% with substantial childhood physical neglect, 23% with substantial childhood emotional neglect, and an additional 51% with two or more other types of trauma. Levels of depressive symptoms in this group were considerably greater than among the general population.

Stigma and Depression

A stressor that is specific to those living with HIV is the psychological distress associated with stigma concerning HIV/AIDS. This includes the stigma associated with populations at-risk for this disease, such as gay men or injection-drug users (Kalichman, 1998; Reece, Tanner, Karpiak, and Coffey, 2007). The stigma attached to HIV is further exacerbated because many wrongly perceive this disease as resulting from a moral failure of personal responsibility, that is engaging in what society judges to be undesirable behaviors (e.g., homosexual activity, drug use), and because the disease is contagious and because the diagnosis is permanent (Reece et al, 2007). HIV/AIDS is also stigmatized because many perceive and judge it as a retribution for sexual activity or drug use through some mechanism of immanent justice (Jue and Lewis, 2001; Raman and Winer, 2002). Sadly, being infected with HIV is unlike any other disease entity in the present day. Those who are living with HIV are subjected to a myriad of negative judgments that can induce psychological distress and may create barriers to health care and social participation. The stigma associated with

HIV/AIDS is present regardless of age, gender, or sexual orientation, and may be particularly demoralizing among persons who have contracted the disease but are not members of high-risk groups (Stanley, 1999). This is the case for many older women with HIV. There is evidence that stigma may be experienced more intensely among women with HIV compared to men. According to Fisher (1999), many women consider HIV to be "...a dirty disease contracted through dirty needles and dirty sex" a self-image that is greatly at odds with society's ideal of being "clean and wholesome." Fisher proposes that for women, the admission of being HIV positive may be "a fate worse than death" due to the social consequences of disclosing one's HIV status. Women are further stigmatized as a result of the assumption by many that they were exposed to HIV through drug use or incarceration (Lichtenstein et al., 2002).

Among older adults, the experience of stigma has been characterized as involving rejection, stereotyping, fear of contagion, violations of confidentiality, and protective silence, i.e., concealing one's HIV status from others to avoid negative reactions (Emlet, 2006a). Thus it is not surprising that stigma has been positively linked to depression among persons with HIV (Emlet, 2007; Flowers, Davis, Hart, Rosengarten, Frankis, and Imrie, 2006; Lichtenstein et al., 2002; Riggs, Vosvick, and Stallings, 2007).

Loneliness and Social Isolation

Loneliness and social isolation are two interrelated constructs that affect the experience of depression among persons with HIV. Loneliness is defined as the subjective emotional experience of dissatisfaction with one's social relationships, such as lack of intimacy or lack of commitment. In contrast, social isolation refers to actual interactions, or lack thereof, with members of one's social network (Chappell and Badger, 1989). Many older adults experience both loneliness and social isolation, and both of these may contribute to depression (Adams, Sanders and Auth, 2004). Among older adults with HIV, increased loneliness has been associated with higher levels of depression (Vance, 2006). In addition, the diagnosis of HIV can also entail social isolation, whether it is in the form of self-protection (Emlet, 2006b) or in instances where the person with HIV faces rejection from members of his or her social network when the diagnosis becomes known, or because of other behaviors associated with HIV infection, such as intravenous drug use or homosexuality (Flowers et al., 2006; Lichtenstein et al., 2002; Mayers and Svartberg, 2001; Tryznka and Erlen, 2004). Emlet (2006b) notes that older adults with HIV are at greater risk for social isolation in comparison with their younger counterparts.

Social Support

A large body of work exists that has examined the effects of social support on mental health outcomes, focusing on both the direct effects of such support, and on the indirect or "buffering" effects of social network participation (Cohen and Wills, 1985). Results of these studies tend to be mixed. Some studies have supported the notion of social support as a buffer to stressful life experiences (e.g., Billings and Moos, 1981; Blake and Vandiver, 1988; Cauce, Hannan, and Sargeant, 1992; Pretorius, 1998; Sumi, 1997), while others have found only direct effects of social support on well-being (e.g., Cohen and Wills). Koenig et al. (2004) have posited that social support may be an important explanatory factor in health research outcomes. This is likely the case among persons with HIV with regard to depression. A central finding in the social support literature has been that the direct receipt of social support, either instrumental or emotional, does not appear to be strongly linked to positive psychosocial outcomes. Rather it is the perception that such support is available and adequate that appears to exert beneficial effects (Cohen and Wills, 1985).

Indeed, similar findings have been noted among persons with HIV in terms of mental health. Stewart and colleagues examined the relation of perceived social support availability (e.g., for caregiving, socialization) to mental health among a sample of persons with HIV of both genders in Alabama (Stewart, Cianfrini, and Walker, 2005). After controlling for demographic, health status, and stress variables, higher perceptions of social support were positively related to better mental health status. Similar results have been found in studies of women with HIV. Catz et al. (2002) found that perceived social support predicted lower levels of depressive symptoms among women with low socioeconomic status. Furthermore, Serovich and colleagues examined both perceived and available social support with regard to depressive symptoms among women with HIV in the Midwest, over one-half of whom were African American. In these analyses, perceived social support, but not actual social support, predicted lower levels of depression in this sample, as well as poor psychosocial well-being in terms of loneliness and anxiety (Serovich, Kimberly, Mosack and Lewis, 2001). Older women with HIV are more likely to perceive that the support they receive is adequate compared with male peers (Shippy and Karpiak, 2005), which may offer an advantage to coping with depression. Thus social isolation among persons with HIV is particularly adverse, given the well-documented function of social support in providing protection against depression in this population.

Spirituality and Depression

Spirituality is distinct from religious beliefs and practices. Spirituality is defined as involving a sense of transcendence over life circumstances, purpose and meaning in life, and a sense of connectedness with others (Howden, 1992; Lindgren and Coursey, 1995; Moberg, 1967; Pargament, 1997). For those living with HIV, spiritual transcendence involves overcoming the boundaries of the self to find purpose and meaning in living with this disease (Mellors, Riley, and Erlen, 1997). Transcendence may serve to alter the perception of having HIV as being a random event or bad luck to that of an experience that has the potential to enrich one's life and that of those around them (Hall, 1998; Jue and Lewis, 2001; Vance and Woodley, 2005). The consoling effects of spirituality may increase one's sense of hope, including the belief that future expectations and life goals are possible (DePalo and Brennan, 2005). By providing positive expectations, hope engendered from spirituality may counteract feelings of depression that are detrimental to quality of life (Dalmida, 2006; Russinova, 1999).

Because persons with HIV, including older women, experience a strong need for meaning and hope, spiritual beliefs and practices can assist in coping and adjustment to this illness (Dalmida, 2006; Dunphy, 1987; Gehr, 2002; Kalichman, 1998). Among one sample of older adults with HIV from 50 to 68 years of age, religious and spiritual beliefs and practices provided the following benefits: a) emotional comfort; b) a greater sense of strength, empowerment, and control; c) lessening the emotional burden of illness; d) improving perceived social support and reducing social isolation; e) fostering spiritual support through relation to a higher power; f) helping to find a sense of meaning and acceptance of HIV; g) maintaining physical health; h) reducing fear and uncertainty around death; and i) increasing self-acceptance while reducing self-blame (Siegel and Schrimshaw, 2002). Spirituality can reinforce a sense of connection to others. This connection facilitates the activation of important social support resources (i.e., Heinrich, 2003; Kendall, 1994), which may be potent protectors against depression. Additionally, research has found higher levels of spirituality to be related to lower levels of stress and psychological distress, both or which are precursors to depression among persons with HIV (Tuck, McCain, and Elswick, 2001). Spirituality also appears to be protective against depression in a range of HIV-positive populations, including males (Yi et al., 2006) and within the racial and ethnic minorities that comprise the majority of older women living with HIV (Simoni and Ortiz, 2003).

Purpose and Rationale

The preceding review of the literature has underscored the problem of depression among older adults and women living with HIV. Given the emergence of a sizable cohort of older women with HIV in the next decade, it is imperative that a better understanding is gained about those factors related to depression in this group, as well as the personal and social resources that may provide protection from depression. For many of these older women, problems with depression may predate their exposure to and diagnosis of HIV. Their depression may well be related to the chronic and acute stressors that typify the life circumstances of persons with low socioeconomic and racial or ethnic minority status. In fact, those two factors describe precisely the status of most older women with HIV in the United States. Such circumstances include inadequate economic resources, crime, high rates of incarceration, substance abuse, and generally poor living conditions. A diagnosis of HIV serves to aggravate what is already an untenable situation for these women. Further, depression may also be related to factors associated with an HIV diagnosis, including comorbid health problems, greater need for assistance, loss of independence, poor health-related quality of life, social isolation, loneliness, and HIV-stigma. However, social and personal resources, such as perceptions of social support availability and adequacy or spirituality, may serve to attenuate depressive symptoms among older women with HIV.

The purpose of the present study is to examine the covariates of depression and putative factors among older women living with HIV in New York City. These women are characterized by many of the factors associated with women having HIV in the United States, being primarily persons of color from disadvantaged socioeconomic backgrounds. The conceptual model for the present analysis is the Stress and Coping Model proposed by

Lazarus and Folkman (1984), which has been employed in other studies of psychosocial outcomes in women with HIV (Gurung et al., 2004). According to this model, stressors, such as HIV, create a sense of threat, challenge, or loss. Coping mechanisms reduce such threats, and lead to better outcomes. For the present analyses, a number of stressors were included in the model, including HIV and non-HIV health indicators (e.g., CD4 count, drug use, comorbid health conditions), economic stressors (e.g., lack of employment, income inadequacy), health-related quality of life (cognitive and social functioning), HIV-related stigma, and loneliness. Coping mechanisms included social resources (i.e., perceptions of social support availability and adequacy, support from religious congregations) and the personal resource of spirituality. The outcome was the level of depressive symptomatology. We hypothesized that stress-related variables would be positively related to higher levels of depressive symptoms, while coping mechanisms of social support and spirituality would be related to lower levels of depressive symptomatology in multivariate analysis controlling for the effects of key sociodemographic factors.

Method

Participants

Data were obtained from the study "Research on Older Adults with HIV" (ROAH; Karpiak et al., 2006), conducted in New York City in 2005 and 2006. ROAH used nonprobabilistic quota sampling with a target of 1,000 participants 50 years of age and older having HIV with the following characteristics: a gender ratio of approximately 2 to 1 (i.e., male and female, respectively); a distribution of race ethnicity of 50% non-Hispanic Black, 35% Hispanic, 15% White; and 15% over the age 60. These quotas were based on available HIV epidemiological data for New York City in early 2005 (New York City Department of Health and Mental Hygiene, 2005). Sample inclusion criteria were: confirmed HIV diagnosis; age 50 years or older; living in or recipient of health care in New York City; community-dwelling; sufficient English-language skills to complete the questionnaire; and no significant cognitive impairments. This resulted in a final sample of 914 older adults (mean age = 55.5, range = 50 to 78 years).

The sample for the present study consisted of a subset of ROAH participants who identified themselves as female (n = 264). The average age of the ROAH women's sample was 55.2 years (SD = 4.6, range = 50 to 76 years; see Table 1). Non-Hispanic Blacks accounted for 58% of the sample, followed by 34% Hispanic, 5% non-Hispanic Whites, and 3% of other/mixed race/ethnicity. Eighty-three percent reported speaking English as a primary language, 15% reported either Spanish or Spanish and English, and 1% reported some other language. With regard to sexual orientation, the vast majority (84%) described themselves as heterosexual, with gay/lesbian and bisexual comprising the remainder (9% and 7%, respectively). Reflecting the lower socioeconomic status of most women with HIV, only 13% had completed college degrees, while nearly one-third (31%) had not obtained a high school diploma. Over one-half of these women (54%) were on disability.

Table 1. Sociodemographic characteristics of Older Women with HIV

Variable	M	SD
Age	55.2	4.6

Variable	N	%
Race/Ethnicity		
Non-Hispanic White	14	5.4
Non-Hispanic Black	150	57.5
Hispanic	88	33.7
Other Race/Ethnicity	9	3.4
Language Usually Spoken		
English	201	83.4
Spanish	17	7.1
Spanish and English	20	8.3
Other	3	1.2
Sexual Orientation		
Heterosexual	208	84.2
Gay/Lesbian	22	8.9
Bisexual	16	6.5
Other	1	0.4
Level of Education		
Less than High School Graduate	81	30.9
High School Graduate	83	31.7
Some College	65	24.8
College Graduate/Post-Graduate	33	12.6

Table 1. (Continued)

Variable	N	%
Employment Status		
Working	24	9.4
Retired	13	5.1
Unemployed	49	19.3
Homemaker	18	7.1
Disability	136	53.5
Volunteer Work	11	4.3
Other	3	1.2
Income Adequacy		
Do Not Have Enough	54	21.8
Just Manage	124	50.0
Enough, a Little Extra	51	20.6
Money Not a Problem	19	7.7
History of Incarceration (yes)	93	36.8
Living Arrangement		
Alone	151	57.6
With Spouse/Partner	58	22.2
With Others	53	20.2

Note. N = 264. Percent shown is valid percent.

Less than 10% reported that they were currently working, and almost 20% reported being unemployed. Thus it is not surprising that approximately three-quarters of these women reported inadequate incomes or were just managing to get by on their current incomes (22% and 50%, respectively). Over one-third (37%) had a past history of incarceration. Over one-half of these women lived alone (58%), with the remainder nearly equally divided between those living with a spouse or partner and those living with someone else, typically a child or other family member.

Measures

Sociodemographic Information. Single items assessed participants' age, gender, race/ethnicity, sexual orientation, level of education, employment status, income adequacy, history of incarceration, and living arrangements (see Table 1).

Health Status. Single items measured months since HIV diagnosis, CD4 count, and receipt of an AIDS diagnosis (see Table 2). Comorbid health conditions were assessed with a checklist of 25 common health conditions experienced in the past year (e.g., arthritis, cancer, and hypertension) and the number of positive responses to this list was summed to obtain the number of conditions. Self-rated health was assessed on a scale ranging from 0 (worst possible health) to 10 (best possible health). Drug and alcohol use in the past 3 months was assessed with a single item. Finally, a single-item assessed if respondents had ever needed emotional, physical or financial help because of HIV/AIDS, with possible responses being; have never needed help, needed help in the past but not now, need help currently.

Health-related Quality of Life. Selected subscales from the Medical Outcomes Study HIV Assessment (MOS-HIV; Wu et al., 1991) were used to assess dimensions of this construct in the areas of cognitive and social function. Responses are made on a 6-point Likert-type scale ranging from 1 (all of the time) to 6 (none of the time). The cognitive subscale consists of the sum of 4 items (e.g., Did you have difficulty reasoning and solving problems, for example, making plans, making decisions, and learning new things?) and high internal consistency in this sample of women with HIV (α = .83). Social function was assessed with a single item that asked, "How much of the time, *during the past 4 weeks*, has your health limited your social activities (like visiting with friends or close relatives)?"

Table 2. Health Status of Older Women with HIV

Variable	M	SD
Months since HIV Diagnosis	137.0	60.2
Number of Comorbid Conditions	3.6	2.7
Self-rated Health (1 to 10)	7.0	1.8
Variable	N	%
CD4 Count		
Less than 200	33	14.0
201 to 350	40	17.0
351 to 500	47	20.0
More than 500	115	48.9
Ever Diagnosed with AIDS (yes)	118	45.0
Drug/Alcohol Use in Past 3 Months (yes)	119	47.0

Note. N = 264. Percent shown is valid percent.

HIV Stigma. The HIV Stigma Scale (Berger, Ferrans, and Lashley, 2001) is a 40-item instrument that uses a 4-point Likert-type scale 1 (strongly disagree) to 4 (strongly agree) for the assessment of perceived stigma related to HIV, with higher scores indicating greater stigma. Two items are reverse scored in order to reduce response bias. Either the total scale score or four subscales scores may be used. The four subscales represent the various domains of stigma. *Personalized Stigma* (18 items; e.g., losing friends, feeling that people avoid you, regretting having told others about one's HIV status) measures perceived consequences of others' knowledge of the individual's HIV status. *Disclosure Concerns* (10 items; e.g., keeping one's HIV status secret, fearing that people will tell others about the individual's HIV status) is related to controlling information. *Negative Self-image* (13 items; e.g., feeling unclean, feeling not as good as other people, feeling bad because you were infected with HIV) assesses internalized stigma. Finally, *Concern with Public Attitudes* (20 items; e.g., when people learn you have HIV, they look for flaws in your character) addresses perceptions about what most people think about HIV-positive individuals or what people living with HIV experience when others discover their HIV status. The range of possible scores for the total HIV Stigma Scale is from 40 to 160. Berger and colleagues (2001) reported a coefficient alpha of .96 for the 40-item instrument, indicating a high level of internal consistency. Cronbach's alpha among the current sample of women for the total scale was .96.

Loneliness. The UCLA Loneliness Scale (Version 3; Russell, 1996) was used to measure emotional loneliness. This scale is a 20-item measure with high reported internal consistency (coefficient αs = .89 to .94) and acceptable one-year test-retest reliabilities (r = .73). There are 11 negatively worded items (e.g., How often do you feel close to people?) and 9 positively-worded items (e.g., How often do you feel alone?). Responses are made on a 4-point Likert-type scale (i.e., never, rarely, sometimes, and always). The nine positively worded items are reverse coded and scores from all 20 items are summed, with higher scores indicating greater emotional loneliness. Internal consistency in this sample of older women with HIV was good with α = .88.

Social Support. Participants were asked to rate the availability and adequacy of social support. The two availability items asked the extent to which either instrumental or emotional social support was available from family or nonkin on a 4-point scale (i.e., most of the time, some of the time, only occasionally, or not at all). The two adequacy items asked whether the instrumental or emotional support received in the past year from family or nonkin was adequate on a 4-point scale (i.e., received all support needed, needed a little more, needed some more, needed a lot more; see Table 3). These social support items have been used previously in other large-scale studies of older adults (e.g., Cantor and Brennan, 1993). Finally, a single dichotomous item asked whether or not respondents sought social support from their places of worship.

Spirituality. Spirituality was measured with Howden's (1992) Spiritual Assessment Scale (SAS), a 28-item measure using a 6-point Likert-type scale (i.e., strongly disagree to strongly agree) with four subscales of *Purpose and Meaning in Life* (e.g., I have goals and aims for my life), *Inner Resources* (e.g., I feel good about myself), *Inter-Connectedness* (e.g., reconciling relationships is important to me), and *Transcendence* (e.g., the boundaries of my universe extend beyond usual ideas of what space and time are thought to be).

Table 3. Need for Help and Social Support Characteristics of Older Women with HIV

Variable	N	%
Ever Needed Help		
Never	38	14.6
Not Presently, But in Past	98	37.7
Currently Need Help	124	47.7
Availability of Instrumental Support		
All/Most of Time	94	35.9
Some of the Time	68	26.0
Only Occasionally	48	18.3
Not at All	52	19.8
Adequacy of Instrumental Support		
Received All That Was Needed	102	39.8
Need a Little More	69	27.0
Need Some More	56	21.9
Need a Lot More	29	11.3
Availability of Emotional Support		
All/Most of Time	133	51.0
Some of the Time	73	28.0
Only Occasionally	22	8.4
Not at All	33	12.6
Adequacy of Emotional Support		
Received All That Was Needed	83	31.9
Need a Little More	62	23.8
Need Some More	51	19.6
Need a Lot More	64	24.6
Received Support from Place of Worship (yes)	127	52.7

Note. N = 264. Percent shown is valid percent.

The four SAS domains have been frequently identified as components of the construct of spirituality (e.g., Brennan, 2004; Chandler et al., 1992; Moberg, 2002), but do not contain references to the sacred or God (e.g., Pargament, 1997). For the present analysis, the total scale score was used with an inter-item reliability of $\alpha = .96$ for this sample of older women with HIV.

Depression. Depressive symptomatology was measured with the Center for Epidemiologic Studies Depression Scale (CES-D; Radloff, 1977). The CES-D is a 20-item self-report scale designed to assess depressive symptomatology in the general population. Four items are reverse coded to prevent response bias. Responses are scored on a 4-point scale ranging from 0 (rarely or none of the time) to 3 (most or all of the time) referring to symptoms experienced in the previous week. Sample items include "I thought my life had been a failure" and "I enjoyed life." Item scores are summed to obtain a total symptom score with a range of 0 to 60; higher scores indicate greater depressive symptomatology. This measure has demonstrated high internal consistency (Cronbach's αs = .85 to .90) across diverse community and clinical samples including women with HIV (e.g., Ickovics, et al., 2001). In the present sample of older women with HIV, the internal consistency of this measure was .88. The Centers for Disease Control and Prevention (2002) have suggested a cutoff of 22 and above on the CES-D as indicative of major depression. In addition, specificity for major depressive disorder is greater than 85% using a cutoff of 23 (Lyness, et al., 1997).

Procedures

The project site was the AIDS Community Research Initiative of America (ACRIA) located in New York City. This study methodology was approved by the Copernicus Group Institutional Review Board prior to data collection. Recruitment materials were mailed to over 1,500 persons living with HIV. Others were recruited by ACRIA's Research Outreach Coordinator and agency staff through on-site trainings, presentations and staff visits, mail contacts, phone contacts, email, and word-of-mouth referral by other ROAH participants. Prior to data collection, participants were given a written informed consent document describing the study's purpose, procedures, possible risks, discomforts, and benefits. Assurance of confidentiality and anonymity was included on the consent form. Data were collected using self-administered questionnaires that were completed at ACRIA, at one of the community recruitment sites, or at the respondent's home and then returned to community recruitment sites where they were retrieved by ACRIA staff. Surveys took approximately one hour to complete. Contact information was provided in the event participants had any concerns or questions about their participation in the study. Participants were reimbursed $25.00 for their participation in the study.

Design and Analysis

The present study of factors related to depression among older women with HIV employed a cross-sectional, correlational design. Statistical analysis consisted of univariate analysis to examine the distribution of study variables, bivariate analyses of the relation between independent covariates and depression using Pearson correlations, and linear multiple regression analysis to examine the relative importance of factors predicting depression. For bivariate and multivariate analyses, nominal and categorical variables were dummy coded using procedures suggested by Cohen and Cohen (1983). For example, race/ethnicity was recoded as non-Hispanic Black, and Hispanic with non-Hispanic Whites and those of other race/ethnicities serving as the reference group.

Bivariate analysis was used to identify significant covariates of depression prior to multivariate analysis; those covariates that did not bear a significant relationship to depression scores and were not conceptually necessary were removed from the regression model. The multiple regression analysis utilized a hierarchical method of entry corresponding to the components of the Lazarus and Folkman (1984) stress and coping model The first block consisted of sociodemographic factors to control for their influence on the dependent variable. The second block consisted of health factors (i.e., months since HIV diagnosis, comorbid conditions) that may be related to depression. The third block consisted of potential stressors (i.e., need for help, income adequacy, QOL measures, loneliness, and stigma). The fourth and final block contained coping mechanisms that were hypothesized to have an impact on depressive symptoms (i.e., social support availability and adequacy, support from religious congregations, spirituality). Prior to regression analysis, correlation coefficients between independent covariates were examined for possible multicollinearity of these factors. In addition, collinearity diagnostics were computed in the regression analysis. Significance of independent predictors was evaluated in terms of t-tests of the individual variables, amount of variance explained by each block of the regression equation (i.e., R^2), and significance of each block of the model as determined with the F-test.

Results

Univariate Analysis

HIV and other Health Status. Women in the present sample could be characterized as long-term HIV survivors; the average length of time since HIV diagnosis 137 months (i.e., 11.4 years; see Table 2). The efficacy of HAART was evident in their CD4 counts; only 14% reported having counts of 200 or less, and almost one-half had CD4 counts of 500 or more. Forty-five percent reported a prior diagnosis of AIDS. The extent of physical health comorbidity was high among these women, with 3.6 comorbid conditions on average (SD = 2.7). However, self-rated health averaged 7.0 (SD = 1.8) on a scale of 0 to 10, with higher scores indicating better health. The use of alcohol and illicit drugs was prevalent, with nearly one-half reporting use in the past 3 months.

Need for Help. Older women with HIV were asked if they had ever needed help (i.e., emotional, physical, or financial) due to HIV/AIDS. Reflecting the difficulty of dealing with this chronic, life-threatening condition, only 15% indicated that they had never needed help in these domains (see Table 3). Approximately two-fifths (38%) reported that they had needed such help in the past, but did not need help at present, while nearly one-half (48%) reported that they were currently in need of emotional, physical or financial help due to HIV/AIDS.

Quality of Life Measures. Despite this high reported need for help among older women with HIV, average QOL measures in cognitive and social domains in this group were in a positive direction (see Table 4). With regard to cognitive function, the mean score was 17.6, above the midpoint of 14 on this measure. In a similar vein, the average for the social functioning item was 4.5, again above the midpoint for 3 on this item. These data suggest that both cognitive and social functioning were relatively high in this group.

HIV Stigma. The average total score on the Berger Stigma Scale (Berger et al., 2001) was 86.5 (SD = 24.2), which was below the midpoint of 95.5 on this measure (see Table 4). However, given the size of the standard deviation, approximately one-third or more of the sample were experiencing significant levels of HIV stigma.

Emotional Loneliness. The average score on the UCLA Loneliness Scale (Russell, 1996) was 41.9, slightly below the midpoint for this measure, indicating a moderate amount of emotional loneliness in the present sample (see Table 4).

Social Support. With regard to the adequacy of instrumental support, only 36% reported that such help was available most of the time, while 26% indicated that such help was available some of the time (see Table 3). Nearly two in five (38%) indicated that instrumental social support was available either occasionally or not at all. For the purposes of comparison, among a sample of community-dwelling New Yorkers age 65 or more, only 32% reported the unavailability of instrumental help (Cantor and Brennan, 1993). Further, one-third of these older women with HIV indicated that such support was inadequate, either needing some more (22%) or a lot more help (11%) in this domain. This compares with only 20% of older New Yorkers in general who reported inadequate instrumental support (Cantor and Brennan).

Table 4. Descriptive Statistics on Major Variables for Correlation and Regression Analyses

Variable	M	SD	Skewness	Range[1]
Cognitive Functioning QOL	17.6	4.8	-0.61	4 to 24
Social Functioning QOL	4.5	1.6	-0.92	1 to 6
Berger Stigma Scale	86.5	24.2	0.33	43 to 154
UCLA Loneliness Scale	41.9	10.7	.21	22 to 69
Spirituality Assessment Scale	140.0	24.0	-1.52	35 to 168
CES-D[2]	20.1	11.1	0.33	0 to 51

Note. N = 264. CES-D = Center for Epidemiological Studies Depression Scale. QOL = Quality of Life.
[1] Observed Range of Scores
[2] Center for Epidemiological Studies Depression Scale

However, the availability of emotional support for the present sample was similar to that of older New Yorkers in general (Cantor and Brennan, 1993). Over one-half of older women with HIV indicated that emotional support was available all or most of the time, while 28% said such support was available some of the time. Over one-fifth reported the unavailability of emotional support, similar to that reported among older New Yorkers in general (19%).

Despite the relatively high availability of emotional help, older women with HIV felt that the emotional support they received was not adequate. Twenty percent indicated the need for some more help in this area, while 25% reported needing a lot more help. This level of emotional support inadequacy far exceeded that found among the general population or older New Yorkers, where only 18% reported this level of inadequate emotional support (Cantor and Brennan). Finally, over one-half (53%) of older women with HIV had received support from their places of worship (see Table 3).

Spirituality. The average total Spiritual Assessment Scale score (Howden, 1992) for the present sample 140.0 indicating a relatively high level of spirituality in this group. Brennan (2004) reported an average score on this measure of 134.5 among a sample of middle-age and older adults vision rehabilitation clients. This finding, along with the high proportion of older women with HIV receiving social support from their places of worship suggests considerable spiritual resilience among this group, despite the well-documented stigma that many people with HIV face in religious settings.

Depression. The average score on the CES-D scale (Radloff, 1977) among older women with HIV was 20.1, approaching the cutoff of 22 suggested by the CDC (2002). Furthermore, 43% of these older women had CES-D scores of 22 or higher. These finding indicate high levels of depressive symptomatology among this group and are suggestive of clinical levels of major depressive disorder.

Bivariate Analysis

Pearson product-moment correlations were calculated between CES-D scores and sociodemographic, heath status, stressors and coping mechanisms (see Table 5).

Overall sociodemographic factors bore little significant relationship to level of depressive symptoms. There was a negative relationship between age and CES-D scores ($r = -.13$) that was significant, suggesting a trend for lower levels of depression with lower age. However, race/ethnicity (i.e., non-Hispanic Black and Hispanic), sexual orientation (bisexual or lesbian), language, education, employment status (i.e.., disabled or unemployed), history of incarceration, and living alone were not significantly related to CES-D scores at the bivariate level.

There were, however, a number of significant relationships between health status variables and depression. The number of months since HIV diagnosis was significantly and positively related to CES-D scores ($r = .12$), such that those older women who had a longer history of being diagnosed with HIV had higher levels of depressive symptoms. However, having received a prior diagnosis of AIDS and CD4 count were not related to levels of depression. The number of comorbid conditions was also significantly and positively related to depression ($r = .33$), so that older women with a greater number of health conditions in addition to HIV were more depressed. Global self-ratings of health had a significant negative relation to CES-D scores ($r = -.19$), in that better perceived health was indicative of fewer depressive symptoms. Finally, use of drugs or alcohol in the previous 3 months was not significantly related to levels of depression.

Table 5. Bivariate Analysis of Correlates of CES-D Depression Scores

Variable	r	p-value
Age	-.13	.041
Non-Hispanic Black	-.06	.368
Hispanic	.01	.871
Bisexual	.01	.895
Lesbian	-.05	.381
Non-English Speaking	-.00	.944
Education	-.01	.857
Disabled	-.08	.194
Unemployed	.09	.168
History of Incarceration	-.03	.630
Live Alone	.01	.894
Months since HIV Diagnosis	.12	.051
AIDS Diagnosis	.01	.886
CD4 Count	.03	.621
Comorbid Health Conditions	.33	.001
Self-Rated Health	-.19	.003
Drugs/Alcohol Past 3 Months	-.04	.521
Need Help	.24	.001
Income Adequacy	-.19	.003
Cognitive QOL	-.38	.001
Social Function QOL	-.31	.001
Berger Stigma Scale	.45	.001
UCLA Loneliness Scale	.59	.001
Instrumental Support Availability	.17	.005
Instrumental Support Adequacy	.20	.001
Emotional Support Availability	.16	.010
Emotional Support Adequacy	.23	.001
Support from Place of Worship	-.10	.119
Spiritual Assessment Scale	-.30	.001

Note. Pairwise N = 264.

There were strong relationships between all of the stressor variables and CES-D scores, highlighting the strong contribution of stress to depression among older women with HIV. The need for help due to HIV was strongly and positively related to depressive symptoms (r = .24), indicating that those with a past or present need for emotional, physical, or financial help had higher levels of depressive symptoms. Income adequacy was significantly related to

CES-D scores ($r = -.19$); older women who reported some degree of income adequacy also reported lower levels of depressive symptoms. Health-related quality of life measures in cognitive and social domains were both negatively related to depressive symptoms ($r = -.38$ and -.31, respectively). Not surprisingly, perceived stigma due to HIV was strongly related to symptoms of depression ($r = .45$), as was emotional loneliness ($r = .59$).

With regard to coping mechanisms, the perceived availability and adequacy of both instrumental and emotional support were consistently related to lower levels of depressive symptomatology among older women with HIV. Correlations of these items with CES-D scores ranged from .17 to .23 (see Table 5). Receiving social support from one's place of worship was negatively related to depressive symptoms; however, this correlation was not statistically significant. Finally, higher levels of spirituality had a strong, negative relationship with depression ($r = -.30$).

Multivariate Analysis

In order to test a parsimonious multivariate model on covariates of depression among older women with HIV, independent factors that were not significantly related to CES-D scores in bivariate analysis and did not have other strong conceptual justification for remaining in the model were omitted from further analysis. The resultant hierarchical model was used to predict CES-D scores in four blocks consisting of sociodemographic factors (i.e., age), health status variables (i.e., months since HIV diagnosis, number of comorbid conditions, self-rated health), stress variables (i.e., need for help, income adequacy, cognitive and social quality of life, HIV stigma, and loneliness), and coping mechanisms (i.e., perceived availability and adequacy of instrumental and emotional support, support from place of worship, spirituality). Diagnostics performed during multivariate analysis did not detect any significant multicollinearity among this set of independent covariates.

The total model explained nearly one-half of the variance in CES-D regression scores (R^2 = .48, see Table 6), with a significant F-value of 12.33. Age accounted for only 1% of the variance in depressive symptoms, and was not a significant predictor of depression in the final model. Among the health status variables, only the number of comorbid conditions emerged as a significant positive predictor of higher levels of depressive symptoms, and accounted for 14% of the variance in CES-D scores. A number of stress-related variables retained their significant relationships to depressive symptoms in multivariate analysis, including the need for help, cognitive quality of life, stigma and loneliness.

This block of stress variables accounted for 33% of the variance in depressive symptoms among older women with HIV. Finally, with regard to coping mechanisms, no predictors emerged as a significant protective factor against depression in the regression model, and explained less than 1% of the variance in CES-D scores.

Table 6. Hierarchical Multiple Regression Analysis of CES-D Depression Scores

Variable	B	SE B	β	p-value	R^2-change
Step One					.01
Age	-0.15	0.13	-.06	.238	
Step Two					.14
Months since HIV Diagnosis	0.02	0.01	.10	.066	
Comorbid Conditions	0.81	0.24	.19	.001	
Self-rated Health	0.16	0.36	.03	.443	
Step Three					.33
Need Help	1.72	0.89	.11	.053	
Income Adequacy	-0.47	0.69	-.04	.496	
Cognitive QOL	-0.40	0.14	-.17	.004	
Social QOL	-0.42	0.41	-.06	.298	
Stigma	0.07	0.03	.14	.023	
Loneliness	0.38	0.07	.37	.001	
Step Four					.00
Instrumental Availability	0.16	0.57	.02	.775	
Instrumental Adequacy	-0.28	0.64	-.03	.665	
Emotional Availability	-0.11	0.66	-.01	.873	
Emotional Adequacy	-0.14	0.55	-.02	.796	
Religious Support	-0.20	1.19	-.01	.863	
Spirituality	-0.02	0.03	-.05	.380	

Note. Pairwise N = 226. Total R^2 = .48. Final Model: F(1,225) = 12.33, p < .001. Regression coefficients shown for final model.

Discussion

The analyses in this chapter underscore the pervasive problem of untreated depression among older women with HIV. Nearly one-half of the older women in this study's sample had CES-D scores indicative of clinically significant depressive symptomatology. A large proportion of these women would likely receive a diagnosis of major depressive disorder if undergoing a full-scale clinical assessment. This high prevalence of clinically significant depressive symptoms is consistent with other studies of women with HIV where the range is typically from 30% to 60% (Ickovics et al., 2001; Tostes et al., 2004; Tryznka and Erlen, 2004). Like other research on depression among the female HIV population, the older women in the present sample face many stresses and strains in their daily lives that undermine psychological well-being. These factors include diminished opportunities for employment, high rates of disability, inadequate incomes, increased rates of health comorbidity, a high level of need for assistance due to HIV, coupled with inadequate instrumental social support, histories of incarceration and substance abuse, HIV stigma, and loneliness. These women did have many positive social and personal resources to help counter such stressors including high positive perceptions of the availability and adequacy of emotional social support, and a high degree of spirituality.

We had predicted that poor health and other stressors would be positively related to greater depressive symptoms. Conversely, social support and spirituality would be predictors of lower levels of depressive symptomatology. This hypothesis was largely supported in bivariate and multivariate analyses. With regard to the bivariate analysis, health factors directly related to HIV, such as CD4 count, prior diagnosis of AIDS, and time since HIV diagnosis, only time since HIV diagnosis was significantly and positively related to depressive symptoms. Significant relationships were found with other health-related stressors; the number of comorbid conditions experienced in the past year and self-rated health. Interestingly, the recent use of drugs or alcohol had no significant relationship to depression in this current sample of older women with HIV at either the bivariate or multivariate level of analysis, in contrast to a number of previous investigations (Brienza et al, 2000; Darke and Ross, 1997; Dodds et al., 2003; 2001; Goggin et al., 1998; Knowlton et al., 2001; Rabkin et al., 1997; Turrina et al.,; Trzunka and Erlen, 2004). This was surprising in that the prevalence of alcohol and substance use in the present study (47%) was similar to the figure of approximately 50% reported in other research (Commerford, Gular, Orr, Reznikoff, and O'Dowd, 1994; Pence et al.; Rabkin et al., 2000).

Stress variables were significantly related to depression at the bivariate levels, including the need for help because of HIV, income adequacy, health-related QOL measures, loneliness and stigma. Greater perceptions of social support availability and adequacy bore an inverse relationship to depressive symptoms. Reported help from religious congregations was not significantly related to lower levels of depression, although the relationship was in the expected direction. Spirituality was indicative of lesser depressive symptomatology among older women with HIV. Among all of the sociodemographic factors, only increased age was significantly related to lower levels of depression. Race/ethnicity, sexual orientation, language use, education, employment, living arrangements, and history of incarceration were not significant correlates of depression.

Using multivariate analyses, many of the covariates described above failed to emerge as significant predictors of CES-D depression scores. With regard to HIV- and health-related variables, only the number of comorbid conditions in the past year was significantly related to greater levels of depression. Among the other stress factors, having a current or past need for help due to HIV predicted higher levels of depression, as did inadequate income. With respect to health-related quality of life, only the cognitive measure emerged as a significant predictor of depression in the regression analysis. HIV stigma and loneliness also remained as positive predictors of depression in multivariate analysis. In terms of putative factors, perceptions of social support availability and adequacy were not related to the level of depressive symptomatology in the multivariate regression model. Greater levels of spirituality were not significantly associated with fewer depressive symptoms, and our hypothesis regarding protective factors against depression was not supported.

The present study is one of the first to explore depression among older women with HIV. Current findings are similar to previous studies of this disorder in other populations living with HIV and older adults in general. In the present analyses, the number of comorbid health conditions in the previous year was a strong predictor of depressive symptoms, which reflects similar findings among older adults in general (Cummings et al., 2003; Dent et al., 1999). In the present study, we did not differentiate comorbid conditions likely associated with HIV (e.g., cardiovascular problems, certain cancers) from those associated with aging (e.g., arthritis, osteoporosis). Future research should examine whether comorbidities that are attributable to HIV have a differential impact on psychological well-being compared with those that are non-HIV related or those that are age related.

Interestingly, the use of alcohol or other substances was not related to depressive symptoms using either bivariate or multivariate analysis. This finding suggests that for this group of older women living with HIV substance use is not likely characterized as a form of self-medication for depression, given the independence of these two factors. It is possible that the high degree of substance use in this population blurred any relationship between this factor and depression. However, it may be that the high prevalence of depression and substance use in the current sample are related to another factor, such as stressful living conditions or past sexual or physical trauma, which are common stressors among women with HIV (Catz et al., 2002; Gurung et al., 2004; Jones et al., 2003; Lesserman et al., 2005; Tarakeshwar, Hansen, Kochman, Fox, and Sikkema, 2006).

We also found that poor functioning, as indexed by the need for help due to HIV, was related to depression in both bivariate and multivariate analyses. This is similar to findings on the general older adult population (Cummings et al., Gitlin et al., 2007; Han and Jylha, 2006; Wolinsky et al., 2007). The levels of depressive symptoms among these older women did not appear to be due to medical factors associated with HIV, namely time since HIV diagnosis, receiving a prior AIDS diagnosis, or CD4 counts. This observation reinforces the view that depression among persons with HIV is not due to the disease *per se*, but rather the personal and social milieu of the person who is infected. In this context, health-related QOL measures in the domain of cognitive functioning were key covariates of depressive symptoms, with higher QOL indicative of being less depressed.

We included two other fundamental factors in our analyses, loneliness and stigma, which are consequences of being diagnosed with HIV. Levels of stigma among the current sample of older women with HIV were high and were significantly associated with greater depressive symptoms in both bivariate and multivariate analysis. HIV-related stigma results from multiple sources, which include the HIV diagnosis itself as well as the association between HIV infection and sexual activity, drug and alcohol use, and a history of incarceration (Lichtenstein et al., 2002). Our findings are consistent with those of others who describe the destructive effects of stigma on persons living with HIV (Emlet, 2007; Flowers et al., 2006, Lichtenstein et al., Riggs et al., 2007). Our findings support the need to address the issue of HIV-related stigma. For this older population of women, who are largely people of color, there are added stigmas of racism, sexism, and ageism. Stigma may be life threatening if it results in delayed testing and diagnosis of HIV or if it discourages those diagnosed with HIV from seeking the treatment and services that they need to live successfully with this chronic condition (Flowers et al., 2006). Emotional loneliness was also prevalent in this group of older women and a consistent predictor of higher levels of depressive symptoms, reinforcing previous findings in this population (Vance, 2006). For older women with HIV, internalized stigma may lead them to feel that they are "dirty" or unclean (Fisher, 1999), discouraging them from seeking close and intimate relationships and thereby exacerbating their loneliness. Future research should examine the interaction between stigma and loneliness among people living with HIV, to better understand how their combined effects may affect psychological well-being.

Findings regarding the protective effects of social support and spirituality on depressive symptoms were mixed. Spirituality was not related to lower levels of depression, even after controlling for all other factors in the multivariate regression model. This finding is not consistent with other studies of persons living with HIV (e.g., Siegel and Scrimshaw, 2002), as well as those with other chronic health conditions (Brennan, 2004). However, our bivariate findings support the view that if programs were available to nurture intrinsic personal resources, such as spirituality, there might well be an amelioration of the levels of depressive symptoms in this population.

In terms of social support, we used indicators of perceived social support availability and adequacy as well as a measure of direct social support received from a religious congregation. Perceptions of social support have consistently emerged as predictors of better psychological well-being and lower depression among persons with HIV (Catz et al., 2002; Serovich et al., 2001; Stewart et al., 2005) and the general population (Cohen and Wills, 1985). It was not surprising that direct social support from a religious congregation was not significantly related to depressive symptoms, given prior empirical findings and the limitation of assessing this factor with a single item. At the bivariate level, however, perceptions of support availability and adequacy were significantly, albeit moderately, related to lower levels of depressive symptoms. Nevertheless, none of these indicators of perceptions of support retained their significant relationship to depressive symptoms in the multivariate analysis. This finding may be the result of other factors in the model interacting with or suppressing the effects of perceptions of social support, which should be investigated in future research.

Study Strengths and Limitations

Although the ROAH sample (Karpiak et al., 2006) is one of the largest studies of older adults with HIV to date, one cannot assess with certainty the representativeness of the current sample of older women with HIV because the parameters of this population are undocumented and unknown. That is to say, the current system of HIV reporting and tracking does not permit one to know exactly who comprises this population as defined by sociodemographic characteristics. However, the high concentration of women of color as well as the lower socioeconomic status of the present sample is congruent with what is generally known about women with HIV (Catz et al., 2002; Gurung et al., 2004; Pence et al., 2006). Furthermore, the ROAH sample closely reflects the most current epidemiological data on HIV/AIDS in New York City (New York City Department of Health and Mental Hygiene, 2007). Another limitation of the present study is the cross-sectional design, which does not permit the examination of covariates of depression over time, or how change in these covariates (e.g., increase in loneliness, reduction of perceived stigma) may affect depressive symptoms. Future research should include longitudinal analyses of the factors related to depression in order to assess the effects of such change, as well as to be able to understand the course of depressive symptoms in this population more thoroughly.

Conclusions

Given the high prevalence of depression among older women with HIV, policy makers, service providers, and HIV advocates need to be made aware of the magnitude of this largely unaddressed public health problem. Medical management is an obvious option, but much more can be done by attending to the other factors that this study and others have identified as contributing to depressive symptoms in this population.

The HIV population continues to age, and the numbers of older women affected by this disease can only be expected to increase. If this group of older women is similar to older women in general with regard to depression, that is, more likely to be depressed than older men with HIV and presenting with more persistent depressive symptoms (see Barry et al., 2008), the situation will have increasingly negative impacts on their health and well-being and place further demands on a health care system that is already strained.

The problem of depression among older women with HIV cannot be minimized given its relationships to poor treatment adherence (Tryznka and Erlen, 2004) and increased levels of mortality (Ickovics et al., 2001). Services targeted at providing community supports of the kind that have been developed for people with serious and persistent mental illnesses are generally not available for people with depressive disorders unless they experience repeated hospitalizations (Brennan, Vega, Garcia, Abad, and Friedman, 2005). Although there is a trend to manage depression among older adults using pharmaceuticals alone (Brennan et al.), recent evidence suggests that cognitive-behavioral interventions for depression among persons with HIV are highly efficacious and thus represent best practices for treating depression in this population (Crepaz et al., 2008). We are watching efforts to mainstream older adults with HIV into those support services in their communities, both medical and social, which will significantly contribute to a successful aging process for this population. Barriers created by stigma and associated guilt must be reduced for this to occur. Thus both traditional providers of services to people with HIV as well as community-based service providers for older adults need to be made aware of the issue of depression among older women with HIV. These providers must be prepared to identify and meet the needs of this population through enhanced outreach and focused service delivery tailored to address depression in this population.

References

Adams, K.B., Sanders, S. and Auth, E.A. (2004). Loneliness and depression in independent living retirement communities: Risk and resilience factors. *Aging and Mental Health, 8*(6), 475-485.

Barry, L. C., Allmore, H. G., Guo, Z., Bruce, M. L., and Gill, T. M. (2008). Higher burden of depression among older women: The effect of onset, persistence and mortality over time. *Archives of General Psychiatry, 65*(2), 172-178.

Berger, B. E., Ferrans, C. E., and Lashley, F. R. (2001). Measuring stigma in people with HIV: Psychometric assessment of the HIV stigma scale. *Research in Nursing and Health, 24*(6), 518-529.

Billings, A. G., and Moos, R. H. (1981). The role of coping responses and social resources in attenuating the stress of life events. *Journal of Behavioral Medicine, 4,* 139-157.

Blake, R. L. Jr., and Vandiver, T. A. (1988). The association of health with stressful life changes, social supports, and coping. *Family Practice Research, 7,* 205-218.

Blazer, D. G. (2002). *Depression in later life,* (3rd ed.). New York: Springer.

Blazer, D. G. (2003). Depression in late life: Review and commentary. *Journal of Gerontology: Series A: Biological Sciences and Medical Sciences: 58,* 249-265.

Boarts, J. M., Sledjeski, E. M., Bogart, L. M., and Delahanty, D. L. (2006). The differential impact of PTSD and depression on HIV disease markers and adherence to HAART in people living with HIV. *AIDS and Behavior, 10*(3), 253-261.

Brennan, M. (2004). Spirituality and religiousness predict adaptation to vision loss among middle-age and older adults. *International Journal for the Psychology of Religion, 14* (3), 193-214.

Brennan, M., Vega, M., Garcia, I., Abad, A., and Friedman, M. B. (2005). Meeting the mental health needs of elderly Latinos affected by depression: Implications for outreach and service provision. *Care Management Journals, 6* (2), 98-106.

Brienza, R., Stein, M., Chen, M., Gugineni, A., Subata, M., Phil, M., et al. (2000). Depression among needle exchange program and methadone maintenance clients. *Journal of Substance Abuse Treatment, 18,* 331–337.

Cantor, M. H., and Brennan, M. (1993). Family and community support systems of older New Yorkers. *Growing older in New York City in the 1990s: A study of changing lifestyles, quality of life, and quality of care, Vol. V.* New York: New York Center for Policy on Aging, New York Community Trust.

Catz, S. L., Gore-Felton, C., and McClure, J. B. (2002). Psychological distress among minority and low-income women living with HIV. *Behavioral Medicine, 28,* 53-60.

Cauce, A. M., Hannan, K., and Sargeant, M. (1992). Life stress, social support, and locus of control during early adolescence: interactive effects. *American Journal of Community Psychology, 20,* 787-798.

Centers for Disease Control and Prevention (CDC). (2002). Impact of September 11 attacks on workers in the vicinity of the World Trade Center – New York City. *MMWR Morbidity and Mortality Weekly Report, 51*(special Sept 11 issue), 8-10.

Centers for Disease Control and Prevention (CDC). (2007). *HIV/AIDS surveillance report, Vol. 17, Revised Edition*, pp.18. Atlanta, GA: CDC.

Chandler, C. K., Holden, J. M., and Kolander, C. A. (1992). Counseling for spiritual wellness: Theory and practice. *Journal of Counseling and Development, 71,* 168-174.

Chappell, N. L., and Badger, M. (1989). Social isolation and well-being. *Journals of Gerontology: SOCIAL SCIENCES, 44*(5), S169-176.

Chen, P., Kales, W. C., Weintraub, D., Blow, F. C., Jiang, L., Ignacio, R. V., and Mellow, A. M. (2007). Depression in veterans with Parkinson's disease: Frequency, comorbidity, and healthcare utilization. *International Journal of Geriatric Psychiatry, 22* (6), 543-548.

Chesney, M. (2000). Factors affecting adherence to antiretroviral therapy. *Clinical Infectious Disease, 30,* S171 – S176.

Cohen, J., and Cohen, P. (1983). *Applied multiple regression and correlation for the behavioral sciences, 2nd ed.,* (pp. 181-220). Hillsdale, NJ: L. Erlbaum Assoc.

Cohen, S., and Wills, T. A. (1985). Stress, social support, and the Buffering Hypothesis. *Psychological Bulletin, 98,* 310-357.

Coleman, C. L., Eller, L. S., Nokes, K. M., et al. (2006).Prayer as a complimentary health strategy for managing HIV-related symptoms among ethnically diverse patients. *Holistic Nursing Practice, 20*(2), 65-72.

Commorford, M., C., Gular, E., Orr, D. A., Reznikoff, M., and O'Dowd, M. A. (1994). Coping and psychological distress in women with HIV/AIDS. *Journal of Community Psychology, 22*(3), 224-30.

Cook, J., Cohen, M., Burke, J., Grey, D., Anastos, K., Kirstein, L., et al. (2002). Effects of depressive symptoms and mental health quality of life on use of highly active antiretroviral therapy among HIV-seropositive women. *Journal of Acquired Immune Deficiency Syndromes, 30,* 401–409.

Crepaz, N., Passin, W. F., Herbst, J. H., et al. (2008). Meta-analysis of cognitive-behavioral interventions on HIV-positive persons' mental health and immune functioning. *Health Psychology, 27*(1), 4-14.

Cummings, S. M., Neff, J. A., and Husaini, B. A. (2003). Functional impairment as a predictor of depressive symptomatology: The role of race, religiosity, and social support. *Health and Social Work, 28* (1), 23-32.

Dalmida, S. G. (2006). Spirituality, mental health, physical health, and health-related quality of life among women with HIV/AIDS: Integrating spirituality into mental health care. *Issues in Mental Health Nursing, 27,* 185-198.

Darke, S. and Ross, J. (1997). Polydrug dependence and psychiatric comorbidity among heroin injectors. *Drug and Alcohol Dependence, 48,* 135–141.

Dent, O. F., Waite, L. M., Bennett, H. P., Casey, B. J., Grayson, D. A., Cullen, J. S., Creasey, H., and Broe, G. A. (1999). A longitudinal study of chronic disease and depressive symptoms in a community sample of older people. *Aging and Mental Health, 3*(4), 351-357.

DePalo, R., and Brennan, M. (2005). Spiritual caregiving for older adults: A perspective from clinical practice. In M. Brennan and D. Heiser (Eds.), *Spiritual assessment and intervention with older adults: Current directions and applications*, (pp. 151-160). Binghamton, NY: Haworth Pastoral Press.

Dodds, S., Blackley, T., Lizzotte, J., Friedman, L., Shaw, K., Martinez, J., et al. (2003). Retention, adherence, and compliance: Special needs of HIV-infected adolescent girls and young women. *Journal of Adolescent Health, 33S*, 39 – 45.

Dunphy, R. (1987). Helping persons with AIDS find meaning and hope. *Health Progress, 68*(4), 58-63.

Emlet, C. A. (2006a). "You're awfully old to have *this* disease": Experiences of stigma and ageism in adults 50 years and older living with HIV/AIDS. *Gerontologist, 46*(6), 781-790.

Emlet, C. A. (2006b). An examination of the social networks and social isolation in older and younger adults living with HIV/AIDS. *Health and Social Work, 31*(4), 299-308.

Emlet, C. A. (2007). Experiences of stigma in older adults living with HIV/AIDS: A mixed-methods analysis. *AIDS Patient Care, 21*(10), 740-752.

Fisher, M. (1999). From the Advisory Council. *Harvard AIDS Review, 1.* Retrieved January 10, 2008 from the World Wide Web: http://www.aids.harvard.edu /news_publications /har /spring_1999/spring99-1.html.

Flowers, P., Davis, M., Hart, G., Rosengarten, M., Frankis, J., and Imrie, J. (2006). Diagnosis and stigma and identity amongst HIV positive Black Africans living in the UK. *Psychology and Health, 21*(1), 109-122.

Gehr, F. C. (2002). Spiritual experiences of HIV-positive gay males: A phenomenological investigation. *Dissertation Abstracts International: Section B: The Sciences and Engineering, 63*(2-B), 1025.

Ghose, S. S., Williams, L. S., and Swindle, R. W. (2005). Depression and other mental health diagnoses after stroke increase inpatient and outpatient medical utilization three years poststroke. *Medical Care, 43* (12), 1259-1264.

Gibbie, T., Mijch, A., Ellen, S., Hoy, J., Hutchison, C., Wright, E., Chua, P. and Judd, F. (2006). Depression and neurocognitive performance in individuals with HIV/AIDS: 2– year follow up. *HIV Medicine, 7,* 112 – 121.

Gitlin, L. N., Hauck, W. W., Dennis, M. P., Schulz, R. (2007). Depressive symptoms in older African-American and white adults with functional difficulties: The role of control strategies. *Journal of the American Geriatrics Society, 55* (7), 1023-1030.

Goggin, K., Engelson, E. S., Rabkin, J. G., and Kotler, D. P. (1998). The relationship of mood, endocrine, and sexual disorders in Human Immunodeficiency Virus positive (HIV+) Women: An exploratory study. *Psychosomatic Medicine, 60*, 11-16.

Gurung, R. A. R., Taylor, S. E., Kemeny, M., and Smyers, H. (2004). "HIV is not my biggest problem": The impact of HIV and chronic burden on depression in women at risk for AIDS. *Journal of Social and Clinical Psychology, 23*(4), 490-511.

Hader, S., Smith, D., Moore, J. and Holmberg, S. (2001). HIV infection in women in the United States: Status at the millennium. *Journal of the American Medical Association, 285*, 1186– 1192.

Hall, B. A. (1998). Patterns of spirituality in persons with advanced HIV disease. *Research in Nursing and Health, 21*(2), 143-53.

Han, B., and Jylha, M. (2006). Improvement in depressive symptoms and changes in self-rated health among community-dwelling disabled older adults. *Aging and Mental Health, 10* (6), 599-605.

Harlow, S. D., Goldberg, E. L., and Comstock, G. W. (1991). A longitudinal study of risk factors for depressive symptomatology in elderly widowed and married women. *American Journal of Epidemiology, 134* (5), 526-538.

Heckman, T. G., Heckman, B. D., Kochman, A., Sikkema, K. J., Suhr, J., and Goodkin, K. (2002). Psychological symptoms among persons 50 years of age and older living with HIV disease. *Aging and Mental Health, 6*(2), 121-8.

Heckman, T. G., Kochman, A., Sikkema, K. J., Kalichman, S. C., Masten, J., Bergholte, J., and Catz, S. (2001). A pilot coping improvement intervention for late middle-aged and older adults living with HIV/AIDS in the USA. *AIDS Care, 13*(1), 129-39.

Heinrich, C. R. (2003). Enhancing the perceived health of HIV seropositive men. *Western Journal of Nursing Research, 25*(4), 383-7.

Holzemer, W., Corless, I., Nokes, K., Eller, L., Bunch, E., Kemppinen, J., et al. (1999). Predictors of self-reported adherence in persons living with HIV disease. *AIDS Patient Care and STDs, 13*, 185 – 197.

Horowitz, A., Reinhardt, J. P., and Kennedy, G. J. (2005). Major and subthreshold depression among older adults seeking vision rehabilitation services. *American Journal of Geriatric Psychiatry, 13* (3), 180-187.

Howden, J. (1992). *Development and psychometric characteristics of the Spirituality Assessment Scale.* Unpublished doctoral dissertation. Texas Women's University.

Ickovics, J. R., Hamburger, M. E., Vlahov, D., Schoenbaum, E. E., Schuman, P., Boland, R. J., and Moore, J. (2001). Mortality, CD4 cell count decline, and depressive symptoms among HIV-seropositive women. *Journal of the American Medical Association, 285* (11), 1466-1474.

Jones, D. J., Beach, S. R. H., Forehand, R., and Foster, S. E. (2003). Self-reported health in HIV-positive African American women: The role of family stress and depressive symptoms. *Journal of Behavioral Medicine, 26*(6), 577-599.

Jue, S., and Lewis, S. Y. (2001). Cultural considerations in HIV ethical decision making: A guide for mental health practitioners. In J. R. Anderson and R. L. Barret (Eds.), *Ethics in HIV-related psychotherapy: Clinical decision making in complex cases* (pp. 61-82). Washington, DC: American Psychological Association.

Kalichman, S. C. (1998). Coping, adjustment, and social support. *Understanding AIDS: Advances in research and treatment* (pp. 257-287). Washington, DC: American Psychological Association.

Karpiak, S. E., Shippy, R. A., and Cantor, M. H. (2006). *Research on older adults with HIV.* New York: AIDS Community Research Initiative of America (ACRIA).

Kempen, G. I. J. M., Ranchor, A. V., van Sonderen, E., van Jaarsveld, C. H. M., Sanderman, R. (2006). Risk and protective factors of different functional trajectories in older persons: Are these the same? *Journals of Gerontology: Series G: Psychological Sciences and Social Sciences, 61B* (2), P95-P101.

Kendall, J. (1994). Wellness spirituality in homosexual men with HIV infection. The *Journal of the Association of Nurses in AIDS Care, 5*(4), 28-34.

Kiecolt-Glaser, J. K., and Glaser, R. (2002). Depression and immune function: Central pathways to morbidity and mortality. *Journal of Psychosomatic Research 53,* 873-876.

Knowlton, A., Latkin, C., Schroeder, J., Hoover, D., Ensminger, M. and Celentano, D. (2001). Longitudinal predictors of depressive symptoms among low income injection drug users. *AIDS Care, 13,* 549–559.

Koenig, H. G., George, L. K., Titus, P., and Meador, K. G. (2004). Religion, spirituality, and acute care hospitalization and long-term care use by older patients. *Archives of Internal Medicine, 164,* 1579-85.

Lazarus, R., and Folkman, S. (1984*). Stress, appraisal, and coping.* New York: Springer.

Leserman, J., Whetten, K., Lowe, K., Stangle, D., Swartz, M. S., and Theilman, N. M. (2005). How trauma, recent stressful events, and PTSD affect functional health status and health utilization in HIV-infected patients in the South. *Psychosomatic Medicine, 67,* 500-507.

Lichtenstein, B., Laska, M. K., and Clair, J. M. (2002). Chronic sorrow in the HIV-positive patient: Issues of race, gender and social support. *AIDS Patient Care and STDs, 16*(1), 27-38.

Lindgren, K. N., and Coursey, R. D. (1995). Spirituality and serious mental illness: A two-part study." *Psychosocial Rehabilitation Journal 18:* 93-107.

Lyness, J. M., King, D. A., Cox, C., Yoediono, Z, and Caine, E. D. (1999). The importance of subsyndromal depression in older primary care patients: Prevalence and associated functional disability. *Journal of the American Geriatrics Society, 47:* 647-652.

Mayers, A. M., and Svartberg, M. (2001). Existential loneliness: A review of the concept, its psychosocial precipitants and psychotherapeutic implications for HIV-infected women. *British Journal of Medical Psychology, 74,* 539-553.

McGrath, E., Keita, G., Strickland, B. and Russo, N. (Eds.). (1990). *Women and Depression: Risk Factors and Treatment Issues:* Final report of the American Psychological Association's Task Force on Women and Depression. Washington DC: American Psychological Association.

McKelroy, J. L., and Vosvick, M. (August, 2006). Spirituality and psychological quality of life in HIV+ adults. Paper session presented at the 114th Annual Convention of the American Psychological Association, New Orleans, LA.

Mehta, S., Moore, R. D., and Graham, N. M. H. (1997). Potential factors affecting adherence with HIV therapy. *AIDS, 11,* 1665-1670.

Mellors, M. P., Riley, T. A., and Erlen, J. A. (1997). HIV, self-transcendence, and quality of life. *The Journal of the Association of Nurses in AIDS Care, 8*(2), 59-69.

Moberg, D. O. (1967). Science and the spiritual nature of man. *Journal of the American Scientific Affiliation, 19,* 12-17.

Moberg, D. O. (2002). Assessing and measuring spirituality: Confronting the dilemmas of universal and particular evaluative criteria. *Journal of Adult Development, 9* (1), 47-60.

Moore, J., Schuman, P., Schoenbaum, E. Boland, B., Solomon, L. and Smith, D. (1999). Severe adverse life events and depressive symptoms among women with, or at risk for, HIV infection in four cities in the United States of America. *AIDS, 13*, 2459 – 2468.

Mueller, T. I., Kohn, R., Leventhal, B. A., et al. (2004). The course of depression in elderly patients. *American Journal of Geriatric Psychiatry, 12*, 22-29.

New York City Department of Health and Mental Hygiene. (2005). *HIV Epidemiology Program First Quarter Report, Vol. 3* (1). New York: Author.

New York City Department of Health and Mental Hygiene. 2007. *HIV Epidemiology and Field Services Semiannual Report, Vol. 2* (1). Retrieved September 10, 2007 from the World Wide Web: http://www.nyc.gov/html/doh/downloads/pdf/dires/dires-2007-report-semi1.pdf .

New York State Department of Health AIDS Institute. (2005). Depression and mania in patients with HIV/AIDS. Retrieved September 25, 2007 from the World Wide Web: http://hivguidelines.org/GuideLine.aspx?pageID=261andguideLineID=39 .

Oursler, K. K., Goulet, J. L., Leaf, D. A., Akingicil, A., Katzel, L. I., Justice, A., and Crystal, S. (2006). Association of comorbidity and physical disability in older HIV-infected adults.*AIDS Patient Care, 20*(11), 782-791.

Pargament, K. I. (1997). *The psychology of religion and coping.* New York: Guilford Press.

Pence, B. W., Miller, W. C., Whetten, K., Eron, J. J., and Gaynes, B. N. (2006). Prevalence of DSM-IV-defined mood, anxiety and substance use disorders in an HIV clinic in the southeastern United States. *Journal of Acquired Immune Deficiency Syndrome, 42*(3), 298-306.

Poindexter, C., and Emlet, C. A. (2006). HIV-infected and HIV-affected older adults. In B. Berkman (Ed.), *Handbook of social work in health and aging* (pp. 91-99). New York: Oxford University Press.

Powell-Cope, G., White, J., Henkelman, E. and Turner, B. (2005). Qualitative and quantitative assessments of HAART adherence of substance abusing women. *AIDS Care, 15*, 239–249.

Pretorius, T. B. (1998). Measuring life events in a sample of South African students: Comparison of the Life Experiences Survey and Schedule of Recent Experiences. *Psychological Reports, 83,* 771-780.

Rabkin, J. G., Ferrando, S. J., Lin, S., Sewell, M., and McElhiney, M. (2000). Psychological effects of HAART: A 2-year study. *Psychosomatic Medicine, 62*, 412-422.

Rabkin, J., Johnson, J., Lin, S-H., Lipsitz, J., Remien, R., Williams, J., et al. (1997). Psychopathology in male and female HIV-positive and negative injecting drug users:Longitudinal course over 3 years. *AIDS, 11*, 507 – 515.

Rabkin, J. G., McElhiney, M. C., and Ferrando, S. J. (2004). Mood and substance use disorders in older adults with HIV/AIDS: Methodological issues and preliminary evidence. *AIDS, 1*(18 Suppl 1), S43-8.

Rabkin, J. G., McElhiney, M. C., Rabkin, R., McGrath, P. J., and Ferrando, S. J. (2006). Placebo-controlled trial of dehydroepiandrosterone (DHEA) for treatment of nonmajor depression in patients with HIV/AIDS. *American Journal of Psychiatry, 163* (1), 59-66.

Rabkin, J. G., and Remien, R. H. (1995). Depressive disorder and HIV disease: An uncommon association. *Focus, 10* (9), 1-4.

Radloff, L. S. (1977). The CES-D scale: A self-report depression scale for research in the general population. *Applied Psychological Measurement, 1,* 385-401.

Raman, L., and Winer, G. A. (2002). Children's and adults' understanding of illness: Evidence in support of a coexistence model. *Genetic, Social, and General Psychology Monographs, 128*(4), 325-55.

Reece, M., Tanner, A. E., Karpiak, S. E., and Coffey, K. (2007). The impact of HIV-related stigma on HIV care and prevention providers. *Journal of HIV/AIDS and Social Services, 6*(3), 55-73.

Riggs, S. A., Vosvick, M., and Stalling, S. (2007).Attachment style, stigma and psychological distress among HIV+ adults. *Journal of Health Psycychology, 12*(6), 922-36.

Riley, E. D., Wu, A. W., Perry, S., Clark, R. A., Moss, A. R., Crane, J., and Bangsberg, D. R. (2003). Depression and drug use impact health status among marginally housed HIV-infected individuals. *AIDS Patient Care and STDs. 17*(8), 401-6.

Russell, D. W. (1996). UCLA Loneliness Scale (Version 3): Reliability, validity and factor structure. *Journal of Personality Assessment, 66*(1), 20-40.

Russinova, Z. (1999). Providers' hope-inspiring competence as a factor optimizing psychiatric rehabilitation outcomes. *Journal of Rehabilitation, 65*(4), 50-57.

Serovich, J. M., Kimberly, J. A., Mosack, K. E., and Lewis, T. L. (2001). The role of family and friend social support in reducing emotional distress among HIV-positive women. *AIDS Care, 13*(3), 335-341.

Shippy, R. A., and Karpiak, S. E. (2005). Perceptions of social support among older adults with HIV. *Research on Aging, 27,* 290-306.

Shor-Posner, G., Lecusay, R., Miguez-Burbano, M., Quesada, J., Rodriguez, A., Ruiz, P., et al. (2000). Quality of Life Measures in the Miami HIV-infected drug abusers cohort: Relationship to gender and disease status. *Journal of Substance Abuse, 11,* 395–404.

Siegel, K., and Schrimshaw, E. W. (2002). The perceived benefits of religious and spiritual coping among older adults living with HIV. *Journal for the Scientific Study of Religion, 41*(1), 91-102.

Simoni, J. M., and Ortiz, M. Z. (2003). Mediational models of spirituality and depressive symptomatology among HIV-positive Puerto Rican women. *Cultural Diversity and Ethnic Minority Psychology, 9*(1), 3-15.

Singh, N., Squier, C., Sivek, C., Wagener, M., Nguyen, M.H. and Yu, V. (1996). Determinants of compliance with antiretroviral therapy in patients with human immunodeficiency virus: Prospective assessment with implications for enhancing compliance. *AIDS Care, 8,* 261–269.

Smallbrugge, M., Pot, A. M., Jongenelis, L., Gundy, C. M., Beekman, A. T. F., Eefsting, J. A. (2006). Impact of depression and anxiety on well being, disability, and use of health care services in nursing home patients. *International Journal of Geriatric Psychiatry, 21* (4), 325-332.

Stanley, L. D. (1999). Transforming AIDS: The moral management of stigmatized identity. *Anthropology and Medicine 6*(1): 103-20.

Stewart, K. E., Cianfrini, L. R., and Walker, J. F. (2005). Stress, social support and housing are related to health status among HIV-positive persons in the Deep South of the United States. *AIDS Care, 17*(3), 350-358.

Sumi, K. Optimism, social support, stress, and physical and psychological well-being in Japanese women. *Psychological Reports, 81,* 299-306.

Tarakeshwar, N., Hansen, N. B., Kochman, A., Fox, A., and Sikkema, K. J. (2006). Resiliency among individuals with childhood sexual abuse and HIV: Perspectives on addressing sexual trauma. *Journal of Traumatic Stress,19*(4), 449-460.

Tiemeier, H. van Tuijl, H. R., Hofman, A., Kiliaan, A. J., and Breteler, M. M. B. (2003). Plasma fatty acid composition and depression are associated in the elderly: The Rotterdam Study. *American Journal of Clinical Nutrition, 78*, 40-46.

Tostes, M. A., Chalub, M., and Botega, N. J. (2004). The quality of life of HIV-infected women is associated with psychiatric morbidity. *AIDS Care, 16* (2), 177-186.

Tryznka, S. L., and Erlen, J. A. (2004). HIV dis*ease susceptibility in women and the barriers to adherence. Medsurg Nursing: Official journal of the Academy of Medical-Surgical Nurses, 13*(2), 97-104.

Tsao, J. C., Dobalian, A., Moreau, C., and Dobalian, K. (2004). Stability of anxiety and depression in a national sample of adults with human immunodeficiency virus. *Journal of Nervous and Mental Disorders, 192* (2), 111-118.

Tuck, I., McCain, N. L., and Elswick, R. K. Jr. (2001). Spirituality and psychosocial factors in persons living with HIV. *Journal of Advanced Nursing, 33*(6), 776-83.

Turrina, C., Fiorazzo, A., Turano, A., Caccniani, P., Regini, C., Castelli, F., et al. (2001). Depressive disorders and personality variables in HIV positive and negative intravenous drug-users. *Journal of Affective Disorders, 65*, 45 – 53.

U. S. Department of Health and Human Services. (1999). *Mental health: A report of the Surgeon General.* Rockville, MD: U. S. Department of Health and Human Services.

Vance, D. A. (2006). The relationship between HIV disclosure and adjustment. *Psychological Reports, 99*(3), 659-663.

Vance, D. A., and Woodley, R. A. (2005). Strengths and distress in adults who are aging with HIV: A pilot study. *Psychological Reports, 96,* 383-86.

Wagner, G., Kanouse, D., Koegel, P. and Sullivan, G. (2003). Adherence to HIV antiretrovirals among persons with serious mental illness. *AIDS Patient Care and STDs, 17*, 179 – 186.

Wolinsky, F. D., Miller, T. R., Malmstrom, T. K., Miller, J. P., Schootman, M., Andresen , E. M., and Miller, D. K. (2007). Four-year lower extremity disability trajectories among African American men and women. *Journals of Gerontology: Series A: Biological Sciences and Medical Sciences, 62A* (5), 525-530.

World Health Organization. (2007). *Depression: What is depression?* Retrieved January 11, 2007 from the World Wide Web: http://www.who.int/mental_health/ management /depression/definition/en/ .

Wu, A. W., Rubin, H. R., Wade, W. C., et al. (1991). A health status questionnaire using 30 items from the Medical Outcomes Study. Preliminary validation in persons with early HIV infection. *Medical Care, 29* (8), 786-798.

Yi, M. S., Mrus, J. M., Wade, T. J., et al. (2006). Religion, spirituality, and depressive symptoms in patients with HIV/AIDS. *Journal of General Internal Medicine, 21*(Suppl 5), S21-S27.

In: Women and Depression ISBN 978-1-60456-647-5
Editors: Paula Hernandez and Sara Alonso © 2009 Nova Science Publishers, Inc.

Chapter 10

Depression During Late Adult Years

Virginia Elderkin-Thompson[7] and Cristine E. Bruzzone
Semel Institute for Neuroscience and Human Behavior, University of California
Los Angeles, USA

Abstract

Between 11 and 30% of older people worldwide suffer from depressive symptoms, and approximately 17 to 35% of depressed patients suffer cognitive loss. Community samples show a doubling of comorbid mood disorder and cognitive deficits every 5 years after the age of 70 until by age 85, approximately 25% of older individuals demonstrate both conditions. Women have almost double the risk of men for suffering these comorbid conditions before the age of 80.

Research on the biological and physiological changes associated with unipolar major depression center on the prefrontal lobes and the fronto-striatal neural loops that are associated with emotional responsiveness, cognition, and behavior. With the advent of new advances in neuroimaging techniques, researchers can explore the anatomical, biochemical and physiological substrates of late-life depression. Imaging studies report that some regions within the prefrontal cortex are selectively reduced in volume during late-life depression. Stable relationships between cognition and brain biochemicals that are seen in healthy elderly are disturbed in depressed individuals, and myelination of white matter tracts appears compromised. This chapter will discuss the 1) diagnosis of late-life depression and how late-onset differs from early-onset depression, 2) medical context in which late-life depression often occurs, 3) neurocognitive profiles of depressed patients, 4) associated anatomic and physiologic brain abnormalities, 5) putative links between late-life depression and the emergence of dementing syndromes, and 6) effects of pharmacological and psychotherapeutic intervention. Knowledge about the characteristics of late-life depression and successful interventions can mitigate and sometimes reverse the onset of a downward spiral in functioning and physical health that frequently accompanies late-life mood disorders.

---

7 Address For Correspondence: Semel Institute for Neuroscience and Human Behavior 760 Westwood Plaza, Rm. C8-688 Los Angeles, CA 90024 310-794-6398 310-206-4996 (fax), velderkin@mednet.ucla.edu.

Keywords: *geriatric, depression, neuroanatomy, neurophysiology, cognition, human, medical, comorbidity, dementia, intervention*

Introduction

Late-life unipolar depression is a major health concern among older women, who have a much higher exposure to risk factors for depression [1] and are twice as likely as men to develop depression.[2, 3, 4] Prevalence estimates of diagnosed major depression in community and clinical samples range from 1 to 2% among community-dwelling residents [5, 6, 7] upwards to 12% in nursing homes and congregate apartments.[8] Prevalence estimates of subthreshold depression or clinically relevant depressive symptomatology range from 9% [7, 9] in a racially mixed sample from urban and rural North Carolina to 35% among patients in nursing homes and congregate apartments.[8] American rural areas tend to have slightly higher rates (16%) [10] with the highest levels found among the oldest old and women. In France, the opposite appears with a slightly greater risk for urban dwellers although women remain at higher risk.[11] Overall, elders are less vulnerable to major depression than young adults, but the odds of developing a major depressive condition increase if cognitive, functional or physical impairment are present.[12, 13, 14, 15] The World Health Organization ranks depression as the number two cause of disability and functional decline in old age, second to cognitive impairment but above disorders such as obesity, vision impairment, social isolation and low physical activity.[16]

Research into late-life depression has focused primarily on understanding the neurobiological correlates of the onset, severity and outcome of the disorder, and less on the psychological context. Greater risk is thought to come from biological sources (genetics and heredity factors, neurotransmitter dysfunction, metabolic disorders, vascular disorders, viral infections, endocrinopathy, malignancy or cardiovascular disease) [17, 18] as depression often arises in the context of a medical condition. Elderly also report more somatic symptoms, feelings of apathy, difficulty sleeping and fatigue problems, which suggest medical etiologies. Alexopoulos and Apfeldorf (2004) note that older adults are likely to report symptoms suggesting anhedonia rather than affective distress,[19] leading to the phrase *depression without sadness* among seniors.[20]

Social and environmental changes can be difficult to assess although there is general agreement that they continue to play a major role in the development and maintenance of depression. Changes in many areas of late-life can initiate stressful readjustments such as retirement, loss of social and recreational outlets, financial hardships, loss of spouse or family members, deteriorating physical health and/or physical disability, relocation from familiar neighborhoods and acquaintances, and the loss of long-term friendships and social support systems. The combination of contradictory reporting of symptoms along with the lack of a previous history of depression in the individual or family equates to difficulty in accurately diagnosing the condition.

Diagnosis of Late-Life Depressive Disorders

The Diagnostic and Statistical Manual of Mental Disorders-IV-TR criteria for clinical diagnosis of depression is the same for older adults as for young and middle-aged adults. However, late-life depression is a more heterogeneous syndrome of disorders than is early-life depression with different psychological, social and medical etiologies, e.g., metabolic disorder or neurodegenerative disease, and each has a unique pathophysiology and outcome. Older adults can vary as much from each other in health status, cognitive abilities, social networks and financial resources as they do from younger adults, [5, 8, 10] so the aspects of the depression that are reported can vary depending on their personal interpretation of symptoms. Elders may also be on medications that can exacerbate the depressive syndrome and the associated cognitive or behavioral features. Consequently, late-life depression is a collection of depressive syndromes with diverse etiologies and a variety of clinical presentations modulated by the individual's characteristics and context.

About 50% of new depression cases occur after age 50 when there is no medical or family history of mood disorders.[19] Depressive symptoms reported by older patients may be attributed to physiological changes that accompany normal aging or to late-onset medical conditions. When elders attribute the symptoms to unavoidable environmental conditions, they may not report them because they do not consider the symptoms medically relevant or amenable to change. Older women tend to report more severe depression, fatigue and somatic complaints such as appetite loss and weight loss,[21] symptoms that may appear related to developing physical frailty or medical complications rather than a mood disorder.[22] Lack of interest in daily activities, apathy, anhedonia and cognitive deficits are common clinical indicators.[17] Older adults are sensitive to cognitive changes and may report them in isolation from the accompanying mood symptoms. Unfortunately, elders may view some symptoms of depression, e.g., feelings of worthlessness or loss of interest in activities, as inevitable aspects of aging and fail to report them unless directly queried.

Early- and Late-Onset Depression

A common method of categorizing late-life depression syndromes outside a medical context is by age of onset. If the initial episode occurs before age 55 or 60, it is referred to as early-onset depression, and if it occurs after age 55 or 60, it is late-onset depression. Individuals with late-onset depression may report greater severity of symptoms, apathy, increased lethargy or agitation, or insomnia. They are less likely to exhibit psychosis, initiate ideas about suicide or report feelings of guilt.[23] On the other hand, early-onset patients frequently present with higher rates of Axis I comorbid conditions,[24, 25] familial histories of psychiatric illness,[26, 27, 28, 29] dysfunctional past maternal relationships [25] and increased medical disorders.[30]

Although late-onset patients are less likely to have accompanying psychopathology, they are more likely to show cognitive deficits and functional impairment. Activities of daily living become more difficult,[12, 14, 31, 32, 33, 34] and they may demonstrate structural brain deficits such as large lateral ventricles,[35] neurosensory hearing impairment,[36] and cerebrovascular disease (e.g., ischemic disease)[18, 23, 37, 38, 39]. A subset of late-onset patients are presumed to have an incipient neurological disease because they show impairment on neuropsychological testing similar to mild cognitive impairment [23], and they are more likely than elders in the general population to convert to an overt dementing disorder.[40, 41] Despite the differences, there are limitations to using the onset age as a distinguishing medical characteristic because late-onset patients may not have recognized earlier episodes if they were mild, and an incipient neurological problem will affect mood regardless of whether or not the patient experienced earlier episodes.[19, 40]

Comorbidity

Late-life depressive syndromes often arise in the context of major medical conditions. Over one-quarter of Parkinson's disease patients demonstrate significant depressive symptoms, and the presence of depression increases the probability of dementia or cognitive impairment.[42] Initially, Parkinson's disease patients show predominantly executive dysfunction,[43] which is consistent with the subcortical origin of the disease. (In contrast, diseases originating in neocortex, such as the temporal lobe, would be likely to show early memory impairment.) Depression is one of the most frequently reported symptoms accompanying Huntington's disease.[44, 45] Although Huntington's disease arises from different subcortical processes than does Parkinson's disease, both diseases soon envelop subcortical structures implicated in the onset of depression. Depression in the context of diabetes, multiple sclerosis or amyotrophic lateral sclerosis increases likelihood of significant cognitive loss [46, 47, 48, 49] and complicates management of the disorder.[50, 51] Depression occurs often in the context of cancer, and mortality is highest among patients with depression.[52] Recently a potential bidirectional pathway has been posited between depression and cancer. In a review of heterogeneous forms of cancer, depression was linked with long-term development of cancer, i.e., over ten years after the first depressive episode.[53]

Cerebrovascular Disease

Depression is most frequently seen as comorbid to cerebrovascular disease, with high rates of depression sequent to the onset of hypertension and ischemic small-vessel disease.[54, 55, 56, 57] Ischemic disease is believed responsible for the development of brain lesions, which occur at an abnormally high rate among depressed individuals. Lesions are small areas of brain tissue with increased signal intensity in balanced, T_2- weighted, and fluid-attenuated inversion recovery (FLAIR) images. T_1- weighted sequences are used to maximize contrast between gray and white matter and to provide anatomical detail. T_2- weighted images are particularly sensitive to water, so they excel at identifying fluid-filled areas that appear as bright spots, or *hyperintense* lesions. In late-life depressed patients, periventricular hyperintensities may line the lateral ventricles and often show fluid leaking into the surrounding white matter.[58] Single or contiguous hyperintensities may be observed in the deep subcortical white matter and may be present in the absence of periventricular lesions. White-matter hyperintensities are of greater size in 80% of patients who are 60 years of age and older at the time of their initial episode compared to patients with an initial episode prior to age 60.[59]

Depressed older women with randomly distributed anterior hyperintense lesions show a stronger negative association between caudate volume and total lesion volume than do comparison subjects.[60] The caudate receives projections from the amygdala and the orbitofrontal and is an important structure in limbic circuitry.[61] The five major fronto-striatal-thalamo neuronal pathways course through some designated section of the caudate after leaving the neocortex, so morphometric deformation in the caudate could occur via "downstream" effects of glial or neuronal compromise in neocortical areas as well as from the geographically closer periventricular lesions.

The Cardiovascular Health Study [62], which imaged approximately 3600 people from 4 communities, found that people over age 65 who had more large cortical white-matter lesions, small lesions in the basal ganglia, or more severe subcortical white matter lesions were at higher risk of developing depressive symptoms.[63] A smaller prospective study by Teodorcsuk and colleagues (2007) assessed patients who were free of depression for white matter hypterintensity burden, quality of life and current disability.[64] They were clinically assessed one year later, at which time the magnitude of change in white matter hyperintense volume predicted development of depression, worsening quality of life and increased disability. Generalized or randomly distributed lesions, such as are found in Alzheimer's disease, multiple sclerosis, HIV, and illnesses with central nervous system involvement, constitute a high risk for developing depression.[65, 66, 67] The rate of increase in the volume of hyperintense tissue is an important predictor of who will respond to treatment. Patients who show a good response to antidepressant treatment show less increase in white matter hyperintense tissue (11.5%), but the individuals with a poor treatment response show a marked increase in volume (31.6%) after one year.[68]

Discrete lesions of tumors, stroke, trauma, surgery and focal seizures are also of interest because brain tumors and stroke are strongly associated with the development of depression.[69] After a stroke, depression may develop immediately or within 3 months and can be a serious obstacle to adhering to the therapy regimen needed to recover function.[70, 71, 72] Stroke researchers note a high incidence of mood disorders following infarctions in the frontal and basal ganglia, particularly in the head of the caudate.[73] Trauma and tumors of the prefrontal dorsolateral cortex are more likely to produce mood changes than tumors of the ventral prefrontal areas,[74] and when the lesions are in the left hemisphere, patients are at particularly high risk.[75] The frequency of the co-occurrence of cerebrovascular disease and depression in late life led Alexopoulos to coin the phrase *vascular depression* [76] for patients who present with comorbid depression and cerebrovascular disease.

Elderly people with vascular depression have greater disability and cognitive impairment than those who are depressed but do not have vascular disease. The most common cognitive deficits occur in language as loss of verbal fluency or ability to name objects spontaneously and in decreased speed of information processing. Behaviorally, patients demonstrate more apathy, retardation, and lack of insight, but they tend toward less agitation and guilt than do elderly individuals who are depressed without vascular risk factors.[77, 78] Treatment is guided by the need to mitigate both disorders concurrently by using an antidepressant that promotes ischemic recovery.

Cardiovascular Disease

Coronary heart disease (CHD) is the most prevalent cause of death in America today, and depression increases the risk of recurrent cardiac morbidity and mortality among patients with established CHD. Depressed women with positive results of coronary angiography [79, 80] or exercise stress testing [81] or who have recently undergone bypass surgery [82, 83] are at greater risk for nonfatal cardiac events than are comparable nondepressed patients.[84] About a quarter of individuals who have a myocardial infarction or who are undergoing cardiac catheterization have major depression, and another 25% have minor depression.[85] If the person is depressed at the time of the first cardiac event, he or she is likely to remain depressed a year later.[84] Additionally, about 40% of patients who initially were not depressed became depressed within the year after the event, and it was likely to be moderate to severe depression (>10 on the Beck Depression Inventory).[84] Depression is also a major determinant of quality of life whereas the somatic indicators of the severity of the cardiovascular problem are not predictive.

Mortality rates are considerably higher among depressed cardiac patients. Patients with depression are at four times greater risk for death during the first six months after a myocardial infarction than are nondepressed older adults.[86, 87] A five-year follow-up study showed both major and minor depression to be independent risk factors for all-cause mortality (hazard ratios = 1.87 and 1.67, respectively).[88] Bush et al (2001) reported that even minor or subclinical depressive symptomatology places myocardial patients at higher risk of death,[89] but not as high as found among patients with major depression.

Depression is suspected of contributing to increased mortality after myocardial infarction as a result of interference in the modulation of the heart rate and rhythm by the autonomic nervous system.[90] A 3-yr follow-up study reported that depressed patients were more likely to have abnormal heart rate turbulence (i.e., elevated heart rate, low heart rate variability, exaggerated heart rate responses to physical stressors, and high variability in ventricular repolarization) and worse chance of survival. [91] When heart rate turbulence was added to a statistical model predicting mortality, the adjusted hazard ratio for depression decreased from 2.4 to 1.9, suggesting that autonomic dysfunction is a likely reason for the association between depression and cardiac mortality. Carney et al (2007) noted that the additional mortality risk does not manifest until the 2nd and 3rd year of follow-up, which is consistent with the long-term development of biophysiological abnormalities associated with depression.[90] Unfortunately, the treatment of depression carries some risk due to the anti-platelet action of selective serotonin reuptake inhibitors (SSRI). (See Rajowska et al. (1999) and van Zyl et al. (2008) for reviews of platelet activity and vascular endothelial dysfunction associated with depression and coronary artery disease.[92, 93]) Administration of an SSRI after a cardiac event increases the risk of bleeding, but on the other hand, if standard antidepressants and cognitive behavior therapy are administered and the patient responds, the risk of mortality decreases compared to those who do not respond. [94]

In a review of unstable angina, Lesperance et al (2000) reported that 40% of patients were depressed,[95] which is slightly higher than seen in other cardiovascular conditions. Angina patients with depression were more likely to die or have a nonfatal myocardial infarction during the follow-up period than were the nondepressed patients, with an adjusted odds ratio of 6.7, which represents a startling risk for angina patients. Most of the reviewed studies did not examine the chronicity or query for time of initial episode, and those that did reported that many patients were unsure of previous depressive episodes. Consequently, it is unknown whether persons with early onset of depression are at significantly greater risk than those with a late onset, potentially inflating the odds of a negative outcome. Many of the above studies were major epidemiological studies with follow-up periods around five years. Longer studies may actually show increased risk for angina patients if the finding by Carney et al (2007)[90] is valid for angina, in that morbidity and mortality begin to manifest during the second or third year after the cardiac event.

A less-well known aspect of late-life depression is that it is a risk factor for the development of life-threatening cardiac conditions as well as a sequel. A history of major depression,[54, 96, 97] current depressive symptoms,[79, 98, 99, 100, 101] diagnosis of clinical depression,[96, 102, 103] and an increase in depressive symptoms with time [103, 104] predict incident coronary heart disease or cardiac mortality in patients without any clinical evidence of coronary heart disease when depression was originally diagnosed. The development of coronary heart disease is the same for depressed women as for depressed men.[84] The reason for the development of cardiovascular disease after depression may have the same biophysiological basis as does the increased risk of subsequent cardiac event or death when the person develops depression sequent to the initial cardiac event. Depression disturbs the functioning of the autonomic nervous system with negative implications for heart stability, platelet activity and neuronal and glial integrity. As we learn more about the biochemical correlates of late-life depression, there are other theories involving immune function and biochemical imbalances that may point to important modulators of the depression-cardiovascular relationship.

Neuropsychological Deficits

Severity of the depressive disorder appears to modulate the severity of any accompanying or developing cognitive deficits. In a comparison of cognitive performance of patients with minor and major depression, composite scores were computed for domains of working memory, nonverbal recognition, resistance to interference, verbal recall and executive function.[105] On four of the five domain scores, means of minor depressed patients fell intermediate to those of comparison subjects and major depressed patients. On the fifth score in executive functioning, minor and major depressed patients scored essentially the same, which was significantly lower than the comparison group. The immediate drop in executive performance for both minor and major depressed individuals supports the theory that late-life depression originates in compromise of fronto-striatal pathways in prefrontal cortex, and this compromise then radiates out to other domains that require support of diverse executive resources. There were few differences between men and women in their performances over the five domains [105].

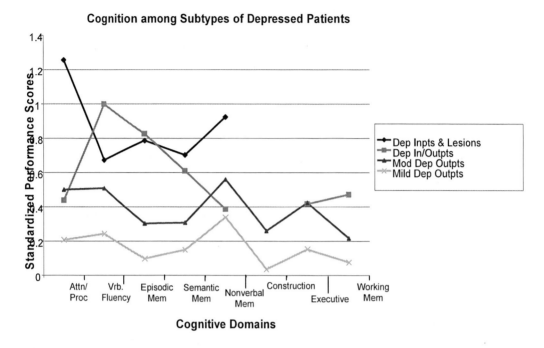

Effect scale was per Cohen's (1988) interpretation: 0.10 = trivial effect, 0.20 = small effect, 0.50=medium effect, and 0.80=large effect. This graph is a modification of one that appeared originally in Elderkin-Thompson, et al., Neurocognitive profiles in elderly patients with frontotemporal degeneration or major depressive disorder, *JINS* 2004; 10:753-771

Figure 1. Effect sizes of cognition deficits across depressed samples categorized by severity of mood disorder.

A meta-analysis of cognitive findings in geriatric major depression demonstrated an overall association with a gradient with illness severity based on the combination of Hamilton Depression Rating Scores (HDRS) [106], severity of biomedical indicators and inpatient status.[107] Depressed patients from 13 studies were categorized into four subgroups: 1) depressed inpatients and patients with severe white matter hyperintensities (WMH) on neuroimaging, 2) mixed groups of in- and outpatients, 3) depressed outpatients with scores of 19 or greater on the HDRS, and 4) mildly to moderately depressed outpatients with HDRS scores between 14 and 19. Mild to moderately depressed individuals demonstrated a small deficit on cognitive performance, and the effect size was consistent across multiple cognitive domains. (See Figure 1) As the severity of depression increased and the sample included both inpatients and outpatients, the effect size of the cognitive deficits increased to large, at which point the impairment is readily apparent.[108] The two subgroups that included inpatients each showed one area of particular weakness. For those with extensive white matter lesions, information processing was noticeably poorer; for in- and outpatient combinations, verbal fluency was the greatest deficit. Given that the most severely depressed also included those with the largest hyperintensity burden, this group can be considered to have the most significant cerebrovascular disease. Impairments for the two subgroups of patients with mild and moderate depression were fairly consistent across the cognitive domains without one area of salient weakness.

Although many individual studies do not show a correlation between cognition and disease severity as defined by the HDRS score, the gradient described in this meta-analysis between cognition and severity of major depression likely occurred because various clinical and outpatient settings were sampled, severity was not limited to HDRS scores, and composite cognitive scores were based on multiple tests within several domains. The following discussion of cognitive deficits comes primarily from this meta-analysis because it provides a valid comparison of performance across domains.[107] The analysis included only results from samples diagnosed per the Diagnostic and Statistical Manual III-R or the Schedule for Affective Disorders with Research Criteria for Major Depression [109, 110]. Test results were converted to weighted effect sizes before averaging to control for sample size. Effect size (ES) guidelines from Cohen (1988) provided the method to compare performances: 0.10 = a trivial effect that would take large samples to detect, 0.20 = a small effect, although noticeable to trained persons; 0.50 = a medium effect size that would be apparent to some untrained observers; and 0.80 = a large effect size, which would be grossly obvious. Please refer to the original analysis for additional source references [107].

Processing Speed

Processing speed is the rate at which a person can perform while being timed on a task that requires processing of information and producing a motor response to complete the task.[111] Tests such as Stroop A/B and Digit Span are used to measure information processing while the Trail Making Test A is used to quantify performance in visual tracking and sequencing. Patients with moderate to severe WMH burden on neuroimaging have the greatest deficit in processing speed of the four subgroups (3.76 ES) (Figure 1). Among nonhospitalized depressed patients, deficits were generally of mild magnitude (0.50 ES). Advanced age, per se, did not result in a large impairment because community depressed patients over age 85 showed a moderate (0.49) effect size for a matching-to-sample task, and another community sample of depressed 70 to 85-year-olds showed processing speeds with trivial to moderate deficits.

Language

Verbal fluency tasks (e.g., naming words that begin with a certain letter or belong to a certain category) assess language productivity. Fluency can be affected differentially in that frontal lesions frequently impair phonemic fluency (i.e., naming words that start with a designated letter) and temporal lesions impair semantic fluency (i.e., naming words that belong to a designated category). Semantic fluency was assessed only in groups of in- and outpatients or patients with moderate to severe WMHs for whom effect sizes were large or very large (ES= 0.70 to 1.22). If no or mild WMHs were present, deficits in phonemic fluency were in the trivial range (0.10 ES). Interestingly, two groups averaged 26 points on the HDRS, but one had large WMHs with significant fluency deficits while the other had no or mild WMHs with a trivial language deficit, indicating a potentially critical association between WMH burden and fluency independent of HDRS scores of depression severity. For the remaining depressed groups, phonemic fluency scores fluctuated within these two extremes.

Episodic Verbal Memory

Depression is most frequently confused with Alzheimer's disease based on tests of recall for recently learned material that is associated with a time and place, i.e., episodic memory. When hyperintensity burden was elevated, inpatients had a severe delayed recall deficit on measures from the Wechsler Memory Scale, Revised (1.45 ES)[112] and a similar deficit on immediate recall (1.96 ES). Hospitalized depressed patients, in general, are strongly impaired on learning word lists, with both free recall and recognition of the previously-presented words showing large effect size differences from nondepressed comparison groups (0.76 recall to 0.95 on recognition). Depressed patients with no or minimal hyperintensity burden showed trivial to small differences on immediate and delayed recall. Patients with mild depressive symptomatology as rated by an HDRS ≤ 18 showed no difference from controls.

Semantic Memory

Semantic memory gives meaning to the objects and sounds of the environment as well as abstractions or conceptualizations shared within a culture, and it is not related to a time or place as is episodic memory. Two studies of depressed outpatients reported trivial (0.02 and 0.10) to moderate (0.41 and 0.57) effect sizes, with the moderate effect sizes occurring among depressed patients with vegetative symptoms. One study of hospitalized patients showed a similar moderate deficit (0.70 ES) but, again, inpatients with high WMH burden showed a severe deficit (1.22 ES).

Nonverbal Construction and Recall

Visuospatial construction involves the ability to observe, manipulate, reason about, and construct nonverbal, spatially represented information.[111] The scale of deficits changed markedly with each categorization of patients. Depressed outpatients with evidence of severe hyperintense lesion volume demonstrated profound loss on visuoconstruction tests, and patients with vegetative symptoms showed moderate to large effects. On the other hand, depressed in- and outpatients with fewer risk factors showed an effect gradient from moderate to trivial. Nonverbal recall tests were similar to construction tasks in that hospitalized depressed patients demonstrated a severe loss of ability across a number of tests (all ES between 0.82 to 1.72). Nonhospitalized depressed patients with vegetative symptoms showed similar large memory deficits: 0.93 ES on a nonverbal recognition test and 1.08 ES on recall of a visual stimulus,[113] which suggests impairment at both the encoding and retrieval stages based on significant deficits for both recall and recognition. However, when cerebrovascular risk and depression severity was within moderate limits, deficits ranged from moderate to trivial.

Working Memory

Working memory tasks, as defined in this review, included tasks presented orally as well as visually. Depressed outpatients and community volunteers demonstrated trivial to mild deficits on almost all tests. Even patients with vegetative symptoms or elevated hyperintensity burdens performed relatively well (ES = 0.42 and 0.62, respectively). An earlier meta-analysis showed similar results, with an approximate overlap in working memory scores between depressed patients and controls of 78%.[114] Attention, sometimes subsumed under working memory, also appears preserved during depression. A meta-analysis of simple attentional tasks reported less than one-quarter standard deviation difference between patients and controls, and another meta-analysis of divided attention found similar results, consistent with the position that working memory and attention processes remain relatively intact despite presence of depression.[114, 115]

Executive Function

Executive function refers to diverse general control processes that involve manipulation and monitoring of other domain processes used to achieve a goal.[74, 116] During the initial stages of learning or executing a complex task, the executive functions determine the efficacy and efficiency of the process.[117, 118, 119] Executive functions of organizing, integrating information for encoding, monitoring information, making complex choices, learning via stimulus-reward situations and adapting to changing environmental conditions demonstrate decline among depressed patients,[113, 120, 121, 122] but it was generally consistent with the level of deficit in other domains. There were no studies on executive functioning of patients with severe WMHs, but patients with vegetative symptoms had moderate to large deficits (0.64 to 0.95 ES). Patients with HDRS scores of 19 or more averaged 0.46 ES on the executive tests, and patients with HDRS scores ≤ 18 had trivial or no deficits on the same tests.

Limited evidence indicates that executive dysfunction may mediate deficits in other cognitive domains for depressed elders. A sample of minor and major depressed patients, screened for indications of mild cognitive impairment, cerebrovascular risk and comorbid medical conditions, was assessed for recall deficits using the California Verbal Learning Test (CVLT).[122] Subjects were asked to recall as many words as possible over five trials in which a 16-word list was read aloud. On the sixth trial, a new word list was presented for recall. After the distractor trial, they were asked to recall the first word list again ("short delayed recall"). They were given twenty minutes of distractor tasks and then asked to recall the first word list ("long delayed recall"). Depressed patients demonstrated a significant impairment on the first presentation of the list of words. However, with each trial, their performance improved, and by the fifth trial they performed at the level of controls. When the new word list was presented, they again scored significantly below the controls. At the two recall measures, however, they performed equal to the controls. Scores assessing executive performance during the task, i.e., organization of the words by semantic categories to facilitate recall, showed deficits among both minor and major depressed patients. When depression and executive scores were entered into a regression analysis predicting the low trial 1 scores, the executive score explained, or statistically mediated, the original recall deficit. Depression, on the other hand, provided no additional explanatory power beyond that provided by the executive score. Another unrelated executive score from a nonverbal abstract conceptualization task also mediated recall scores, suggesting that multiple executive abilities might be similarly affected by depression. Processing speed, on the other hand, was tested as a mediator but was not successful. This hypothesis of executive function being the mediator of recall was replicated using nonverbal stimuli, and again executive organization mediated recall.[121] The findings strongly support the theory that fronto-striatal dysfunction is attenuating the ability of depressed people to mobilize executive skills to facilitate abilities in other domains.

One cannot generalize these findings regarding mediation to other depressed patients not as rigorously screened for comorbid medical conditions or signs of developing dementia. For example, one study reported that 45% of patients with late-life depression were impaired after one year later compared to 8% of the comparison group.[123] However, at baseline, 30% of the depressed subjects and 10% of the comparison group were already impaired (i.e., below the 10th percentile on normed performance) and people who became demented over the follow-up year were not excluded from the study. Visuospatial ability, information-processing speed and delayed memory were most frequently impaired, and the biggest increase in impairment over the intervening year was in visuospatial performance. The combination of neurocogntive deficits suggests neurodegeneration of the parietal region, a key indicator of spreading Alzheimer's disease. Some people develop depression during early Alzheimer's disease, and this type of clinical presentation has its own unique cognitive profile and pathophysiology.

Although depressed elderly patients often complain of forgetfulness and distractibility, for those without an underlying neurodegenerative disease the primary problem may well be an underlying executive dysfunction. These patients are least likely to return to baseline performance after remission of the depression because executive dysfunction -- but not memory impairment -- are associated with relapse and recurrence of depression in the follow-up period.[124, 125] Memory impairment, disability, medical burden, social support, and history of previous episodes do not significantly influence the outcome of depression in this subgroup of patients. van Gorp et al. (2004) concluded in his review of neurocognitive profiles during late-life depression that the reduced ability to remember new information was based largely upon a deficiency in learning or acquisition of material,[111] and this conclusion likely applies to a sizeable percentage of depressed older patients.

Neuroanatomy and Pathophysiology of Depression

Magnetic Resonance Imaging

One of the most consistent findings among depressed elders are changes in the morphometry of the brain. Enlarged ventricle size has been noted for several years among patients of all ages, and among geriatric cases of depression, the finding is more prominent among late-onset patients than early-onset.[126] The fact that late-onset patients are more vulnerable to the morphometric change is particularly important because it appears to rule out the concern that the ventricular enlargement might be consequent to previous anti-depressant medications or ECT treatment.[126] The majority of late-onset patients are imaged during their index episode, so accelerated atrophic processes becomes a more likely explanation. The effects of aging, also, present a concern because ventricular brain ratios begin to increase after age 60 in cross-sectional studies.[58] One prospective study reported that ventricular enlargement at baseline was predictive of development of late-onset depression within a four-year follow-up period [127] indicating that ventricular enlargement may begin at a younger age, but it may become associated with depression after senescence in an interaction with aging processes.

Among minor depressed patients, total prefrontal cortex volumes are intermediate to those of comparison subjects and major depressed elders [128]. The prefrontal brain volumes are not associated with age of onset, so duration of illness does not appear to modulate them. Patients with major late-life depression show decreased volume in prefrontal and subcortical structures, specifically the caudate [129], subgenual anterior cingulate [130], putamen,[131] orbitofrontal cortex,[132, 133] anterior cingulate and gyrus rectus,[132] and dorsolateral prefrontal cortex.[133] Consensus is growing that volume of the hippocampus is also decreased [134, 135] and is most pronounced in late-onset patients.[136] Ballmaier and colleagues (2007) did a mesh-based geometrical modeling that produced statistically-generated maps of the hippocampus.[136] Distances between the statistical center point of the hippocampus and the surface data points were measured at hundreds of points over the surface of the hippocampus. Significant reductions were noted in the CA1, CA3 and subiculum areas. According to post-mortem analyses, the reduced volume likely does not involve neuronal death as in Alzheimer's disease, but increased density of neurons and glia in the dentate gyrus and pyramidal cells in all cell fields in the hippocampus.[137, 138] Stockmeier et al (2004) also found a decrease in neuronal soma size.[138] A similar finding emerged from a post-mortem analysis of the anterior cingulate of middle-aged patients in their forties,[139] i.e., neuronal somal size was reduced and neuronal density was increased.

The paralimbic orbitofrontal cortex appears to be affected quite differently than the limbic structures of hippocampus and anterior cingulate. A post-mortem analysis reported *reduced* density that occurred primarily in layers III and V of the orbitofrontal cortex, layers that are the origins of projections to the striatum, amygdala and neocortex.[140] Rajkowska and colleagues speculated that the reduced density may result from increased hyperintensities in the neuronal pathways. Glia cell density has also been reported as decreased among some astrocytes and oligodendrocytes in the prefrontal cortex and amygdala during depression.[141] The pathological changes in oligodendrocytes, which provide the myelin sheath around neuronal axons, may be a factor in the degeneration of white matter tracts and the creation of the WMHs.[141] Reduced density extends to Brodmann's area 9 of the dorsolateral surface where reduced glial density in layer 5 and reduced neuronal soma size in layer 6 have been reported.[139]

Corpus callosum neuronal pathways in both splenium and genu of depressed elders are thinner than in a comparison group when measured with statistical imaging maps.[142] Significant callosal thinning is restricted to the genu in early-onset patients, but patients with late-onset depression exhibit significant callosal thinning in both genu and splenium relative to controls. In both the analysis of the hippocampus and the corpus callosum, Ballmaier and colleagues found that the thinning correlated with verbal and nonverbal recall measures. Hickie et al. (2005) found similar correlations between hippocampal and cognitive results in late-life depression,[143] so even if there is no temporal neurodegenerative condition, morphemetric change within the hippocampus appears to impair spontaneous recall.

Functional Imaging

Functional imaging relies on the assumption that increased perfusion in a region represents increased glucose intake and metabolic action, which underlies increased neural activity. Originally, ventral limbic and paralimbic structures, e.g., amygdala, medial orbital and cingulate were reported as having increased metabolism,[144, 145, 146, 147, 148] while more dorsal structures of lateral and dorsolateral prefrontal cortex, dorsal anterior cingulate and caudate [145, 149, 150] were thought to be hypometabolic. Evidence soon became contradictory.[151, 152] A recent hypothesis posits that different subregions within the same structure may show different rates of perfusion, and the rate may be dependent on the particular cytoarchitecture and mood regulatory function of the subregion.[153] Metabolic activity could decrease among depressed individuals in posterior lateral and medial orbitofrontal regions but increase in the ventromedial orbitofrontal cortex. Simultaneously, some areas of the orbitofrontal may enhance emotional expression while others may inhibit it. Effective antidepressant treatment is associated with a normalization of the perfusion rates in all areas.[153] More refined analyses under this new theory will undoubtedly lead to more precise understanding of how functioning within a brain structure might become unbalanced with varying behavioral implications, depending on the relationships between the subregions. Interactions with aging and atrophic processes also remain to be clarified.

Magnetic Resonance Spectroscopy

Magnetic resonance spectroscopy is a recently developed imaging technique that allows determination of levels of various biochemical compounds in the brain in vivo. Three biochemicals have received interest in terms of depression. N-acetyl asparate (NAA) is an abundant molecule in the brain and is contained almost exclusively within neurons.[154] It is considered to act as an in vivo marker of neuronal loss and/or viability.[155, 156] Reduced regional NAA concentrations have been reported in conditions that are characterized by neuronal or axonal loss such as Alzheimer's disease.[157, 158] Choline (Cho) is an essential precursor of the neurotransmitter acetylcholine [159] and its signal represents about 40% of the phospholipid contents of cell membranes.[157] It is considered a biomarker for the status of membrane phospholipid metabolism.[160, 161] Elevated Cho suggests altered membrane synthesis and degradation.[162] Myo-Inositol (mI) is a marker of phospoholipid turnover, a component of cell membrane structure and growth, and a messenger for hormones and neurotransmitters [163] and for some types of neurons.[161] mI is also a metabolic precursor to phospoinositide (PI), a key component of central G-protein coupled receptor signaling systems, including several subtypes of adrenergic, cholinergic, serotonergic and metabotropic glutamatergic receptors.[164]

In a meta-analysis of MRS findings in depressed subjects of all ages no differences were found between depressed patients and controls in levels of NAA/creatine ratios.[165] A voxel-based analysis in the dorsolateral cortex of elderly patients found elevated Cho/creatine ratios in the white but not gray matter.[166] According to Kumar and colleagues (2002), higher levels of Cho resonance on MRS may reflect alterations in the structure of neuronal membranes of which Cho components are an integral part. Four of five depression studies found higher Cho in the basal ganglia.[167, 168, 169, 170] mI/creatine levels among depressed patients have been contradictory. One study reported ratios of mI/creatine in middle-aged depressed patients as lower than a comparison group in a prefrontal/anterior cingulate voxel,[171] but another study reported higher mI/creatine levels in dorsolateral white matter of elderly patients.[166] In a follow-on analysis of the latter study by Kumar and colleagues (2002), levels of Cho and mI were correlated with cognitive functioning to determine if differences in biochemical levels might be implicated in task performance.[244] See Figure 2. When the four biochemicals were entered into a regression equation predicting performance in six different cognitive domains, controls showed a strong correlation between cognition and biochemical levels, but depressed patients showed no systematic relationship between cognition and biochemicals. It appears that depressed patients must function despite biophysiologic disorganization, which may contribute to the global nature of behavioral and cognitive deficits.

Diffusion Tensor Imaging (DTI)

Diffusion tensor imaging utilizes a pulse sequence sensitive to microscopic random water motion. The forward motion of fluid is represented as fractional anisotropy (FA), a directional measure that is a ratio of the forward motion by motion in two perpendicular directions. A high FA represents unidimensional movement constrained by intact vascular membranes. A low FA indicates that fluid is moving in multiple directions and suggests low membrane integrity or even seepage into the surrounding tissue. Hyperintense lesions have lower FA than comparison tissue, as does the tissue surrounding the lesion.[172, 173] If surrounding tissue is impacted by the lesion, then the microstructural organization of an area's vascular system may be damaged by the development of the lesion. Among elderly depressed patients, white matter of right anterior cingulate and middle and superior gyri of the dorsolateral region show lower FA.[174] This degraded membrane organization is consistent with conclusions from lesion analyses suggesting that membrane compromise in one area of a neuronal pathway can disturb physiologic, and even anatomic, integrity at geographically removed locations. Unexpectedly, early-onset patients demonstrate lower anisotropy than late-onset or controls. [174] This finding is particularly intriguing because late-onset patients usually are attributed with larger volumes of hyperintense tissue. The low FA of early-onset patients raises the question as to whether they might have a differential vulnerability to white matter disorganization or even a neurodevelopmental difference that begins early in life.

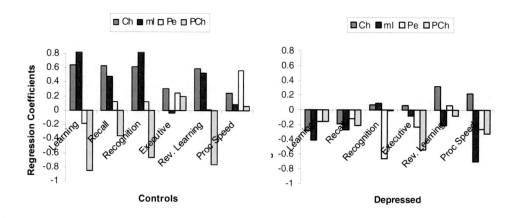

Note: Ch=Choline, mI=myo-Inositol, Pe=Phospethanolamine, PCh=Phosphocholine
Controls showed significant associations between cognition and biochemical concentrations, but the associations in the depressed group were small and insignificant.

This graph is a modification of one that appeared originally in Elderkin-Thompson, et al., Brain metabolites and cognitive function among older depressed and healthy individuals using 2D MR spectroscopy, *Neuropsychoparmacology* 2004; 29: 2251-2257.

Figure 2. Regression coefficients for biochemicals predicting domains of cognition for nondepressed controls and depressed patients.

Another new MRI-related imaging technique called magnetization transfer assesses the macromolecular protein content of white and gray brain matter. The MT ratio is a measure of the biological integrity of myelin and axonal density in white matter and a more composite index of macromolecular proteins in gray matter regions. Magnetization transfer ratios of outpatients with moderate late-life depression show evidence of change in the macromolecular protein pool of white matter tissue that appears normal on traditional MR images.[175] This finding may represent an early stage of biophysiological change associated with late-life depression. Thus, all forms of imaging continue to point toward gradual tissue dysregulation and insult, with abnormalities occurring in multiple areas with varying magnitudes.

Neurochemical Abnormalities

The overactivity of the hypothalamic-pituitary-adrenal axis has been well documented in young depressed adults, but unlike younger adults who demonstrate hypercortesolemia during depression, results in late-life depression are contradictory. We now know that older depressed individuals demonstrate both low and high cortisol levels, and hypocortisolemic depression is associated with female sex, joint diseases, smoking, low urinary cortisol [176] and recurrent depression.[177, 178] Hypercortisolemic depression, on the other hand, is associated with older age, male sex, cardiovascular diseases, nonsteroidal anti-inflammatory use and borderline cognitive impairment. The possibility of a dichotomous association between cortisol and depression in late life underscores the divergent clinical presentations of geriatric patients.

Changes in the pro-inflammatory cytokine interleukin-6 (IL-6) level occurs with age due to several factors, such as a high fat diet,[179] reduced exercise,[180] adipose fat levels,[181] and declines in circulating levels of steroid hormones.[182, 183] Increased IL-6 levels are also associated with late-life depression.[184, 185] However, IL-6 has a complex regulatory role because it simultaneously regulates pro-inflammatory and anti-inflammatory activities through different mechanisms, thus contributing to both development and resolution of the acute inflammatory response.[186] Elderly women with depressive symptomatology have poor T-cell responses to mitogens,[187, 188] and they have high concentrations of both plasma interleukin 1 beta (IL-1b) [189] and IL-6 [190]. The IL-1b levels are associated with the duration of the current episode, but not age of onset.[189]

One of the more confusing but interesting aspects of IL-6 is that in its regulatory role, it can limit the inflammatory response by suppressing the production of IL-1b.[191, 192] The question becomes whether the elevated levels of IL-6 are aimed at resolving the inflammatory response that is inappropriately long, or whether dysregulation of IL-6 production is a response to a chronic pro-inflammatory state, which would negatively impact health status.[186] One interpretation of the inflammatory response problem in late-life depression is that IL-6 is unable, for some unknown reason, to control the activity of IL-1b despite increased plasma levels of IL-6, and the increased production just represents its effort to modulate IL-1b. In contrast, a negative interpretation of increased levels of IL-6 would posit that IL-6 is functioning as a pro-inflammatory agent in addition to IL-1b. Whatever the function, the elevated levels of IL-6 are implicated in a number of chronic medical conditions and are found in frail, but not non-frail, age-matched individuals.[193] (See Maggio, Guralnik, Longo et al (2006) for a review.[186]) High levels of IL-6 also increase the risk for bone resorption,[194] a concern of elderly patients on anti-depressant medications due to increased risk of falls.

While past research has established the link between depression and increased pro-inflammatory cytokines, recent preliminary evidence establishes a putative link between prolonged immune activation and the onset of depression [195]. Peripherally-produced cytokines coordinate the body's reaction to infection, but they also act on the brain to produce the accompanying sickness behavior, which has considerable overlap with depressive symptomatology. Unlike sickness behavior that recedes when the infection is resolved, cytokine-induced depression is a maladaptive response that may occur because the innate immune response is exacerbated in intensity and/or duration and precipitates a cascade of biochemical reactions that the body is unable to suppress.[195] Elderly women often deal with several major stressors concurrently that involve negative emotions such as care-giving, bereavement, relocation, or medical events, which can modulate immune status [196]. Chronic medical conditions frequently elevate immunoreactivity. Furthermore, the combination of aging and environmental stress may be synergistic [197, 198]. Older women find it more difficult than young women to return to homeostasis after increased pro-inflammatory cytokine mRNA expression in the central nervous system from all sources. [199, 200, 201] Consequently, older women may be more vulnerable to the cascading effect of exaggerated immune response. Cytokine-induced depression is not the biological equivalent of major depressive disorder, but growing evidence indicates that depression in chonically ill or chronically stressed individuals may account for a substantial number of cases involving depressive syndromes. Van den Biggelaar and colleagues (2007) recently reported intriguing results in which 85-year-old nondepressed subjects with no psychiatric history were followed prospectively.[202] Elevated biomarkers of IL-1b and C-reactive protein were associated with the emergence of depressive symptoms.

Late-Life Depression and Dementia

Depression as prodromal to Alzheimer's disease has received considerable attention. Van Reekum et al (2005) studied patients of a geriatric day hospital who met criteria for major depression, were medically stable, and did not suffer from dementia or other central nervous system disease or injury at initial interview.[203] Both early- and late-onset individuals, with a mean age of 75 years, were included. A neurologist, psychiatrist and neuropsychologist reviewed each case and diagnosis was by consensus. Patients were screened with a neurological assessment, cognitive testing, metabolic screening, and CT scanning. After 7 years of follow-up, 27% converted to dementia per *Diagnostic and Statistical Manual* criteria. Although this study had a thorough screening process, there are some questions about the generalizability of the findings. The participants were not demented at baseline, but they scored an average of 128 on the Mattis Dementia Rating Scale, which is below the 130 breakpoint that represents no cognitive loss.[204] Alzheimer's disease was the most common dementia at follow-up, but recruiting from a geriatric day care center introduces a selection bias toward elderly with initial functional deficits. In fact, persons with the lowest Mattis' scores were also the most likely to convert and there was no difference in conversion rates between early- and late-onset individuals (annual incidence 4.2% for late-onset and 3.0% for early-onset). The authors point out that both rates are higher than the annual incidence rate of 2% for the general population of 75-year-olds [205], but marginal levels of cognitive function present a high risk of dementia conversion for nondepressed 75-year-olds as well as depressed ones. As might be expected, in the regression model, scores on the Mattis Dementia Rating Scale (MDRS) were the strongest predictor of conversion, reducing odds of both age and onset status to 1.0. Thus, a low level of cognitive function presents a conversion risk for all older individuals, and the nature of the role of depression in precipitating or hastening this decline has yet to be resolved.

Lopez and colleagues (2000) have investigated the effect of Lewy Body disease (LBD) on the clinical presentation of Alzheimer's disease (AD).[206] A retrospective analysis of patients with autopsy-confirmed Alzheimer's and Lewy Body disease (AD+LBD) showed a nonsignificant increase in confusional episodes and bradykinesia compared to AD alone when the dementia was in the mild stages, although specificity was low. Depression was associated with moderate disease progression of AD + LBD, at which time patients had more overall extrapyramidal signs, syncopal episodes, confusional episodes and diurnal hypersomnia. In the advanced stage of AD+LBD dementia, the depression remitted, which is consistent with other evidence indicating that depression remits during severe dementia. The post-mortem analysis [207] showed that depression manifested when Lewy bodies were concentrated in the amygdala. Patients with diffuse neocortical LBD did not manifest depression, suggesting that the deposition of the LBs in the amygdala is a critical development for the onset of depression in patients with AD. Furthermore, the deposition in the amygdala is not a late-stage phenomena because depression appeared in the mild/moderate stages of dementia, and occasionally preceded the onset of dementia.

Currently, late-onset depression appears more problematic for the development of dementia than is early-onset.[208] Late-onset of depression, particularly when concurrent with mild cognitive impairment and apathy, becomes a risk factor for the development of Alzheimer's disease (AD).[209] However, the nature of a causal connection between depression and dementia is likely to be complex. The cognitive loss of Alzheimer's disease and that of depression appear to be quite different. The early brain anomalies that lead to the typical Alzheimer's cognitive deficits may precipitate a secondary response that manifests as a mood disorder, with its additional cognitive deficits. The secondary disorder then masks the primary pathodegenerative condition in its initial stages. The cognitive losses assumed to be associated with depression would be very mild Alzheimer's deficits coupled with fronto-striatal deficits of depression.

The role of cognitive deficits was highlighted in a postmortem study examining depressed and nondepressed individuals. It reported that individuals with Alzheimer's pathology but *no* cognitive decline before death had significantly lower rates of depression than cognitively normal controls with no Alzhemier pathology and individuals with Alzheimer pathology plus clinical diagnoses of dementia [210]. The conclusion is that, in the absence of cognitive decline, Alzheimer's patients are less likely to demonstrate depression than either healthy controls or diagnosed Alzheimer's patients. Healthy controls would still develop late-onset depression, but their etiologies would be of a different origin as long as they remain free of a neurodegenerative condition.

A postmortem analysis from the University of Pittsburgh [211] found similar rates of Alzheimer's pathology between patients with late-onset of depression and dementia patients without depression: 70% of depressed patients and 89% of the control dementia patients from the Alzheimer's Disease Research Center showed the expected neuropathology. Although the severity of depression was not predictive of conversion, the presence of the apolipoprotein E ε3 or ε4 (*APOE* ε3 or ε4) allele significantly increased the risk of developing MCI among depressed subjects.[212] (APOE ε4 allele is a known genetic risk factor for the development of Alzhemier's disease.) Compared to those without the combined ε3 or ε4 allele, nondepressed subjects with the ε3/ε4 or ε4/ε4 alleles had a hazard ratio of 1.6 for developing MCI or dementia; depressed subjects with the same genotype, i.e., carrier of either ε3/ε4 or ε4/ε4, had a hazard ratio of 5.1. The significant interaction between the *APOE* genotype and depression indicates that those with late-onset of depression who are also carriers of the ε3/ε4 allele are at markedly higher risk of cognitive decline.

The association between smaller hippocampal volumes and incipient AD is well-established, and apoptosis in the medial temporal region is known to begin before the disease is clinically apparent. However, hippocampal findings among depressed individuals have not supported the hypothesis that depression is prodromal to Alzheimer's disease despite findings that late-onset patients have smaller hippocampal volumes than comparison elderly. Post-mortem analysis of brains of depressed individuals has found no indication of massive neuronal die-off that would suggest a neurodegenerative process or a suppression of dentate neurogenesis.[137] Instead, the post-mortem histopatholgical evidence points to changes in neuronal and glial density,[92] reduced membrane integrity,[166] and intracellular changes like alterations in somatodendritic, axonal and synaptic components.[137] Suppression of dentate neurogenesis occurs in patients with depression who are also hypercortisolemic, such as Cushing's disease patients, and have increased exposure to high glucocorticoid toxicity,[213] but this condition is not characteristic of most depression cases. Yet the evidence suggests that depression may exacerbate the severity of this pathophysiology if it has developed concurrently. Rapp and colleagues (2006) reported that brains of patients with AD and a lifetime history of depression showed higher levels of both plaque and tangle formation within the hippocampus than brains of patients with AD without a history of depression [214]. Sweet (2004) found that patients with depression and AD had significantly shorter times before death than did patients with AD alone.

The possibility that we are relying too heavily on retrospective or cross-sectional data from clinical samples presents a clear threat to interpretation of a large portion of the depression and dementia literature. The central issue appears to be the stability of cognition, with depression increasing the risk of decline. A longitudinal study found that while cross-sectional analysis showed an association between depression and dementia, longitudinal analysis did not show the same relationship [215]. Among those in whom dementia later developed, depression was associated with worse performance in some but not all baseline cognitive composite scores. Cognitive decline was minimal in one group who remained free of dementia, but the other group who developed dementia had marked cognitive decline over the 12 years of the prospective study. Moreover, depressive symptoms were not associated with rate of cognitive decline in either group. Clearly, conclusions regarding an association between late-life depression and dementia need to be limited according to each study's patient sample, genetic risk, methodology and biophysical vulnerabilities. More longitudinal studies are needed to clarify the multiple influences and their intereactions with aging to sort out the reliable markers of incipient cognitive decline.

Interventions in Late-Life

A review by Pollock (2004; Table 15.2) itemizes published and unpublished reports of the pharmokinetics of newer antidepressants among elderly patients.[216] He also discusses the altered pharmokinetics that must be considered when treating elderly patients, such as decreased absorption rates, increased/decreased free concentration of drugs in plasma, decreased renal clearance of active metabolites, altered volume of distribution of lipid-soluble drugs that leads to increased elimination half-life, and decreased hepatic clearance. In general, older patients are more sensitive than younger ones to adverse side effects of antidepressants at lower concentrations, but they require similar levels to precipitate a response.[217] Homeostatic indicators may be less robust among elderly,[216] and selective serotonin reuptake inhibitors (SSRI) may increase the risk of falls and broken hips.[218] Pollock also discusses the problem of prescribing anticholinergic agents among elderly, which can lead to parkinsonism. Even mild anticholinergic agents can be associated with cognitive impairment in depressed and nondepressed elders.[219, 220]

Treatment of late-life depression usually involves an antidepressant regimen, sometimes combined with psychotherapy. Meta-analyses have shown considerable heterogeneity in treatment effects, with the mean level of improvement of depressive symptoms ranging from 0.61 ES [221] to 1.22 ES [222]. The differences may be attributed to different selection criteria for depression in that some studies include only patients with clinically diagnosed major depression and others include subthreshold depression. Cases of refractory depression are more common among patients who meet thresholds for diagnosis of major depression, and the increased likelihood of cognitive deficits complicates their treatment protocols. A meta-analysis of 89 controlled studies of pharmacotherapy or psychotherapy treatments included patients with major depression, minor depression and dysthymia, included dropout rate as a criterion, computed weighted effect sizes per Cohen,[108] and adjusted results for bias due to differences in pre-tests between therapy and control conditions.[223, 224] The analysis included studies that administered SSRIs, other agents with varied mechanisms (e.g., venlafaxine, mirtazapione) and tricyclic antidepresssants and monoamine oxidase inhibitors (MAOIs). Although SSRIs are the standard drugs of choice for most physicians, some patients prefer psychotherapeutic treatments to avoid side effects or drug-drug interactions, or because of personal choice. Cognitive behavioral treatment was included as well as studies of interpersonal psychotherapy, psychodynamic therapy and electro-convulsive therapy.

Overall, large effect sizes in improvements were found. Improvements in depression showed a large average effect size for clinician-rated improvement over the three diagnostic groups (major depression, minor depression and dystymia) (0.93 ES) and a moderate to large effect size for self-rated improvement (0.84 ES).[224] Cognitive behavioral therapy (CBT) was the most effective therapeutic approach (1.06 ES) when compared to other psychotherapies (eclectic psychotherapies, focused visual imagery group therapy, interpersonal psychotherapy, psychodynamic therapy and reminiscence). The other psychotherapies except interpersonal therapy showed moderate to large effect sizes, with reminiscence (1.00 ES) showing the second strongest effect size; other methods were in the moderate range (0.52 to 0.73 ES). Effects of CBT were analyzed with the different patient groups, and it had its smallest effect in studies of major depressed individuals (0.76 ES) compared to more heterogeneous samples (1.26 ES).

Among clinicians, psychotherapeutic interventions showed larger effect sizes than pharmacologic interventions, although the difference was small (72.4% to 66.3% respectively showed improvement).[223] The effect of CBT on clinican-rated improvement in depression was greater than the effects of other forms of psychotherapy, SSRIs, other drugs, and all medications combined (ES=1.22 for CBT, 0.48 for SSRIs, 0.93 for tricyclics, and 0.79 for MAOI). Patients rated SSRIs as less effective (0.22 ES) than tricyclic antidepressants (0.83 ES), MAOIs (0.80 ES), other drugs (0.67 ES) and group and individual therapy. In groups that included minor depressed and dysthymia patients, clinicians rated the effect of psychotherapy as larger than pharmacotherapy by a marked margin (ES of 1.21 *vs* ES of 0.59), but patients' ratings of the two methods did not differ.

Recent intervention studies show specific physiologic changes with pharmacotherapy. After 13.7 weeks, geriatric patients randomized to treatment with paroxetine, mulnacipran or tricyclic antidepressant had significantly increased regional cerebral blood flow in left dorsolateral prefrontal cortex and right parieto-occiptal regions, although other areas of reduced cerebral blood flow at baseline did not show improvement.[225] Two studies directly compared responses to paroxetine with responses to cognitive behavioral therapy (CBT). Remission with paroxetine was associated with metabolic increases in prefrontal cortex and decreases in subgenual cingulate and hippocampus. In contrast, CBT-mediated response was associated with a prefrontal decrease along with hippocampal and rostral cingulate increase. [226] The disparate findings likely can be attributed to the complex nature of late-life depression. It is unlikely to be caused by a single brain region or neurotransmitter system. Instead, it more likely results from a failure of multiple systems involved in limbic-cortical interactions, including failure of the homeostatic system to maintain emotional control in times of intrinsic or extrinsic stress.[227] If so, amelioration of the depression might well be effected by quite different mechanisms of action. Increasing the functional integrity of any one of these pathways might explain the clinical efficacy of both pharmacological and cognitive treatments in randomized controlled trials. It would also explain why combined pharmacotherapy and psychotherapy has the most pronounced effect because disturbances in more than one system would be ameliorated. This hypothesis may be transferable to situations in which depression is comorbid to medical conditions.

Due to the association between depression and cerebrovascular disease, improving depression outcome may depend on arresting or improving the cerebrovascular disease. One type of treatment combines the use of an antidepressant and a calcium channel blocker.[228] One hundred and one patients with cerebrovascular disease and depression received standard antidepressant treatment, and a subsample of 50 had augmented treatment with a L-type calcium antagonist (nimodipine). Depression was reduced in 63% of the patients, but those whose treatment was enhanced with nimodipine had greater improvements overall with higher rates of full remission, and fewer developed recurrence of major depression compared to those treated with an antidepressant alone. Among those whose HDRS rating fell by over 50% in the first 2 months, only 7.4% of those taking the combined antidepressant and calcium antagonist had a recurrence compared to 32% in the comparator group. Repetition of this protocol using fluoxetine augmented with nimodipine compared to fluoxetine alone showed similar results: 54% compared to 27% achieved full remission and 3.7% compared to 35.7% developed recurrence of major depression.[229]

Mickusch and colleagues (2008) found a reduction in depressive symptomatology after implanting a stent for carotid atherosclerosis [230] and an improvement in cognitive functioning.[231] Prior to the surgery, 33.6% of the sample had depressive symptoms, but after four weeks, 9.8% continued to have depressive symptoms. A control group undergoing lower-limb percutaneous angioplasty for advanced peripheral artery disease showed no change in rate of depressive symptoms. A neuropsychological evaluation six months after the carotid artery stenting showed improved executive function and processing speed compared to baseline evaluation. However, there appeared to be no correction for expected test-retest improvement [231] so the validity of the improvement is not clear.

Contrary to expectations, large scale studies that have examined the use of preventive interventions such as taking aspirin have not shown reduction in depressive symptoms. On the contrary, according to the "treatment paradox," high risk cardiovascular disease (CVD) patients are less compliant than low risk CVD patients due to their higher risk of depressive symptoms. [232, 233] Administering a SSRI in addition to traditional aspirin therapy has been shown to yield additional antiplatelet and endothelium-protective properties that benefit cardiovascular patients. [234, 235] However, administering a selective serotonin reuptake inhibitor and aspirin after patients have experienced an acute coronary syndrome increases the likelihood of in-hospital bleeding (37.3% vs 26.6%). On the other hand, patients were less likely to experience recurrent ischemia, heart failure, or asymptomatic cardiac enzyme elevation while in the hospital.[236]

Bereavement

For many older adults, the loss of a spouse is a common experience in later life. Over half of all women and over 10% of all men who are over age 65 years will experience bereavement.[237] Bereavement can include a wide variety of emotions such as grief or sadness (the most common), depression, yearning for and pining over the deceased, hallucinatory episodes, anger, and guilt. While not all emotions or even the bulk of them must be experienced during bereavement, the variability in bereavement experiences contributes to the difficulty in identifying normal versus pathological responses.

Research on late-life bereavement has been limited due to an expectation that these symptoms are normal reactions to life's events rather than clinically relevant depression. The DSM-IV defines six symptoms during bereavement that indicate a major depressive episode as opposed to normal grief reaction. These symptoms include feelings of 1) guilt about things other than actions that were taken or not taken by the survivor at the time of death, 2) thoughts of death other than those of the survivor thinking he or she would be better off dead or should have died with the deceased person, 3) a morbid preoccupation with worthlessness, 4) marked psychomotor retardation, 5) prolonged and marked functional impairment, and 6) hallucinatory experiences other than thinking that the survivor hears the voice of, or transiently sees the image of, a deceased person.[238] Based upon recent studies, a distinction has been made between *symbols of grief* (e.g., searching, yearning, preoccupation with thoughts of the deceased) and the *symbols of bereavement-related depression* (e.g., worthlessness, psychomotor retardation, apathy, sad mood).[239, 240, 241]

These symptoms may last up to two years and beyond. Zisook's (2007) review of bereavement and depression noted findings from a study of 350 younger and older age widows and widowers that contradict the common assumption that depression or depressive symptoms will be at their most intense early in the bereavement and then gradually decrease as time passes.[242] During the first year, the late-aged bereaved group had lower rates of depression compared to the younger group. During the second year, however, the pattern changed as the younger age bereaved group's level of depression improved with time, but the late-age bereaved group's level of depression increased and eventually matched that of the younger age bereaved group's level after two years. By that time, 14% of the late-age bereaved group met DSM-IV-TR criteria for major depressive disorder. Many more of the same group experienced a substantial number of depressive symptoms that, although they did not meet the criteria in the DSM-IV-TR for diagnosis of clinical depression, did affect their quality of life. Irwin and Pike (1993) demonstrated an association between natural killer cell activity and the severity of depression in bereaved women. The bereaved may experience problems with sleep including insomnia and waking up many times during a sleep cycle, which can also identify a depressive episode.[243] To date, treatment with a combination of SSRI's and psychotherapy has been found to be the most effective regime.

Conclusion

Medical outcomes of late-life depression can vary significantly not only because late-life depression is itself a heterogeneous syndrome of disorders with dissimilar etiologies, pathophysiologies and outcomes, but because they are embedded within a heterogeneous group of patients. When late-life depression occurs in the context of a medical condition, treatment must address both conditions or both conditions may deteriorate. If the depression is left untreated, the pathophysiology surrounding the depressive state is vulnerable to precipitous decline, which can hasten mortality. Evidence is growing that a reverse causal path also exists in which the onset of untreated depression can disturb anatomical and physiological systems sufficiently to precipitate major illnesses either shortly after or years after the initial episode of depression.

New neuroimaging methodologies are providing a window into the complex neuropathology that accompanies late-life depression and making clearer why different subgroups of patients differ in functional status, cognitive performance and likely medical outcomes. Imaging studies are beginning to identify how depression might precipitate other medical conditions by tracing individual bioanatomical, biophysiological and biochemical substrates and looking for overlap with known medical conditions. In combination with clinical trials that have shown the efficacy and effectiveness of pharmacotherapeutic and psychotherapeutic interventions, imaging results show that the mechanisms used by both approaches differ markedly. Consequently, it appears that depression involves disruption or failure of multiple biological systems to monitor and adapt to intrinsic or extrinsic environments, creating a cascading effect that is more troubling and threatening to the health of elderly individuals than to young adults.

Depression has long been associated with patients suffering neurodegenerative diseases, so it was assumed that the depression was a reaction to the pathology or a secondary result of the neuropathology. However, determining how depression develops when it is sequent to a neuropathological condition remains elusive. The majority of patients who experience late-life depression do not continue into dementia, just as many dementing patients do not display depression. Some forms of dementia pose a greater risk to elderly depressed patients than other forms, such as vascular dementia resulting from cerebrovascular disease. The relationship between Alzheimer's disease, on the other hand, is not as clear. The new evidence that the presence of Lewy Body disease concurrent with developing Alzheimer's increases the risk of depression offers a new path of inquiry into the relationship between dementing syndromes and depression. Separating the two trajectories of incipient dementia and mood disorders is one of the primary concerns of geriatric psychologists and psychiatrists, and considerable progress has been made, yet post-mortem analyses show that specificity before death remains poor.

A side effect of the widening interest in late-life depression has been research into the aging process itself. Life spans continue to increase, but far less is known about the years at the end of the life cycle than at the beginning. An almost universal desire among older adults is for preservation of mood and cognitive resources as they age, and current depression research is elucidating both the strengths and weaknesses of multiple biological systems that contribute to both abilities. With age, some early adulthood mental health problems wane, but the persistence of depression suggests that permanent alterations in the biological systems perpetuate vulnerabilities well into late adulthood that interact with aging processes.

Medical research focuses on the medical contexts of late-life depression, although the importance of social and environmental concerns are widely accepted. Medical care of an elderly depressed patient far exceeds that of a comparable nondepressed patient, so the costs to health care resources will be substantial unless effort is made to address as many of the causal paths to depression as possible. Pharmacologic and psychotherapeutic interventions used on younger populations are similarly effective in elderly populations, but better understanding of what primary interventions could be used are necessary. The more we understand the biological substrates of depression, the clearer it becomes that simply trying to make opportunities for increased productivity and social engagement available after senescence will not make substantial contributions. Changes in lifestyle, health care, interpersonal relationships and professional activities will likely have to start in young and middle adulthood to reduce the biological weaknesses that become increasingly vulnerable when late-life aging processes begin.

References

[1]   Sonnenberg CM, Beekman AT, Deeg DJ et al. Sex differences in late-life depression. *Acta Psychiatr. Scand.,* 2000, 101, 286-92.

[2]   Alexopoulos GS. Depression in the elderly. *Lancet,* 2005, 365, 1961-70.

[3]   Barefoot JC, Mortensen EL, Helms MJ et al. A longitudinal study of gender differences in depressive symptoms from age 50 to 80. *Psychol. Aging,* 2001, 16, 342-5.

[4]   Bergdahl E, Allard P, Alex L et al. Gender differences in depression among the very old. *Int. Psychogeriatr.,* 2007, 19, 1125-40.

[5]   Beekman AT, Deeg DJ, van TT et al. Major and minor depression in later life: a study of prevalence and risk factors. *J Affect Disord,* 1995, 36, 65-75.

[6]   Beekman AT, Copeland JR, Prince MJ. Review of community prevalence of depression in later life. *Br. J Psychiatry,* 1999, 174, 307-11.

[7]   Blazer D, Hughes DC, George LK. The epidemiology of depression in an elderly community population. *Gerontologist,* 1987, 27, 281-7.

[8]   Parmelee PA, Katz IR, Lawton MP. Depression among institutionalized aged: assessment and prevalence estimation. *J. Gerontol.,* 1989, 44, M22-M29.

[9]   Blazer D, Williams C. The epidemiology of dysphoria and depression in an elderly population. *Am. J. Psychiatry,* 1980, 137, 439-44.

[10]   Murrell SA, Himmelfarb S, Wright K. Prevalence of depression and its correlates in older adults. *Am. J. Epidemiol.,* 1983, 117, 173-85.

[11]   Dufouil C, Dartigues JF, Fuhrer R. Depressive symptoms in elderly persons: comparison between rural and urban populations. *Rev. Epidemiol. Sante Publique,* 1995, 43, 308-15.

[12]   Alexopoulos GS, Meyers BS, Young RC et al. Recovery in geriatric depression. *Arch. Gen. Psychiatry,* 1996, 53, 305-12.

[13]   Blazer D, Burchett B, Service C et al. The association of age and depression among the elderly: an epidemiologic exploration. *J. Gerontol.,* 1991, 46, M210-M215.

[14]   Blazer D, Hughes DC, George LK. Age and impaired subjective support. Predictors of depressive symptoms at one-year follow-up. *J. Nerv. Ment. Dis,* 1992, 180, 172-8.

[15]   Bruce ML. Depression and disability in late life: directions for future research. *Am. J. Geriatr. Psychiatry,* 2001, 9, 102-12.

[16]   Stuck AE, Walthert JM, Nikolaus T et al. Risk factors for functional status decline in community-living elderly people: a systematic literature review. *Soc. Sci.Med,* 1999, 48, 445-69.

[17]   Alexopoulos GS, Schultz SK, Lebowitz BD. Late-life depression: a model for medical classification. *Biol. Psychiatry,* 2005, 58, 283-9.

[18]   Blazer DG, Hybels CF. Origins of depression in later life. *Psychol. Med,* 2005, 35, 1241-52.

[19]   Alexopoulos GS, Apfeldorf WJ. Unipolar depression. In: Roose SP, HA Sackeim, *Late-Life Depression*. New York: Oxford University Press; 21-33.

[20]   Gallo JJ, Rabins PV. Depression without sadness: alternative presentations of depression in late life. *Am. Fam. Physician,* 1999, 60, 820-6.

[21]   Brodaty H, Luscombe G, Parker G et al. Increased rate of psychosis and psychomotor change in depression with age. *Psychol. Med,* 1997, 27, 1205-13.

[22]   Leng SX, Xue QL, Tian J et al. Inflammation and frailty in older women. *J. Am. Geriatr. Soc.,* 2007, 55, 864-71.

[23]   Salloway S, Malloy P, Kohn R et al. MRI and neuropsychological differences in early- and late-life-onset geriatric depression. *Neurology,* 1996, 46, 1567-74.

[24]   Albert PS. Longitudinal data analysis (repeated measures) in clinical trials. *Stat. Med.,* 1999, 18, 1707-32.

[25]   Brodaty H, Luscombe G, Parker G et al. Early and late onset depression in old age: different aetiologies, same phenomenology. *J. Affect Disord.,* 2001, 66, 225-36.

[26]   Baldwin RC, Tomenson B. Depression in later life. A comparison of symptoms and risk factors in early and late onset cases. *Br. J. Psychiatry,* 1995, 167, 649-52.

[27] Heun R, Papassotiropoulos A, Jessen F et al. A family study of Alzheimer disease and early- and late-onset depression in elderly patients. *Arch. Gen. Psychiatry*, 2001, 58, 190-6.

[28] Katon W, Lin E, von KM et al. The predictors of persistence of depression in primary care. *J. Affect Disord.*, 1994, 31, 81-90.

[29] Devanand DP, Adorno E, Cheng J et al. Late onset dysthymic disorder and major depression differ from early onset dysthymic disorder and major depression in elderly outpatients. *J. Affect Disord.*, 2004, 78, 259-67.

[30] Holroyd S, Duryee JJ. Differences in geriatric psychiatry outpatients with early- vs late-onset depression. *Int. J. Geriatr. Psychiatry*, 1997, 12, 1100-6.

[31] Patterson MB, Schnell AH, Martin RJ et al. Assessment of behavioral and affective symptoms in Alzheimer's disease. *J. Geriatr. Psychiatry Neurol.*, 1990, 3, 21-30.

[32] Reifler BV, Larson E, Hanley R. Coexistence of cognitive impairment and depression in geriatric outpatients. *Am. J. Psychiatry*, 1982, 139, 623-6.

[33] Murphy E. The prognosis of depression in old age. *Br. J. Psychiatry*, 1983, 142, 111-9.

[34] Reynolds CF, III, Frank E, Perel JM et al. Nortriptyline and interpersonal psychotherapy as maintenance therapies for recurrent major depression: a randomized controlled trial in patients older than 59 years. *JAMA*, 1999, 281, 39-45.

[35] Alexopoulos GS, Young RC, Shindledecker RD. Brain computed tomography findings in geriatric depression and primary degenerative dementia. *Biol. Psychiatry*, 1992, 31, 591-9.

[36] Kalayam B, Meyers BS, Kakuma T et al. Age at onset of geriatric depression and sensorineural hearing deficits. *Biol. Psychiatry*, 1995, 38, 649-58.

[37] Alexopoulos GS. The vascular depression hypothesis: 10 years later. *Biol. Psychiatry*, 2006, 60, 1304-5.

[38] Artero S, Tiemeier H, Prins ND et al. Neuroanatomical localisation and clinical correlates of white matter lesions in the elderly. *J. Neurol. Neurosurg. Psychiatry*, 2004, 75, 1304-8.

[39] van Reekum R, Simard M, Clarke D et al. Late-life depression as a possible predictor of dementia - Cross-sectional and short-term follow-up results. *Am. J. Geriatr. Psychiatry*, 1999, 7, 151-9.

[40] Alexopoulos GS, Meyers BS, Young RC et al. The course of geriatric depression with reversible dementia - a controlled study. *Am. J. Psychiatry*, 1993, 150, 1693-9.

[41] Yaffe K, Blackwell T, Gore R et al. Depressive symptoms and cognitive decline in nondemented elderly women - A prospective study. *Arch. Gen. Psychiatry*, 1999, 56, 425-30.

[42] Riedel O, Klotsche J, Spottke A et al. Cognitive impairment in 873 patients with idiopathic Parkinson's disease : Results from the German Study on Epidemiology of Parkinson's Disease with Dementia (GEPAD). *J. Neurol.*, 2008, 255, 255-64.

[43] Caballol N, Marti MJ, Tolosa E. Cognitive dysfunction and dementia in Parkinson disease. *Mov. Disord.*, 2007, 22, S358-S366.

[44] Shen YC. Lamotrigine in motor and mood symptoms of Huntington's disease. *World J. Biol. Psychiatry*, 2007, 8, 1-3.

[45] van Duijn E., Kingma EM, van der Mast RC. Psychopathology in verified Huntington's disease gene carriers. *J. Neuropsychiatry Clin. Neurosci.*, 2007, 19, 441-8.

[46] Buchanan RJ, Wang S, Huang C et al. Profiles of nursing home residents with multiple sclerosis using the minimum data set. *Mult. Scler.*, 2001, 7, 189-200.

[47] Julian L, Merluzzi NM, Mohr DC. The relationship among depression, subjective cognitive impairment, and neuropsychological performance in multiple sclerosis. *Mult. Scler.*, 2007, 13, 81-6.

[48] Kilani M, Micallef J, Soubrouillard C et al. A longitudinal study of the evolution of cognitive function and affective state in patients with amyotrophic lateral sclerosis. *Amyotroph. Lateral. Scler. Other Motor Neuron Disord,* 2004, 5, 46-54.

[49] Watari K, Letamendi A, Elderkin-Thompson V et al. Cognitive function in adults with type 2 diabetes and major depression. *Arch. Clin. Neuropsychol.*, 2006, 21, 787-96.

[50] Lynch SG, Kroencke DC, Denney DR. The relationship between disability and depression in multiple sclerosis: the role of uncertainty, coping, and hope. *Mult. Scler.*, 2001, 7, 411-6.

[51] Odegard PS, Capoccia K. Medication taking and diabetes: a systematic review of the literature. *Diabetes Educ.*, 2007, 33, 1014-29.

[52] Onitilo AA, Nietert PJ, Egede LE. Effect of depression on all-cause mortality in adults with cancer and differential effects by cancer site. *Gen. Hosp. Psychiatry,* 2006, 28, 396-402.

[53] Oerlemans ME, van den AM, Schuurman AG et al. A meta-analysis on depression and subsequent cancer risk. *Clin. Pract. Epidemol. Ment. Health,* 2007, 3, 29.

[54] Cohen HW, Madhavan S, Alderman MH. History of treatment for depression: risk factor for myocardial infarction in hypertensive patients. *Psychosom. Med.*, 2001, 63, 203-9.

[55] Harman JS, Edlund MJ, Fortney JC et al. The influence of comorbid chronic medical conditions on the adequacy of depression care for older Americans. *J. Am. Geriatr. Soc.*, 2005, 53, 2178-83.

[56] Kales HC, Maixner DF, Mellow AM. Cerebrovascular disease and late-life depression. *Am. J. Geriatr. Psychiatry,* 2005, 13, 88-98.

[57] Wright JW, Mizutani S, Harding JW. Pathways involved in the transition from hypertension to hypertrophy to heart failure [online]. Treatment strategies. *Heart Fail. Rev.,* [cited 1.10.2007]. Available from PM:17987382.

[58] Sackeim HA. Structural and functional brain imaging in late-life depression. In: Roose SP, Sackeim HA editors, *Late-Life Depression.* New York: Oxford University Press; 2004; 129-147.

[59] Figiel GS, Krishnan KR, Doraiswamy PM et al. Subcortical hyperintensities on brain magnetic resonance imaging: a comparison between late age onset and early onset elderly depressed subjects. *Neurobiol. Aging,* 1991, 12, 245-7.

[60] Hannestad J, Taylor WD, McQuoid DR et al. White matter lesion volumes and caudate volumes in late-life depression. *Int. J. Geriatr. Psychiatry,* 2006, 21, 1193-8.

[61] Ongur D, Price JL. The organization of networks within the orbital and medial prefrontal cortex of rats, monkeys and humans. *Cereb .Cortex,* 2000, 10, 206-19.

[62]   Steffens DC, Helms MJ, Krishnan KR et al. Cerebrovascular disease and depression symptoms in the cardiovascular health study. *Stroke*, 1999, 30, 2159-66.

[63]   Steffens DC, Krishnan KR, Crump C et al. Cerebrovascular disease and evolution of depressive symptoms in the cardiovascular health study. *Stroke*, 2002, 33, 1636-44.

[64]   Teodorczuk A, O'Brien JT, Firbank MJ et al. White matter changes and late-life depressive symptoms: longitudinal study. *Br. J. Psychiatry*, 2007, 191, 212-7.

[65]   Berger-Greenstein JA, Cuevas CA, Brady SM et al. Major depression in patients with HIV/AIDS and substance abuse. *AIDS Patient. Care STDS.*, 2007, 21, 942-55.

[66]   Cummings JL, Mega MS. Focal brain disorders and related conditions. In: Cummings JL, Mega MS editors. *Neuropsychiatry and behavioral neuroscience*. New York: Oxford University Press; 2003; 385-406.

[67]   Nemeroff CB. Clinical significance of psychoneuroendocrinology in psychiatry: focus on the thyroid and adrenal. *J. Clin. Psychiatry*, 1989, 50 Suppl, 13-20.

[68]   Taylor WD, Steffens DC, MacFall JR et al. White matter hyperintensity progression and late-life depression outcomes. *Arch. Gen. Psychiatry*, 2003, 60, 1090-6

[69]   Starkstein SD, Robinson RG. Depression in neurologic diseases. Baltimore; Johns Hopkins University Press; 1993.

[70]   Gabaldon L, Fuentes B, Frank-Garcia A et al. Poststroke depression: importance of its detection and treatment. *Cerebrovasc. Dis.*, 2007, 24 Suppl 1, 181-8.

[71]   Gaete JM, Bogousslavsky J. Post-stroke depression. *Expert. Rev. Neurother.*, 2008, 8, 75-92.

[72]   Robinson RG. Poststroke depression: prevalence, diagnosis, treatment, and disease progression. *Biol. Psychiatry*, 2003, 54, 376-87.

[73]   Vataja R, Leppavuori A, Pohjasvaara T et al. Poststroke depression and lesion location revisited. *J. Neuropsychiatry Clin Neurosci*, 2004, 16, 156-62.

[74]   Stuss DT, Benson DF. The Frontal Lobes. New York; Raven Press; 1986.

[75]   Barker-Collo SL. Depression and anxiety 3 months post stroke: prevalence and correlates. *Arch Clin Neuropsychol*, 2007, 22, 519-31.

[76]   Alexopoulos GS, Meyers BS, Young RC et al. Clinically defined vascular depression. *Am. J. Psychiatry*, 1997, 154, 562-5.

[77]   Krishnan KR, Hays JC, Blazer DG. MRI-defined vascular depression. *Am J Psychiatry*, 1997, 154, 497-501.

[78]   Baldwin RC, O'Brien J. Vascular basis of late-onset depressive disorder. *Br. J. Psychiatry*, 2002, 180, 157-60.

[79]   Barefoot JC, Helms MJ, Mark DB et al. Depression and long-term mortality risk in patients with coronary artery disease. *Am. J. Cardiol..*, 1996, 78, 613-7.

[80]   Carney RM, Rich MW, Freedland KE et al. Major depressive disorder predicts cardiac events in patients with coronary artery disease. *Psychosom. Med.*, 1988, 50, 627-33.

[81]   Herrmann C, Brand-Driehorst S, Buss U et al. Effects of anxiety and depression on 5-year mortality in 5,057 patients referred for exercise testing. *J. Psychosom. Res.*, 2000, 48, 455-62.

[82]   Burg MM, Benedetto MC, Rosenberg R et al. Presurgical depression predicts medical morbidity 6 months after coronary artery bypass graft surgery. *Psychosom. Med.*, 2003, 65, 111-8.

[83] Connerney I, Shapiro PA, McLaughlin JS et al. Relation between depression after coronary artery bypass surgery and 12-month outcome: a prospective study. *Lancet*, 2001, 358, 1766-71.

[84] Carney RM, Freedland KE. Depression, mortality, and medical morbidity in patients with coronary heart disease. *Biol. Psychiatry*, 2003, 54, 241-7.

[85] Carney RM, Blumenthal JA, Catellier D et al. Depression as a risk factor for mortality after acute myocardial infarction. *Am. J. Cardiol.*, 2003, 92, 1277-81.

[86] Ahern DK, Gorkin L, Anderson JL et al. Biobehavioral variables and mortality or cardiac arrest in the Cardiac Arrhythmia Pilot Study (CAPS). *Am. J. Cardiol.*, 1990, 66, 59-62.

[87] Frasure-Smith N, Lesperance F, Talajic M. Depression following myocardial infarction. Impact on 6-month survival. *JAMA*, 1993, 270, 1819-25.

[88] Carney RM, Freedland KE, Steinmeyer B et al. Depression and five year survival following acute myocardial infarction: A prospective study [online]. *J. Affect. Disord.*, 2008, [cited 2/9/2008] Available from: PM:18191208.

[89] Bush DE, Ziegelstein RC, Tayback M et al. Even minimal symptoms of depression increase mortality risk after acute myocardial infarction. *Am. J. Cardiol..*, 2001, 88, 337-41.

[90] Carney RM, Howells WB, Blumenthal JA et al. Heart rate turbulence, depression, and survival after acute myocardial infarction. *Psychosom. Med.*, 2007, 69, 4-9.

[91] Carney RM, Freedland KE, Veith RC. Depression, the autonomic nervous system, and coronary heart disease. *Psychosom. Med.*, 2005, 67 Suppl 1, S29-S33.

[92] Rajkowska G, Miguel-Hidalgo JJ, Wei JR et al. Morphometric evidence for neuronal and glial prefrontal cell pathology in major depression. *Biol. Psychiatry*, 1999, 45, 1085-98.

[93] van Zyl LT, Lesperance F, Frasure-Smith N et al. Platelet and endothelial activity in comorbid major depression and coronary artery disease patients treated with citalopram: the Canadian Cardiac Randomized Evaluation of Antidepressant and Psychotherapy Efficacy Trial (CREATE) biomarker sub-study [online]. *J. Thromb. Thrombolysis* [cited 1/28/2008]. Available from PM:18188512.

[94] Carney RM, Blumenthal JA, Freedland KE et al. Depression and late mortality after myocardial infarction in the Enhancing Recovery in Coronary Heart Disease (ENRICHD) study. *Psychosom. Med.*, 2004, 66, 466-74.

[95] Lesperance F, Frasure-Smith N, Juneau M et al. Depression and 1-year prognosis in unstable angina. *Arch. Intern. Med.*, 2000, 160, 1354-60.

[96] Pratt LA, Ford DE, Crum RM et al. Depression, psychotropic medication, and risk of myocardial infarction. Prospective data from the Baltimore ECA follow-up. *Circulation*, 1996, 94, 3123-9.

[97] Vaccarino V, McClure C, Johnson BD et al. Depression, the metabolic syndrome and cardiovascular risk. *Psychosom. Med.*, 2008, 70, 40-8.

[98] Anda R, Williamson D, Jones D et al. Depressed affect, hopelessness, and the risk of ischemic heart disease in a cohort of U.S. adults. *Epidemiology*, 1993, 4, 285-94.

[99] Ferketich AK, Schwartzbaum JA, Frid DJ et al. Depression as an antecedent to heart disease among women and men in the NHANES I study. National Health and Nutrition Examination Survey. *Arch. Intern. Med.,* 2000, 160, 1261-8.

[100] Mendes de Leon CF, Krumholz HM, Seeman TS et al. Depression and risk of coronary heart disease in elderly men and women: New Haven EPESE, 1982-1991. Established Populations for the Epidemiologic Studies of the Elderly. *Arch. Intern. Med.,* 1998, 158, 2341-8.

[101] Sesso HD, Kawachi I, Vokonas PS et al. Depression and the risk of coronary heart disease in the Normative Aging Study. *Am. J. Cardiol..,* 1998, 82, 851-6.

[102] Aromaa A, Raitasalo R, Reunanen A et al. Depression and cardiovascular diseases. *Acta Psychiatr. Scand. Suppl,* 1994, 377, 77-82.

[103] Penninx BW, Guralnik JM, Mendes de Leon CF et al. Cardiovascular events and mortality in newly and chronically depressed persons > 70 years of age. *Am. J. Cardiol.,* 1998, 81, 988-94.

[104] Wassertheil-Smoller S, Applegate WB, Berge K et al. Change in depression as a precursor of cardiovascular events. SHEP Cooperative Research Group (Systoloc Hypertension in the elderly). *Arch. Intern. Med.,* 1996, 156, 553-61.

[105] Elderkin-Thompson V, Kumar A, Bilker WB et al. Neuropsychological deficits among patients with late-onset minor and major depression. *Arch .Clin. Neuropsychol.,* 2003, 18, 529-49.

[106] Hamilton MA. A rating scale for depression. *J. Neurol., Neurosurg Psychiatry,* 1960, 23, 56-62.

[107] Elderkin-Thompson V, Boone KB, Hwang S et al. Neurocognitive profiles in elderly patients with frontotemporal degeneration or major depressive disorder. *JINS,* 2004, 10, 753-71.

[108] Cohen J. Statistical power analysis for the behavioral sciences. Hillsdale, NJ; Lawrence Erlbaum Assoc.; 1988.

[109] Endicott J, Spitzer RL. A diagnostic interview: the schedule for affective disorders and schizophrenia. *Arch. Gen. Psychiatry,* 1978, 35, 837-44.

[110] Spitzer RL, Endicott J, Robins E. Research diagnostic criteria: rationale and reliability. *Arch. Gen. Psychiatry,* 1978, 35, 773-82.

[111] van Gorp WG, Root JC, Sackeim HA. Neuropsychological assessment of late-life depression. In: Roose SP, Sackeim HA editors. *Late-life depression.* New York: Oxford University Press; 2004; 117-125.

[112] Wechsler D. Wechsler Memory Scale - Revised manual. New York; The Psychological Corporation; 1987.

[113] Boone EB, Lesser IB, Miller BL et al. Cognitive functioning in older depressed outpatients: relationship of presence and severity of depression to neuropsychological test scores. *Neuropsychology,* 1995, 9, 390-8.

[114] Zakzanis KK, Leach L, Kaplan E. Neuropsychological differential diagnosis. Lisse, The Netherlands; Swets and Zeitlinger; 1999.

[115] Veiel HO. A preliminary profile of neuropsychological deficits associated with major depression. *J. Clin. Exp. Neuropsychol.,* 1997, 19, 587-603.

[116] Miyake A, Friedman NP, Emerson MJ et al. The unity and diversity of executive functions and their contributions to complex "frontal lobe" tasks: A latent variable analysis. *Cogn Psychol*, 2000, 41, 49-100.

[117] Cummings JL. Frontal-subcortical circuits and human behavior. *Arch. Neurol.*, 1993, 50, 873-80.

[118] Fuster JM. A theory of prefrontal functions: The prefrontal cortex and the temporal organization of behavior. In: Fuster JM editor. *The Prefrontal Cortex: Anatomy, Physiology and Neuropsychology of the Frontal Lobes*. New York: Raven Press; 1989; 157-192.

[119] Fuster JM. Cognitive functions of the frontal lobes. In: Miller BL, Cummings JL editors. *The Human Frontal Lobes*. New York: The Guilford Press; 1999; 187-195.

[120] Butters MA, Becker JT, Nebes RD et al. Changes in cognitive functioning following treatment of late-life depression. *Am. J. Psychiatry*, 2000, 157, 1949-54.

[121] Elderkin-Thompson V, Kumar A, Mintz J et al. Executive dysfunction and visuospatial ability among depressed elders in a community setting. *Arch. Clin. Neuropsychol,.* 2004, 19, 597-611.

[122] Elderkin-Thompson V, Mintz J, Haroon E et al. Executive dysfunction and memory in older patients with major and minor depression. *Arch. Clin. Neuropsychol.*, 2007, 22, 261-70.

[123] Bhalla RK, Butters MA, Mulsant BH et al. Persistence of neuropsychologic deficits in the remitted state of late-life depression. *Am J Geriatr Psychiatry*, 2006, 14, 419-27.

[124] Alexopoulos GS, Kiosses DN, Klimstra S et al. Clinical presentation of the "depression-executive dysfunction syndrome" of late life. *Am. J. Geriatr. Psychiatry*, 2002, 10, 98-106.

[125] Alexopoulos GS, Meyers BS, Young RC et al. Executive dysfunction and long-term outcomes of geriatric depression. *Arch. Gen. Psychiatry*, 2000, 57, 285-90.

[126] Dahabra S, Ashton CH, Bahrainian M et al. Structural and functional abnormalities in elderly patients clinically recovered from early- and late-onset depression. *Biol. Psychiatry*, 1998, 44, 34-46.

[127] Bird JM, Levy R, Jacoby RJ. Computed tomography in the elderly: changes over time in a normal population. *Br. J. Psychiatry*, 1986, 148, 80-5.

[128] Kumar A, Jin ZS, Bilker W et al. Late-onset minor and major depression: early evidence for common neuroanatomical substrates detected by using MRI. *Proc. Nat. Acad. Sci. U. S. A.* 1998, 95, 7654-8.

[129] Krishnan KR, McDonald WM, Escalona PR et al. Magnetic resonance imaging of the caudate nuclei in depression. Preliminary observations. *Arch. Gen. Psychiatry*, 1992, 49, 553-7.

[130] Ongur D, Drevets WC, Price JL. Glial reduction in the subgenual prefrontal cortex in mood disorders. *Proc. Nat .Acad. Sci .U. S. A.*, 1998, 95, 13290-5.

[131] Husain MM, McDonald WM, Doraiswamy PM et al. A magnetic resonance imaging study of putamen nuclei in major depression. *Psych. Res. Neuroimaging*, 1991, 40, 95-9.

[132] Ballmaier M, Toga AW, Blanton RE et al. Anterior cingulate, gyrus rectus, and orbitofrontal abnormalities in elderly depressed patients: an MRI-based parcellation of the prefrontal cortex. *Am. J .Psychiatry,* 2004, 161, 99-108.

[133] Vasic N, Walter H, Hose A et al. Gray matter reduction associated with psychopathology and cognitive dysfunction in unipolar depression: A voxcl-bascd morphometry study [online]. *J Affect Disord.* [cited 1/22/2008]. Available from PM:18191459.

[134] Steffens DC, Byrum CE, McQuoid DR et al. Hippocampal volume in gcriatric depression. *Biological Psychiatry,* 2000, 48, 301-9.

[135] O'Brien JT, Lloyd A, McKeith I et al. A longitudinal study of hippocampal volume, cortisol levels, and cognition in older depressed subjects. *Am. J. Psychiatry,* 2004, 161, 2081-90.

[136] Ballmaier M, Narr KL, Toga AW et al. Hippocampal morphology and distinguishing late-onset from early-onset elderly depression. *Am J Psychiatry,* 2008, 165, 229-237.

[137] Czeh B, Lucassen PJ. What causes the hippocampal volume decrease in depression? Are neurogenesis, glial changes and apoptosis implicated? *Eur. Arch. Psychiatry Clin. Neurosci.,* 2007, 257, 250-60.

[138] Stockmeier CA, Mahajan GJ, Konick LC et al. Cellular changes in the postmortem hippocampus in major depression. *Biol. Psychiatry,* 2004, 56, 640-50.

[139] Chana G, Landau S, Beasley C et al. Two-dimensional assessment of cytoarchitecture in the anterior cingulate cortex in major depressive disorder, bipolar disorder, and schizophrenia: evidence for decreased neuronal somal size and increased neuronal density. *Biol. Psychiatry,* 2003, 53, 1086-98.

[140] Rajkowska G, Miguel-Hidalgo JJ, Dubey P et al. Prominent reduction in pyramidal neurons density in the orbitofrontal cortex of elderly depressed patients. *Biol. Psychiatry,* 2005, 58, 297-306.

[141] Rajkowska G, Miguel-Hidalgo JJ. Gliogenesis and glial pathology in depression. *CNS. Neurol. Disord. Drug Targets.,* 2007, 6, 219-33.

[142] Ballmaier M, Kumar A, Elderkin-Thompson V et al. Mapping callosal morphology in early- and late-onset elderly depression: an index of distinct changes in cortical connectivity [online]. *Neuropsychopharmacology* [cited 2/23/2007]. Available from PM:17712348.

[143] Hickie I, Naismith S, Ward PB et al. Reduced hippocampal volumes and memory loss in patients with early- and late-onset depression. *Br. J. Psychiatry,* 2005, 186, 197-202.

[144] Bench CJ, Friston KJ, Brown RG et al. The anatomy of melancholia--focal abnormalities of cerebral blood flow in major depression. *Psychol. Med.,* 1992, 22, 607-15.

[145] Biver F, Goldman S, Delvenne V et al. Frontal and parietal metabolic disturbances in unipolar depression. *Biol .Psychiatry,* 1994, 36, 381-8.

[146] Buchsbaum MS, Wu J, Siegel BV et al. Effect of sertraline on regional metabolic rate in patients with affective disorder. *Biol. Psychiatry,* 1997, 41, 15-22.

[147] Drevets WC, Raichle ME. Reciprocal suppression of regional cerebral blood flow during emotional versus higher cognitive processes: Implications for interactions between emotion and cognition. *Cogn. and Emotion,* 1998, 12, 353-85.

[148] Drevets WC. Prefrontal cortical-amygdalar metabolism in major depression. *Advancing from the Ventral Striatum to the Extended Amygdala,* 1999, 877, 614-37.

[149] Liotti M, Mayberg HS, McGinnis S et al. Unmasking disease-specific cerebral blood flow abnormalities: mood challenge in patients with remitted unipolar depression. *Am. J. Psychiatry,* 2002, 159, 1830-40.

[150] Drevets WC, Videen TO, Price JL et al. A functional anatomical study of unipolar depression. *J. Neurosci.,* 1992, 12, 3628-41.

[151] Mayberg HS, Lewis PJ, Regenold W et al. Paralimbic hypoperfusion in unipolar depression. *J. Nucl. Med,* 1994, 35, 929-34.

[152] Mayberg HS. Frontal lobe dysfunction in secondary depression. *J. Neuropsychiatry Clin. Neurosci.,* 1994, 6, 428-42.

[153] Drevets WC. Orbitofrontal cortex function and structure in depression. *Ann. N. Y. Acad. Sci.,* 2007, 1121, 499-527.

[154] Urenjak J, Williams SR, Gadian DG et al. Proton nuclear magnetic resonance spectroscopy unambiguously identifies different neural cell types. *J .Neurosci.,* 1993, 13, 981-9.

[155] Metastasio A, Rinaldi P, Feliziani F et al. Role of proton magnetic resonance spectroscopy (H-1-MRS) in predicting the conversion of mild cognitive impairment to dementia. *Neurobiol. Aging,* 2004, 25, S276-S277.

[156] Metastasio A, Rinaldi P, Tarducci R et al. Conversion of MCI to dementia: Role of proton magnetic resonance spectroscopy. *Neurobiol. Aging,* 2006, 27, 926-32.

[157] Martin WR. MR spectroscopy in neurodegenerative disease. *Mol. Imaging Biol.,* 2007, 9, 196-203.

[158] Stanley JA. In vivo magnetic resonance spectroscopy and its application to neuropsychiatric disorders. *Can. J .Psychiatry,* 2002, 47, 315-26.

[159] Kusumakar V, MacMaster FP, Gates L et al. Left medial temporal cytosolic choline in early onset depression. *Can. J. Psychiatry,* 2001, 46, 959-64.

[160] Glitz DA, Manji HK, Moore GJ. Mood disorders: treatment-induced changes in brain neurochemistry and structure. *Semin. Clin. Neuropsychiatry,* 2002, 7, 269-80.

[161] Moore GJ, Galloway MP. Magnetic resonance spectroscopy: neurochemistry and treatment effects in affective disorders. *Psychopharmacol Bull,* 2002, 36, 5-23.

[162] Ende G, Braus DF, Walter S et al. The hippocampus in patients treated with electroconvulsive therapy: a proton magnetic resonance spectroscopic imaging study. *Arch. Gen. Psychiatry,* 2000, 57, 937-43.

[163] Ross BD. Biochemical considerations in 1H spectroscopy. Glutamate and glutamine; myo-inositol and related metabolites. *NMR Biomed.,* 1991, 4, 59-63.

[164] Brink CB, Viljoen SL, de Kock SE et al. Effects of myo-inositol versus fluoxetine and imipramine pretreatments on serotonin 5HT2A and muscarinic acetylcholine receptors in human neuroblastoma cells. *Metab. Brain Dis.,* 2004, 19, 51-70.

[165] Yildiz-Yesiloglu A, Ankerst DP. Review of 1H magnetic resonance spectroscopy findings in major depressive disorder: a meta-analysis. *Psychiatry Res.,* 2006, 147, 1-25.

[166] Kumar A, Thomas A, Lavretsky H et al. Frontal white matter biochemical abnormalities in late-life major depression detected with proton magnetic resonance spectroscopy. *Am. J .Psychiatry*, 2002, 159, 630-6.

[167] Vythilingam M, Charles HC, Tupler LA et al. Focal and lateralized subcortical abnormalities in unipolar major depressive disorder: An automated multivoxel proton magnetic resonance spectroscopy study. *Biol .Psychiatry*, 2003, 54, 744-50.

[168] Hamakawa H, Kato T, Murashita J et al. Quantitative proton magnetic resonance spectroscopy of the basal ganglia in patients with affective disorders. *Eur. Arch. Psychiatry Clin Neurosci*, 1998, 248, 53-8.

[169] Charles HC, Lazeyras F, Krishnan KR et al. Brain choline in depression: in vivo detection of potential pharmacodynamic effects of antidepressant therapy using hydrogen localized spectroscopy. *Prog. Neuropsychopharmacol. Biol. Psychiatry*, 1994, 18, 1121-7.

[170] Renshaw PF, Lafer B, Christensen JD et al. Proton MRS of basal ganglia in major depression. *Biol. Psychiatry*, 1994, 35, 685.

[171] Coupland NJ, Ogilvie CJ, Hegadoren KM et al. Decreased prefrontal Myo-inositol in major depressive disorder. *Biol. Psychiatry*, 2005, 57, 1526-34.

[172] Taylor WD, Payne ME, Krishnan KR et al. Evidence of white matter tract disruption in MRI hyperintensities. *Biol. Psychiatry*, 2001, 50, 179-83.

[173] Taylor WD, MacFall JR, Payne ME et al. Late-life depression and microstructural abnormalities in dorsolateral prefrontal cortex white matter. *Am. J. Psychiatry*, 2004, 161, 1293-6.

[174] Bae JN, MacFall JR, Krishnan KR et al. Dorsolateral prefrontal cortex and anterior cingulate cortex white matter alterations in late-life depression. *Biol. Psychiatry*, 2006, 60, 1356-63.

[175] Kumar A, Gupta RC, Albert TM et al. Biophysical changes in normal-appearing white matter and subcortical nuclei in late-life major depression detected using magnetization transfer. *Psychiatry Res*, 2004, 130, 131-40.

[176] Oldehinkel AJ, van dB, Flentge F et al. Urinary free cortisol excretion in elderly persons with minor and major depression. *Psychiatry Res*, 2001, 104, 39-47.

[177] Bremmer MA, Deeg DJ, Beekman AT et al. Major depression in late life is associated with both hypo- and hypercortisolemia. *Biol. Psychiatry*, 2007, 62, 479-86.

[178] Penninx BW, Beekman AT, Bandinelli S et al. Late-life depressive symptoms are associated with both hyperactivity and hypoactivity of the hypothalamo-pituitary-adrenal axis. *Am. J. Geriatr. Psychiatry*, 2007, 15, 522-9.

[179] Esposito K, Marfella R, Ciotola M et al. Effect of a Mediterranean-style diet on endothelial dysfunction and markers of vascular inflammation in the metabolic syndrome: a randomized trial. *JAMA*, 2004, 292, 1440-6.

[180] Weigert C, Hennige AM, Lehmann R et al. Direct cross-talk of interleukin-6 and insulin signal transduction via insulin receptor substrate-1 in skeletal muscle cells. *J. Biol. Chem.*, 2006, 281, 7060-7.

[181] Fried SK, Bunkin DA, Greenberg AS. Omental and subcutaneous adipose tissues of obese subjects release interleukin-6: depot difference and regulation by glucocorticoid. *J. Clin. Endocrinol. Metab*, 1998, 83, 847-50.

[182] Straub RH, Konecna L, Hrach S et al. Serum dehydroepiandrosterone (DHEA) and DHEA sulfate are negatively correlated with serum interleukin-6 (IL-6), and DHEA inhibits IL-6 secretion from mononuclear cells in man in vitro: possible link between endocrinosenescence and immunosenescence. *J. Clin. Endocrinol. Metab.*, 1998, 83, 2012-7.

[183] Maggio M, Basaria S, Ble A et al. Correlation between testosterone and the inflammatory marker soluble interleukin-6 receptor in older men. *J. Clin. Endocrinol. Metab.*, 2006, 91, 345-7.

[184] Glaser R, Robles TF, Sheridan J et al. Mild depressive symptoms are associated with amplified and prolonged inflammatory responses after influenza virus vaccination in older adults. *Arch. Gen. Psychiatry*, 2003, 60, 1009-14.

[185] Penninx BW, Kritchevsky SB, Yaffe K et al. Inflammatory markers and depressed mood in older persons: results from the Health, Aging and Body Composition study. *Biol. Psychiatry*, 2003, 54, 566-72.

[186] Maggio M, Guralnik JM, Longo DL et al. Interleukin-6 in aging and chronic disease: a magnificent pathway. *J. Gerontol.A Biol. Sci. Med. Sci.*, 2006, 61, 575-84.

[187] Castle S, Wilkins S, Heck E et al. Depression in caregivers of demented patients is associated with altered immunity: impaired proliferative capacity, increased CD8+, and a decline in lymphocytes with surface signal transduction molecules (CD38+) and a cytotoxicity marker (CD56+ CD8+). *Clin Exp. Immunol.*, 1995, 101, 487-93.

[188] Fortes C, Farchi S, Forastiere F et al. Depressive symptoms lead to impaired cellular immune response. *Psychother. Psychosom*, 2003, 72, 253-60.

[189] Thomas AJ, Davis S, Morris C et al. Increase in interleukin-1beta in late-life depression. *Am J Psychiatry*, 2005, 162, 175-7.

[190] Dentino AN, Pieper CF, Rao MK et al. Association of interleukin-6 and other biologic variables with depression in older people living in the community. *J. Am. Geriatr. Soc.*, 1999, 47, 6-11.

[191] Xing Z, Gauldie J, Cox G et al. IL-6 is an antiinflammatory cytokine required for controlling local or systemic acute inflammatory responses. *J. Clin. Invest*, 1998, 101, 311-20.

[192] Schindler R, Mancilla J, Endres S et al. Correlations and interactions in the production of interleukin-6 (IL-6), IL-1, and tumor necrosis factor (TNF) in human blood mononuclear cells: IL-6 suppresses IL-1 and TNF. *Blood*, 1990, 75, 40-7.

[193] Leng SX, Cappola AR, Andersen RE et al. Serum levels of insulin-like growth factor-I (IGF-I) and dehydroepiandrosterone sulfate (DHEA-S), and their relationships with serum interleukin-6, in the geriatric syndrome of frailty. *Aging .Clin. Exp. Res.*, 2004, 16, 153-7.

[194] Michelson D, Stratakis C, Hill L et al. Bone mineral density in women with depression. *N. Engl. J. Med*, 1996, 335, 1176-81.

[195] Dantzer R, O'Connor JC, Freund GG et al. From inflammation to sickness and depression: when the immune system subjugates the brain. *Nat. Rev. Neurosci*, 2008, 9, 46-56.

[196] Esterling BA, Kiecolt-Glaser JK, Glaser R. Psychosocial modulation of cytokine-induced natural killer cell activity in older adults. *Psychosom Med*, 1996, 58, 264-72.

[197] Graham JE, Christian LM, Kiecolt-Glaser JK. Stress, age, and immune function: toward a lifespan approach. *J .Behav. Med.,* 2006, 29, 389-400.

[198] Kiecolt-Glaser JK, Glaser R. Depression and immune function: central pathways to morbidity and mortality. *J. Psychosom. Res.,* 2002, 53, 873-6.

[199] Ferrucci L, Corsi A, Lauretani F et al. The origins of age-related proinflammatory state. *Blood,* 2005, 105, 2294-9.

[200] Hager K, Machein U, Krieger S et al. Interleukin-6 and selected plasma proteins in healthy persons of different ages. *Neurobiol. Aging,* 1994, 15, 771-2.

[201] Wei J, Xu H, Davies JL et al. Increase of plasma IL-6 concentration with age in healthy subjects. *Life Sci,* 1992, 51, 1953-6.

[202] van den Biggelaar AH, Gussekloo J, de Craen AJ et al. Inflammation and interleukin-1 signaling network contribute to depressive symptoms but not cognitive decline in old age. *Exp. Gerontol.,* 2007, 42, 693-701.

[203] van Reekum R, Binns M, Clarke D et al. Is late-life depression a predictor of Alzheimer's disease? Results from a historical cohort study. *Int. J .Geriatr. Psychiatry,* 2005, 20, 80-2.

[204] McDowell I, Newell C. Measuring health. New York; Oxford University Press; 1996.

[205] Bachman DL, Wolf PA, Linn RT et al. Incidence of dementia and probable Alzheimer's disease in a general population: the Framingham Study. *Neurology,* 1993, 43, 515-9.

[206] Lopez OL, Hamilton RL, Becker JT et al. Severity of cognitive impairment and the clinical diagnosis of AD with Lewy bodies. *Neurology,* 2000, 54, 1780-7.

[207] Lopez OL, Becker JT, Sweet RA et al. Lewy bodies in the amygdala increase risk for major depression in subjects with Alzheimer disease. *Neurology,* 2006, 67, 660-5.

[208] Geda YE, Knopman DS, Mrazek DA et al. Depression, apolipoprotein E genotype, and the incidence of mild cognitive impairment: a prospective cohort study. *Arch. Neurol.,* 2006, 63, 435-40.

[209] Teng E, Lu PH, Cummings JL. Neuropsychiatric symptoms are associated with progression from mild cognitive impairment to Alzheimer's disease. *Dement. Geriatr. Cogn. Disord,* 2007, 24, 253-9.

[210] Morgan MD, Mielke MM, O'Brien R et al. Rates of depression in individuals with pathologic but not clinical Alzheimer disease are lower than those in individuals without the disease: findings from the Baltimore Longitudinal Study on Aging (BLSA). *Alzheimer Dis. Assoc. Disord.,* 2007, 21, 199-204.

[211] Sweet RA, Hamilton RL, Butters MA et al. Neuropathologic correlates of late-onset major depression. *Neuropsychopharmacology,* 2004, 29, 2242-50.

[212] Lavretsky H, Ercoli L, Siddarth P et al. Apolipoprotein epsilon4 allele status, depressive symptoms, and cognitive decline in middle-aged and elderly persons without dementia. *Am. J. Geriatr. Psychiatry,* 2003, 11, 667-73.

[213] Brown ES, Varghese FP, McEwen BS. Association of depression with medical illness: does cortisol play a role? *Biol. Psychiatry,* 2004, 55, 1-9.

[214] Rapp MA, Schnaider-Beeri M, Grossman HT et al. Increased hippocampal plaques and tangles in patients with Alzheimer disease with a lifetime history of major depression. *Arch. Gen .Psychiatry,* 2006, 63, 161-7.

[215] Ganguli M, Du Y, Dodge HH et al. Depressive symptoms and cognitive decline in late life: a prospective epidemiological study. *Arch. Gen .Psychiatry,* 2006, *63,* 153-60.

[216] Pollock BG. Pharmacokinetics and pharmacodynamics in late life. In: Roose SP, Sackeim HA editors. *Late-Life Depression.* New York: Oxford University Press; 2004; 185-191.

[217] Pollock BG. Adverse reactions of antidepressants in elderly patients. *J Clin Psychiatry,* 1999, 60 Suppl 20, *4-8.*

[218] Liu B, Anderson G, Mittmann N et al. Use of selective serotonin-reuptake inhibitors of tricyclic antidepressants and risk of hip fractures in elderly people. *Lancet,* 1998, *351,* 1303-7.

[219] Mulsant BH, Pollock BG, Kirshner M et al. Serum anticholinergic activity in a community-based sample of older adults: relationship with cognitive performance. *Arch. Gen. Psychiatry,* 2003, *60,* 198-203.

[220] Nebes RD, Pollock BG, Mulsant BH et al. Low-level serum anticholinergicity as a source of baseline cognitive heterogeneity in geriatric depressed patients. *Psychopharmacol Bull,* 1997, *33,* 715-20.

[221] Engels GI, Vermey M. Efficacy of nonmedical treatments of depression in elders: A quantitative analysis. *Journal of Clinical Geropsychology,* 1997, *3,* 17-35.

[222] Koder D, Brodarty H, Anstey K. Cognitive therapy for depression in the elderly. *Internat J. Geriatr. Psychiatry,* 1996, *11,* 97-107.

[223] Pinquart M, Duberstein PR, Lyness JM. Treatments for later-life depressive conditions: a meta-analytic comparison of pharmacotherapy and psychotherapy. *Am. J. Psychiatry,* 2006, *163,* 1493-501.

[224] Pinquart M, Duberstein PR, Lyness JM. Effects of psychotherapy and other behavioral interventions on clinically depressed older adults: A meta-analysis. *Aging Ment. Health,* 2007, *11,* 645-57.

[225] Ishizaki J, Yamamoto H, Takahashi T et al. Changes in regional cerebral blood flow following antidepressant treatment in late-life depression [online]. *Int. J Geriatr Psychiatry* [cited 2/10/2008]. Available from PM:18214999.

[226] Kennedy SH, Evans KR, Kruger S et al. Changes in regional brain glucose metabolism measured with positron emission tomography after paroxetine treatment of major depression. *Am. J. Psychiatry,* 2001, *158,* 899-905.

[227] Mayberg HS. Modulating dysfunctional limbic-cortical circuits in depression: towards development of brain-based algorithms for diagnosis and optimised treatment. *Br. Med. Bull,* 2003, *65,* 193-207.

[228] Taragano FE, Allegri R, Vicario A et al. A double blind, randomized clinical trial assessing the efficacy and safety of augmenting standard antidepressant therapy with nimodipine in the treatment of 'vascular depression'. *Int. J .Geriatr. Psychiatry,* 2001, *16,* 254-60.

[229] Taragano FE, Bagnatti P, Allegri RF. A double-blind, randomized clinical trial to assess the augmentation with nimodipine of antidepressant therapy in the treatment of "vascular depression". *Int. Psychogeriatr.,* 2005, *17,* 487-98.

[230] Mlekusch W, Mlekusch I, Minar E et al. Is there improvement of "vascular depression" after carotid artery stent placement? *Radiology,* 2006, *240,* 508-14.

[231] Mlekusch W, Mlekusch I, Haumer M et al. Improvement of neurocognitive function after protected carotid artery stenting. *Catheter. Cardiovasc. Interv.*, 2008, 71, 114-9.

[232] McAlister FA, Oreopoulos A, Norris CM et al. Exploring the treatment-risk paradox in coronary disease. *Arch. Intern. Med*, 2007, 167, 1019-25.

[233] Rieckmann N, Gerin W, Kronish IM et al. Course of depressive symptoms and medication adherence after acute coronary syndromes: an electronic medication monitoring study. *J. Am. Coll. Cardiol.*, 2006, 48, 2218-22.

[234] Serebruany VL, Glassman AH, Malinin AI et al. Selective serotonin reuptake inhibitors yield additional antiplatelet protection in patients with congestive heart failure treated with antecedent aspirin. *Eur. J Heart Fail.*, 2003, 5, 517-21.

[235] Serebruany VL, Suckow RF, Cooper TB et al. Relationship between release of platelet/endothelial biomarkers and plasma levels of sertraline and N-desmethylsertraline in acute coronary syndrome patients receiving SSRI treatment for depression. *Am J Psychiatry*, 2005, 162, 1165-70.

[236] Ziegelstein RC, Meuchel J, Kim TJ et al. Selective serotonin reuptake inhibitor use by patients with acute coronary syndromes. *Am. J. Med.*, 2007, 120, 525-30.

[237] Rosenzweig A, Prigerson H, Miller M et al. Bereavement and late-life depression: grief and its complications in the elderly. *Annu. Rev. Med*, 1997, 48, 421.

[238] American Psychiatric Assocation. Diagnostic and Statistical Manual of Mental Disorders IV-TR. Washington, D.C.: American Psychiatric Association; 2000.

[239] Prigerson HG, Maciejewski PK, Reynolds CF, III et al. Inventory of Complicated Grief: a scale to measure maladaptive symptoms of loss. *Psychiatry Res.*, 1995, 59, 65-79.

[240] Prigerson HG, Frank E, Kasl SV et al. Complicated grief and bereavement-related depression as distinct disorders: preliminary empirical validation in elderly bereaved spouses. *Am. J. Psychiatry*, 1995, 152, 22-30.

[241] Prigerson HG, Shear MK, Newsom JT et al. Anxiety among widowed elders: is it distinct from depression and grief? *Anxiety*, 1996, 2, 1-12.

[242] Zisook S, Shear K, Kendler KS. Validity of the bereavement exclusion criterion for the diagnosis of major depressive episode. *World Psychiatry*, 2007, 6, 102-7.

[243] Irwin M, Pike J. Bereavement, depressive symptoms, and immune function. In: Stroebe M, Stroebe W, Hansson RO editors. *Handbook of Bereavement, Theory, Research, and Intervention*. New York: Cambridge University Press; 1993; 160-171.

[244] Elderkin-Thompson V, thomas MA, Binesh N, Mintz J, Haroon E, Dunkin JJ, Kumar A. Brain metabolites and cognitive function among older depressed and healthy individuals using 2D MR spectroscophy. *Neuropsychopharmacology*, 2004, 29, 2251-2257.

In: Women and Depression
Editors: Paula Hernandez and Sara Alonso

ISBN 978-1-60456-647-5
© 2009 Nova Science Publishers, Inc.

Chapter 11

Depression in Women with Diabetes: A Review and Methodological Critique

Julie Wagner and Howard Tennen
University of Connecticut Health Center, USA

Abstract

Diabetes and depression are both significant public health concerns for women. Depression is a risk factor for incident type 2 diabetes, and it also increases risk for poor diabetes outcomes. Research linking depression to health risks is limited in several important ways, particularly by common practices employed to measure depression. In this chapter we review evidence linking depression and diabetes in women, and describe limitations of the extant literature. We then review our own work that begins to address these limitations. We conclude with a review of the treatment literature and recommendations for addressing depression in women with diabetes.

Diabetes: Relevance to Women's Health

A Growing Problem

In 2005, 7% of the US population, or 20.8 million people, had diabetes. Of them, 30% were undiagnosed (Centers for Disease Control [CDC], 2005). The prevalence of type 2 diabetes is high and its incidence is rising, with a 33% increase nationwide in the 1990s (Mokdad et al., 2000). This increase can be attributed to national changes in risk-factor patterns including rising rates of obesity and overweight, an ageing population, a larger proportion of racial and ethnic minorities in the general population, as well as lower thresholds for diabetes diagnosis. Diabetes incurs tremendous economic costs. In 2002, direct costs for diabetes (such as medication and medical professional services) were estimated to be $92 billion, and indirect costs (such as lost income and disability) were estimated to be

$40 billion (CDC, 2005). Approximately half the cost is spent on treatment of the metabolic condition per se, while the other half is spent on treatment of the long-term complications of diabetes. Thus, prevention of long-term complications is a primary goal of diabetes treatment.

Women and Diabetes

Changing patterns of gender and age distribution in the general population are important for understanding diabetes incidence. The greater number of women than men in the total population is the result of greater life expectancy for women in all age groups. While the female survival advantage is narrowing, greater longevity among women is projected to persist for several decades. Between 1995 and 2010, the female population is projected to grow by 17.7 million, and more than three quarters of that growth will comprise women aged 45-64 years (United States Bureau of the Census, 1996).

Women have slightly higher rates of diabetes than men. Rates of diabetes double as women age out of the reproductive years (Harris et al., 1998). Approximately 6% of women aged 45-64 years, and 13% over 60 years have diabetes (CDC, 2002) and rates are increasing (Beckles and Thompson-Reid, 2001). Older women with diabetes outnumber men with diabetes of the same age (4.5 vs. 3.7 million; Beckles and Thompson-Reid, 2001), are hospitalized for diabetes 55% more days (Aubert, 1995), and have more diabetes-related disability than diabetic men (CDC, 2000).

Minority Women and Diabetes

The US population will also become more racially and ethnically diverse over time. Population growth will rise faster for minority groups than for non-Hispanic whites. From 1995-2010, the number of Hispanic and Asian American women is expected to double, the number of African American women to increase by two thirds, and the number of American Indian women will increase by almost half (Beckles and Thompson-Reid, 2001). Minority women suffer disproportionately from diabetes; the prevalence is at least 2-4 times higher among African American, Hispanic, American Indian, and Asian Pacific Islander women compared to White women (CDC, 2005).

Classification and Prevention of Diabetes

Diabetes is a heterogeneous group of disorders characterized by glucose dysregulation including type 1 diabetes, type 2 diabetes, gestational diabetes, pre-diabetes, and latent autoimmune diabetes in adults. An important related problem common to type 2 diabetes is the metabolic syndrome which is the constellation of hypertension, dyslipidemia, hypercoagulability, glucose dysregulation, and adiposity. The two major subtypes of diabetes, type 1 and type 2, will be the focus of this chapter.

People with type 1 diabetes suffer from an autoimmune disorder which results in an absolute insulin deficiency. They require exogenous insulin for survival. Approximately 5% of individuals with diabetes have type 1 diabetes. Risk for type 1 diabetes includes a genetic predisposition and exposure to as yet unknown contagion(s) which activate the autoimmune response. Risk factors for type 1 include younger age and western European ancestry. There is currently no cure or prevention for type 1 diabetes, but promising experimental protocols include stem cell therapies.

People with type 2 diabetes suffer from a relative lack of insulin due to progressive insulin resistance and gradual loss of insulin production, with individual variation in the contribution of each. Because hyperglycemia develops gradually in type 2 diabetes, this form of diabetes frequently goes undiagnosed for many years.

Risk factors for type 2 diabetes include female sex, increasing age, genetic vulnerability, obesity/overweight, physical inactivity, and race/ethnicity, with Native Americans, Hispanics, and African Americans at increased risk relative to non-Hispanic Whites. Importantly, it is well demonstrated that type 2 diabetes can be prevented or delayed. The Diabetes Prevention Program showed that among individuals at high risk for type 2, weight loss and physical activity decreased the conversion to overt type 2 diabetes by 58% (Knowler et al., 2002), and metformin, a medication traditionally used to treat diabetes, decreased conversion by 31%.

Complications of Diabetes

Long term complications of diabetes can be categorized as those affecting the macrovascular, microvascular, and neurological systems. The majority of morbidity and mortality in diabetes is due to cardiovascular disease. People with diabetes are more likely to develop cardiovascular disease compared to individuals without diabetes even after controlling for other risk factors (Kannel and McGee, 1979). In fact, individuals with diabetes have a risk of a myocardial infarction equal to individuals without diabetes who have already experienced an infarction (Haffner, Lehto, Ronnemaa, Pyorala, and Laakso, 1998). Women with type 2 are at particular risk. Indeed, type 2 diabetes is the only disorder in which women have higher risk of coronary artery disease than men. Our work has shown that people with diabetes lack knowledge of their risk for cardiovascular disease. Women with diabetes are largely unaware of the additional risk their sex confers (Wagner, Lacey, Abbott, de Groot, and Chyun, 2006).

There are well documented racial disparities in diabetes outcomes, including among women. Mortality rates for diabetes are greater for African Americans compared to Whites, with a larger gap for women than men (Department of Health and Human Services, 1999; American Diabetes Association [ADA], 2001). Relative to Whites, African Americans are more likely to suffer some long term complications including blindness (Harris, Klein, Rowland, and Byrd-Holt, 1998), tissue injury that requires amputation (ADA, 2004), and nephropathy (United States Renal Data System, 1999). The reason for these disparities is almost certainly multifactorial, and may include genetic, physiological, behavioral, and cultural factors. African American diabetic women have higher rates of hypertension than White diabetic women (Cowie and Harris, 1995) and a worse profile of diurnal blood pressure patterns. Diabetic African Americans also have worse glycemic control than Whites even after adjustment for treatment status (Haffner, Rosenthal, Hazuda, Stern, and Franco, 1984). Relative to Whites, African Americans have poorer diabetes self care behaviors (Auslander, Thompson, Dreitzer, White, and Santiago, 1997) even when financial barriers to medication are equalized (Charles, Good, Hanusa, Chang, and Whittle 2003). As we discuss later in the chapter, depression screening, diagnosis, and treatment initiation also varies by race in diabetes.

Several well controlled trials with decades of follow up show that the risk of some long-term complications can be reduced with proper diabetes treatment. (Diabetes Control and Complications Trial Research Group, 1993; The United Kingdom Prospective Diabetes Study Group, 1998). These studies showed definitively that tighter glycemic control decreases the likelihood of long term complications. Glycemic control is measured with glycosylated hemoglobin in the blood (HbA1c), which provides an indication of average blood glucose levels over 6-10 weeks. These studies also demonstrate that blood-pressure and lipid management are important treatment targets.

Unfortunately, tight glycemic control continues to be elusive for many people with diabetes. The diabetes regimen is a complex balancing act, coordinating medication, carbohydrate intake, and physical activity. When this delicate balance is disrupted, as is often the case, short-term complications occur, which include episodes of hypo- and hyper-glycemia. There are numerous cognitive, psychological, social, and environmental barriers to diabetes self-care. Ruggiero, Glasgow, Dryfoos, Rossi, Prochaska, Orleans, et al. (1997) found that in their large sample, more than 20% did not usually self-monitor blood glucose as prescribed, nearly 60% did not usually exercise as prescribed, and more than a third did not eat according to their prescribed meal plan.

Depression in Diabetes: A Women's Health Issue

Major Depressive Disorder is Prevalent among Women with Diabetes

A major depressive episode—also referred to as major depression or clinical depression—is characterized by at least two weeks of depressed mood or loss of interest or pleasure most of the day, nearly every day. These symptoms impair the affected person's social, occupational and/or educational functioning. In addition to mood disturbance or loss of interest, the depressed individual manifests at least four of the following symptoms every day or nearly every day: significant weight loss or weight gain, motor agitation or slowing, insomnia or hypersomnia, fatigue or loss of energy, feelings of worthlessness or excessive guilt, impaired concentration or indecisiveness, or recurrent thoughts of death. Depression here is distinguished from more general diabetes distress, which is defined as patient concerns about disease management, support, emotional burden, and access to care (Fisher, Skaff, Mullan, Arean, Mohr, et al. 2007).

Major depressive disorder is common in the general population, with 17% lifetime prevalence (Kessler et al., 2004). Associated impairments (Wells et al., 1989; Hays, Wells, Sherbourne, Rogers, and Spritzer, 1995) make it the 4th most disabling illness globally

(Ustün, Ayuso-Mateos, Chatterji, Mathers, and Murray 2004). Lifetime prevalence in the general population is twice as high in women (10-25%) as men (5-12%; Kessler et al.; 2004) and twice as high in persons with type 1 and type 2 diabetes as controls (Anderson, Freedland, Clouse, and Lustman, 2001). Approximately 1 in 4 people with diabetes experience major depression in their lifetime (Anderson et al., 2001). As in the general population, prevalence is higher among diabetic women than diabetic men. Women with diabetes have 1.6 times the risk of depression compared to their male counterparts, with 28.2% of women and 18% of men reporting significant depressive symptoms. Among people with diabetes, evidence comparing African Americans and Latinos with Whites suggests that rates of depression in minorities with diabetes are commensurate with, or slightly exceed that of, rates of depression in Whites with diabetes (Gary, Crum, Cooper-Patrick, Ford, and Brancati, 2000; Grandinetti et al., 2000; Gross et al., 2004). Higher rates for Native Americans have also been reported recently (Sahmoun, Markland, and Helgerson, 2007; Li, Ford, Strine, and Mokdad, 2008).

There are scant data regarding depression and diabetes in pregnancy. What data do exist suggest that pregnant diabetic women and pregnant nondiabetic controls do not differ on depressive symptoms (Langer and Langer, 1994). Additionally, women with gestational diabetes and women with pregnancy in existing diabetes do not differ on depressive symptoms. Women with gestational diabetes do show higher anxiety, though, than women with pregnancy in existing diabetes (York et al., 1996). Diabetes (gestational or pre-existing) in pregnancy usually entails an increasingly rigorous regimen, including frequent self-monitoring of blood glucose and multiple daily insulin injections. Langer and Langer (1994) showed that intensified management of newly diagnosed gestational diabetes mellitus does not increase patient anxiety and depression, and in fact is perceived as reassuring to patients. This is an important consideration, as treatment of gestational diabetes reduces serious perinatal morbidity and may also improve the woman's health-related quality of life (Crowther et al., 2004). Two studies compared depressive symptoms of pregnant women prior to and then again after being screened for gestational diabetes (Rumbold and Crowther, 2002; Kerbel, Glazier, Holzapfel, Yeung, and Lofsky, 1997). Both studies found that compared to pre-screening, women who were positive for gestational diabetes had decreased perceptions of their own health post-screening, however they showed no changes in levels of depression.

Because type 2 diabetes can be prevented or delayed, and because interventions to prevent type 1 diabetes are being tested, individuals are sometimes screened for diabetes risk. Eborall et al. (2007) investigated over 7000 individuals who were screened for type 2 diabetes. After the initial screen, compared with participants who screened negative, those who screened positive reported more depressive symptoms, although effect sizes were small. Keruish and colleagues (2007) investigated depressive symptoms among mothers of infants tested at birth for genetic susceptibility to type 1 diabetes. Mothers of high risk, low risk, and untested infants showed similar levels of depression over 1 year after screening. Similarly, Hood et al. (2005) assessed depression among mothers of at-risk infants who were identified through newborn genetic screening. For the most part, mothers of infants genetically at risk for type 1 diabetes did not report elevated depressive symptoms. This suggests that most mothers are resilient when notified of infant risk. However, certain maternal characteristics such as ethnic minority status, less than a high school education, postpartum depressive symptoms, and a history of major depression, were associated with a depressive maternal response to the news of an infant's increased genetic risk for type 1 diabetes.

Among individuals with diabetes, additional risk factors for depression include younger age, low education attainment, being unmarried, smoking, overweight, treatment with insulin, and presence of diabetes complications (Ruggiero, Wagner, and de Groot, 2006). The nature of the relationship between diabetes and depression, and any common underlying genetic, environmental, behavioral, and hormonal mechanisms have not been fully elucidated. The relationship is likely multifactorial with individual variability in the relative contribution of each factor. It is possible that slightly different mechanisms are influential in men and women. For example, Suarez (2006) investigated glucose metabolism and emotion in nondiabetic men and women. Insulin resistance and insulin levels were associatd with depressive symptoms, hostility, and anger expression among women, but not among men.

Course and Costs of Depression in Diabetes

The trajectory of comorbidity is different for type 1 and type 2 diabetes. Type 1 diabetes tends to be diagnosed prior to a first depressive episode. This is likely a reflection of the typical age of onset for the two disorders; i.e., type 1 diabetes tends to be diagnosed in childhood with average onset during puberty, whereas a first depressive episode tends to present during the second or third decade of life. In type 2 diabetes, the first depressive episode tends to occur prior to a diabetes diagnosis. In fact, prospective data show that depression is a risk factor for onset of type 2 diabetes. Taken together, the data do not support depression as simply a psychological reaction to diagnosis of type 2 diabetes, its treatment, or its complications, although this may certainly occur in some individuals.

The duration of depressive episodes in individuals with diabetes may be longer and more persistent than those documented in the general population (Peyrot and Rubin, 1999). One study of persons enrolled in a diabetes education program found that 34% of participants continued to report clinically significant depressive symptoms 6 months after initial evaluation. Relapse may also be more common, and inter-episode recovery less complete, among depressed individuals with diabetes. In a review of the literature, Lustman, Clouse, and Freedland (1998) concluded that diabetic patients who have experienced depression are subsequently seldom free of depressive symptoms for more than a year.

Depression has a clinically meaningful detrimental association with glycemic control in persons with both type 1 and type 2 diabetes (Lustman et al., 2000). Some evidence suggests that the relationship between depression and glycemic control may be stronger for women than for men (Pouwer and Snoek, 2001). The relationship is likely bi-directional, with depression contributing to hyperglycemia, and hyperglycemia in turn contributing to mood disturbance. Depression may affect glycemic control directly via metabolic and hormonal perturbations. Depression may also affect glycemic control indirectly through compromised self-care behaviors. People with comorbid depression and diabetes show decrements in adherence to multiple components of their diabetes self-care regimen (Ciechenowski, Katon, and Russo, 2000). Some data suggest this relationship is stronger for men than women (Nau,

Aikens, and Pacholski, 2007). Hyperglycemia also diminishes response to depression treatment, thus increasing risk of depression recurrence (Lustman, Freedland, Griffith, and Clouse, 1998).

Depression has also been shown to have a moderate relationship with worsened long-term diabetes complications, including neurological, macrovascular, and microvascular complications. Meta-analysis shows a consistent cross-sectional relationship between depression and macrovascular complications of type 2 diabetes (de Groot, Anderson, Freedland, Clouse, and Lustman, 2001). One longitudinal study assessed diabetic women annually for 10 years, and found that depression at baseline accelerated the development of heart disease (Clouse et al., 2003). Although depression is associated with hyperglycemia, and hyperglycemia is implicated in complications, the available evidence suggests that depression is not related to complications simply via hyperglycemia.

The costs associated with comorbid diabetes and depression are considerable, including costs for ambulatory care and prescription use (Egede, Zhen, and Simpson, 2002). Depression in diabetes also increases disability (Egede, 2004) and risk for mortality (Zhang et al., 2005). Much of the disability and financial burden of depression in diabetes is due to long-term complications.

Limitations of Previous Studies and Findings Using Alternative Approaches

Previous studies of depression and diabetes outcomes are limited by common practices in depression measurement, which influence determination of 'case' and 'control' participants in controlled studies. We now describe these limitations, the approaches used in our own program of research to address them, and the findings that have resulted from our approaches. Outcomes have included psychological well-being, self-care behaviors, medical and mental health symptoms, and markers of cardiovascular function.

The findings discussed below are drawn from our ongoing program of research which has essentially employed a 2 (diabetes vs non-diabetic) X 2 (history of major depressive disorder [MDD] vs never depressed) design to study diabetes outcomes among postmenopausal women who are not depressed at the time of their study participation. Women with type 2 diabetes (n=79) were over-sampled and compared to non-diabetic controls (n=74). Participants in the diabetes sub-sample were diagnosed on average nearly 6 years prior to study participation, with HbA1c M=6.7 indicating adequate glycemic control. Participants with a history of depression were over-sampled (n=62) and compared to never depressed controls (n=84). The previously depressed sub-sample had their first MDD episode when they were, on average, 36 years old. Forty-three percent of the previously depressed participants had a single lifetime major depression, and another 34% had experienced two or more depressive episodes. The average time since remission of their most recent episode was nearly twelve years. To be eligible for the study, individuals were required to be free of current mood disorder and antidepressant use for at least 12 months. Among the diabetic women with a history of depression, the vast majority (96%) experienced their first depressive episode prior to being diagnosed with diabetes, with an average lag time of 18.2

years. What follows is a methodological critique of the literature, and findings from our program of research that speak to the importance of addressing these limitations.

Relying Solely on Depression Symptom Questionnaires

Rates of depression vary by type of depression measurement. Studies using diagnostic interviews show lower rates of clinically significant depression (11.4%) than those using self-report questionnaires (31.0%; Anderson et al., 2001). This difference may reflect two issues. First, as Fisher and colleagues point out, most diabetic patients with high levels of depressive symptoms do not meet diagnostic criteria for major depression (Fisher et al., 2007). They assessed more than 500 diabetic patients for major depressive disorder by a structured interview (Composite International Diagnostic Interview [CIDI]), a questionnaire for depressive symptoms (Center for Epidemiological Studies Depression Scale [CESD; Radloff et al., 1977]), and on the Diabetes Distress Scale. They found that of individuals who scored above 16 on the CESD, 70% were not clinically depressed. Furthermore, diabetes distress was minimally related to major depression, but substantively linked to CESD scores. They concluded that the CESD may be more reflective of general emotional and diabetes-specific distress than major depressive disorder.

Second, there is an inherent difficulty associated with assessing depression in medical samples. Symptoms of diabetes can easily be confounded with symptoms of depression on a self-report questionnaire. For example, changes in appetite or weight may be attributable to either depression or the metabolic condition that is the hallmark of diabetes; sleep disruption may be attributable to either depression or frequent nighttime urination due to hyperglycemia; fatigue may be due to depression or glucose fluctuations. Because of overlapping symptoms, depression in diabetes is best measured by clinical interview rather than symptom questionnaire, whenever feasible. Lustman and colleagues (1997) evaluated the ability of the Beck Depression Inventory (BDI) to distinguish between depressed and non-depressed diabetic patients. The presence of depression was determined using the National Institute of Mental Health Diagnostic Interview Schedule (DIS; Robins et al., 1989) in accordance with the Diagnostic and Statistical Manual of Mental Disorders (DSM-III-R) criteria. The BDI total score, the somatic items alone, and the cognitive items alone all distinguished between groups. However, the somatic items performed less well than the cognitive items.

We use both approaches in tandem, employing self-report depression symptoms scales, and structured clinical interviews such as the Structured Clinical Interview for DSM-IV (SCID; First, Spitzer, Gibbon, Williams, 1998). Our determination of presence or absence of mood disorder is made from clinical information gathered through the interviews. We assess symptom severity with the CESD.

We have explored the relationship between depressive symptoms and diabetes symptoms among women with type 2 diabetes. Current depressive symptoms were measured with the CESD, which assesses the presence and frequency of depressive symptoms during the preceding week. Diabetes symptoms were measured with the Diabetes Symptom Checklist (Grootenhuis, Snoek, Heine, Heine, and Bouter, 2004) which asks about the frequency and burden of 34 diabetes symptoms over the past month. In our study sample, aggregated diabetes symptoms were correlated with depressive symptoms on the order of r=.45. In partial correlation, both frequency and burden of diabetes symptoms were independently correlated with depressive symptoms. When diabetes symptoms were examined individually, those diabetes symptoms that can mimic depression, such as fatigue, were correlated with depressive symptoms, whereas those symptoms that would not likely mimic depression, such as vision changes, were not correlated with depressive symptoms. These findings underscore the importance of diagnostic interviewing to assess mood disorder so that judgment can be made about whether symptoms suggestive of depression might be better accounted for by diabetes.

Incomplete Characterization of the Course of Depression

Controlled studies linking depression to diabetes and its complications almost invariably compare individuals with current depression to those not currently depressed. This approach may be prone to the following limitations: (a) ignoring history of depression, thereby including in the comparison group individuals with a depression history; (b) failing to capture duration of exposure to depression; (c) overlooking the fact that the majority of people with a current depression have also had a previous depression, thus confounding current and previous depression; and (d) confounding depression and its treatment. Each of these methodological issues is discussed below.

History of Depression

By measuring only depression at study baseline, individuals who are not currently depressed are assumed to be free from the effects of depression. If previous depression is ignored, individuals who are not currently depressed, but who had experienced a depression prior to study baseline, may be misclassified into a group thought to be free from the effects of depression. In our program of research, we more accurately group participants by 'previous major depression' and 'never depressed.' This approach has yielded interesting findings.

Available evidence suggests that previous depression is associated with health problems that are temporally distant from the depressive episode (e.g., Fifield et al., 2001). For example, in the Women's Health Initiative, mortality survival curves for depressed and non-depressed study participants diverged over several years of follow up, indicating that the effect of depression on mortality is not necessarily proximal to depression assessment (Wassertheil-Smoller et al., 2004). Major depressive disorder is associated with cellular alterations that remain abnormal in remission (Post, 1999; Sheline, Sanghavi, Mintun, and Gado, 1992). This helps to explain why patients with a history of major depressive disorder prior to myocardial infarction have higher mortality than those who experience their first episode post-infarct (Lesperance, Frasure-Smith, and Talajic, 1996). Certainly there are state dependent depression effects which are perhaps even stronger than any effects that might be detected during depression remission (e.g., insulin resistance is worse in the presence of depression and improves with depression treatment; Okamura et al., 2000). Nonetheless, objective functional and structural changes, as well as subjective physical symptom changes, are documented after depression remission.

We investigated history of MDD and glycemic control among women with type 2 diabetes. Compared with their never-depressed counterparts, women with a history of major depressive disorder had higher HbA1c (7.0 vs. 6.5%), after controlling for confounding variables including CESD-derived current depressive symptoms.

We also investigated history of MDD and diabetes self-care behaviors among women with type 2 diabetes. Physical activity was assessed with the Framingham Physical Activity scale (Kannel, 1997); self-monitoring of blood glucose (SMBG) was measured with the Measure of Invasiveness and Skipping SMBG (MISS; Wagner, Malchoff, and Abbott, 2005). After controlling for confounders including current depressive symptoms on the CESD, women with a history of depression showed lower physical activity scores and more frequent skipping SMBG compared to their never depressed counterparts. These findings suggest that women with a history of depression show poor self-care behaviors, even in the absence of current mood disorder and controlling for current depressive symptoms.

In examining each of these questions, had we examined only current depression, previously depressed persons who were no longer depressed would have been included with never depressed participants, increasing variance within groups, and thus making group differences more difficult to detect.

Duration of Exposure to Depression

Most studies of depression treat the mood disorder as a binary independent variable, i.e., depressed vs. not depressed, or occasionally, history of depression vs. never depressed. This approach does not consider duration of exposure to depression over the lifespan. Major depressive disorder is often a chronic, progressive condition with each episode increasing the likelihood of an additional episode, and subsequent inter-episode recovery periods of shorter duration with decreased symptom relief. Of those individuals with an episode of major depression, 41% will have a second episode within a year, 59% within 2 years, and 74% within 5 years (American Psychiatric Association; DSM-IV). Studies suggest that single episode depression may be taxonomically different from recurrent depression. For example, compared to individuals with a single prior depressive episode, those with recurrent depression manifest greater sleep disturbance (Jindal et al., 2002), memory deficits (Basso and Bornstein, 1999), and less response to placebos (Bialik, Ravindran, Bakish, and Lapierre, 1995). They also generate more stressful life events than their single-episode or never-depressed counterparts (Harkness, Monroe, Simons, and Thase, 1999). In light of this evidence, we measure the number of major depressive episodes experienced over the lifespan.

We studied the effect of number of depressive episodes on cardiovascular functioning. Flow mediated dilation (FMD) is a noninvasive measure of endothelial functioning, which is an early marker of cardiovascular disease. Diseased vessels dilate less fully; in some severely impaired vessels, paradoxical vasoconstriction can occur. Unlike the women who had experienced a single depression and never depressed women who showed similar levels of vasodilation, women with history of recurrent depression showed vasoconstriction. Controlling for confounds including CESD derived current depressive symptoms, history of recurrent depressive disorder predicted greater likelihood of vasoconstriction, but history of single depressive disorder did not. Women with single episode depression histories more closely resembled never depressed women than they resemble women with multiple episodes. These findings are consistent with a literature suggesting that recurrent depression is associated with a more severe neurophysiologic substrate and more environmental insults than phenotypically similar single episode cases (Jindal et al., 2002). Determination of number of episodes, particularly single or recurrent, may improve our understanding of who among those with MDD is at risk for poor health outcomes, including diabetes outcomes, and how MDD may confer that risk.

Current Plus Previous Depression

With very few exceptions, studies of depression as a health risk confound current and previous depression. Over the course of the depressive illness, the onset of depressive episodes may become decreasingly related to environmental adversities. This presumably results from sensitization to the state of depression, referred to as the 'kindling effect' (Solomon et al., 2000; Segal, Williams, Teasdale, and Gemar, 1996; Kendler, Thornton, and Gardner, 2000; Kendler, Thornton, and Gardner, 2001). Because the modal age of first major depressive episode is in young adulthood (Bijl, De Graff, Ravelli, Smit, and Vollebergh, 2002), this 'kindling' effect can be reasoned backwards, i.e., that a late middle-aged woman with a major depressive disorder at study baseline has a reasonable probability of having had a prior depressive episode, or numerous prior episodes. To the extent that this is the case, using baseline major depressive disorder as a predictor of health outcomes confounds 'current' major depressive disorder with 'lifetime exposure' to major depressive disorder (Tennen, Hall, and Affleck, 1995a; Tennen, Hall, Affleck, 1995b). We propose that both lifetime and current mood disorder should be considered as simultaneous predictors of health outcomes. This approach would shed light on the relative contributions of state-dependent effects of depression versus effects of accumulated exposure to depression on health risk.

We addressed this issue in a secondary data analysis of the relationship between mood disorder and coronary heart disease risk among 10,573 adults aged 60 and older from the National Epidemiologic Survey on Alcohol and Related Conditions (Herbst, Pietrzak, Wagner, White, and Petry, 2007). In the first analysis, along with covariates, past-year mood disorder predicted presence of coronary heart disease. In the second analysis, along with all covariates, both any lifetime and any past-year mood disorder were entered into the equation simultaneously to ascertain whether recency of mood disorders was more closely associated with coronary heart disease than a lifetime history of a mood disorder. Any lifetime mood disorder continued to be associated with coronary heart disease, but any past-year mood disorder was not. These data support the hypothesis that in older persons, current mood disorder may function as a proxy for history of mood disorder.

Depression and its Treatment

Many epidemiological studies that rely on medical record reviews or registry data use antidepressant use as a surrogate for presence of depression. However, resulting differences in clinical indicators between persons taking antidepressant medication, and those not taking antidepressant medication, may be difficult to interpret. Differences could be due to either depression or its treatment. In our research, we investigate depression and its treatment separately. In fact, to be eligible for our studies on history of depression and health outcomes, participants must be free from antidepressant medications for at least one year. This way, differences between previously depressed and never depressed groups cannot be better accounted for the potential effects of antidepressant medication.

Many participants, even those not currently taking antidepressants, have taken antidepressant medications in the past. We carefully assess medication history using the same measurement strategy that we employ for history of depression. Even so, findings must be interpreted cautiously. For example, in our sample of diabetic women; those who endorse a history of antidepressant use show higher diabetes symptom scores compared to nonusers. One might (mis)interpret this as indicating that a side effect of antidepressants is to cause, potentiate, or exacerbate diabetes symptoms. However, when we limit our analyses to those women with a history of depression, those who endorse a history of antidepressant use show *lower* diabetes symptom scores than nonusers, even after controlling for CESD scores. Studies that use chart reviews, registries, and other types of medical record data must be cautious in their use of treatment as a marker for disease.

Measurement of Depression

In order to address the limitations of depression measurement noted thus far, we have combined several established methods to assess lifetime depressive episodes and their treatment. At its core, our measurement strategy employs the Structured Clinical Interview for DSM-IV (First, Spitzer, Gibbon, and Williams, 1998), expanded to collect diagnostic information on every past episode.

Reliability of retrospective data is limited by participant recall and bias. Bias is most likely a problem when current mood colors recollection. For example, Aneshensel and colleagues (1987) examined lifetime history of depression in 601 participants over five waves of data collection. They found that follow-up reports of history of depression were inconsistent with reports made three to four years earlier; the predominant inconsistency was failure to report a previously reported depressive episode. The presence of internal symptom cues or external stress cues prompted recollection of past disorder. Aneshensel et al. concluded that individuals seem to alter their reports of past experience to make past states consistent with current states.

Reliability is also limited by poor recall. In order to enhance recall, we have adapted for use with the SCID, a reliable, validated, and widely used method for assessing past behaviors. The TimeLine Follow-Back (TLFB; Sobell and Sobell 1995) is a measure of past behavior widely used in behavioral studies with both clinical and non-clinical populations.

The method is recommended for use when relatively precise estimates are necessary, especially when assessment of intra-individual variability is required. TLFB provides more precise information than standard questionnaires or unaided recall strategies. Our TLFB interviews include memory aids. For example, key dates and life events serve as anchors, and a visual timeline calendar is constructed with the participant to graphically represent this information (see Figure 1). By reviewing the timeline, the interviewer can assist the participant in providing a detailed picture of the time period under study (e.g., onset, duration, intensity, remission, relapse, treatment initiation and termination).

The TLFB was used in the NIH-funded Project MATCH, a multisite randomized controlled trial of alcohol treatment (Project MATCH Research Group, 1993). It has been used with adults and adolescents, men and women, different racial groups, individuals of varying educational backgrounds, the mentally ill (Sokya et al., 2003; Carey, Cocco, and Simons, 1996), both in the US and abroad (Shimizu et al., 1997; Gastpar et al., 2002). Originally designed to assess past alcohol use, the TLFB has been applied to past sexual behavior (Weinhardt et al., 1998; Midanik et al., 1998; Wickramasinghe, 1998; Crosby, Stall, Paul, Barrett, and Midanik, 1996; Stein, Anderson, Charuvastra, and Friedmann, 2001), past binge eating (Bardone, Krahn, Goodman, and Searles, 2000), past gambling (Weinstock, Whelan, and Meyeres, 2004; Hodgins and Makarchuk 2003), and past substance use (Stephens, Babor, Kadden, and Miller, 2002; Hersh, Mulgrew, Van Kirk, and Kranzler, 1999). We have adapted the TLFB to assess past depression with the SCID. To our knowledge, ours is the first application of the TLFB to psychiatric symptoms.

The TLFB has demonstrated high test-retest reliability, content validity, concurrent criterion validity, collateral (informant) validity, and construct validity in both general and clinical samples (National Institute on Alcohol Abuse and Addiction, 2004). Validity of the method is related to respondent motivation, i.e., validity is highest when the respondent is willingly engaged in the interview procedure, as participants in our study are (Vinson, Reidinger, and Wilcosky, 2003). We use the TLFB to create a visual timeline in collaboration with the participant. Such timeline construction has many benefits. First, asking research participants to anchor their memories to specific events facilitates their recall. For example, a participant may not be able to recall the date of symptom onset, but may be able recall that symptoms began 'just prior to my wedding in 1978,' or 'the week my son was born.' This is particularly true for ageing individuals and those with substance abuse, physical or emotional trauma histories that interfere with recall. Second, making differential diagnosis is facilitated by the clear outline of an individual's intertwined medical, psychiatric, and psychosocial histories. Third, people who are attempting to deceive the interviewer will have fewer opportunities to obfuscate their symptoms when they are laid out sequentially.

Traditional assessments using structured interviews such as the SCID explore clusters of symptoms at a time, jumping from past to present repeatedly, leaving both clinician and patient with a disjointed sense of events. Key information for accurate diagnosis often includes the manifestation of symptoms prior to a certain age, duration of symptoms, symptoms occurring in absence of another disorder, or the presence of symptoms in relation to life events. It can be helpful to organize disparate information into a multilayered, linear format.

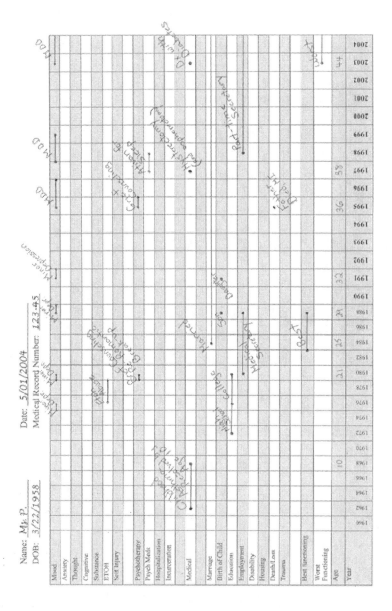

Figure 1. Visual timeline calendar which uses key dates and life events as anchors to aid recall.

We designed a timeline (see figure 1 for data from a fictional participant) to visually represent, along the Y-axis, the sequence of significant life events, psychiatric and medical symptoms and treatments, as well as subjective psychosocial functioning. The X axis displays both calendar year and patient age. An average lifespan is displayed in two year intervals with the most recent two decades (in bold) laid out annually for more detailed accounting of recent symptoms and functioning. All of these features can be modified to suit the needs of the user for a useful "at a glance" window into multiple dimensions of a complex history. In our experience, a brief explanation of the timeline to research participants is sufficient.

Our preliminary data show 100% inter-rater reliability for presence/absence of lifetime history of major depressive disorder. As would be expected, the inter-rater reliability for any individual SCID symptom is in fact lower than 100% (ranging from 60%-100%, averaging 94%). It is not unusual to have inter-rater agreement for presence/absence of Axis I disorders (including major depressive disorder) in the 'excellent' range when using the SCID (Skre, 1991). However, we attribute our unusually high reliability to our use of the TLFB, and visual timeline construction.

Why it Matters: Depression in Persons with Diabetes is Modifiable

Depression Treatment in Diabetes

Depression is an important predictor of diabetes outcomes not only because it is common and burdensome, but also because it is modifiable. Behavioral, pharmacological, and case management treatments for major depressive disorder and elevated depressive symptoms have been shown to be effective in diabetes. Available evidence suggests that when diabetes patients receive a depression intervention, whether psychological or pharmacological, they are largely satisfied with the treatment (de Groot, Pinkerman, Wagner, and Hockman, 2006). Factors related to diabetes, such as self-care behaviors, glycemic control, and weight influence response to treatment. These factors should be addressed in treatment in order to optimize treatment response. The available data regarding depression treatment response either do not address sex, or do not show differences by sex. Our knowledge of diabetic women in depression treatment is limited, but there is no indication that women respond differently to depression treatment than diabetic men.

Lustman and colleagues (1998) conducted a randomized, double-blind, placebo-controlled trial to evaluate the effects of nortriptyline on depression among individuals with diabetes. Treatment was effective at reducing depressive symptoms, and depression improvement had an independent beneficial effect on glycemic control. Improved glycemic control could not be attributed to weight change or to change in diabetes self-care. However, while decreased depression improved glycemic control, an additional direct effect of nortriptyline was to *worsen* glycemic control. Thus, while effective for depression, nortriptyline is not the medication of choice for people with diabetes.

Lustman and colleagues (2000) also conducted a randomized, double-blind, placebo-controlled trial to evaluate the effects of fluoxetine on depression and glycemic control.

Participants in fluoexetine treatment showed a greater reduction in depressive symptoms, compared to a placebo group. The fluoxetine group also showed a trend toward greater improvement in glycemic control, compared to placebo-treated participants. In an uncontrolled study, Amsterdam and colleagues (2006) examined the effect of s-citalopram on depression and diabetes. After sixteen weeks, they observed a statistically significant decrease in depressive symptoms, and a marginal decrease in various indices of glycemic control. Animal studies further suggest that the selective serotonin reuptake inhibitor (SSRI) sertraline may protect, and potentially restore, counterregulatory responses that enable diabetic patients to detect and respond to acute episodes of hypoglycemia (Sanders, Wilkinson, Taborsky, Al-Noori, Daumen, et al., 2008).

In another randomized, controlled trial, Lustman, Griffith, Freedland, Kissel, and Clouse (1998) compared the effects of ten weeks of cognitive behavior therapy (CBT) to no antidepressant treatment among individuals with type 2 diabetes and major depression. A greater proportion of CBT-treated participants compared to controls achieved remission; and at 6-month follow-up, CBT-treated participants had better glycemic control. In the sample as a whole, non-remission of depression was associated with poor diabetes self-care, poor glycemic control, higher weight, and a history of previous treatment for depression. In the CBT-treated group, the presence of diabetes complications and poor diabetes self-care were independent predictors of diminished response.

Finally, the Pathways study randomized 329 patients with diabetes and major depression and/or dysthymia to either collaborative case management, or usual care (Katon, Von Korff, Lin, Simon, Ludman, Russo, et al., 2004). Compared to usual care, the collaborative care model improved depression levels and outcomes, but improved depression alone did not result in improved glycemic control. Effects were also observed for patients with multiple diabetes complications (Kinder et al., 2006). This intervention also demonstrated economic benefit. Over 24 months, patients assigned to the intervention accumulated a mean of 61 additional days free of depression and had outpatient health services costs that averaged $314 less than usual care patients. When an additional day free of depression is valued at $10, the net benefit of the intervention is $952 per patient treated (Simon et al., 2007).

Patient characteristics may influence depression treatment outcomes. Ciechanowski (2006) examined the interpersonal style of patients enrolled in the depression case management intervention described above (Katon, Von Korff, Lin, Simon, Ludman, Russo, et al., 2004). He found that the collaborative care intervention resulted in better attendance at therapy visits, more positive depression outcomes, and greater satisfaction with depression care for patients with an 'independent' interpersonal style, but not for patients with an 'interactive' style. Key components of collaborative care, including proactive follow-up and treatment adapted to the patients' preferred mode of interaction, may have provided greater possibilities for interaction on patients' terms. The investigators hypothesize that this contributed to the differences in process and outcomes for patients with a less flexible relationship style.

As mentioned previously, depression in diabetes is characterized by incomplete symptom remission and high rates of recurrence. To date, one trial (Lustman et al., 2006) has examined the effect of maintenance medication on depression relapse. Patients who recovered from depression during open-label sertraline treatment continued to receive sertraline or placebo and were followed for up to 52 weeks or until depression recurred. Among patients whose depression recurred (1/3 of the study sample), the depression free interval was longer with sertraline maintenance treatment than placebo. Glycemic control improved with depression treatment, and remained improved as long as remission was sustained, regardless of treatment.

The effects of depression care on mortality among individuals with diabetes has also been also examined. Bogner et al. (2007) performed secondary analyses on data from a prospective depression management intervention. A depression care manager worked with primary care physicians to provide algorithm-based depression care. Older depressed primary care patients with diabetes in practices implementing depression care management were less likely to die over the course of a 5-year interval than depressed patients with diabetes in usual-care practices.

Together, these studies suggest that depression in individuals with diabetes can be treated effectively. Evidence for medical and financial outcomes is limited, but growing. Antidepressant medications should be chosen prudently because of iatrogenic effects of some agents on glycemic control. To improve outcomes, the role of diabetes self-care in depression treatment should be addressed directly in the context of depression treatment.

Barriers to Effective Depression Treatment

Lack of screening is a significant barrier to detection and treatment of depression. Unfortunately, as in the general population, detection of depression in persons with diabetes by healthcare providers is inadequate. Katon, Simon, Russo, Von Korff, Lin, Ludman, et al. (2004) examined rates of detection and treatment in a large HMO population. Approximately half the cases of depression in diabetes went undetected by healthcare providers. Depression in women was more likely to be detected than depression in men. Among all of those detected, only 43% received antidepressant therapy, and only 7% received 4 or more sessions of psychotherapy. From the perspective of a healthcare provider, there are many barriers to detection and treatment. Short visit times, lack of convenient referrals, reimbursement issues, and low confidence about one's own ability to measure and manage depression may all play a role.

Furthermore, patient depression itself may interfere with a healthcare providers' ability to communicate effectively with a patient. Swensen, Rose, Vittinghoff, Stewart, and Schillinger (2008) found that compared with patients with no depressive symptoms, patients with severe depressive symptoms were more likely to report suboptimal communication across multiple domains of communication, particularly those involving interactive and patient-centered communication. Domains that were suboptimal in the presence of patient depression were elicitation of patient problems, concerns, and expectations; explanations of condition; empowerment; and decision-making. These are the interactive, bi-directional components of the clinician–patient relationship that may be crucial to detecting depression and negotiating its treatment.

Rates of depression detection and treatment also vary by race and ethnicity. We surveyed a community sample of 740 persons with diabetes attending diabetes health fairs in the northeastern US (Wagner, Tsimikas, Heapy, de Groot, and Abbott, 2007). Only half of those indicating elevated depressive symptoms responded affirmatively that a healthcare provider had diagnosed depression. Rates of depressive symptoms were similar among White, African-American, and Latino participants. One quarter of the sample endorsed physician-diagnosed depression, and among those who had been diagnosed, only 40% reported pharmacological treatment. Despite equivalent symptoms among racial/ethnic groups, African-Americans reported lower rates of physician-diagnosed depression than Whites. Those African Americans who did endorse physician-diagnosed depression reported lower rates of pharmacotherapy than Whites.

One explanation for this racial difference in pharmacotherapy may be the frequent use of alternative depression treatments, especially among minorities. de Groot, Pinkerman, Wagner, and Hockman (2006) surveyed 222 persons with diabetes about depression and depression treatment. Of those who endorsed clinically significant depressive symptoms, 19% reported receiving depression treatment from alternative healers (e.g., preachers, folk doctors), and 16% reported using herbal remedies. Twenty four percent reported receiving no treatment at all. Compared to Whites, African Americans were less likely to receive antidepressant medications, receive treatment from a mental health professional, or to report any depression treatment. These differences were evident even after controlling for sociodemographic factors. The Institute of Medicine report on health disparities (Smedley, Stith, and Nelson, 2003) suggests that when differences in outcomes are noted even when sociodemographic characteristics are equalized, the source of the difference may lie in subtle or unintended discrimination in the patient-provider healthcare interaction.

While substantial gains towards societal equity for African Americans have been made, there is still evidence of considerable discrimination against African American women. Discrimination is defined as "unfair treatment received because of one's ethnicity, where ethnicity refers to various groups of individuals based on race or culture of origin" (Contrada, Ashmore, and Gary, 2000). Racial disparities in education, income, and employment are more pronounced among diabetic than nondiabetic women (Beckles and Thompson-Reid, 2001), suggesting discrimination may be particularly relevant for diabetic African American women.

We surveyed 120 African Americans with diabetes about experiences with discrimination, depression, and depression treatment (Wagner and Abbott, 2007). We found that whereas men and women reported a similar frequency of discriminatory events, these events were experienced as more stressful to women. We also found that perceived discrimination was related to depression. More perceived discrimination was related to higher depressive symptoms, greater likelihood of clinically significant symptoms, and greater likelihood of patient-reported physician-diagnosed depression. Additionally, perceptions of discrimination within healthcare settings were associated with not taking antidepressant medication. Individuals who perceive discrimination in their healthcare system may have more depressive symptoms, but those same individuals may be less trusting of providers or the medications they recommend. Although it is true that some individuals may perceive a given situation as discriminatory while others may not, the objective nature of the stressor may have less impact on health outcomes than the event's subjective meaning (Lazarus,1978; Brondolo, Rieppi, Kelly, and Gerin, 2003).

In order to realize the benefits of efficacious depression treatment, screening must first be implemented to detect depression. Implementing pharmacotherapy for depression may be challenging among minorities and those individuals who perceive discrimination in their environment, particularly in the healthcare setting.

Conclusions and Future Directions

Rates of diabetes are high and rising. Depression is common in diabetes, especially among women. When depression occurs in diabetes, it increases risk for psychological, behavioral, and health problems. Depression may be one factor that explains diabetic women's higher rates of cardiovascular disease compared to both diabetic men and nondiabetic individuals.

Research investigating the effect of depression on diabetes outcomes has several limitations, the most important of which is an overly simplistic approach to depression assessment. Surprising data have emerged from studies that use clinical interviews rather than symptoms questionnaires, that investigate history of remitted depression, that assess number of episodes, that control for current depressive symptoms, and that differentiate depression and its treatment. Our studies of diabetic women illustrate that depression is associated with long-term health outcomes that are distal from the depressive episode. We encourage investigators to employ the strategies outlined in this chapter to assess history of depression, to establish appropriate control groups, and to more fully elucidate the relationship between depression and health outcomes in diabetes.

Efficacious treatments for depression in diabetes are available, some of which show benefits for health. However, under-detection and under-treatment of depression remains problematic, especially in minorities. Recommendations for gender-specific care of women with diabetes include screening for depression (Legato, et al. 2006). Clinicians are encouraged to screen, treat, or refer for treatment their patients with diabetes.

References

American Diabetes Association. (2001). *Diabetes 2001 vital statistics.* Alexandria, VA: American Diabetes Association.

American Diabetes Association. (2004). *Diabetes statistics for African Americans.* Retrieved April 20, 2004, from www.diabetes.org/ diabetes-statistics/african-americans.jsp

American Psychiatric Association (1994). *Diagnostic and Statistical Manual of Mental Disorders, 4th edition (DSM-IV^{TM}).* Washington, DC: American Psychiatric Association.

Amsterdam, J.D., Shults, J., Rutherford, N., Schwartz, S. (2006). Safety and efficacy of s-citalopram in patients with co-morbid major depression and diabetes mellitus. *Neuropsychobiology, 54,* 208-214.

Anderson, R. J., Freedland, K. E., Clouse, R. E., and Lustman, P. J. (2001). The prevalence of comorbid depression in adults with diabetes. *Diabetes Care, 24,* 1069-1078.

Aneshensel, C. S., Estrada, A. L., Hansell, M. J., and Clark, V. A. (1987). Social psychological aspects of reporting behavior: Lifetime depressive episode reports. *Journal of Health and Social Behavior, 28,* 232-246.

Aubert, R. (1995). Diabetes-related hospitalization and hospital utilization. In National Diabetes Data Group (Eds.), *Diabetes in America (2ⁿᵈ ed.) (NIH Publication No. 95-1468).* Bethesda, MD: National Institutes of Health.

Auslander, W. F., Thompson, S., Dreitzer, D., White N. H., and Santiago, J. V. (1997). Disparity in glycemic control and adherence between African-American and Caucasian youths with diabetes. Family and community contexts. *Diabetes Care, 20,* 1569-1575.

Bardone, A. M., Krahn, D. D., Goodman, B. M., and Searles, J. S. (2000). Using interactive voice response technology and timeline follow-back methodology in studying binge eating and drinking behavior: Different answers to different forms of the same question? *Addictive Behaviors, 25,* 1-11.

Basso, M. R. and Bornstein, R. A. (1999). Relative memory deficits in recurrent versus first-episode major depression on a word-list learning task. *Neuropsychology, 13,* 5557-63.

Beckles, G. and Thompson-Reid, A. (Eds.). (2001). *Diabetes and women's health across the life stages: A public health perspective.* Atlanta, GA: United States Department of Health and Human Services, Centers for Disease Control, National Center for Chronic Disease Prevention and Health Promotion, Division of Diabetes Translation.

Bialik, R. J., Ravindran, A. V., Bakish, D., and Lapierre, Y. D. (1995). A comparison of placebo responders and nonresponders in subgroups of depressive disorder. *Journal of Psychiatry and Neuroscience, 20,* 265-270.

Bijl, R. V., De Graff, R., Ravelli, A., Smit, F., and Vollebergh, W. A. (2002). Netherlands mental health survey and incidence study: Gender and age-specific first incidence of DSM-III-R psychiatric disorders in the general population. Social Psychiatry and Psychiatric Epidemiology, *37,* 372-379.

Bogner, H. R., Morales, K. H., Post, E. P., and Bruce, M. L. (2007). Diabetes, depression, and death: a randomized controlled trial of a depression treatment program for older adults based in primary care (PROSPECT). *Diabetes Care, 30,* 3005-3010.

Brondolo, E., Rieppi, R., Kelly, K. P., and Gerin, W. (2003). Perceived racism and blood pressure: A review of literature and conceptual and methodological critique. *Annals of Behavioral Medicine, 25,* 55-65.

Carey, K. B., Cocco, K. M., and Simons, J. S. (1996). Concurrent validity of clinicians' ratings of substance abuse among psychiatric outpatients. *Psychiatric Services, 7,* 842-847.

Centers for Disease Control (2000). State-specific prevalence of disability among adults - 11 states and the District of Columbia, 1998. *Mortality and Morbidity Weekly Report, 49,* 711-714.

Centers for Disease Control. (2002). http://www.cdc.gov/diabetes/statistics/survl99/chap2/table10.htm.

Centers for Disease Control and Prevention. (2005). National diabetes fact sheet: general information and national estimates on diabetes in the United States, 2005. Atlanta, GA: U.S. Department of Health and Human Services, Centers for Disease Control and Prevention.

Charles, H., Good, C. B., Hanusa, B. H., Chang, C. C., and Whittle, J. (2003). Racial differences in adherence to cardiac medications. *Journal of the National Medical Association, 95*, 17-27.

Ciechanowski, P.S., Russo, J.E., Katon, W.J., Von Korff, M., Simon, G.E., Lin, E.H.B., Ludman, E.J., Young, B. (2006). The association of patient relationship style and outcomes in collaborative care treatment for depression in patients with diabetes. *Medical Care, 44*, 283-291.

Ciechanowski, P. S., Katon, W. J., and Russo, J. E. (2000). Depression and diabetes: Impact of depressive symptoms on adherence, function, and costs. *Archives of Internal Medicine, 160*, 3278-3285.

Clouse, R. E., Lustman, P. J., Freedland, K. E., Griffith, L. S., McGill, J. B., and Carney, R. M. (2003). Depression and coronary heart disease in women with diabetes. *Psychosomatic Medicine, 65*, 376-383.

Contrada, R. J., Ashmore, R. D., and Gary, M. L. (2001). Measures of ethnicity-related stress: Psychometric properties, ethnic group differences, and associations with well-being. *Journal of Applied Social Psychology, 31*, 1775-1820.

Cowie, C. C. and Harris, M. I. (1995). Physical and metabolic characteristics of persons with diabetes. In National Diabetes Data Group (Eds.), *Diabetes in America (2nd ed.)*. (NIH Publication No. 95-1468), Bethesda MD: National Institutes of Health, 117-133.

Crosby, G. M., Stall, R. D., Paul, J. P., Barrett, D. C., and Midanik, L. T. (1996). Condom use among gay/bisexual male substance abusers using the TLFB method. *Addictive Behaviors, 21*, 249-57.

Crowther, C.A., Hiller, J.E., Moss, J.R., McPhee, A.J., Jeffries, W.S., Robinson, J.S., Australian Carbohydrate Intolerance Study in Pregnant Women (ACHOIS) Trial Group (2005). Effect of treatment of gestational diabetes mellitus on pregnancy outcomes. *New England Journal of Medicine, 352*, 2477-86.

de Groot, M., Anderson, R., Freedland, K. E., Clouse, R. E., and Lustman, P. J. (2001). Association of depression and diabetes complications: a meta-analysis. *Psychosomatic Medicine, 63*, 619-30.

de Groot, M., Pinkerman, B., Wagner, J., and Hockman, E. (2006). Depression treatment and satisfaction in a multicultural sample of type 1 and type 2 diabetic patients. *Diabetes Care, 29*, 549-553.

Department of Health and Human Services. (1999). *Diabetes Surveillance, 1999*. Atlanta, GA: Dept. of Health and Human Services, Public Health Service.

Diabetes Control and Complications Trial Research Group (1993). The effect of intensive treatment of diabetes on the development and progression of long-term complications in insulin-dependent diabetes mellitus. *New England Journal of Medicine, 329*, 977-985.

Eborall, H.C., Griffin, S.J., Prevost, A.T., Kinmonth, A.L., French, D.P., Sutton, S. (2007). Psychological impact of screening for type 2 diabetes: controlled trial and comparative study embedded in the ADDITION (Cambridge) randomised controlled trial. *British Medical Journal, 335*, 486-494.

Egede, L. E. (2004). Diabetes, major depression and functional disability among U.S. adults. *Diabetes Care, 27*, 421-428.

Egede, L. E., Zheng, D., and Simpson, K. (2002). Comorbid depression is associated with increased health care use and expenditures in individuals with diabetes. *Diabetes Care, 25*, 464-70.

Fifield, J., McQuillan, J., Tennen, H., Sheehan, T. J., Reisine, S., Hesselbrock, V., and Rothfield, N. (2001). History of affective disorder and the temporal trajectory of fatigue in rheumatoid arthritis. *Annals of Behavioral Medicine, 23*, 34-41.

First, M., Spitzer, R., Gibbon, M., and Williams, J. (1998). *Structured clinical interview from DSM-IV, axis disorders- patient edition* (SCID-I/P Version 2.0, 8/98 revision). New York, NY, New York State Psychiatric Institute.

Fisher, L., Skaff, M.M., Mullan, J.T., Arean, P., Mohr, D., Masharani, U., Glasgow, R., and Laurencin, G. (2007). Clinical depression versus distress among patients with type 2 diabetes: not just a question of semantics. *Diabetes Care, 30*, 542-548.

Gary, T. L., Crum, R. M., Cooper-Patrick, L., Ford, D., Brancati, F. L. (2000). Depressive symptoms and metabolic control in African-Americans with type 2 diabetes. *Diabetes Care, 23*, 23-29.

Gastpar, M., Bonnet, U., Böning, J., Mann, Schmidt, L. G., Soyka, M., Wetterling, T., Kielstein, V., Labriola, D., and Croop, R. (2002). Lack of efficacy of naltrexone in the prevention of alcohol relapse: Results from a German multicenter study. *Journal of Clinical Psychopharmacology, 22*, 592-598.

Grandinetti, A., Kaholokula, J., Crabbe, K., Kenui, C., Chen, R., and Chang, H. (2000). Relationship between depressive symptoms and diabetes among native Hawaiians. *Psychoneuroendocrinology, 25*, 239-46.

Grootenhuis, P. A., Snoek, F. J., Heine, R. J., Heine, R. J., and Bouter, L. M. (2004). Development of a type 2 diabetes symptom checklist: a measure of symptom severity. *Diabetic Medicine, 11*, 253-261.

Gross, R., Olfson, M., Gameroff, M. J., Carasquillo, O., Shea, S., Feder, A., Lantigua, R., Fuentes, M., and Weissman, M. M. (2004). Depression and glycemic control in Hispanic primary care patients with diabetes. *Journal of General Internal Medicine, 20*, 460-466.

Gu, K., Cowie, C. C., and Harris, M. I. (1998). Mortality in adults with and without diabetes in a national cohort of the U.S., 1971-1993. *Diabetes Care, 21*, 1138-1145.

Haffner, S. M., Lehto, S., Rönnemaa, T., Pyörälä, K., and Laakso, M. (1998). Mortality from coronary heart disease in subjects with type 2 diabetes and in nondiabetic subjects with and without prior myocardial infarction. *New England Journal of Medicine, 339*, 229-234.

Haffner, S. M., Rosenthal, M., Hazuda, H. P., Stern, M. P., and Franco, L. J. (1984). Evaluation of three potential screening tests for diabetes mellitus in a biethnic population. *Diabetes Care, 7*, 347-353.

Harkness, K.L., Monroe, S.M., Simons, A.D., and Thase, M. (1999). The generation of life events in recurrent and non-recurrent depression. *Psychological Medicine, 29*, 135-144.

Harris, M. I., Flegal, K. M., Cowie, C. C., Eberhardt, M. S., Goldstein, D. E., Little, R. R., Wiedmeyer, H. M., and Byrd-Holt, D. D. (1998). Prevalence of diabetes, impaired fasting glucose, and impaired glucose tolerance in U.S. adults: The third national health and nutrition examination survey, 1988-1994. *Diabetes Care, 21*, 518-524.

Harris, M. I., Klein, R., Cowie, C., Rowland, M., and Byrd-Holt, D. D. (1998). Is the risk of diabetic retinopathy greater in non-Hispanic AAs and Mexican Americans than in non-Hispanic Whites with type 2 diabetes? A U.S. population study. *Diabetes Care, 21,* 1230-1235.

Hays, R. D., Wells, K. B., Sherbourne, C. D., Rogers, W., and Spritzer, K. (1995). Functioning and well-being outcomes of patients with depression compared with chronic general medical illnesses. *Archives of General Psychiatry, 52,* 11-19.

Herbst, S., Pietrzak, R.H., Wagner, J., White, W.B., and Petry, N.M. (2007). Lifetime major depression is associated with coronary heart disease in older adults: Results from the national epidemiologic survey on alcohol and related conditions. *Psychosomatic Medicine, 69,* 729-735.

Hersh, D., Mulgrew, C. L., Van Kirk, J., and Kranzler, H. R. (1999). The validity of self-reported cocaine use in two groups of cocaine abusers. *Journal of Consulting and Clinical Psychology 67,* 37-42.

Hodgins, D. and Makarchuk, K. (2003). Trusting problem gamblers: Reliability and validity of self-reported gambling behavior. *Psychology of Addictive Behaviors, 17,* 244-248.

Hood, K.K., Bennett Johnson, S., Carmichael, S.K., Laffel, L.M.B., She, J.X., Schatz, D.A. (2005). Depressive symptoms in mothers of infants identified as genetically at risk for type 1 diabetes. *Diabetes Care, 28,* 1898-1903.

Jindal, R.D., Thase, M.F., Fasiczka, A.L., Friedman, E.S., Buysse, D.J., Frank, E., and Kupfer, D.J. (2002). Electroencephalographic sleep profiles in single episode and recurrent unipolar forms of major depression: II. Comparison during remission. *Biological Psychiatry, 51,* 230-236.

Kannel, W.B. and McGee, D.L. (1979). Diabetes and glucose tolerance as risk factors for cardiovascular disease: the Framingham study. *Diabetes Care, 2,* 120-126.

Kannel, W. and Sorlie, P. (1997). Framingham physical activity index. In M Pereira et al (Eds.). A collection of physical activity questionnaires for health-related research: *Medicine and Science in Sports and Exercise, 29,* S33-5.

Katon, W. J., Simon, G., Russo, J., Von Korff, M., Lin, E. H., Ludman, E., Ciechanowski, P., and Bush, T. (2004). Quality of depression care in a population-based sample of patients with diabetes and major depression. *Medical Care, 42,* 1222-1229.

Katon, W.J., Von Korff, M., Lin, E.H., Simon, G., Ludman, E., Russo,J., Ciechanowski, P., Walker, E., and Bush, T. (2004). The pathways study: a randomized trial of collaborative care in patients with diabetes and depression. *Archives of General Psychiatry, 61,* 1042-1049.

Kendler, K., Thornton, L., and Gardener, C. (2000). Stressful life event and previous episodes in the etiology of major depression in women: An evaluation of the 'kindling' hypothesis. American *Journal of Psychiatry, 157,* 1243-1251.

Kendler, K., Thornton, L., and Gardner, C. (2001). Genetic risk, number of previous depressive episodes, and stressful life events in predicting onset of major depression. *American Journal of Psychiatry, 158,* 582-586.

Kerbel, D., Glazier, R., Holzapfel, S., Yeung ,M., Lofsky, S. (1997). Adverse effects of screening for gestational diabetes: a prospective cohort study in Toronto, Canada. *Journal of Medical Screening, 4,* 128-32.

Kessler, R. C., McGonagle, K. A., Zhao, S., Nelson, C. B., Hughes, M., Eshleman, S., Wittchen, H-U., and Kendler, KS. (1994). Lifetime and 12-month prevalence of DSM-III-R psychiatric disorders in the United States. *Archives of General Psychiatry*, *51*, 8-19.

Kinder, L. S., Katon, W. J., Ludman, E., Russo, J., Simon, G., Lin, E. H., Ciechanowski, P., Von Korff, M., and Young, B. (2006). Improving depression care in patients with diabetes and multiple complications. *Journal of General Internal Medicine*, *21*, 1036-1041.

Knowler, W.C., Barrett-Connor, E., Fowler, S.E., Hamman, R.F., Lachin, J.M., Walker, E.A., and Nathan, D.M. (2002). Reduction in the incidence of type 2 diabetes with lifestyle intervention or metformin. *New England Journal of Medicine, 346*, 393-403.

Kerruish, N.J., Campbell-Stokes, P.L., Gray, A., Merriman, T.R., Robertson, S.P., Taylor, B.J. (2007). Maternal psychological reaction to newborn genetic screening for type 1 diabetes. *Pediatrics, 120,* 324-35.

Langer, N., and Langer, O. Emotional adjustment to diagnosis and intensified treatment of gestational diabetes. *Obstetrics and Gynecology, 84*, 329-334.

Lazarus, R. S. (1978). A strategy for research on psychological and social factors in hypertension. Journal of Human Stress, *4*, 35-40.

Legato, M.J., Gelzer A, Goland, R., Ebner, S..A, Rajan, S., Villagra, V., Kosowski, M., Writing Group for The Partnership for Gender-Specific Medicine (2006). Gender-specific care of the patient with diabetes: review and recommendations. *Gender Medicine, 3,* 131-158.

Lesperance, F., Frasure-Smith, N., and Talajic, M. (1996). Major depression before and after myocardial infarction: its nature and consequences. *Psychosomatic Medicine*, *58*, 99-110.

Li, C., Ford, E.S., Strine, T.W., Mokdad, A.H. (2008). Prevalence of depression among U.S. adults with diabetes: Findings from the 2006 Behavioral Risk Factor Surveillance System. *Diabetes Care 31,* 105-107.

Lustman, P.J., Anderson, R.J., Freedland, K.E., de Groot, M., Carney, R.M. and Clouse, R.E. (2000). Depression and poor glycemic control.: A meta-analytic review of the literature. *Diabetes Care*, *23*, 934-942.

Lustman, P.J., Clouse, R.E., Ciechanowski, P.S., Hirsch, I.B., and Freedland, K.E. (2005). Depression-related hyperglycemia in type 1 diabetes: A mediational approach. *Psychosomatic Medicine*, *67*, 195-199.

Lustman, P. J., Clouse, R. E., and Freedland, K. E. (1998). Management of major depression in adults with diabetes: Implications of recent clinical trials. *Seminars in Clinical Neuropsychiatry. 3*, 102-114.

Lustman, P. J., Clouse, R. E., Griffith, L. S., Carney, R. M., and Freedland, K. E. (1997). Screening for depression in diabetes using the Beck Depression Inventory. *Psychosomatic Medicine*, *59*, 24-31.

Lustman, P. J., Clouse, R. E., Nix, B. D., Freedland, K. E., Ribin, E. H., McGill, J. B., Williams, M. M., Gelenberg, A. J., Ciechanowski, P. S., and Hirsch, I. B.(2006). Sertraline for prevention of depression recurrence in diabetes mellitus: a randomized, double-blind, placebo-controlled trial. *Archives of General Psychiatry*, *63*, 521-529.

Lustman, P.J., Frank, B.L., and McGill, J.B. (1991). Relationship of personality characteristics to glucose regulation in adults with diabetes. *Psychosomatic Medicine, 53,* 305-312.

Lustman, P. J., Freedland, K. E., Griffith, L. S., and Clouse, R. E. (1998). Predicting response to cognitive behavior therapy of depression in type 2 diabetes. *General Hospital Psychiatry, 20,* 302-306.

Lustman, P. J., Freedland, K. E., Griffith, L. S., and Clouse, R. E. (2000). Fluoxetine for depression in diabetes: A randomized double blind placebo-controlled trial. *Diabetes Care, 23,* 618-623.

Lustman, P. J., Griffith, L. S., Clouse, R. E., Freedland, K. E., Eisen, S. A., Rubin, E. H., Carney, R. M., and McGill, J. B. (1995). Effects of alprazolam on glucose regulation in diabetes. Results of double-blind, placebo-controlled trial. *Diabetes Care, 18,* 1133-1139.

Lustman, P. J., Griffith, L. S., Clouse, R. E., Freedland, K. E., Eisen, S. A., Rubin, E. H., Carney, R. M., and McGill, J. B. (1998). Effects of nortryptyline on depression and glycemic control in diabetes: results of a double blind, placebo-controlled trial. *Psychosomatic Medicine, 59,* 241-250.

Midanik, L. T., Hines, A. M., Barrett, D. C., Paul, J. P., Crosby, G. M., and Stall, R. D. (1998). Self-reports of alcohol use, drug use and sexual behavior: Expanding the TLFB technique. *Journal of Studies on Alcohol, 59,* 681-689.

Mokdad, A. H., Ford, E. S., Bowman, B.A., Nelson, D. E., Engelgau, M. M., Vinicor, F., and Marks, J. S. (2000). The continuing increase of diabetes in the US. *Diabetes Care, 24,* 412.

National Institute on Alcohol Abuse and Alcoholism.(2004). Retrieved December 16, 2004 from the NIAAA website: http://www.niaaa.nih.gov/publications/publications-text.htm

Nau, D.P., Aikens, J.E., and Pacholski, A.M. (2007). Effects of gender and depression on oral medication adherence in persons with type 2 diabetes mellitus. *Gender Medicine, 4,* 205-213

Okamura, F., Tashiro, A., Utumi, A., Imai, T., Suchi, T., Tamura, D., Sato, Y., Suzuki, S., and Hongo, M. (2000). Insulin resistance in patients with depression and it changes during the clinical course of depression: Minimal model analysis. *Metabolism, 49,* 1255-1260.

Peyrot, M. and Rubin, R. R. (1999). Persistence of depressive symptoms in diabetic adults. *Diabetes Care, 22,* 448-452.

Post, RM. (1992). Transduction of psychosocial stress into the neurobiology of recurrent affective disorder. *American Journal of Psychiatry, 49,* 999-1010.

Pouwer, F., Snoek, F.J. (2001). Association between symptoms of depression and glycaemic control may be unstable across gender. *Diabetic Medicine, 18,* 595-598.

Project MATCH Research Group. (1993). Rationale and methods for a multisite clinical trial matching patients to alcoholism treatment. *Alcoholism, Clinical and Experimental Research, 17,* 1130-1145.

Radloff, L. S. (1977). The CES-D scale: A self-report depression scale for research in the general population. Applied Psychological Measurement, 1, 385-401.

Robins, L.N., Helzer, J.E., Cottler, L.B., and Goldring, E. The Diagnostic Interview Schedule-Version III-R. St. Louis, Washington University, 1989.

Ruggiero, L., Glasgow, R., Dryfoos, J. M., Rossi, J. S., Prochaska, J. O., Orleans, C. T., Prokhorov, A. V., Rossi, S. R., Greene, G. W., Reed, G. R., Kelly, K., Chobanian, L., and Johnson, S. (1997). Diabetes self-management: Self-reported recommendations and patterns in a large population. *Diabetes Care, 20,* 568-576.

Ruggiero, L., Wagner, J., and de Groot, M. (2006). Understanding the individual. In Walker, E. (Ed.), *The Art and Science of Diabetes Self-Management Education: A Desk Reference for Healthcare Professionals*, 2nd ed. Chicago, American Association of Diabetes Educators.

Rumbold, A.R., and Crowther, C.A. (2002). Women's experiences of being screened for gestational diabetes mellitus. Australian and New Zealand Journal of Obstetrics and Gynaecology 42, 131-137.

Sahmoun, A.E., Markland, M.J., and Helgerson, S.D. (2007). Mental health status and diabetes among Whites and Native Americans: is race an effect modifier? Journal of Health Care for the Poor and Underserved, 18, 599-608.

Sanders, N.M., Wilkinson, C.W., Taborsky, G.J., Al-Noori, S., Daumen, W., Zavosh, A., Figlewicz, D.P. (2008). The selective serotonin reuptake inhibitor sertraline enhances counterregulatory responses to hypoglycemia. American Journal of Physiolical Endocrinology and Metabolism, 294, E853-60.

Segal, Z., Williams, J., Teasdale J., and Gemar, M. (1996). A cognitive science perspective on kindling and episode sensitization in recurrent affective disorder. Psychological Medicine, 26, 371-180.

Sheline, Y. I., Sanghavi, M., Mintun, M. A., and Gado M. H.(1999). Depression duration but not age predicts hippocampal volume loss in medically healthy women with recurrent major depression. Journal of Neuroscience, 19, 5034-5043

Shimizu. S., Ito, N., Fujiwara, M., Takanashi, K., Weerakoon, S., Deshapriya, E. B. (1997). Is the TLFB method applicable to Japanese drinking population?: Methodological study on measurement of alcohol consumption. Nihon Arukoru Yakubutsu Igakkai Zasshi, 32,163-181.

Simon, G. E., Katon, W. J., Lin, E. H., Rutter, C., Manning, W. G., Von Korff, M., Ciechanowski, P., Ludman, E. J., and Young, B. A. (2007). Cost-effectiveness of systematic depression treatment among people with diabetes mellitus. *Archives of General Psychiatry, 64,* 65-72.

Skre, I. (1991). High interrater reliability for the Structured Clinical Interview for DSM Axis 1. *Acta Psychiatrica Scandinavica, 84,* 167-173.

Smedley, B. D., Stith, A. Y., Nelson, A. R. (Eds.). (2003). *Unequal treatment: Confronting racial and ethnic disparities in health care*. Washington, DC, National Academies Press.

Sobell, L. and Sobell, M. (1995). *Alcohol timeline followback user's manual.* Toronto, ON: Addiction Research Foundation.

Solomon, D., Keller, M., Leon, A., Mueller, T. I., Lavori, P. W., Shea, M. T., Coryell, W., Warshaw, M., Turvey, C., Maser, J. D., and Endicott, J. (2000). Multiple recurrences of major depressive disorder. *American Journal of Psychiatry, 157,* 229-233.

Soyka, M., Aichmüller C., v Bardeleben, U., Beneke, M., Glaser, T., Hornung-Knobel, S., Wegner, U. (2003). Flupenthixol in relapse prevention in schizophrenics with comorbid alcoholism. *European Addition Research, 9*, 65-72.

Stein M. D., Anderson, B., Charuvastra A., and Friedmann, P. D. (2001). Alcohol use and sexual risk taking among hazardously drinking drug injectors who attend needle exchange. *Alcoholism, Clinical and Experimental Research, 25*, 1487-1493.

Stephens, R. S., Babor, T. F., Kadden, R., and Miller, M. (2002). The marijuana treatment project: Rationale, design and participant characteristics. Addiction, 97(S1), 109-124.

Suarez, E.C. (2006). Sex differences in the relation of depressive symptoms, hostility, and anger expression to indices of glucose metabolism in nondiabetic adults. Health Psychology, 25, 484-92.

Swenson, S.L., Rose, M., Vittinghoff, E., Stewart, A., Schillinger, D. (2008). The influence of depressive symptoms on clinician-patient communication among patients with type 2 diabetes. Medical Care, 46, 257-65.

Tennen, H., Eberhardt, T., and Affleck, G. (1999). Depression research methodologies at the social-clinical interface: Still hazy after all these years. *Journal of Social and Clinical Psychology, 18*, 121-159.

Tennen, H., Hall, J., and Affleck, G. (1995a). Depression research methodologies in Journal of Personality and Social Psychology: A review and critique. *Journal of Personality and Social Psychology, 68*, 870-884.

Tennen, H., Hall, J., and Affleck, G. (1995b). Rigor, rigor mortis, and conspiratorial views of depression research. *Journal of Personality and Social Psychology, 68*, 895-900.

United Kingdom Prospective Diabetes Study (UKPDS)Group (1998). Intensive blood-glucose control with sulphonylureas or insulin compared with conventional treatment and risk of complications in patients with type 2 diabetes. *Lancet, 12*, 837-53.

United States Bureau of the Census. (1996). Population projections of the United States by age, sex, race, and Hispanic origins: 1995 to 2050. Current Population Reports, Series P25, No. 1130. Washington DC: US Government Printing Office.

United States Renal Data System. (1999). *USRDS 1999 Annual Data Report*, NIH, NIDDK, Bethesda MD 1999; CDCP, Division of Diabetes Translation: ESRD.

Ustün, T. B., Ayuso-Mateos, J. L., Chatterji, S., Mathers, C., and Murray, C. J. (2004). Global burden of depressive disorders in the year 2000. *British Journal of Psychiatry, 184*, 386-392.

Vinson, D., Reidinger, C., and Wilcosky, T. (2003). Factors affecting the validity of a TLFB interview. *Journal of Studies on Alcohol ,64*, 733-740.

Wagner, J. and Abbott, G. (2007). Depression and depression care in diabetes: Relationship to perceived discrimination in African Americans. *Diabetes Care, 30*, 364-366.

Wagner, J., Lacey, K., Abbott, G., de Groot, M., and Chyun, D. (2006). Knowledge of heart disease risk in a multicultural community sample of people with diabetes. *Annals of Behavioral Medicine, 31*, 224-230.

Wagner, J., Malchoff, C., and Abbott, G. (2005). Invasiveness as a barrier to self-monitoring of blood glucose in people with diabetes. *Diabetes Technology and Therapeutics, 7*, 612-619.

Wagner, J. and Tennen, H. (2007). History of major depressive disorder and diabetes outcomes among diet and tablet treated postmenopausal women: A case control study. *Diabetic Medicine, 24*, 211-216.

Wagner, J., Tennen, H., Mansoor, G., and Abbott, G. (in press). Endothelial dysfunction and history of depression in post-menopausal women with type 2 diabetes: A case control study. *Journal of Diabetes and its Complications.*

Wagner, J., Tsimikas, J., Heapy, A., de Groot, M., and Abbott, G. (2007). Ethnic and racial differences in diabetic patients' depressive symptoms, diagnosis, and treatment. *Diabetes Research and Clinical Practice, 75*, 119-122.

Wassertheil-Smoller, S., Shumaker, S., Ockene, J., Talavera, G. A., Greenland, P., Cochrane, B., Robbins, J., Aragaki, A., and Dunbar-Jacob J. (2—4). Depression and cardiovascular sequelae in postmenopausal women. The Women's Health Initiative (WHI). *Archives of Internal, 164*, 289-298.

Weinhardt, L. S., Carey, M. P., Maisto, S. A., Carey, K. B., Cohen, M. M., and Wickramasinghe, S. M. (1998). Reliability of the timeline follow-back sexual behavior interview. *Annals of Behavioral Medicine, 20,* 25-30.

Weinstock, J., Whelan, J. P. and Meyers, A. W. (2004). Behavioral assessment of gambling: an application of the TLFB method. *Psychological Assessment,16,* 72-80.

Wells, K. B., Stewart, A., Hays, R. D., Burnam, M. A., Rogers, W., Daniels, M., Berry, S., Greenfield, S., and Ware, J. (1989). The functioning and well-being of depressed patients: results from the medical outcomes study. J*ournal of the American Medical Association, 262*, 914-919.

Wickramasinghe, S. (1998). Reliability of the timeline follow-back sexual behavior interview. *Annals of Behavioral Medicine, 20*, 25-30.

York, R., Brown, L.P., Persily, C.A., Jacobsen, B.S. (1996). Affect in diabetic women during pregnancy and postpartum. *Nursing Research, 45*, 54-6.

Zhang, X., Norris, S. L., Gregg, E. W., Cheng, Y. J., Beckles, G., and Kahn, H. S. (2005). Depressive symptoms and mortality among persons with and without diabetes. *American Journal of Epidemiology, 161*, 652-660.

In: Women and Depression
Editors: Paula Hernandez and Sara Alonso

ISBN 978-1-60456-647-5
© 2009 Nova Science Publishers, Inc.

Chapter 12

Risk and Resilience Factors for Depression in Women with Cancer

Laurie E. Ching[1], Linda E. Carlson[1,2] and Keith Dobson[1]
[1]University of Calgary Department of Psychology, Canada
[2] University of Calgary Department of Oncology, Canada

Abstract

The psychological and physical challenges associated with cancer often result in considerable distress and symptoms of depression. Major Depression is a significant mental health concern among patients with cancer, as it affects 20 – 25% of all patients diagnosed with cancer. This chapter examines the factors that both increase and decrease the risk of developing depression following a cancer diagnosis. Cancer related variables including the type of cancer, stage of disease, and level of pain and physical impairment are examined as they relate to depression in women with cancer. Other risk factors including age, prior history of depression, and coping style are also examined. In addition, spirituality and religiosity, as well as level and quality of social support are discussed as buffering factors against the negative effects of a cancer diagnosis. Knowledge and understanding of these factors are imperative for appropriate assessment and diagnosis of depression in oncology patients, and the implications and limitations of this body of research are briefly examined.

Introduction

A diagnosis of cancer is often accompanied by stress, fear, emotional distress, and uncertainty regarding the future. For many individuals, a diagnosis of cancer evokes fears of dying, becoming dependent on one's family members, and the possibility of changes to their appearance and bodily functioning (Massie and Popkin, 1998). The psychological and physical challenges associated with cancer can result in considerable distress and symptoms of depression. Given the weight and impact of such a diagnosis individuals typically respond with shock, disbelief, anxiety, difficulty concentrating, sadness, and changes in mood, appetite, and sleep patterns. For many individuals, the initial distress and fear begin to dissipate as a plan of action is put into place, and the individual receives support from those around them (Massie and Popkin, 1998). However, for a smaller number of individuals, the symptoms of anxiety and depression do not dissipate over time and may interfere with daily functioning. Differentiating between the normal grief response associated with receiving a potentially lethal diagnosis, and that which constitutes a maladaptive response is imperative in distinguishing between individuals who may benefit from support and information and those that require treatment and additional assistance. This chapter provides a comprehensive examination of the factors that affect the development of depression in women with cancer.

Depression in Patients with Cancer

The lifetime prevalence of Major Depression in the general population has been estimated at approximately 10% - 25% in women and 5% - 12% in men (APA, 2004). There is a large body of literature examining depression associated with cancer; however, there is significant variability in the prevalence of depression in cancer patients reported from study to study. This variability is due to the lack of uniformity in the definition of depression utilized in each study, the criteria used to identify individuals with depression, the methods used to assess for depression, and the heterogeneity in the populations studied (Massie, 2004). As a result, estimates of the prevalence of depression in cancer patients range between 0% - 38% for Major Depression, and 0% - 58% for depressive symptoms and other depressive disorders (e.g., adjustment disorder with depressed mood) (Massie, 2004).

A review of the literature conducted by Pirl (2004) identified eleven studies which utilized *Diagnostic and Statistical Manual of Mental Disorders* (DSM) version III or IV criteria to diagnose depression in individuals with cancer. Ten of these studies utilized an interview which included DSM criteria, and one utilized the Structured Clinical Interview for the DSM. All but two studies assessed depression in hospitalized cancer patients. Despite the use of standardized criteria for diagnosing depression in patients with cancer, the reported rates of depression ranged from 1% - 42% for Major Depressive Disorder (MDD) and 10% - 24% for elevated levels of depression symptoms, or adjustment disorder with depressed mood (Alexander, Dinesh, and Vidyasagar, 1993; Berard, Boermeester, and Viljoen, 1998; Breitbart et al., 2000; Bukberg, Penman, and Holland, 1984; Colon, Callies, Popkin, and McGlare, 1991; Derogatis et al., 1983; Evans et al., 1986; Golden et al., 1991; Grandi et al., 1987; Morton, Davies, Baker, Baker, and Stell; 1984; Sneeuw et al., 1993). Six of the eleven studies found rates of MDD in the 10% - 25% range (Alexander, Dinesh, and Vidyasagar, 1993; Berard, Boermeester, and Viljoen, 1998; Breitbart et al., 2000; Evans et al., 1986; Golden et al., 1991; Grandi et al., 1987). Pirl determined that this variability makes it difficult to draw conclusions about the prevalence of MDD in patients with cancer. The variability in prevalence rates reported was due in large part to the heterogeneity of the samples used in each study. For example, several different types of cancers were examined across studies including lung cancer, breast cancer, lymphoma, head and neck cancers, and gynecologic cancers. Studies were also heterogeneous in the stage of cancer examined. Some studies included patients with early stage cancer while others examined patients with late stage cancer. Several studies did not note the stage of cancer at all, and other studies included patients regardless of the stage of disease. One study also included patients with no evidence of current disease who had completed treatment three years prior (Morton et al., 1984).

Pirl (2004) also reviewed twelve studies which assessed symptoms of depression using the Hospital Anxiety and Depression Scale (HADS). The HADS is the most commonly used screening measure in this population. It identifies individuals who endorse a large number of depressive symptoms and who are therefore at elevated risk for a diagnosis of depression. Unlike those studies that employed DSM criteria to diagnose individuals with depression, those using the HADS assessed outpatient populations, and only 2 of the twelve studies assessed hospitalized patients. Despite using a consistent depression measure there was wide variability in the estimated prevalence rates, ranging from 1.5% - 45% for significant depressive symptoms, and 7% - 21% for probable cases of depression. In addition to the heterogeneity of samples used in these studies, the use of different cutoff scores to identify individuals with clinically significant levels of depressive symptoms contributed to the variability in prevalence rates.

It is clear that estimates of the prevalence of depression in cancer patients vary dramatically depending on the measures used to assess for depression, the diagnostic criteria used, and the patient population examined in each study. While there has been wide variation in the rates of depression found in this group, the emerging consensus is that MDD affects 20% - 25% of all patients with cancer, and that an even greater number of patients endorse a significant number of depression symptoms at some point during their illness (Breitbart, 1995; Massie and Holland, 1990). Further complicating our understanding of the prevalence of depression in cancer patients, however, are factors such as type of cancer, stage of cancer, and other variables unrelated to the disease which play an important role in increasing the risk that a patient with cancer will develop depression. Unfortunately, much of the literature fails to specify these factors, even though they likely account for a large amount of the variability in reported rates of depression. Thus, the following sections will examine the prevalence of depression across different types of cancer and later, the role of stage of cancer and other risk factors will be examined as they relate to depression in patients with cancer.

Gender Difference in the Prevalence of Depression in Patients with Cancer

The gender difference in depression is a well established finding in the general population (APA, 2004), as the prevalence rate of depression in adult women is roughly double that of men. However, the research examining the prevalence of depression in patients with cancer indicates that women with cancer are no more likely than men with cancer to be depressed. Thus, while Plumb and Holland (1981) found more men than women with Hodgkin's disease, multiple myeloma, and a variety of solid tumors to be severely depressed, DeFlorio and Massie (1995) found no gender difference in 23 of the 30 studies in their review of gender differences. A small number of studies have reported higher rates of depression in women (Craig and Abeloff, 1974; Lloyd, Parker, Ludlam, and McGuire, 1984;

Pettingale, , Burgess, and Greer, 1987); however, the majority of studies in this area indicate no gender difference, or gender differences in subsets of patients with both men and women having higher rates of depression depending on the sample, and the measures used to identify individuals with depression (Massie, 2004). Thus, it does not appear that the same gender difference present in the general population is found in patients with cancer.

Notwithstanding the lack of gender difference in the rates of depression in patients with cancer, it is possible that the factors associated with risk of depression vary between the genders. Depression in women with cancer is complex and affected by multiple risk and resilience factors, examined below with specificity to women where possible.

Difficulty Diagnosing Depression in Cancer Patients

One of the dilemmas that face mental health professionals who diagnose depression in cancer patients is the overlap among the somatic symptoms of cancer and the associated treatments, and the somatic symptoms experienced in depression (e.g., sleep disturbance, changes in appetite, changes in motor functioning). It has been argued that the inclusion of somatic symptoms in the diagnosis of depression in cancer patients can result in an over-diagnosis of depression in this group. The concern regarding over-diagnosis has resulted in several different approaches to diagnosing depression in cancer patients (Newport and Nemeroff, 1998). The *inclusive* approach assesses and includes all of the symptoms of depression, even if they may be secondary to the medical disorder. The *exclusive* approach excludes fatigue and loss of appetite from the symptoms used to diagnose depression. The *substitutive* approach replaces somatic symptoms with cognitive symptoms to make a diagnosis. Finally, the *etiological* approach requires that each symptom be included only if it is clearly not secondary to the comorbid medical disorder. The exclusion of the somatic symptoms of depression in patients with cancer may result in the under-recognition and under-treatment of depression in this population.

A barrier to the recognition and treatment of depression in patients with cancer is that sadness and psychological distress are, to a certain extent, normal responses to a diagnosis. In many cases physicians and health care professionals believe patients are rightfully depressed given the potentially life threatening nature of cancer. This minimization of depression symptoms can result in the under-recognition and hence under-treatment of clinically significant depression. There is currently no standardized approach for diagnosing depression in patients with cancer, however, the somatic symptoms of depression are often not considered in diagnosing depression in oncology patients.

Risk Factors

Cancer-Related Variables

Several risk factors for depression in patients with cancer are the direct result of the cancer and its treatment. Cancer-related risk factors include the type of cancer, the stage of cancer, and the level of pain and physical impairment experienced by the individual.

Type of Cancer. All types of cancer are not equally associated with risk of depression in those who contract them. A review conducted by Massie (2004) found a lower prevalence of depression in patients with colon cancer (13% - 25%), gynecological cancer (12% - 23%), and lymphoma (8% - 19%), compared to those patients with lung (11% - 44%), oropharyngeal (22% - 57%), pancreatic (33% - 50%), and breast (1.5% - 46%) cancers, which were most highly associated with depression. In addition to these cancers, liver cancer (54.4%) and leukemia (54.2%) were highly associated with depression (Zabora, Brintzenhofeszoc, Curbow, Hooker, and Piantadosi, 2001). In considering why lung cancer may be associated with higher rates of distress, Zabora et al. propose that poor prognosis, as well as guilt and self-blame often associated with smoking in lung cancer patients, may result in the high level of distress seen in these individuals. Similarly, head and neck cancers are often associated with lifestyle behaviors such as smoking and excess alcohol consumption. Smoking itself is associated with higher levels of depression and so may be a confounding variable in smoking-related cancers. Other cancers such as oropharyngeal and liver cancer may be associated with substance abuse, and also require multi-modality treatments. Thus, these patients may experience more distress as a result of the demanding treatments and potential complications from these treatments. Oropharyngeal cancer can also be associated with physical disfigurement, and impairments in speech, vision, hearing, taste, and smell. These changes can affect self-image and interpersonal relationships, as well as the individual's ability to participate in and derive pleasure from everyday tasks (Moadel, Ostroff, and Schantz, 1998). Pancreatic cancer is also associated with poor prognosis as many of the therapies available for this form of cancer are relatively ineffective and physically taxing. Thus, patients may accurately experience more negative beliefs about their prognosis from doctors and family members, compared to those whose cancers have a better prognosis. Pancreatic cancer has also been associated with an increased risk of depression due to the enzymes, hormones, neurotransmitters, and acid-base imbalances common with this type of cancer (Green and Austin, 1993).

Of particular interest in this chapter are breast cancer and gynecologic cancer, not only because of their exclusivity in women, but because of the relatively large amount of literature conducted on women with these two types of cancers. Several factors may account for an increased risk of depression in patients with breast cancer. Breast cancer is the most common form of cancer among women, and as many as 46% of women with breast cancer may develop depression. Breast cancer affects a region of the body with particular significance for a woman's sense of femininity, attractiveness, and self-esteem. Treatments can be invasive, and may result in disfigurement which can also affect a women's self-image.

Gynecologic cancer is a form of cancer unique to women, and as many as one third of women with this type of cancer develop depression. Like breast cancer, gynecologic cancer affects a part of the body with particular significance for a woman's sense of female identity, fertility, attractiveness, and sexuality. Treatments for gynecologic cancers may have detrimental effects on reproductive ability and interpersonal relationships given the lasting impact on the reproductive and sexual organs. Many women with this type of cancer, particularly cervical cancer, experience guilt and self-blame due to self-attributions regarding the etiology of the cancer (Gotheridge, Dresner, 2002). For example, the etiology of cervical cancer is often associated with sexual activity. As a result, some women believe that their past sexual practices have resulted in the development of cervical cancer.

Stage of Cancer. In several studies of patients with mixed diagnoses (Ciaramella and Poli, 2001; Friedman, Baer, Lewy, Lane, and Smith, 1989; Kugaya, Akechi, Okamura, Mikami, and Uchitomi, 1999; Sellick and Crooks, 1999) and women with cancer (Norton et al., 2004), advanced stage of disease has been correlated with a higher prevalence of depression. For example, Ciaramella and Poli (2001) found higher rates of depression in patients with metastases than those without. Patients in the advanced stages of disease face complex and unique challenges associated with their shortened life expectancy. These challenges include the confrontation of feelings about death and dying, preparations for family members left behind, and an increased likelihood and fear of pain, physical impairment, and hospitalization.

Pain and Physical Impairment. The presence of pain has been consistently replicated as a risk factor for depression in patients with cancer. Derogatis et al. (1983) conducted a study which examined the prevalence of psychiatric disorders among 215 cancer patients from three cancer centers. Thirty-nine percent of the patients with a psychiatric diagnosis experienced significant pain, in contrast to 19% of patients who did not receive a psychiatric diagnosis. The majority of patients who experienced significant pain were diagnosed with Adjustment Disorder with Depressed or Mixed Mood, and 15% had symptoms of major depression. A group of 40 cancer patients experiencing pain had more symptoms of depression than a similar sized comparison group of patients who were pain-free (Ahles, Blanchar, and Ruckdeschel, 1983). These results have been replicated across studies, regardless of the tool used to assess depression (Aukst-Margetić, Jakovljević, Margetić, Bišćan, and Šamija, 2005; Bukberg et al., 1984; Ciaramella and Poli, 2001; Lansky et al., 1985; Williams and Schulz, 1995). Based on this research, Massie and Holland (1992) concluded that the risk of developing a psychiatric disorder such as depression is greater in cancer patients with pain than in those without pain.

Despite agreement on the co-occurrence of pain and depression, there has been some disagreement in the literature regarding the causal relationship between pain and depression. Some authors have argued that depression increases the intensity of pain experienced by an individual (Massie and Holland, 1987), whereas others suggest that pain plays a causal role in the onset of depression (Spiegel, Sand, and Koopman, 1994). A longitudinal study examining the association between pain, functional disability and symptoms of depression in both young and older cancer patients found that as pain increased over time, so did the individual's level of physical impairment, which predicted increases in depression (Williamson and Schulz, 1995), supporting the latter view.

While the evidence clearly indicates that cancer patients who experience pain are at higher risk of developing depression, no studies to date have examined whether female cancer patients who experience pain are at a higher risk for developing depression than male cancer patients who also experience pain. Despite the lack of research comparing males and females, research evidence has demonstrated a higher level of pain in breast cancer (Aukst-Margetić et al., 2005), gynecologic malignancies, melanoma, bowel cancer, and lymphoma (Lansky et al., 1985) patients with depression when compared to patients without depression, and higher rates of depression in breast cancer patients experiencing pain than those not experiencing pain (Gaston-Johansson, Fall-Dickson, Bakos, and Kennedy, 1999).

Physical impairment has also been associated with an increased risk of developing depression in patients with cancer. Several studies have found depressed cancer patients to be significantly more likely to be experiencing physical impairment than those patients without depression (Bukberg et al., 1984; Lansky et al., 1985; Williams and Schulz, 1995). Given the cross-sectional nature of the studies conducted examining physical impairment, it is yet unclear whether physical impairment causes depression. Much like pain, no studies have been done examining gender differences in this area. However, as with pain, Lansky et al. (1985) found depressed female cancer patients diagnosed with breast cancer, gynecologic malignancies, melanoma, bowel cancer, and lymphoma to experience significantly greater physical disability than non-depressed female patients with these same cancer types.

Individual Difference Factors

Other risk factors for depression in patients with cancer are the result of individual differences between patients. Individual difference factors that increase the risk for developing cancer include age, prior history of depression, and coping style.

Age. The study of risk factors for depression in individuals with cancer has included a large body of literature examining distress and depression in women diagnosed with cancer at different ages. Of the research conducted in this area, much has examined women with breast cancer. Younger women with breast cancer may be more likely to experience prolonged distress and depression in response to their diagnosis than their older counterparts, despite the higher incidence of breast cancer in women over the age of 65. Younger women are typically defined in the literature as under the age of 50. Compas et al. (1999) found age to be inversely correlated with symptoms of depression shortly after diagnosis, even when disease severity was controlled for. However, there was not the same inverse correlation at 3-month and 6-month follow-ups. Similarly, Vinokur, Threatt, Vinokur-Kaplan, and Satariano (1990) found age to be associated with increased levels of distress at the time of diagnosis, but not at a 10-month follow-up. These results suggest that younger women display a more distressed response to a diagnosis of breast cancer, however, once the initial stress of the diagnosis has subsided, younger women are equally able to adapt as older women.

However, not all studies examining depression in women with breast cancer have revealed age differences in levels of depression. For example, a study of 731 women with breast cancer between the ages of 23 and 60 years old found that while anxiety was higher in younger women, elevated levels of depressive symptoms were not associated with age (Osborne, Elsworth, and Hopper, 2003). However, this study did not have a very wide age range as the oldest patients were only 60, whereas the average age of diagnosis of breast cancer is 65 years. A review examining the age differences in psychological adjustment to breast cancer also identified seven studies that failed to find an inverse relationship between age and distress (Mosher and Danoff-Burg, 2005). Despite this finding, Mosher and Danoff-Burg concluded that while some studies have failed to find age effects, there is a greater body of literature that supports the finding that younger women are at an increased risk for depression following a diagnosis of cancer. There is growing evidence that older women (typically defined as women over the age of 50) report less depression than women younger than 50. Age appears to be a fairly consistent predictor of depressive symptoms in women with breast cancer, but primarily close to the time of diagnosis and not further along the disease trajectory.

While the majority of studies conducted examining age as a risk factor for depression in women with cancer have looked at breast cancer, a meta-analysis conducted by van't Spijker, Trijsburg, and Duivenvoorden (1997) examining cancers in men and women included a wide range of cancers including Hodgkin's lymphoma, colon, gynecological, head and neck, testicular, pancreatic, and lung cancer. Studies conducted with younger patients (mean age less than 50) reported significantly more depression than studies conducted with older patients (mean age greater than 50). Thus, while much of the research on women has examined breast cancer patients, there is some evidence suggesting that younger age is a risk factor for depression in other forms of cancer experienced by women, and also for men.

Several factors are thought to account for the increased risk of depression in younger women diagnosed with cancer. Baucom, Porter, Kirby, Gremore, and Keefe (2006) proposed both developmental and physical reasons for this age difference. Developmentally, women under the age of 50 are more likely to be married, well-established in their careers (i.e. mid-career not yet near retirement), have young children, or be considering having children. A diagnosis of breast cancer may reduce a woman's ability to fulfill these multiple roles, and may result in significant distress, a sense of increased burden, and symptoms of depression. Younger women are also more likely to be diagnosed with more advanced tumors than older women, and thus, may have to endure more aggressive, multi-component treatments (Mosher and Danoff-Burg, 2005). Younger women have not yet experienced menopause, thus the treatments for breast cancer can result in very different physical effects for women under the age of 50. Treatments for breast cancer, such as chemotherapy and tamoxifen, can induce early menopause with more severe symptoms than naturally occurring menopause, such as hot flashes, sweats, and vaginal dryness. Estrogen reduced states have also been associated with increased depression in general (Monti, Mago, and Shakin Kunkel, 2005). Treatment for breast cancer may also result in the loss of fertility, or changes in sexual functioning, and changes in physical appearance affecting body image. The difficulties that result from treatment not only disrupt areas of the woman's functioning during treatment, but can have a lasting impact on functioning. For example, Bloom, Stewart, Change, and Banks (2004) examined the sexual functioning of young women previously treated for breast cancer, and found that 5 years after the completion of treatment for breast cancer there were still no improvements in sexual functioning or in the frequency of sexual activity (as cited in Baucom et al., 2006).

Younger women diagnosed with breast cancer may also experience an increased sense of unfairness related to their diagnosis, given that breast cancer is typically diagnosed in women over the age of 65 (Rowland and Massie, 1998). Women of a younger age often feel as though they have more to lose as a result of a cancer diagnosis given the milestones they have yet to experience. There is also some evidence that younger women may be at higher risk for depression due to differences in coping. Compas et al. (1999) found that ventilation coping (i.e., expressing or losing control of emotions) mediated the relationship between age and symptoms of depression in women diagnosed with breast cancer. These results suggest that younger women are more likely to use less adaptive coping than older women, which may account for the increased level of depression seen in younger women following diagnosis.

There are several limitations to the research conducted on age as a risk factor for depression in women with cancer. Studies differ in how they stratify age groups, which makes comparisons across studies difficult (Mosher and Danoff-Burg, 2005). In addition, studies often failed to include very young participants diagnosed with cancer due to the low incidence of breast cancer in these ages. However, this group may be at highest risk for depression and represent an important group in need of study. Studies also differ in the way in which they measure depression, and timing of measurement limiting comparison across studies (Mosher and Danoff-Burg, 2005). Finally, a large portion of the research conducted in this area has focused exclusively on women with breast cancer. As a result, the ability to draw strong conclusions regarding age as a risk factor for women with other types of cancer is limited.

Younger women face unique challenges when diagnosed with cancer. In addition to differences in the severity of cancer often seen in younger women, differences in role demands and developmental level place this group at increased risk for depression. Knowledge and recognition that younger women are at increased risk for depression is imperative to identifying those individuals in need of additional support or intervention.

Prior History of Depression. An episode of Major Depression generally puts individuals at increased risk for subsequent episodes, and the risk for recurrent episodes is also present in patients with cancer. For example, a study examining the current and past psychological functioning of patients with cancer found that those cancer patients who experienced depression prior to receiving a cancer diagnosis were more likely to have severe depression following a diagnosis of cancer than those without a history of mood disturbance (Plumb and Holland, 1981). In a study of female cancer patients, Lansky et al. (1985) found a prior episode of depression to be more likely in depressed female cancer patients than those patients without depression. Finally, high levels of psychological distress were found in 63% of women with a history of depression compared with 14% of those without a history of depression following initial treatment for breast cancer (Maunsell, Brisson, and Deschênes, 1992). Several other studies have found a prior history of depression to be predictive of depression following a cancer diagnosis (Weisman, 1976; Hughes, 1985a; Hughes, 1985b; Robinson, Boshier, Dansak, and Peterson, 1985). Thus, previous episodes of depression appear to place individuals at increased risk for depression following a cancer diagnosis. These findings have important implications for the monitoring mood disturbance in cancer patients with a history of depression.

Coping. Coping is the means by which an individual deals with stress, including the attitudes and behaviors that help an individual to react to stressors (Kneier, 2003). There is general recognition that how one copes with cancer can significantly influence both psychological adjustment and emotional well-being. Lazarus and Folkman (1984) identified 2 types of coping: problem-focused coping and emotion-focused coping. Problem-focused coping is a response in which an individual focuses their attention and energy on finding solutions to the problem or ways to remove the stressor (Osowiecki and Compas, 1999). Several variants of problem-focused coping exist in the literature including engagement coping and active coping, however, each of these three forms of coping involve intentional and purposeful attempts to manage the stressor. Emotion-focused coping includes responses in which the individual focuses on processing and expressing emotions associated with the stressor (Osowiecki and Compas, 1999). Avoidant coping has also been described in the literature, and is characterized by both cognitive and behavioral efforts to escape from the stressor, or the negative thoughts and emotions related to the stressor (Compas et al., 2006). Avoidant coping has also been labeled disengagement coping. The trends in this literature are reviewed here, although it is noted that differences in the way in which coping has been defined and measured makes firm conclusions in this area difficult.

A fairly consistent finding is that coping characterized by avoidance or escape behaviors is associated with higher emotional distress and poorer psychological adjustment in cancer patients in general (Osowiecki and Compas, 1999; Rodrigue, Behen, and Tumlin, 1994; Schnoll, Knowles, and Harlow, 2002) as well as women with breast cancer (Carver et al., 1993; Compas et al., 2006; Epping-Jordan et al., 1999; McCaul et al., 1999; Stanton and Snider, 1993). It is generally thought that problem-focused or active coping results in lower levels of psychological distress, and several studies of women with breast cancer support this conclusion (Carver et al., 1993; Hilton, 1989; Osowiecki and Compas, 1999; Taylor et al., 1985). Finally, there is some evidence that the use of emotion-focused coping is related to more emotional distress and poorer adjustment in cancer patients in general (Osowiecki and Compas, 1999; Osowiecki and Compas, 1998) and in women with breast cancer (Ben-Zur, Gilbar, and Lev, 2001; Carver et al., 1993; Epping-Jordan et al., 1999; Stanton et al., 2000).

The finding that emotion-focused coping is related to more emotional distress may be affected by limitations in this body of research. In particular, many of the measures used to assess emotion-focused coping include items that actually assess avoidant coping, and the unregulated expression of negative emotions. Thus, it may be premature to conclude that emotion-focused coping increases distress in women with cancer (Compas et al., 2006). Stanton et al. (2000) found that women who completed treatment for breast cancer and who expressed emotions related to cancer as a form of coping had fewer medical appointments for cancer related difficulties, showed better physical health, and had lower levels of distress than those who had low levels of emotional expression in the first three months following diagnosis. However, the authors caution that while the use of emotional expression to cope with cancer may be adaptive as a short-term coping mechanism, prolonged use of emotional coping may become maladaptive and result in higher levels of distress.

It is possible that it is not the particular coping strategy that is used that matters, but rather the "fit" between the coping strategy and situation (Suls and Feltcher, 1985 as cited in Rowland and Massie, 1998). Flexible coping may result in the least amount of distress. For example, active coping may be particularly beneficial during treatment planning as seeking information and solutions may facilitate choosing a treatment, however avoidant coping may be more useful during treatment when active coping approaches may do little to reduce distress (Rowland and Massie, 1998). Further support for the "fit" model of coping was presented in a study examining the role of control beliefs on coping in patients with cancer (Osowiecki and Compas, 1998). Patients had less emotional distress when perceived control was high and they utilized problem-focused coping. However, patients experienced more emotional distress when perceived control was low and problem-focused coping was used. In these types of situations managing emotions may be more useful than trying to solve unsolvable problems. These authors suggest that adjustment is related to the fit between the coping style used, the situation, and the individual's perceived control over the situation. Further research should examine the role of "situational fit" in the relationship between coping and distress.

There is a growing body of evidence which suggests that optimism plays an important role in coping with and responding to a diagnosis of cancer and the prolonged stress associated with cancer. Carver et al. (1993) found women with breast cancer who were high in optimism were more likely to accept the reality of their situation, were less likely to make conscious efforts to avoid or refuse to deal with the stress associated with the cancer, and were less likely to experience feelings of giving up or hopelessness when compared to women low in optimism. In contrast, low levels of optimism, and helpless, hopeless, pessimistic coping strategies have been associated with depression (Epping-Jordan et al., 1999; Schou, Ekeberg, Ruland, Sandvik, and Kåresen, 2004) and poor adjustment (Schnoll et al., 2002) in women with breast cancer.

There are several limitations to the body of research that examines coping style and depression in women with cancer. The studies on coping style have predominantly examined breast cancer to the exclusion of all other forms of cancer experienced by women. In addition, this body of research has examined the role of coping style on psychological adjustment and overall emotional distress, but few studies have examined depression directly. Finally, the broad categories of problem-focused and emotion-focused coping have been criticized as too vague and insufficient to account for the different forms of coping employed by women with cancer (Compas et al., 2006). These measurement issues have resulted in variation in the conceptualization and measurement of coping across studies. This variation in turn makes it difficult to compare studies and draw strong conclusions from the literature.

Resilience Factors

Much of the research has examined factors that increase the risk of developing depression in patients with cancer. However, there is growing recognition that certain factors may decrease the risk the depression, or buffer against the negative effects of a cancer diagnosis and treatment. Included in these protective factors are religion and spirituality, and social support.

Religion and Spirituality. An important way individuals may choose to cope with a diagnosis of cancer is through spirituality or religion. Spirituality is a controversial topic and has been defined in a number of different ways. For example, it has been defined as a set of beliefs or attitudes regarding one's purpose and the meaning of life, illness, and death (Boscaglia, Clarke, Jobling, and Quinn, 2005). Spirituality can be strengthened through a connectedness with self, others, the environment, and in some cases, a higher power. It may provide a basis from which an individual can gain an understanding of him or herself and cope with stress and hardship. Spirituality and religion are not synonymous constructs, as spirituality is a broader concept than religion (Boscaglia et al., 2005). Religion refers to a system of beliefs, practices, and ways of worship centered on a deity or the divine, and may include a spiritual component or, instead, focus on rituals and traditions (Nelson, Rosenfeld, Breitbart, and Galietta, 2002). Religiosity generally refers to participation in activities associated with organized religion, whereas spirituality is a more personal construct. Individuals can be both spiritual and religious; however, many individuals who consider themselves to be spiritual do not adhere to a particular religion or set of religious practices.

Until recently the role of spirituality and religion has been relatively neglected in the empirical literature despite the move toward a holistic approach to treating and understanding the psychological sequelae of cancer. Whereas early research in this area failed to differentiate religion from spirituality, the recognition of the possible importance of spirituality and religion has resulted in increased attention to both as possible mechanisms for coping with cancer. Many early studies examined the relationship between religion and depression in patients with cancer utilizing either a traditional definition of religion devoid of a spiritual component, or a conceptualization of religion that combined religion and spirituality. The results of these early studies indicate that the use of religious coping (i.e., seeking religious or spiritual meaning, solace, and/or inspiration when faced with problems or difficulties) was associated with lower levels of depression in both cancer patients (Aukst-Margetić et al., 2005; Ferraro and Kelley-Moore, 2000; Musick, Koenig, Hays, and Cohen, 1998) and their spouses (Abernethy et al., 2002).

More recently, researchers have begun to differentiate spirituality and religion and look at the differential impact of both on depression in patients with cancer. The evidence shows that spirituality can help buffer against depression in individuals with cancer, while religion may have no benefit, and in some cases a negative effect on depression in patients with cancer. Nelson, Rosenfeld, Breitbart, and Galietta (2002) conducted the first study examining the association between spirituality, religion, and depression in terminally ill cancer patients and patients with AIDS. They found that individuals higher in spirituality had lower levels of depressive symptomatology, but that individuals who were self-rated as more religious had more symptoms of depression than individuals who considered themselves nonreligious. These results were replicated in a study of patients with advanced cancer conducted by McCoubrie and Davies (2006). Studies of spirituality, religion, and depression in women with breast cancer and gynecological cancer have also found individuals high in spirituality to have fewer symptoms of depression (Boscaglia, Clarke, Jobling, and Quinn, 2005; Romero et al., 2006).

In an attempt to explain these findings, Nelson et al. propose that the positive benefits related to spirituality may largely be due to an individual's ability to look internally for strength and meaning, and to accept their circumstances. Individuals high in spirituality are better able to place their illness in a broader social context and find inner peace and meaning in their lives than others low in spirituality. Spirituality may also provide individuals with emotional support in the face of an emotionally distressing period of their lives (Feher and Maly, 1999). Nelson et al. also suggest that the association between depression and high religiosity may be due to the negative effect that cancer has on one's ability to participate in religious activities and rituals. One's religion may also be a source of stress for individuals with cancer who feel anger towards a higher power for causing them and their loved one's pain. These feelings of anger may result in psychological distress and feelings of unfairness.

While these results suggest that spirituality rather than religion is associated with lower levels of depression, as in previous sections, this body of research is not without its limitations. All of the research conducted in this area is cross-sectional in nature, and thus, causal conclusions about the relationship between spirituality and depression in cancer patients can not be drawn. Some authors have suggested that more depressed individuals may seek religion as a form of coping and this effect may account for the positive association found between religion and depression. Further, the majority of the research in this area has been conducted on terminally ill cancer patients, who may have increased interest in religious coping and spirituality as they near the end of life. Thus, more research is needed to elucidate the relationship between spirituality, religion, and depression in cancer patients who are not facing terminal diagnoses.

Finally, the differentiation of religion and spirituality is a relatively recent endeavor. For this reason, only tentative conclusions regarding the relationship between religion, spirituality, and depression can be drawn on the basis of this new body of research. While spirituality and religion are distinct concepts, many religions include a spiritual component. Religions which incorporate a spiritual component, and spirituality alone, may constitute resiliency factors against depression, or buffer negative effects of depression in patients with cancer.

Social Support. The physical stress and psychological burden associated with a diagnosis of cancer and cancer treatments result in an increased need for support. Social support is a broad term that refers to the functions performed for an individual by others within their social environment (Helgeson, 2003). The multi-dimensional nature of social support has resulted in the identification of three forms of social support. For example, Helgeson (2003) distinguished among emotional support, informational support, and instrumental support. Emotional support is defined as having others to talk to, provide understanding and reassurance, and to make one feel loved, valued, and cared for. Informational support is defined as providing information, guidance, or advice such as that needed for medical decision-making. Instrumental support refers to providing an individual with tangible assistance for daily tasks and chores such as running errands or cooking. Social support has also been further broken down in other measures with the inclusion of affectionate support and positive social interaction. The distinction can also be made between *perceived* support, the extent to which an individual believes support is available to them should they need it, *received* support, which is the extent to which the individual feels they were given needed support, and *objective* support, such as the number of friends or confidantes available in a person's network.

A number of studies have shown that social support can decrease or protect against the negative impact of a cancer diagnosis (Parker, Baile, De Moor, Cohen, 2003). For example, social support buffered against the development of depression in patients with mixed diagnoses of cancer (DeLeeuw et al., 2000; Grassi, Malacarne, Maestri, and Ramelli, 1997; Hann et al., 2002) and more specifically, in women with breast cancer (Bloom and Spiegel,

1984; Bloom, Stewart, Johnston, Banks, and Fobair, 2001; Simpson, Carlson, Beck, and Patten, 2002). Both the size of the social network (Bloom et al., 2001; Lugton, 1997) and marital status (Kugaya et al., 1999; Simpson et al., 2002) have been associated with symptoms of depression. More specifically, having a larger social network and being married has been associated with fewer depressive symptoms, possibly due to increased availability of accessible social support. De Leeuw et al. (2000) examined the positive and negative effects of social support on depression in patients with head and neck cancer before and after treatment and found that following treatment, individuals with higher levels of support had fewer depressive symptoms. However, prior to treatment, high levels of social support were associated with more depressive symptoms

The finding that individuals with more received support have higher levels of depression has been shown elsewhere in the literature. De Leeuw et al. (2000) suggest that this result may be due to the fact that individuals who are high in distress seek out and obtain more social support. Support for this hypothesis has been found in studies that indicate the severity of depressive symptoms influence the level of social support received from others, rather than social support predicting later symptoms of distress (Brady and Helgeson, 1991; Simpson et al., 2002). Another possible explanation for this finding is that the support received from others has a detrimental effect on the patient's well-being or coping ability, which results in more symptoms of depression (De Leeuw et al., 2000).

It is often assumed that the social support offered by others is universally beneficial; however, a growing body of literature suggests that members of a social support network may inadvertently engage in aversive or unhelpful behaviors (Dakof and Taylor, 1990; Koopman, Hermanson, Diamond, Angell, and Spiegel, 1998; Manne, Ostroff, Winkel, and Grana, 2005; Schroevers, Ranchor, and Sanderman, 2003). Women with breast cancer report other's behaviors of being critical, forcing cheerfulness, avoiding cancer related discussions, or trying to minimize the cancer experience to be particularly detrimental (Dakof and Taylor, 199). Often significant others fear that talking about cancer, and the cancer patient's experience, will result in feelings of hopelessness and sadness in the cancer patient. However, the suppression of negative emotions by cancer patients can result in elevated levels of depression (Iwamitsu et al., 2005). Thus, it appears that the perceived helpfulness of the social support delivered by significant others, rather than more objective measures of support, plays a large role in determining whether social support is associated with fewer depressive symptoms.

Patients with cancer may find different forms of support to be more beneficial from different members of their support network. A study of 55 cancer patients examining which social support behaviors were perceived as most helpful from spouse, family, and friends, overwhelmingly found emotional support to be most helpful (Dakof and Taylor, 1990). Patients reported the physical presence, expression of concern and affection, and acceptance of the illness to be helpful behaviors when offered by their spouse, family, and friends. Some patients also found informational and instrumental support to be helpful from their spouse, family, and friends. Informational support in the form of medical information and the provision of competent medical care was found to be particularly helpful from physicians, and insufficient informational support was found to be the most unhelpful form of social support from physicians. Informational support was also found to be most helpful from other cancer patients. Thus, different forms of social support appear to be particularly helpful from different members of the social network, and likely at different times during treatment and recovery. These findings have implications for the provision of adequate and beneficial support to patients with cancer.

The influence of social support on depression in women with cancer changes over time. Given the beneficial nature of social support, knowledge of the fluctuations and changes from the time of diagnosis to post-treatment and remission are important in buffering against depression resulting from inadequate support. Immediately following a diagnosis, the severity of the stressor and associated distress experienced by the patient often lead to the mobilization and increased provision of support (Dunkel-Schetter and Skokan, 1990). However, due to the considerable stress posed by a cancer diagnosis, significant others may find it difficult to maintain their support over time, particularly after the salience of the diagnosis and treatment has decreased (Coyne and Fiske, 1992). One study found that while significant others provided support for a patient's physical impairment, the emotional support provided in response to the patient's emotional distress eroded over time (Bolger, Foster, Vinokur, and Ng, 1996). This erosion of support is particularly detrimental given that emotional support is typically found to be the most beneficial form of support offered by family members. More research is needed to determine the relationship between the decline in social support over time and the resulting impact on levels of depression.

Social support is a multi-dimensional construct that plays an important role in buffering against the negative effects of cancer and its treatments. While it is typically assumed that social support is always beneficial, a growing body of literature suggests that not all social support is perceived equally. Spouses, family members, and friends may inadvertently provide, or fail to provide, adequate social support, thus increasing the risk for depression. In addition, cancer patients appear to find different types of social support to be particularly useful from different members of their social network. The compatibility between the perceived helpfulness of social support and the support received by patients with cancer plays an important role in the effect of social support on patient mental health. Finally, recognition and understanding of the changes in social support over time is imperative to monitoring periods of high risk for depression in patients with cancer.

Limitations in the Depression and Cancer Literature

As cited above, there is a large body of literature which examines depression in patients with cancer. Despite the breadth of research in this area, there are several limitations to the extant literature. There is wide heterogeneity in the conceptualization and measurement of depression across studies. Not only do studies differ in the extent to which they examine individuals high in depressive symptoms versus those meeting diagnostic criteria for depression, but studies also differ in whether or not they include somatic symptoms when identifying patients with depression. In many cases patients are identified as depressed if they meet "caseness" criteria on a screening measure such as the HADS. While these measures are meant to identify individuals at increased risk for depression, they are not diagnostic and only identify levels of severity of depressive symptoms. There is also extreme heterogeneity in the samples of cancer patients examined in different studies. Across studies, patients differ in age, gender, type of cancer, stage of cancer, and type of treatment, all of which can impact the level of depression experienced by patients in the study. This heterogeneity makes comparisons across studies difficult, and limits the extent to which conclusions can be drawn about cancer patients more generally.

For some of the risk factors for depression that have been examined in patients with cancer, research about depression *per se* is limited. For example, most of the research on coping has examined levels of psychological distress rather than assessing specifically for symptoms of depression. Studies which explicitly examined risk factors related to depression are sparse in several areas. There is also a lack of research on culturally diverse females with cancer, as the bulk of the research has been conducted with middle class Caucasian females with breast cancer. While some studies have involved Asian women with cancer, other cultural groups have been relatively neglected. As cultural factors can affect the development of depression in women in the general population, understanding the risk factors for women of different cultures is needed.

A major limitation in the research related to depression in women with cancer is the bias to examine women with breast cancer. Of the studies that looked only at women, it is estimated that as many as 85% involved patients who had breast cancer. The exclusion of most other forms of cancer in women limits the conclusions that can be drawn regarding women with cancer to women with breast cancer. For example, a significantly smaller number of studies on female cancer patients have looked at depression in patients with gynecologic cancer. However, more research is needed in this area, as well as the gender-specific risk for depression in patients with cancers found in both men and women. Finally, questions remain as to whether or not depression in patients with cancer differs from that experienced by patients with other chronic medical illnesses.

Conclusion

A diagnosis of cancer is a stressful time of change and uncertainty for many cancer patients and their family. A period of distress following diagnosis is normative, and in most patients, dissipates over time. However, for some, the psychological and physical challenges associated with cancer can result in considerable distress and symptoms of depression (Giese-Davis et al., 2006). Major Depression is a significant mental health concern among patients with cancer, as it affects approximately 20 – 25% of all patients diagnosed with cancer. Depression negatively affects the quality of life in this group (Onitilo, Nietert, and Egede, 2006). While gender differences in the prevalence of depression exist in the general population, no gender differences in the prevalence of depression appears to exist in patients with cancer. Complicating the treatment of depression in patients with cancer is the difficulty diagnosing depression in this group due to the overlap between the somatic symptoms of cancer and the associated treatments, and the somatic symptoms experienced in depression (e.g., sleep disturbance, change in appetite, change in motor functioning).

There are several factors that increase the risk that women with cancer will develop depression. Included in these are factors that are the direct result of the cancer and/or the treatments associated with cancer. Research evidence suggests that lung, oropharyngeal, pancreatic, and breast cancer are most highly associated with depression. Advanced stage of illness as well as increased pain and physical impairment have also been shown to increase risk for the development of depression in patients with cancer. Several individual difference factors also affect the risk for developing depression. For example, younger women appear to be at higher risk for depression, as well as those with a prior history of depression and those who adopt an avoidant coping style. While several factors increase the risk that cancer patients will develop depression, several factors can decrease or buffer against the negative effects of a cancer diagnosis. For example, spirituality, optimism, and high levels of effective social support have all been associated with lower levels of depression in oncology patients.

Although there is a large body of research examining depression in patients with cancer, several limitations exist, including the heterogeneity in the conceptualization and measurement of depression across studies, varied characteristics of the samples used, and the focus on breast cancer in the research examining women with cancer. While the area has suffered from methodological limitations thus far, the importance of conducting research on patients with cancer remains. Future research that illuminates both risk and resilience factors for depression in patients with cancer will be useful, both to identify those individuals at increased risk for depression, and to provide these individuals with resources and support to prevent the prolonged psychological distress associated with cancer.

References

Abernethy, A. D., Chang, T. H., Seidlitz, L., Evinger, J. S., and Duberstein, P. R. (2002). Religious coping and depression among spouses of people with lung cancer. *Psychosomatics, 43,* 456-463.

Ahles, T. A., Blanchard, E. B., and Ruckdeschel, J. C. (1983). The multidimensional nature of cancer-related pain. *Pain, 17,* 277-288.

Alexander, P. J., Dinesh, N., and Vidyasagar, M. S. (1993). Psychiatric morbidity among cancer patients and its relationship with awareness of illness and expectations about treatment outcome. *Acta Oncologica, 32,* 623-626.

American Psychiatric Association. (2004). *Diagnostic and statistical manual of mental disorders* (4th ed.-Text revision). Washington, DC: American Psychiatric Association.

Aukst-Margetić, B., Jakovljević, M., Margetić, B., Bišćan, M., and Šamija, M. (2005). Religiosity, depression and pain in patients with breast cancer. *General Hospital Psychiatry, 27,* 250-255.

Baucom, D. H., Porter, L. S., Kirby, J. S., Gremore, T. M., and Keefe, F. J. (2006). Psychosocial issues confronting young women with breast cancer. *Breast Disease, 23,* 103-113.

Ben-Zur, H., Gilbar, O., and Lev, S. (2001). Coping with breast cancer: Patient, spouse, and dyad models. *Psychosomatic Medicine, 63,* 32-39.

Berard, R. M., Boermeester, F., and Viljoen, G. Depressive disorders in an outpatient oncology setting: prevalence, assessment, and management. *Psychooncology, 7, 112-120.*

Bloom, J. R., and Spiegel, D. (1984). The relationship of two dimensions of social support to the psychological well-being and social functioning of women with advanced breast cancer. *Social Science and Medicine, 19,* 831-837.

Bloom, J. R., Stewart, S. L., Johnston, M., Banks, P., and Fobair, P. Sources of support and the physical and mental well-being of young women with breast cancer. *Social Science and Medicine, 53,* 1513-1524.

Bolger, N., Foster, M., Vinokur, A. D., and Ng, R. (1996). Close relationships and adjustment to a life crisis: The case of breast cancer. *Journal of Personality and Social Psychology, 70*(2), 283-294.

Boscaglia, N., Clarke, D. M., Jobling, T. W., and Quinn, M. A. (2005). The contribution of spirituality and spiritual coping to anxiety and depression in women with a recent diagnosis of gynecological cancer. *International Journal of Gynecological Cancer, 15,* 755-761.

Brady, S. S., and Helgeson, V. S. (1991). Social support and adjustment to recurrence of breast cancer. *Journal of Psycho-social Oncology, 17,* 37-55.

Breitbart, W. (1995). Identifying patients at risk for, and treatment of major psychiatric complications of cancer. *Support Care Cancer, 3,* 45-60.

Breitbart, W., Rosenfeld, B., Pessin, H., Kaim, M., Funesti-Esch, J., Gallietta, M, et al. (2000).

Depression, hopelessness, and desire for hastened death in terminally ill patients with cancer. *Journal of the American Medical Association, 284,* 2907-2911.

Bukberg, J., Penman, D., and Holland, J. C. (1984). Depression in hospitalized cancer patients. *Psychosomatic Medicine, 46,* 199-212.

Carver, C. S., Pozo, C., Harris, S. D., Noriega, V., Scheier, M. F., Robinson, D. S., Ketcham, A. S., Moffat, F. L., and Clark, K. C. (1993). How coping mediates the effect of optimism on distress: A study of women with early stage breast cancer. *Journal of Personality and Social Psychology, 65,* 375-390.

Ciaramella, A., and Poli, P. (2001). Assessment of depression among cancer patients: The role of pain, cancer type and treatment. *Psycho-oncology, 10,* 156-165.

Colon, E. A., Callies, A. L., Popkin, M. K., and McGlare, P. B. Depressed mood and other variables related to bone marrow transplantation survival in acute leukemia. *Psychosomatics, 32,* 420-425.

Compas, B. E., Beckjord, E., Agocha, B., Sherman, M. L., Langrock, A., Grossman, C. I., Dausch, B., Glinder, J., Kaiser, C., Anderson-Hanley, C., and Luecken, L. (2006). Measurement of coping and stress responses in women with breast cancer. *Psycho-oncology, 15,* 1038-1054.

Compas, B. E., Stoll, M. F., Thomsen, A. H., Oppedisano, G., Epping-Jordan, J. E., and Krag, D. N. (1999). Adjustment to breast cancer: Age-related differences in coping and emotional distress. *Breast Cancer Research and Treatment, 54,* 195-203.

Coyne, J. C., and Fiske, V. (1992). Couples coping with chronic and catastrophic illness. In T. J. Akamatsu, J. H. Crowther, S. E. Hobfoll, and M. A. Stevens (Eds.), *Family health psychology* (pp. 129-149). Washington, DC: Hemisphere.

Craig, T. J., and Abeloff, M. D. (1974). Psychiatric symptomatology among hospitalized cancer patients. *American Journal of Psychiatry, 131,* 1323-1327.

Dakof, G. A., and Taylor, S. E. (1990). Victims' perceptions of social support: What is helpful from whom? *Journal of Personality and Social Psychology,* 58, 80-89.

DeLeeuw, J. R. J., De Graeff, A., Ros, W. J. G., Hordijk, G. J., Blijham, G. H., and Winnubst, J. A. M. Negative and positive influences of social support on depression in patients with head and neck cancer: A prospective study. *Psycho-oncology, 9,* 20-28.

Derogatis, L. R., Morrow, G. R., Fetting, J., Penman, S., Piasetsky, S., Schmale, A. M., Henrichs, M., and Carnicke, L. M. (1983). The prevalence of psychiatric disorders among cancer patients. *Journal of the American Medical Association, 249,* 751-757.

Dunkel-Schetter, C., and Skokan, L. A., (1990). Determinants of social support provision in personal relationships. *Journal of Social and Personal Relationships, 7,* 437-450.

Epping-Jordan, J. E., Compas, B. E., Osowiecki, D. M., Oppedisano, G., Gerhardt, C., Primo, K., and Krag, D. N. (1999). Psychological adjustment in breast cancer: Processes of emotional distress. *Health Psychology, 18,* 315-326.

Evans, D. L., McCartney, C. F., Nemeroff, C. B., Raft, D., Quade, D., Golden, R. N., Haggerty, J. J., Holmes, V. Simon, J. S., Droba, M., et al. (1986). Depression in women treated for gynecological cancer: Clinical and neuroendocrine assessment. *American Journal of Psychiatry, 143,* 447-452.

Ferraro, K. F., and Kelley-Moore, J. A. (2000). Religious consolation among men and women: Do health problems spur seeking?

Friedman, L. C., Baer, P. E., Lewy, A., Lane, M., and Smith, F. E. (1989). Predictors of psychosocial adjustment to breast cancer. *Psychosocial Oncology, 6,* 75-94.

Gaston-Johansson, F., Fall-Dickson, J. M., Bakos, A. B., and Kennedy, M. J. (1999). Fatigue, pain, and depression in pre-autotransplant breast cancer patients. *Cancer Practice, 7,* 240-247.

Giese-Davis, J., Wilhelm, F. H., Conrad, A., Abercrombie, H. C., Sephton, S., Yutsis, M., Neri, E., Taylor, C. B., Kraemer, H. C., and Spiegel, D. (2006). Depression and stress reactivity in metastatic breast cancer. Psychosomatic Medicine, 68(5), 675-683.

Golden, R. N., McCartney, C. F., Haggerty, J. J., Raft, D., Nemeroff, C. B., Ekstrom, D., et al. (1991). The detection of depression by patient self-report in women with gynecologic cancer. *International Journal of Psychiatry In Medicine, 21,* 17-27.

Gotheridge, S. M., and Dresner, N. (2002). Psychological adjustment to gynecologic cancer. *Primary Care Update for Ob/Gyns, 9,* 80-84.

Grandi, S., Fava, G. A., Cunsolo, A., Saviotti, F. M., Ranieri, M., Trombini, G., et al. (1987). Major depression associated with masectomy. *Medical Science Research, 15,* 283-284.

Grassi, L., Malacarne, P., Maestri, A., and Ramelli. (1997). Depression, psychosocial variables and occurrence of life events among patients with cancer. *Journal of Affective Disorders, 44,* 21-30.

Green, A. I., and Austin, C. P. (1993). Psychopathology of pancreatic cancer, a psychobiologic probe. *Psychosomatics, 34,* 208-221.

Hann, D., Baker, F., Denniston, M., Gesme, D., Reding, D., Flynn, T., Kennedy, J., and Kieltyka, L. R. The influence of social support on depressive symptoms in cancer patients: Age and gender differences. *Journal of Psychosomatic Research, 52,* 279-283.

Helgeson, V. S. (2003). Social support and quality of life. *Quality of Life Research, 12*(Suppl. 1), 25-31.

Hilton, B. A. The relationship of uncertainty, control, commitment, and threat of recurrence to coping strategies used by women diagnosed with breast cancer. *Journal of Behavioral Medicine, 12,* 39-54.

Hughes, J. E. (1985a). Depressive illness and lung cancer. I. Depression before diagnosis. *European Journal of Surgical Oncology, 11,* 15-20.

Hughes, J. E. (1985b). Depressive illness and lung cancer. II. Follow-up of inoperable patients. *European Journal of Surgical Oncology, 11,* 21-40.

Iwamitsu, Y., Shimoda, K., Abe, H., Tani, T., Okawa, and M., Buck, R. (2005). The relation between negative emotional suppression and emotional distress in breast cancer diagnosis and treatment. *Health Communication, 18,* 201-215.

Kneier, A. W. (2003). Coping with melanoma – Ten strategies that promote psychological adjustment. *Surgical Clinics of North America, 83,* 417-430.

Koopman, C., Hermanson, K., Diamond, S., Angell, K., and Spiegel, D. (1998). Social support, life stress, pain and emotional adjustment to advanced breast cancer. *Psycho-oncology, 7,* 101-111.

Kugaya, A., Akechi, T., Okamura, H., Mikami, I., and Uchitomi, Y. Correlates of depressed mood in ambulatory head and neck cancer patients. *Psycho-oncology, 8,* 494-499.

Lansky, S. B., List, M. A., Herrman, C. A., Ets-Hokin, E. G., DasGupta, T. K., Wilbanks, G. D., and Hendrickson, F. R. (1985). Absence of major depressive disorder in female cancer patients. *Journal of Clinical Oncology, 3,* 1553-1560.

Lazarus, R. S., and Folkman, S. (1984). *Stress, appraisal and coping.* New York: Springer-Verlag.

Lloyed, G. G., Parker, A. C., Ludlam, C. A., and McGuire, R. J. (1984). Emotional impact of diagnosis and early treatment of lymphomas. *Journal of Psychosomatic Research, 28,* 157-162.

Lugton, J. (1997). The nature of social support as experienced by women treated for breast cancer. *Journal of Advanced Nursing, 25,* 1184-1191.

Manne, S. L., Ostroff, J., Winkel, G., and Grana, G. (2005). Partner unsupportive responses, avoidant coping, and distress among women with early stage breast cancer: patient and partner perspectives. *Health Psychology, 24,* 635-641.

Massie, M. J. (2004). Prevalence of depression in patients with cancer. *Journal of the National Cancer Institute Monographs, 32,* 57-71.

Massie, M. J., and Holland, J. C. (1992). The cancer patient with pain: Psychiatric complication and their management. *Journal of Pain and Symptom Management, 7,* 99-109.

Massie, M. J., and Holland, J. C. (1990). Depression and the cancer patient. *Journal of Clinical Psychiatry, 51,* 12-17.

Massie, M. J., and Popkin, M. K. (1998). Depressive disorders. In J. C. Holland (Ed.), *Psycho-oncology* (pp. 518-540). New York: Oxford University Press.

Maunsell, E., Brisson, J., and Deschênes, L. (1992). Psychological distress after initial treatment of breast cancer. *Cancer, 70,* 120-125.

McCaul, K. D., Sandgren, A. K., King, B., O'Donnell, S., Branstetter, A., and Foreman, G. (1999).

Coping and adjustment to breast cancer. *Psycho-oncology, 8,* 230-236. McCoubrie, R. C., and Davies, A. N. (2006). Is there a correlation between spirituality and anxiety and depression in patients with advanced cancer? *Support Care Cancer, 14,* 379-385.

Moadel, A. B., Ostroff, J. S., and Schantz, S. P. (1998). Head and neck cancer. In J. C. Holland (Ed.), *Psycho-oncology* (pp. 518-540). New York: Oxford University Press.

Monti, D. A., Mago, R., and Shakin Kunkel, E. J. (2005). Depression, cognition, and anxiety among postmenopausal women with breast cancer. *Psychiatric services, 56,* 1353-1355.

Morton, R. P., Davies, A. D., Baker, J., Baker, G. A., and Stell, P. M. (1984). Quality of life in treated head and neck cancer patients: a preliminary report. *Clinical Otolaryngology, 9,* 181-185.

Mosher, C. E., and Danoff-Burg, S. (2005). A review of age differences in psychological adjustment to breast cancer. *Journal of Psychosocial Oncology, 23,* 101-114.

Musick, M. A., Koenig, H. G., Hays, J. C., Cohen, H. J. (1998). Religious activity and depression among community-dwelling elderly persons with cancer: The moderating effect of race. *Journal of Gerontology: Social Sciences, 53B,* 218-227.

Nelson, C. J., Rosenfeld, B., Breitbart, W., and Galietta, M. (2002). Spirituality, religion, and depression in the terminally ill. *Psychosomatics, 43,* 213-220.

Norton, T. R., Manne, S. L., Rubin, S., Carlson, J., Hernandez, E., Edelson, M. I., Rosenblum, N., Warshal, D., and Bergman, C. (2004). Prevalence and predictors of psychological distress among women with ovarian cancer. *Journal of Clinical Oncology, 22,* 919-926.

Onitilo, A. A., Nietert, P. J., and Egede, L. E. (2006). Effect of depression on all-cause mortality in adults with cancer and differential effects by cancer site. *General Hospital Psychiatry, 28*(5), 396-402.

Osborne, R. H., Elsworth, G. R., and Hopper, J. L. (2003). Age-specific norms and determinants of anxiety and depression in 731 women with breast cancer recruited through a population-based cancer registry. *European Journal of Cancer, 39,* 755-762.

Osowiecki, D. M., and Compas, B. E. (1999). A prospective study of coping, perceived control, and psychological adaptation to breast cancer. *Cognitive Therapy and Research, 23,* 169-180.

Osowiecki, D., and Compas, B. E. (1998). Psychological adjustment to cancer: Control beliefs and coping in adult cancer patients. *Cognitive Therapy and Research, 22,* 483-499.

Parker, P. A., Baile, W. F., De Moor, C., and Cohen, L. (2003). Psychosocial and demographic predictors of quality of life in a large sample of cancer patients. *Psycho-Oncology, 12,* 183-193.

Pettingale, K. W., Burgess, C., and Greer, S. (1987). Psychological response to cancer diagnosis.I.Correlations with prognostic variables. *Journal of Psychosomatic Research, 32,* 255-261.

Pirl, W. F. (2004). Evidence report on the occurrence, assessment, and treatment of depression in cancer patients. *Journal of the National Cancer Institute Monographs, 32,* 32-39.

Plumb, M., and Holland, J. (1981). Comparative studies of psychological function in patients with advanced cancer. II. Interviewer rated current and past psychological symptoms. *Psychosomatic Medicine, 43,* 243-254.

Robinson, J. K., Boshier, M. L., Dansak, D. A., and Peterson, K. J. Depression and anxiety in cancer patients: Evidence for different causes. *Journal of Psychosomatic Research, 29,* 133-138.

Rodrigue, J. R., Behen, J. M., and Tumlin, T. (1994). Multidimensional determinants of psychological adjustment to cancer. *Psycho-oncology, 3,* 205-214.

Rowland, J. H., and Massie, M. J. (1998). Breast cancer. In J. C. Holland (Ed.), *Psycho-oncology* (pp. 518-540). New York: Oxford University Press.

Schnoll, R. A., Knowles, J. C., and Harlow, L. (2002). Correlates of adjustment among cancer survivors. *Journal of Psychosocial Oncology, 20,* 37-59.

Schou, I., Ekeberg, O., Ruland, C. M., Sandvik, L., and Kåresen, R. (2004). Pessimism as a predictor of emotional morbidity one year following breast cancer surgery. *Psycho-oncology, 13,* 309-320.

Schroevers, M. J., Ranchor, A. V., and Sanderman, R. (2003). The role of social support and self esteem in the presence and course of depressive symptoms: A comparison of cancer patients and individuals from the general population. *Social Science and Medicine, 57,* 375-385.

Sellick, S. M., and Crooks, D. L. (1999). Depression and cancer: An appraisal of the literature for prevalence, detection, and practice guidelines development for psychological interventions. *Psycho-oncology, 8,* 315-333.

Simpson, S. J. A., Carlson, L. E., Beck, C. A., and Patten. S. (2002). Effects of a brief intervention on social support and psychiatric morbidity in breast cancer patients. *Psycho-oncology, 11,* 282-294.

Sneeuw, K. C., Aaronson, N. K., van Wouwe, M. C., Sergeant, J. A., van Dongen, Bartelink, H., et al. (1993). Prevalence and screening of psychiatric disorder in patients with early stage breast cancer [abstract]. *Quality of Life Research, 2,* 50-51.

Spiegel, D., Sand, S., and Koopman, C. (1994). Pain and depression in patients with cancer. *Cancer, 74,* 2570-2578.

Stanton, A. L., and Snider, P. R. (1993). Coping with a breast cancer diagnosis: A prospective study. *Health, Psychology, 12,* 16-23.

Stanton, A. L., Danoff-Burg, S., Twillman, R., Cameron, C. L., Bishop, M., Collins, C. A., Kirk, S. B., and Sworowski, L. A. (2000). Emotionally expressive coping predicts psychological and physical adjustment to breast cancer. *Journal of Consulting and Clinical Psychology, 68,* 875-882.

Taylor, S. E., Lichtman, R. R., Wook, J. V., Bluming, A. Z., Dosik, G. M., and Leibowitz, R. L. (1985). Illness-related and treatment-related factors in psychological adjustment to breast cancer. *Cancer, 55,* 2506-2513.

van't Spijker, A., Trijsburg, R. W., and Duivenvoorden, H. J. (1997). Psychological sequelae of cancer diagnosis: A meta-analytical review of 58 studies after 1980. *Psychosomatic Medicine, 59,* 280-293.

Vinokur, A. D., Threatt, B. A., Vinokur-Kaplan, D., and Satariano, W. A. (1990). The process of recovery from breast cancer for younger and older patients: Changes during the first year. *Cancer, 65,* 1242-1254.

Weisman, A. D. (1976). Early diagnosis of vulnerability in cancer patients. *American Journal of the Medical Sciences, 271,* 187-196.

Williamson, G. M., and Schulz, R. (1995). Activity restriction mediates the association between pain and depressed affect: A study of younger and older adult cancer patients. *Psychology and Aging, 10,* 369-378.

Zabora, J., Brintzenhofeszoc, K., Curbow, B., Hooker, C., and Piantadosi, S. (2001). The prevalence of psychological distress by cancer site. *Psycho-Oncology, 10,* 19-28.

In: Women and Depression
Editors: Paula Hernandez and Sara Alonso

ISBN 978-1-60456-647-5
© 2009 Nova Science Publishers, Inc.

Chapter 13

Depression in Women with Epilepsy

A.E. Cavanna [1,2], *S. Cavanna* [3], *L. Bertero* [3], *and M.M. Robertson* [1,4,5]

[1]Institute of Neurology, Queen Square, London, United Kingdom
[2]Department of Neurology, Amedeo Avogadro University, Novara, Italy
[3]University of Turin Medical School, Turin, Italy
[4]St Georges Hospital and Medical School, London, United Kingdom
[5]Department of Mental Health Sciences University College, London United Kingdom

Abstract

Converging evidence suggests that patients affected by epilepsy show a considerably higher incidence of depression than the average population (about 65% versus 25%). Since women are twice as likely as men to suffer from depression, female gender could be considered a major risk factor to develop this condition, although gender-related epidemiological data are somewhat controversial. Overall, it is recommended that clinicians pay particular attention, when dealing with women with epilepsy, to examine for early signs of depression. With regards to the neurobiological and psychological underpinnings of these conditions, the key elements to be considered are the partial overlapping in neuro-chemical mechanisms involved both in depression and epilepsy, and the large number of interlinked psychosocial determinants, including clinical features of epilepsy such as seizure type, frequency, and cortical focus. Moreover, sex hormones are important, since they are known to contribute remodelling the hippocampus, a structure which plays a pivotal role in both epilepsy and depression. In women, as opposed to men, the levels of sex hormones are more relevant because of their physiological cyclic fluctuations. Estrogens, rather than other ovarian hormones, show an effect similar to antidepressant drugs by stimulating hippocampal synaptogenesis. With regards to epilepsy, a decrease in estrogen levels is linked to a significant increase in seizures frequency. The exact relationship between epilepsy and depression is not fully understood. However, an emerging picture may suggest potential therapeutic strategies to improve the clinical management of women with epilepsy: first and foremost, an optimal control of seizures can be obtained by using an appropriate pharmacological regimen or neurophysiological devices, such as vagus nerve stimulation. The choice of the antiepileptic drug should take into due account the behavioral profile of the medication, as some of them (e.g. lamotrigine, carbamazepine) can have a positive effect on mood. Selective serotonin reuptake inhibitors and dual-action antidepressant medications are also considered first-line therapy. Finally, electroconvulsive therapy and vagus nerve stimulation can prove useful in selected cases.

Keywords: *Antiepileptic drugs; Depression; Suicide; Epilepsy; Sexual hormones; Women.*

Introduction

The term epilepsy, or more correctly, the epilepsies, refers to a group of chronic neurologic conditions characterized by recurrent epileptic seizures. The diagnosis of epilepsy implies the existence of a neurologic dysfunction responsible for generating epileptic seizures. Thus, epileptic seizures represent the clinical manifestations (signs and symptoms) of excessive and/or hyper-synchronous, usually self-limited, abnormal activity of neurons in the brain. It was once believed that epileptic seizures reflect disturbances involving the cerebral cortex only; however it has become increasingly recognized that sub-cortical structures can also be involved, and some epileptic seizures may be primarily generated at a sub-cortical level [Engel et al. 2005]. Overall, the behavioral features of epileptic seizures reflect the functions of the brain areas involved, and may therefore take a plethora of signs and symptoms including impaired higher mental function or altered consciousness, involuntary jerk-like movements or cessation of movement, sensory or psychic experiences, autonomic disturbances, or combination of these. Specific epileptic seizure types are defined by their ictal behavioral and electroencephalogram (EEG) features. The epileptic focus is defined electro-physiologically as the brain area that appears to generate the most prominent interictal epileptiform EEG discharges. Accordingly, epileptic conditions may be due to a single focus, bilateral independent foci, multiple foci, or there may be diffuse unilateral or generalized epileptiform abnormalities with no focal features. The current classification scheme of the International League Against Epilepsy [ILAE 1989], makes a fundamental distinction between partial (or focal) epilepsies and generalized epilepsies, based on clinical and electrophysiological evidence for the presence of a clear-cut epileptogenic focus. On the other hand, seizures are classified into the simple/complex dichotomy according to the presence/absence of ictal consciousness [ILAE 1981].

The exact figure of the prevalence of epilepsy varies amongst different countries, but it is estimated that there are about 50 million people affected by epilepsy worldwide. An increasing amount of evidence suggests that people with epilepsy (PWE) show a considerably higher incidence of depression [Robertson and Trimble 1983; Mendez et al. 1986; Robertson et al. 1987; Robertson 1991a; Robertson 1992; Harden 2002; Kanner and Barry 2003; Swinkels 2005], which is four- to five-fold greater than the average population (about 85% versus 25%). Moreover, since depression is one of the major psychiatric diagnoses associate with suicide, PWE have a five-fold greater incidence of suicide than the general population [Standage and Fenton 1975; Matthews and Barabas 1981; Barraclough

1987; Robertson 1997]. Several studies have shown that 80% of PWE report feelings of depression [Barraclough 1987; Robertson 1983; Harden 2002], whereas endogenous depression has been found in up to 40% in some series [Betts 1981; Robertson 1991a; Swinkels 2005]. Other studies seemed to suggest that 20% of patients with temporal lobe epilepsy (TLE) will eventually become depressed and that up to 62% of patients with intractable complex partial seizures (CPS) have a history of previous depressive episodes which may also be recurrent [Currie et al. 1971; Blumer and Zielinski 1988]. The prevalence of mood disorders is lower in population-based studies, as shown by Jacoby et al. [1996] which found a 10% prevalence of depression amongst patients with less than one seizure/month, 21% in those whose seizure frequency was >1/month, and 4% in seizure-free patients, which is in accord with the prevalence rate in the general population [Anthony et al. 1995; Gaitatzis et al. 2004; Mensah et al. 2006].

These results are, however, not free from possible bias or methodological problems. For example, some investigators relied on data derived from self-rating scales or personality inventories, whereas others derived their data from standardized psychiatric interviews performed by clinicians. Most studies were undertaken in specialist centers, which attract patients with more severe epileptic disorders, and therefore are likely to report a higher prevalence of psychopathology (referral bias) [Kanner and Balabanov 2002]. Even though the different prevalence rates reported in the literature could result from differences in methodology for detecting psychiatric symptomatology and for different selection of the patient populations studied or possible errors, the existence of a link between these two pathologies is not to be discarded. Although the data derived from such studies cannot be generalized to all PWE, there is nevertheless a consensus that depression is more common among patients with poorly controlled seizures [Anthony et al. 1995].

A relationship between depression and epilepsy has been observed since antiquity. Temkin, for example, quotes Aretaeus as saying that subjects with epilepsy were "languid, spiritless, and dejected" [Temkin 1971], whereas nearer our own time Griesinger noted that a "misanthropic perversion of sentiment, sometimes even actual melancholia with suicidal tendency, is observed in a great many epileptics" [Griesinger 1857]. The co-morbidity of epilepsy and depression can present with two main forms: peri-ictal depression and inter-ictal depression. The first type occurs when the depressive symptomatology is present around the seizure, including prodromata, epileptic aura, ictal and postictal disturbances [Monaco et al. 2005; Mula et al. 2006; Cavanna et al. 2007; Cavanna 2008]. The second type is characterized by chronic psychiatric disturbances which are not directly related to the ictal electroclinical disturbances [Krishnamoorthy et al. 2007].

Furthermore, intermittent affective-somatoform symptoms are frequently present in chronic epilepsy; they manifest in a pleomorphic pattern and can include several symptoms: these include irritability, depressive moods, anergia, insomnia, atypical pains, anxiety, phobic fears, and euphoric moods. These symptoms occur at various intervals and tend to last from hours to a few days. If intermittent dysphoric symptoms (at least three of the above) are present, each to a troublesome degree, a few authors have proposed a diagnosis of interictal dysphoric disorder [Blumer 2000; Mula et al. 2008]. In women, the disorder is accentuated in the premenstrual phase.

Since women are twice as likely as men to suffer from depression, female gender could be considered a major risk factor to develop this condition, although gender-related epidemiological data are somewhat controversial. Overall, women with epilepsy have a greater risk of developing depression than the general population [Kanner and Balabanov 2002; Cramer et al. 2005].

A small group of female patients showing a much higher risk of developing depressive disorders are those who undergo surgical treatment because of pharmacological failure in obtaining seizures control. In the past two decades the rate of surgical resection of antero-temporal lobes substantially increased leading to a proportional increase in iatrogenic epilepsy [Savarad et al. 1998]. In fact it is not unusual to see mood lability within the initial 6 weeks after surgery. Often these symptoms subside, but in up to 30% of patients overt symptoms of depression become apparent within the first 6 months. Characteristically, symptoms of depression vary in severity from mild to very severe, including suicidal attempts. In most instances these patients respond readily to pharmacologic treatment with antidepressant drugs. Patients with a prior history of depression are at greater risk. Interestingly, this risk is independent of the postsurgical control of seizures. All patients undergoing epilepsy surgery should therefore be advised of this potential complication before surgery.

These preliminary data highlight that special attention should be paid when evaluating a female patient affect by epilepsy, in order to correctly diagnose the early warning signs of depression. The following sections discuss the main clinical issues concerning women with epilepsy and depression.

Female Physiology and Epilepsy

Over the last few years, several authors have investigated the neurobiological links between epilepsy and depression [Kanner and Balabanov 2002; Hecimovic 2003; Jobe 2003; Hajszan and MacLusky 2006]. In female patients, these links are further complicated by gender-specific physiological issues. It is currently acknowledged that following menarche, ovarian steroid hormones affect seizure activity. Women may have changes in seizure threshold related to their menstrual cycle, as well as at other times in their reproductive life including puberty, pregnancy, and after the menopause: that is when important changes take place in both the estrogen and progesterone levels in the body. Fertility and reproductive functions may also be affected in some women with epilepsy [Wallace et al. 1998]. There is a significant relationship between hormones and epilepsy, in that hormones influence epilepsy, and epilepsy influences hormones, in several ways. Converging evidence showed that seizures can compromise sexual development, with impairment of libido and sexual potency [Cramer et al 2007].

The main ovarian steroid hormones are estrogens (estradiol, estrone, and estriol) and progesterone; their secretion is controlled by the hypothalamus and pituitary gland through a complex neuroendocrinological feedback system. The hypothalamic–pituitary–ovarian axis regulates the menstrual cycle [Wooley and Schwartzkroin 1998]. Gonadotropin-releasing hormone (GnRH) secreted by the hypothalamus stimulates the release of follicle-stimulating hormone (FSH) by the pituitary. FSH stimulates the formation of the ovarian follicles, which in turn secrete estradiol as they develop. FSH is inhibited, whereas GnRH is stimulated, by estrogen. One result is a surge of luteinizing hormone (LH), which induces oocyte maturation, ovulation, and conversion of the follicle into the corpus luteum. This marks the end of the follicular phase of the cycle, preceding ovulation by about 36 hours. Following ovulation is the luteal phase, when the corpus luteum secretes progesterone, which inhibits secretion of GnRH, FSH, and LH. If the ovule is not fecundated, the corpus luteum regresses, and production of progesterone and estradiol declines. When progesterone secretion tapers off and GnRH inhibition decreases, the cycle repeats, forming a loop [Foldvary-Schaefer et al. 2003].

Ovarian steroid hormones affect the activity of the central nervous system (CNS) by altering excitability of neurons. This modifies both the frequency and the severity of seizures. Animal models have interestingly demonstrated both the proconvulsant effects of estrogen and anticonvulsant effects of progesterone [Logothetis et al 1959; Herzog 1995; Rodgers and Johnson 1998; Herzog 1999; Lonsdale and Burham 2003; Lonsdale et al. 2006]. Estrogen increases activity of excitatory neurotransmitters and also alters dopamine pathways, thus disrupting inhibitory neurotransmission. Estradiol-like hormones may also alter the structure of the synaptic area of neurons, increasing the number of dendritic spines and synapses. Estrogen and progesterone are highly lipophilic and easily cross the blood–brain barrier and diffuse through cell membranes, binding to intracellular receptors and forming hormone–receptor complexes. The fluctuations in ovarian steroids and peptides directly affect the brain. Hormones secreted by hypothalamus and pituitary gland regulate the amounts of estrogen and progesterone circulating in the body. The hypothalamus receives many direct connections from temporal lobes which are involved in the generation of seizures. Alteration of normal LH pulsatile secretion has been documented in women with epilepsy [Bilo et al. 1991; Drislane et al. 1994]. Research has shown that seizure discharges can disrupt the output of hormones such as FSH and LH, which, in turn, can alter the balance of estrogen and progesterone and affect seizure control. Progesterone metabolites produce anticonvulsant, anti-anxiety, and sedative effects similar to, but in a narrower range than those of the benzodiazepines. The effects of estrogen and progesterone demonstrated in experimental models of epilepsy have also been seen clinically [Logothetis et al. 1959; Herzog 1995]. Women with epilepsy have exhibited a variety of endocrine disturbances [Morrel et al. 2001; Pack and Morrel 2002]. Several lines of evidence suggest that changes in the levels of the female sex steroids may contribute to the risk for depression.

Depression in Women with Epilepsy

Clinical data show that distinct events of reproductive physiology in women, especially those accompanied by abrupt declines in gonadal hormone levels, are frequently associated with mood disorders, including postpartum, peri-menopausal or postmenopausal depression [Seeman 1997; Shors and Leuner 2003; Steiner et al. 2003; Stewart et al. 2004]. In particular, alteration of estrogen secretion, which is common in women affected by epilepsy, appears to be a critical contributor to the etiology of these depressive disorders [Dalla et al. 2004; Stoffel and Craft 2004; Imwalle 2005; Lund et al. 2005]. Consistent with animal studies, estrogen appears to be effective in treating postpartum and peri-menopausal depression [Gregoire et al. 1996; Ahokas et al. 2001; Rasgon et al. 2002; Studd and Panay 2004]. Moreover, since androgens appear to have an antidepressant effect comparable to those of estrogens [Barret-Connor et al. 1999; Allolio and Arlt 2002; Almeida et al. 2004; Orengo et al. 2004; Studd and Panay 2004], the higher incidence of depression in women may be easily explained by the different pattern of gonadal hormone secretion. In men, testosterone levels remain constant since puberty, declining because of aging only in a few cases [Jockenhovel 2004]. By contrast, levels of estrogen in women go through cyclical variations during adult life and rapidly decline with menopause. The mechanisms responsible for the antidepressant effect of gonadal steroids are not yet fully understood. However, current evidence suggests that the effects of sex hormones on the brain mimic those of antidepressants, including effects on the structure and function of the hippocampus. Estrogen seems to modulate the reuptake of serotonin [Bethea et al. 2000], leading to increase of this neurotransmitter concentration in mood-determining key areas, in a way which is reminiscent of selective serotonin reuptake inhibitors (SSRI) antidepressants. The hippocampus itself is also sensitive to both estrogen and androgen [Leranth et al. 2003; MacLusky et al. 2005], containing receptors for both of these steroids [Clancy et al. 1992; Shughrue et al. 1997]. Thus, estrogen induces brain-derived neurotrophic factor (BDNF) synthesis in the hippocampus [Gibbs 1999], determining significant increments in hippocampal BDNF expression with every ovarian cycle [Scharfman et al. 2003]. In conclusion, elevated circulating levels of gonadal steroids have been found to revert both hippocampal structure and functional changes associated with depression. Finally, as additional supporting evidence, gonadectomy in experimental animals has been shown to reduce the density of dendritic spines and spine synapses on pyramidal neurons in hippocampus [Leranth et al. 2004a], but this effect is rapidly revertible by treatment with either androgens [Leranth et al. 2003; Leranth et al. 2004b] or estrogens [Leranth et al. 2000; Leranth et al. 2002]. If one considers these data and the actual understanding of the mechanisms of action of antidepressant drugs, a remarkable parallel is provided between the actions of female sex hormones and those of antidepressants. This parallel suggests that, at the level of the hippocampus, the mood-enhancing effects may be based on convergent mechanisms. The observation that loss of gonadal steroids leads to atrophic changes in the hippocampus explains why the risk of developing depression appears to be higher when estrogen levels are low. These data are also consistent with the findings, from both animal research and clinical trials, that hormone replacement therapy may potentiate the effects of antidepressant therapy [Grigoriadis and Kennedy 2002; Nowakowska and Kus 2005]. A possible explanation for this observation might be that the effects of gonadal steroids on hippocampus could synergize with those of antidepressants. Moreover, the difference in time delay before obtaining a measurable therapeutic effect is also consistent with clinical observations. Improvements after treatment of postpartum depression using antidepressant drugs can take up to 6 weeks, whereas estrogen appears to be effective within a week [Ahokas et al. 2001; Wong and Licinio 2001]. Further research in experimental animal models has shown that these timings are necessary to obtain a hippocampal neuroplastic response to estrogen and antidepressant drugs. Estrogens are likely to induce rapid increases in hippocampal spine synapse density [Woolley and McEwen 1992; Leranth et al. 2003] as well as rapid but transient increases in dentate gyrus neurogenesis [Tanapat et al. 2005]. Although the time course of antidepressant effects on synaptogenesis has not yet been clearly demonstrated, neurogenetic changes appear to require weeks of antidepressant treatment to become fully established [Malberg et al. 2000]. Why these different molecules, which appear to act in a similar way on the same targets, require different timings to exert their full action? The answer is likely to be provided by further study aimed at investigating the underlying neurobiological mechanisms.

It has been shown how female sex hormones influence both epilepsy and depression, and that these disorders, when they coexist at the same time, are deeply intertwined in each other's pathophysiology. Hippocampal plasticity, which is affected by female sex hormones, appears to be involved in both mood disorders and epilepsy. This common mechanism could provide a theoretical basis for the increased frequency of depression in women with epilepsy. Certain consequences of recurrent seizures may be directly related to the actions of gonadal steroids and depression. Nevertheless, aspects of the endocrine and anatomic sequelae of epilepsy appear to be consistent with the observations in depression, suggesting possible parallels between the two disorders. First, epileptic seizures can lead to a derangement of the hypothalamic circuitry controlling pituitary gonadotropin release [Nappi et al. 1993; Morrel 2003] and consequently deregulation of female sex hormones. However, this alteration leads to relevant physiological and anatomical changes in hippocampus. Attention should be paid to possible similar adverse effects due to antiepileptic medication. Therefore, it is possible that the increased incidence of depression observed in women with epilepsy could reflect a hormonal deficiency state consisting of abnormally low levels of estrogen contributing to the intrahippocampal deficits that predispose toward depressive symptoms.

Moreover, changes in gonadal steroid production probably represent a critical contributing factor in determining seizure frequency in women with catamenial epilepsy, a condition defined by variation in seizure frequency in relation to stages of the menstrual cycle. Using a criterion of at least a twofold increase in daily seizure frequency, catamenial epilepsy is seen in approximately 30% of women with epilepsy [Foldvary-Schaefer and Falcone 2003]. The proconvulsive effects of estradiol mentioned earlier and the anticonvulsive effects of progesterone seem to play a central role in the etiology of catamenial epilepsy, which is not entirely understood. In particular, 5α-reduced metabolites of progesterone, such as allopregnanolone, modulate $GABA_A$ receptor function [Smith and Woolley 2004], while estradiol mediates an increment in hippocampal excitation increasing hippocampal expression of BDNF. A decrease of hippocampal excitability threshold means easier seizure generation. Circumstantial evidence supporting this view also comes from observations on one of the potential adverse effects of antidepressant drugs which consist in an increased susceptibility to seizures [Settle 1998; Cavus and Duman 2003; De Foubert et al. 2004]. These findings seem to explain the link between estrogen activity, depression, and seizure frequency, thus providing a plausible explanation for both the aspects of epilepsy and the response to antidepressants. However they also raise an apparent paradox. An extensive body of evidence indicates that the seizure activity itself is associated with marked increases in hippocampal neurogenesis and BDNF synthesis [Cha et al. 2004; Mohapel et al. 2004; Scharfman 2004]. Since an insufficient hippocampal neurogenesis and BDNF synthesis are critical contributory factors in depression [Duman et al. 2001; Shirayama et al. 2002], it seems difficult to accept that depression has a higher prevalence in epilepsy, under conditions of increased neurogenesis and facilitated BDNF release. A possible explanation could be found in the particular hippocampal environment as resulting from recurrent seizures activity. In this situation the positive effect of increased neurogenesis acts as a compensatory attempt to balance the massive seizures-induced loss of neurons. Normally, increases in BDNF synthesis and neurogenesis are likely to contribute to the enhancement of hippocampal function, increasing the pool of developing neurons available for incorporation into the circuitry and stimulating synaptogenesis. But under the aberrant conditions of recurrent seizures, neurogenesis is likely to be an insufficient response. Despite increased cell proliferation, there may be a net loss of neurons in the hippocampus as a result of seizure-induced cell death [Bengzon et al. 1997; Engel 2002]. Moreover this continuous pathological neurogenesis appears to happen in a deregulated way, whereas some of the newly created neurons end up at ectopic sites, where they form inappropriate connections [Scharfman 2004]. In addition to cells number, also their connections are crucial in developing a correctly functioning hippocampal circuitry. Several studies indicate that there is a fairly consistent loss of dendritic spines both in epilepsy patients [Isokawa 2000; Swann et al. 2000] and in animal models of epilepsy [Drekew et al. 1996; Isokawa 1998]. These data provide another explanation to the inefficacy of post-seizure neurogenesis. An important factor in determining the likelihood of developing depression, is the extent to which the hippocampal circuitry retains the capacity for growth and repair. If this capacity is diminished, no matter how it occurs, the final result may be an increase in the risk of developing clinical depression. Moreover, it should be noted that at a cellular and molecular basis, these changes in epilepsy are probably different from those in idiopathic depression or after hormone withdrawal, even though the clinical consequences may be similar.

In summary, the reviewed literature suggests an increased incidence of depression in epilepsy: however much work remains to be done in order to fully understand the underlying neurological basis of this relationship. It is often difficult to obtain experimental data and therefore evidence is usually circumstantial. Despite this, it is possible to postulate a reasonable and acceptable theory to explain clinical manifestations shared by epilepsy and depression. The hippocampus seems to play a pivotal role in these processes [Hajszan and MacLusky 2006]. This structure is subject to rapid structural changes, in order to effectively respond to an ever changing environment. Neurological disorders, like epilepsy, or conditions causing deficient gonadal steroids trophic stimulation, heavily undermine its plasticity and eventually predispose to the development of depression. Moreover, in women, hippocampus is also physiologically under stress by cyclic fluctuation of sex hormones levels, and consequently this phenomenon is exacerbated and accounts for the increased prevalence of depression.

Diagnostic and Therapeutic Issues

Clinical aspects have been thoroughly reviewed and studied by several authors, in order to effectively approach patients affected by both epilepsy and depression [Lambert and Robertson 1999; Harden 2002; Kanner 2003a; Kanner 2003b; Mensah 2006]. Diagnosis often represents a difficult challenge. In fact, PWE usually experience forms of depressive disorders identical to those of non-epileptic patients. Nevertheless, depressive disorders can have an atypical presentation in a significant percentage of patients who fail to meet any of the DSM Axis I categories [Kanner and Barry 2001]. The temporal relationship to seizure occurrence is an important factor when classifying depressive symptoms and disorders. Thus, symptoms can be present before or after the onset of seizures. Moreover, depressive symptoms can be a manifestation of the actual seizure or appear completely unrelated to the seizure occurrence [Mulder and Daly 1952; Weil 1955; Williams 1956; Daly 1958; Weil 1959; Blanchet and Frommer 1986; Kanner et al. 1999; Kanner et al. 2000a; Kanner et al. 2000b]. Symptoms occurring very closely to a seizure are usually unrecognized by clinicians and account for the paucity of data regarding their prevalence and response to treatment.

Not surprisingly, female patients affected by epilepsy and depression are in a very particular situation where many important mechanisms are compromised. It has been pointed out that the specific form that the depressive illness will take in a given individual depends on the interaction of several factors, including genetic vulnerability, developmental events (and their disruption by epileptic seizures), psychosocial events (e.g. unemployment and stigma), physiological stressors (seizures themselves), and personality traits [Robertson 1991b]. As a consequence, the issues of making a correct diagnosis and targeting an effective treatment can pose serious difficulties.

Although the exact relationship between epilepsy and depression is not fully understood, the emerging picture informs potential therapeutic strategies to improve the clinical management of women with epilepsy. The goal is to obtain both seizure and depression control, but it should be taken into account that several anticonvulsant and antidepressant drugs partially overlap in their mechanisms of action, potentially leading to significant interactions and thus probable interference in efficacy [Gilliam and Kanner 2002; Krish 2003; Barry and Jones 2005; Pennell 2006; Mula et al. 2007]. For example, depression is more common in patients treated with poly-drug anticonvulsant therapy, especially when barbiturates, phenytoin, and vigabatrin are concomitantly administered, while other anticonvulsants (e.g. lamotrigine, carbamazipine) seem to be effective in stabilizing and improving mood. On the other hand, antidepressant drugs are not always indicated because of their potential seizure-inducing activity and their foreseeable partial inefficacy due to one of their supposed mechanisms of action, the stimulation of hippocampal neurogenesis and BDNF synthesis, consistently shown to be ineffective in PWE. Clinical trials and practice, however, seem to suggest that this problem is often overestimated. Results from preliminary clinical trials indicate that SSRIs can be effective in controlling major depressive symptoms in PWE without incurring unacceptable increases in seizure frequency [Robertson and Trimble 1985; McConnell and Duncan 1998; Kanner et al. 2000; Kuhn et al. 2003]. Specifically, paroxetine and citalopram are drugs of choice because they do not interact with the most common antiepileptic drugs and are known to have a lower epileptogenic potentials [Andersen et al. 1991]. Moreover, converging evidence suggests the use of moclobemide because of its double activity in improving depression and in seizure status [Bonnet 2003] may be a suitable antidepressant in PWE. Clinical data have also shown that the dual antidepressant venlafaxine, which modulates both serotonergic and noradrenergic pathways, has a low epileptogenic potential [Pisani et al. 2002]. The multiple mechanisms of action of antidepressant drugs partly explain their efficacy in populations with epilepsy. Although their influence on hippocampal plasticity may be ineffective, their ability to inhibit serotonin reuptake and direct stimulate aminergic receptors seem to be adequate to effectively contrast depression [Hajszan et al. 2005]. These latter effects, in fact, may be quantitatively more important in determining the behavioral effects of these drugs, at least under the specific conditions of epilepsy. Moreover, some of what are now recognized to be the best known and most widely used mood stabilizers - i.e. carbamazepine, sodium valproate, and lamotrigine – have long been known to also show an anticonvulsant activity [Post et al. 1996; Krishnamoorthy 2003].

Electro-convulsive therapy (ECT), which is used in selected patients to treat psychiatric disorders, can have significant effects on PWE. This treatment can result in at least transient cessation of seizures by increasing the seizure threshold [Kellner and Bernstein 1993]. For obvious reasons, ECT as a treatment is generally restricted to specialist settings and is most often used for severe or treatment-resistant depression [McCall 2001]. The main benefit of ECT is the rapidity of response, which may not always be sustained.

Counseling and or psychotherapy can also be effectively used in the management and in the prevention of clinical relapses in depression [Scott 1996; Fava et al. 1998], in particular cognitive-behavioral therapy (CBT) and interpersonal therapy (IPT). These psychological therapies are especially used when patients are reluctant to take antidepressant medications, often because of social acceptance issues [Priest et al. 1996]. Several treatment protocols based on psychotherapy alone and on psychotherapy combined with antidepressant drugs have been evaluated and shown to be effective [Klerman and Weissmann 1987; Fava et al. 1994; FAva et al. 1996; Fava et al. 1998; Blackburn and Moore 1997; Thase et al. 1997; Paykel et al. 1999; Frank et al. 2000; Teasdale et al. 2000; Segal et al. 2002].

Vagus nerve stimulation (VNS) has recently gained considerable support in order to approach patients with treatment-refractory partial seizures unable to undergo surgical procedures. The advantage of VNS in epilepsy and co-morbid depression is that it has proved effective for both disorders [Elger et al. 2000; Hareden et al. 2000; Schmidt 2001].

In conclusion, the choice of the antiepileptic drug should take into due account the behavioral profile of the medication. Special attention must be paid to potential drug interactions in order to exploit the mood stabilizing activity showed by some anticonvulsive drugs. SSRIs and dual-action antidepressant medications are considered first-line therapy for depression in epilepsy. Moreover, ECT can prove useful in selected cases where antidepressant drugs showed no efficacy. New treatment options, including the recently developed VNS, should also be taken into consideration when facing treatment-resistant forms of depression associated with epilepsy.

Conclusion

In conclusion much evidence suggests that patients affected by epilepsy show a considerably higher incidence of depression than the average population. As women are twice as likely as men to suffer from depression, female gender could be considered a major risk factor to develop depression although gender-related epidemiological data are somewhat controversial. With regards to the neurobiological and psychological underpinnings of these conditions, the key elements to be considered are the partial overlapping in neuro-chemical mechanisms involved both in depression and epilepsy, and the large number of interlinked psychosocial determinants, including clinical features of epilepsy such as seizure type, frequency, and cortical focus. Moreover, sex hormones are also important as they effect the hippocampus which plays an important role in both epilepsy and depression. With regards to epilepsy, a decrease in estrogen levels is linked to a significant increase in seizures frequency. The exact relationship between epilepsy and depression remains not fully understood. It is however important to control seizures by medication or newer strategies. The choice of the antiepileptic drug should take into due account the behavioral profile of the medication, as some of them (e.g. lamotrigine, carbamazepine) can have a positive effect on mood. Selective serotonin reuptake inhibitors and dual-action antidepressant medications are also considered first-line therapy.

References

Ahokas A, Kaukoranta J, Wahlbeck K, Aito M. Estrogen deficiency in severe postpartum depression: successful treatment with sublingual physiologic 17beta-estradiol: a preliminary study. *J. Clin. Psychiatry* 2001;62:332–336.

Allolio B, Arlt W. DHEA treatment: myth or reality? *Trends Endocrinol. Metab.* 2002;13:288–294.

Almeida OP, Waterreus A, Spry N, Flicker L, Martins RN. One year follow-up study of the association between chemical castration, sex hormones, beta-amyloid, memory and depression in men. *Psychoneuroendocrinology* 2004;29:1071–1081.

Andersen BB, Mikkelsen M, Vesterager A, et al. No influence of the antidepressant paroxetine on carbamazepine, valproate and phenytoin. *Epilepsy Res.* 1991;10:201–204.

Anthony JC, Eaton WW, Henderson AS. Looking to the future in psychiatric epidemiology. *Epidemiol. Rev.* 1995;17:240–242.

Barraclough B. The suicide rate of epilepsy. *Acta Psychiatr. Scand.* 1987;76:339–345.

Barrett-Connor E, von Muhlen D, Laughlin GA, Kripke A. Endogenous levels of dehydroepiandrosterone sulfate, but not other sex hormones, are associated with depressed mood in older women: the Rancho Bernardo Study. *J. Am. Geriatr. Soc.* 1999;47:685–691.

Barry JJ, Jones JE. What is effective treatment of depression in people with epilepsy? *Epilepsy Behav.* 2005;6:520-528.

Bengzon J, Kokaia Z, Elmer E, Nanobashvili A, Kokaia M, Lindvall O. Apoptosis and proliferation of dentate gyrus neurons after single and intermittent limbic seizures. *Proc. Natl. Acad. Sci. USA.* 1997;94:10432–10437.

Bethea CL, Mirkes SJ, Shively CA, Adams MR. Steroid regulation of tryptophan hydroxylase protein in the dorsal raphe of macaques. *Biol. Psychiatry* 2000;47:562–576.

Betts TA. Depression, anxiety and epilepsy. In: Reynolds EH,. Trimble MR, editors. Epilepsy and psychiatry. Edinburgh: Churchill Livingstone, 1981:60–71.

Bilo L, Meo R, Valentino R, et al. Abnormal patterns of luteinizing hormone pulsatility in women with epilepsy. *Fertil. Steril.* 1991;55:705–711.

Blackburn IM, Moore RG. Controlled acute and follow-up trial of cognitive therapy and pharmacotherapy in outpatients with recurrent depression. *Br. J. Psychiatry.* 1997;171:328–334.

Blanchet P, Frommer GP. Mood change preceding epileptic seizures. *J. Nerv. Ment. Dis.* 1986; 174: 471–476.

Blumer D, Zielinski J. Pharmacologic treatment of psychiatric disorders associated with epilepsy. *J. Epilepsy.* 1988;1:135–150.

Blumer D. Dysphoric disorders and paroxysmal affects: recognition and treatment of epilepsy-related psychiatric disorders. *Harv. Rev. Psychiatry* 2000;8:8-17.

Bonnet U. Moclobemide: therapeutic use and clinical studies. CNS Drug Rev. 2003;9:97–140.

Cavanna AE, Mula M, Monaco F. Epilepsy and consciousness. In: Hollaway HJ (Ed) New research on epilepsy and behavior. New York: Nova Science Publishers 2007, 295-317.

Cavanna AE. Seizures and consciousness. In: Schachter SC, Holmes G, Kasteleijn-Nolst Trenite D (Eds) Behavioral aspects of epilepsy: principles and practice. New York: Demos 2008, 99-104.

Cavus I, Duman RS. Influence of estradiol, stress, and 5-HT2A agonist treatment on brain-derived neurotrophic factor expression in female rats. *Biol. Psychiatry* 2003;54:59–69.

Cha BH, Akman C, Silveira DC, Liu X, Holmes GL. Spontaneous recurrent seizure following status epilepticus enhances dentate gyrus neurogenesis. *Brain Dev.* 2004;26:394–397.

Clancy AN, Bonsall RW, Michael RP. Immunohistochemical labeling of androgen receptors in the brain of rat and monkey. *Life Sci.* 1992;50: 409–417.

Cramer JA, Gordon J, Schachter S, Devinsky O. Women with epilepsy: Hormonal issues from menarche through menopause. *Epilepsy Behav.* 2007;11:160–178.

Currie S, Heathfield K, Henson R. Clinical course and prognosis of temporal lobe epilepsy. A survey of 666 patients. *Brain.* 1971;94:173–190.

Dalla C, Antoniou K, Papadopoulou-Daifoti Z, Balthazart J, Bakker J. Oestrogen-deficient female aromatase knockout (ArKO) mice exhibit depressive-like symptomatology. *Eur. J. Neurosci.* 2004;20:217–228.

Daly D. Ictal affect. *Am. J. Psychiatry.* 1958; 115: 97–108.

De Foubert G, Carney SL, Robinson CS, et al. Fluoxetine-induced change in rat brain expression of brain-derived neurotrophic factor varies depending on length of treatment. *Neuroscience* 2004;128:597–604.

Drakew A, Muller M, Gahwiler BH, Thompson SM, Frotscher M. Spine loss in experimental epilepsy: quantitative light and electron microscopic analysis of intracellularly stained CA3 pyramidal cells in hippocampal slice cultures. *Neuroscience.* 1996;70:31–45.

Drislane FW, Coleman AE, Schomer DL, et al. Altered pulsatile secretion of lutenizing hormone in women with epilepsy. *Neurology* 1994;44:306–310.

Duman RS, Nakagawa S, Malberg J. Regulation of adult neurogenesis by antidepressant treatment. *Neuropsychopharmacology* 2001;25:836–844.

Elger G, Hoppe C, Falkai P, Rush AJ, Elger CE. Vagus nerve stimulation is associated with mood improvements in epilepsy patients. *Epilepsy Res.* 2000;42:203–210.

Engel J Jr, Birbeck GI, Diop AG, et al. Epilepsy: global issues for the practicing neurologist. World Federation of Neurology: seminars in clinical neurology. New York: Demos; 2005

Engel J Jr. So what can we conclude–do seizures damage the brain? *Prog. Brain. Res.* 2002;135:509–512.

Fava G, Grandi S, Zielezny M, Canestrari R, Morphy MA. Cognitive behavioral treatment of residual symptoms in primary major depressive disorder. *Am. J. Psychiatry.* 1994; 151:1295–1299.

Fava G, Silvana G, Zielezny M, Canestrari R, Morphy MA. Six year outcome for cognitive behavioral treatment of residual symptoms in major depression. *Am. J. Psychiatry.* 1998;155:1443–1445.

Fava G, Silvana G, Zielezny M, Rafanelli C, Canestrari R. Fouryear outcome for cognitive behavioral treatment of residual symptoms in major depression. *Am. J. Psychiatry.* 1996;153: 945–947.

Fava GF, Rafanelli C, Grandi S, Conti S, Belluardo P. Prevention of recurrent depression with cognitive behavioral therapy. *Arch. Gen. Psychiatry.* 1998;55:816–820.

Foldvary-Schaefer N, Falcone T. Catamenial epilepsy: pathophysiology, diagnosis, and management. *Neurology* 2003;61(Suppl. 2):S2–15.

Frank E, Grochocinski VJ, Spanier CA, et al. Interpersonal psychotherapy and antidepressant medication: evaluation of a sequential treatment strategy in women with recurrent major depression. *J. Clin. Psychiatry.* 2000;61:51–57.

Gaitatzis A, Carroll K, Majeed A, Sander JW. The epidemiology of the comorbidity of epilepsy in the general population. *Epilepsia* 2004;45:1613-1622.

Gibbs RB. Treatment with estrogen and progesterone affects relative levels of brain-derived neurotrophic factor mRNA and protein in different regions of the adult rat brain. *Brain Res.* 1999;844:20–27.

Gilliam F, Kanner AM. Treatment of depressive disorders in epilepsy patients. *Epilepsy Behav.* 2002;3:S2-S9

Gregoire AJ, Kumar R, Everitt B, Henderson AF, Studd JW. Transdermal oestrogen for treatment of severe postnatal depression. *Lancet* 1996;347:930–933.

Griesinger W. Mental pathology and therapeutics [Translated by Lockhart Robertson C, Rutherford J]. 1857 London: New Sydenham Society.

Grigoriadis S, Kennedy SH. Role of estrogen in the treatment of depression. *Am. J. Ther.* 2002;9:503–509.

Hajszan T, MacLusky NJ, Leranth C. Short-term treatment with the antidepressant fluoxetine triggers pyramidal dendritic spine synapse formation in the rat hippocampus. *Eur. J. Neurosci.* 2005;21:1299–1303.

Hajszan T, MacLusky NJ. Neurologic links between epilepsy and depression in women: is hippocampal neuroplasticity the key? *Neurology.* 2006;66:S13-22.

Harden CL, Pulver MC, Ravdin LD, Nikolov B, Halper JP, Labar DR. A pilot study of mood in epilepsy patients treated with vagus nerve stimulation. *Epilepsy Behav.* 2000;1:93–99.

Harden CL. The co-morbidity of depression and epilepsy: epidemiology, etiology, and treatment. *Neurology.* 2002;59(6 Suppl 4):S48-55.

Hecimovic H, Goldstein JD, Sheline YI, Gilliam FG. Mechanisms of depression in epilepsy from a clinical perspective. *Epilepsy Behav.* 2003;4:S25-S30.

Herzog AG. Hormonal changes in epilepsy. *Epilepsia* 1995;36:323–324.

Herzog AG. Progesterone therapy in women with complex partial and secondary generalized seizures. *Neurology* 1995;45:1660–1662.

Herzog AG. Progesterone therapy in women with epilepsy: a 3-year follow-up. *Neurology* 1999;52:1917–1918.

ILAE. Proposal for revised classification of epilepsy and epileptic syndromes. *Epilepsia* 1989;30:389–399.

ILAE. Proposal for revised clinical and electroencephalographic classification of epileptic seizures. *Epilepsia* 1981;22: 489–501.

Imwalle DB, Gustafsson J, Rissman EF. Lack of functional estrogen receptor beta influences anxiety behavior and serotonin content in female mice. *Physiol. Behav.* 2005;84:157–163.

Isokawa M. Remodeling dendritic spines in the rat pilocarpine model of temporal lobe epilepsy. *Neurosci.Lett.* 1998;258:73–76.

Isokawa M. Remodeling dendritic spines of dentate granule cells in temporal lobe epilepsy patients and the rat pilocarpine model. *Epilepsia.* 2000;41(suppl 6):S14–17.

Jacoby A, Baker GA, Steen N, Potts P, Chadwick DW. The clinical course of epilepsy and its psychosocial correlates: findings from a UK community study. *Epilepsia.* 1996;37:148–161.

Jobe PC. Common pathogenic mechanisms between depression and epilepsy: an experimental perspective. *Epilepsy Behav.* 2003;4:S14-S24

Jockenhovel F. Testosterone therapy–what, when and to whom? Aging Male. 2004;7:319–324.

Kanner AM, Balabanov A. Depression in Epilepsy: How closely related are these two disorders? *Neurology.* 2002;58(Suppl 5):S27-39.

Kanner AM, Barry J. Is the psychopathology of epilepsy different from that of non-epileptic patients? *Epilepsy Behav.* 2001; 2: 170–186.

Kanner AM, Barry JJ. The impact of mood disorders in neurological disease: should neurologists be concerned? *Epilepsy Behav.* 2003;4:S3-S13.

Kanner AM, Kozak AM, Frey M. The use of sertraline in patients with epilepsy: is it safe? *Epilepsy Behav.* 2000;1:100–105.

Kanner AM, Kuzniecky RI. Psychiatric phenomena as an expression of postictal and paraictal events. In: Ettinger AB, Kanner AM, eds. Psychiatric issues in epilepsy. Baltimore: Lippincott, Williams and Wilkins, 2000:163–180.

Kanner AM, Rabinovich A, Soto A, et al. The prevalence of postictal symptoms of depression in patients treated in tertiary epilepsy centers: a transcultural perspective [Abstract]. *Epilepsia.* 1999; 40 (Suppl. 2): A147.

Kanner AM, Soto A, Kanner-Gross HR. There is more to epilepsy than seizures: a reassessment of the postictal period [Abstract]. Neurology. 2000;54:7(Suppl. 3): A352.

Kanner AM. Depression in epilepsy: a frequently neglected multifaceted disorder. *Epilepsy Behav.* 2003b;4: S11-S19.

Kanner AM. Depression in epilepsy: prevalence, clinical semiology, pathogenic mechanisms, and treatment. *Biol. Psychiatry* 2003a;54:388-398.

Kellner CH, Bernstein HJ. ECT as a treatment for neurologic illness. In: Coffey CE, editor. The clinical science of electroconvulsive therapy. Spiegel D, series editor. Progress in psychiatry. Washington, DC: American Psychiatric Press; 1993;38:183-312.

Klerman GL, Weissmann MM. Interpersonal psychotherapy and drugs in the treatment of depression. *Pharmacopsychiatry.* 1987;20:3–7.

Krishnamoorthy ES, Trimble MR, Blumer D. The classification of neuropsychiatric disorders in epilepsy: a proposal by the ILAE Commission on Psychobiology of Epilepsy. *Epilepsy Behav.* 2007;10:349-353.

Krishnamoorthy ES. Treatment of depression in patients with epilepsy: problems, pitfalls, and some solutions. *Epilepsy Behav.* 2003;4 Suppl 3:S46-54.

Kuhn KU, Quednow BB, Thiel M, Falkai P, Maier W, Elger CE. Antidepressive treatment in patients with temporal lobe epilepsy and major depression: a prospective study with three different antidepressants. *Epilepsy Behav.* 2003;4:674–679.

Lambert MV, Robertson MM. Depression in epilepsy: etiology, phenomenology, and treatment. *Epilepsia* 1999;40(Suppl 10):S21-47.

Leranth C, Hajszan T, MacLusky NJ. Androgens increase spine synapse density in the CA1 hippocampal subfield of ovariectomized female rats. *J. Neurosci.* 2004b;24:495–499.

Leranth C, Petnehazy O, MacLusky NJ. Gonadal hormones affect spine synaptic density in the CA1 hippocampal subfield of male rats. *J. Neurosci.* 2003;23:1588–1592.

Leranth C, Prange-Kiel J, Frick KM, Horvath TL. Low CA1 spine synapse density is further reduced by castration in male non-human primates. *Cereb. Cortex.* 2004a;14:503–510.

Leranth C, Shanabrough M, Horvath TL. Hormonal regulation of hippocampal spine synapse density involves subcortical mediation. *Neuroscience* 2000;101:349–356.

Leranth C, Shanabrough M, Redmond DE Jr. Gonadal hormones are responsible for maintaining the integrity of spine synapses in the CA1 hippocampal subfield of female nonhuman primates. *J. Comp. Neurol.* 2002;447:34–42.

Logothetis J, Harner R, Morrell F, Torres F. The role of estrogens in catamenial exacerbation of epilepsy. *Neurology* 1959;9:352–360.

Lonsdale D, Burnham WM. The anticonvulsant effects of progesterone and 5alpha-dihydroprogesterone on amygdala-kindled seizures in rats. *Epilepsia* 2003;44:1494–1499.

Lonsdale D, Nylen K, McIntyre Burnham W. The anticonvulsant effects of progesterone and its metabolites on amygdala-kindled seizures in male rats. *Brain Res.* 2006;1101:110–116.

Lund TD, Rovis T, Chung WC, Handa RJ. Novel actions of estrogen receptor-beta on anxiety-related behaviors. *Endocrinology* 2005;146: 797–807.

MacLusky NJ, Luine VN, Hajszan T, Leranth C. The 17alpha and 17beta isomers of estradiol both induce rapid spine synapse formation in the CA1 hippocampal subfield of ovariectomized female rats. *Endocrinology* 2005;146:287–293.

Malberg JE, Eisch AJ, Nestler EJ, Duman RS. Chronic antidepressant treatment increases neurogenesis in adult rat hippocampus. *J. Neurosci.* 2000;20:9104–9110.

Matthews W, Barabas G. Suicide and epilepsy: A review of the literature. *Psychosomatics.* 1981; 22:515–524.

McCall WV. Electroconvulsive therapy in the era of modern psychopharmacology. *Int. J. Neuropsychopharmacol* .2001;4:315–324.

McConnell HW, Duncan D. Treatment of psychiatric comorbidity in epilepsy. In: McConnell HW, Snyder PJ, editors. Psychiatric comorbidity in epilepsy: basic mechanisms, diagnosis, and treatment. Washington, DC: American Psychiatric Press; 1998;245–361.

Mendez MF, Cummings JL, Benson DF, et al. Depression in epilepsy. Significance and phenomenology. *Arch. Neurol.* 1986;43:766–770.

Mensah SA, Beavis JM, Thapar AK, Kerr M. The presence and clinical implications of depression in a community population of adults with epilepsy. *Epil. Behav.* 2006;8:213-219.

Mohapel P, Ekdahl CT, Lindvall O. Status epilepticus severity influences the long-term outcome of neurogenesis in the adult dentate gyrus. *Neurobiol. Dis.* 2004;15:196–205.

Monaco F, Mula M, Cavanna AE. Consciousness, epilepsy and emotional qualia. *Epilepsy Behav.* 2005;7:150-160.

Morrell MJ, Flynn L, Seale CG, et al. Reproductive dysfunction in women with epilepsy: antiepileptic drug effects on sex-steroid hormones. *CNS Spectr* 2001;6:771–786.

Morrell MJ. Reproductive and metabolic disorders in women with epilepsy. Epilepsia 2003;44(Suppl. 4):11–20.

Mula M, Cavanna AE, Collimedaglia L, Barbagli D, Magli E, Monaco F. The role of aura in psychopathology and dissociative experiences in epilepsy. *J. Neuropsy. Clin. Neurosci.* .2006;18:536-542.

Mula M, Cavanna AE, Monaco F. New anticonvulsant drugs and psychopathology: an update. In: Hollaway HJ (Ed) New research on epilepsy and behavior. New York: Nova Science Publishers 2007, p. 127-140.

Mula M, Jauch R, Cavanna AE, Collimedaglia L, Barbagli D, Gaus V, Kretz R, Viana M, Tota G, Israel H, Reuter U, Martus P, Cantello R, Monaco F, Schmitz B. Clinical and psychopathological definition of the interictal dysphoric disorder of epilepsy. *Epilepsia* 2008; 49: 650-656.

Mulder D, Daly D. Psychiatric symptoms associated with lesions of the temporal lobe. *JAMA.* 1952; 150: 173–176.

Nappi C, Meo R, Di Carlo C, Estraneo A, Bilo L. Reduced fertility and neuroendocrine dysfunction in women with epilepsy. *Gynecol. Endocrinol* .1994;8:133–145.

Nowakowska E, Kus K. Antidepressant and memory affecting influence of estrogen and venlafaxine in ovariectomized rats. *Arzneimittelforschung* 2005;55:153–159.

Orengo CA, Fullerton G, Tan R. Male depression: a review of gender concerns and testosterone therapy. *Geriatrics* 2004;59:24–30.

Pack AM, Morrell MJ. Treatment of women with epilepsy. *Semin. Neurol.* 2002;22:289–298.

Paykel ES, Scott J, Teasdale JD, et al. Prevention of relapse in residual depression by cognitive therapy. *Arch. Gen. Psychiatry.* 1999;56:829–835.

Pennell PB. Evidence used to treat women with epilepsy. *Epilepsia* 2006;47(Suppl 1):S46-53.

Pisani F, Oteri G, Costa C, Di Raimondo G, Di Perri R. Effects of psychotropic drugs on seizure threshold. *Drug Saf.* 2002;25:91–110.

Post RM, Ketter TA, Denicoff K, et al. The place of anticonvulsant therapy in bipolar illness. *Psychopharmacology* (Berl) 1996;128:115–129.

Priest RG, Vize C, Roberts A, Roberts M, Tylee A. Lay people's attitudes to treatment of depression: results of an opinion poll for the Defeat Depression campaign just before launch. *Br. Med. J.* 1996;313:858–859.

Rasgon NL, Altshuler LL, Fairbanks LA, et al. Estrogen replacement therapy in the treatment of major depressive disorder in perimenopausal women. *J. Clin. Psychiatry* 2002;63(suppl 7):45– 48.

Robertson M, Trimble M, Townsend H. Phenomenology of depression in epilepsy. *Epilepsia.* 1987; 28:364–372.

Robertson MM, Trimble MR. Depressive illness in patients with epilepsy: a review. *Epilepsia.* 1983;24(Suppl 2):S109-116.

Robertson MM, Trimble MR. The treatment of depression in patients with epilepsy: a double-blind trial. *J. Affect. Disord.* 1985;9:127–136.

Robertson MM. Affect and mood in epilepsy: an overview with focus on depression. *Acta Neurol. Scand.* 1992;140(Suppl.):127–132.

Robertson MM. Depression in patients with epilepsy: an overview. *Semin. Neurol.* 1991a;11:182-189.

Robertson MM. Women and depression in epilepsy. In: Trimble MR, ed. Women and epilepsy. Chichester, Sussex: John Wiley and Sons, 1991b: 223-242.

Robertson MM. Suicide and parasuicide in epilepsy. In: Engel J Jr et al, eds. The American Textbook of Epilepsy. New York: Raven Press, 1997: 2141-2151.

Rodgers RJ, Johnson NJ. Behaviorally selective effects of neuroactive steroids in plus-maze anxiety in mice. *Pharmacol. Biochem. Behav.* 1998;59:221–232.

Savard G, Andermann LF, Reutens D, Andermann F. Epilepsy, surgical treatment and postoperative psychiatric complications: a re-evaluation of the evidence. In: Trimble MR, Schmitz B, eds. Forced normalization and alternative psychosis of epilepsy. Petersfield: Writson Biomedical Publishing, 1998: 179–192.

Scharfman HE, Mercurio TC, Goodman JH, Wilson MA, MacLusky NJ. Hippocampal excitability increases during the estrous cycle in the rat: a potential role for brain-derived neurotrophic factor. *J. Neurosci* .2003;23:11641–11652.

Scharfman HE. Functional implications of seizure-induced neurogenesis. *Adv. Exp. Med. Biol.* 2004;548:192–212.

Schmidt D. Vagus nerve stimulation for the treatment of epilepsy. *Epilepsy Behav.* 2001;2:S1–5.

Scott J. Cognitive therapy of affective disorders: a review. *J. Affect. Disord.* 1996;37:1–11.

Seeman MV. Psychopathology in women and men: focus on female hormones. *Am. J. Psychiatry.* 1997;154:1641–1647.

Segal Z, Vincent P, Levitt A. Efficacy of combined, sequential, and crossover psychotherapy and pharmacotherapy in improving outcomes in depression. *J. Psychiatry Neurosci.* 2002;27:281–290.

Settle EC Jr. Antidepressant drugs: disturbing and potentially dangerous adverse effects. *J. Clin. Psychiatry* 1998;59(suppl 16):25–30.

Shirayama Y, Chen AC, Nakagawa S, Russell DS, Duman RS. Brainderived neurotrophic factor produces antidepressant effects in behavioral models of depression. *J. Neurosci.* 2002;22:3251–3261.

Shors TJ, Leuner B. Estrogen-mediated effects on depression and memory formation in females. *J. Affect .Disord.* 2003;74:85–96.

Shughrue PJ, Lane MV, Merchenthaler I. Comparative distribution of estrogen receptor-alpha and -beta mRNA in the rat central nervous system. *J. Comp .Neurol .*1997;388:507–525.

Smith SS, Woolley CS. Cellular and molecular effects of steroid hormones on CNS excitability. *Cleve Clin. J. Med.* 2004;71(Suppl. 2):S4–10.

Standage K, Fenton G. Psychiatric symptom profiles of patients with epilepsy: a controlled investigation. *Psychol. Med.* 1975;5:152–160.

Steiner M, Dunn E, Born L. Hormones and mood: from menarche to menopause and beyond. *J. Affect Disord.* 2003;74:67–83.

Stewart DE, Rolfe DE, Robertson E. Depression, estrogen, and the Women's Health Initiative. *Psychosomatic*s 2004;45:445–447.

Stoffel EC, Craft RM. Ovarian hormone withdrawal-induced "depression" in female rats. *Physiol. Behav.* 2004;83:505–513.

Studd J, Panay N. Hormones and depression in women. *Climacteric* 2004;7:338–346.

Swann JW, Al-Noori S, Jiang M, Lee CL. Spine loss and other dendritic abnormalities in epilepsy. *Hippocampus.* 2000;10:617–625.

Swinkels WAM, Kuyk J, van Dyck R, Spinhoven Ph. Psychiatric comorbidity in epilepsy. *Epilepsy Behav.* 2005;7:37-50.

Tanapat P, Hastings NB, Gould E. Ovarian steroids influence cell proliferation in the dentate gyrus of the adult female rat in a dose and time-dependent manner. *J. Comp. Neurol.* 2005;481:252–265.

Teasdale JD, Segal ZV, Williams JM, Ridgeway VA, Soulsby JM, Lau MA. Prevention of relapse/recurrence in major depression by mindfulness-based cognitive therapy. *J. Consult. Clin. Psychol.* 2000;68:615–623.

Temkin O. The falling sickness. 1971 Baltimore: John Hopkins Press.

Thase ME, Greenhouse JB, Frank E, et al. Treatment of major depression with psychotherapy or psychotherapy–pharmacotherapy combinations. *Arch. Gen. Psychiatry* 1997;54:1009–1015.

Wallace H, Shorvon S, Tallis R. Age specific incidence and prevalence rates of treated epilepsy in an unselected population of 2,052,922 and age-specific fertility rates of women with epilepsy. *Lancet* 1998;352:1970–1973.

Weil A. Depressive reactions associated with temporal lobe uncinate seizures. *J. Nerv. Ment. Dis.* 1955; 121: 505–510.

Weil A. Ictal emotions occurring in temporal lobe dysfunction. *Arch. Neurol.* 1959; 1: 87–97.

Williams D. The structure of emotions reflected in epileptic experiences. *Brain.* 1956; 79: 29–67.

Wong ML, Licinio J. Research and treatment approaches to depression. *Nature Rev. Neurosci.* 2001;2:343–351.

Wooley CS, Schwartzkroin PA. Hormonal effects on the brain. *Epilepsia* 1998;39(Suppl. 8):52–58.

Woolley CS, McEwen BS. Estradiol mediates fluctuation in hippocampal synapse density during the estrous cycle in the adult rat. *J. Neurosci.* 1992;12:2549–2554.

In: Women and Depression
Editors: Paula Hernandez and Sara Alonso

ISBN 978-1-60456-647-5
© 2009 Nova Science Publishers, Inc.

Chapter 14

Temporomandibular Disorders (TMD) and Depression

Kirsi Sipilä[8]
Department of Prosthetic Dentistry and Stomatognathic Physiology,
Institute of Dentistry, University of Oulu, P.O. Box 5281, FIN-90014 Oulu, Finland,
and Oral and Maxillofacial Department, Oulu University Hospital, Oulu, Finland

Abstract

Temporomandibular disorders (TMD) are characterized as a heterogeneous set of clinical problems involving the masticatory musculature and/or the temporomandibular joint (TMJ). TMD are considered to be one of the musculoskeletal disorders, and are usually subclassified as myogenous, arthrogenous or combined disorders. The symptoms and clinical signs of TMD include joint sounds, TMJ and masticatory muscle pain and restricted mandibular movements.

Several population-based studies indicate that women experience more TMD-related pain than men, usually at a ratio of two to one. The most prominent sex differences have been found at the age of 20-40 years. Altogether, there seem to be both local and central factors involved in the aetiology of TMD. Epidemiological and clinical studies have shown that besides local pain, facial pain is related to pain condition in different parts of the body. It has also been shown that psychological factors are related to TMD, especially those involving muscular problems.

It has been shown that chronic pain conditions and depressive disorders have some pathophysiologic characteristics in common. Additionally, an association between depression and TMD-related pain has been found in several studies, both in clinical and epidemiological ones. It has been suggested that especially TMD pain as part of a generalised pain condition is connected with depression. The comorbidity has been found to be stronger among women than men.

8 e-mail: kirsi.sipila@oulu.fi, tel:+358-40-7137075, fax:358-8-537 5560.

The diagnosis and treatment of TMD pain may be complicated, especially when the condition is linked with psychological problems. Depression may have an effect on the outcome of the treatment of TMD. Especially when TMD are related to chronic pain conditions, a multidisciplinary approach is needed, besides conservative treatment of TMD. Dentists can provide an important contribution to health care by identifying depression in patients and referring them for treatment.

Introduction

Facial pain originating from the musculoskeletal structures of the masticatory system is included in a category of pain complaints known as temporomandibular disorders (TMD). The term TMD refers to a group of heterogeneous pain and dysfunction conditions involving the masticatory structure. TMD are defined as "a collective term embracing a number of clinical problems that involve the masticatory muscles, the temporomandibular joints (TMJs) and associated structures, or both" [1]. Besides pain in the facial area, typical signs and symptoms of TMD are sounds, i.e. clicking or crepitus, of the TMJs, restriction of the jaw movements, and deviation in the movement patterns of the mandible [2]. In addition to specific symptoms, TMD patients may also report nonspecific symptoms affecting the ears, eyes or throat, as well as headaches typically involving frontal, parietal, occipital or neck regions. Moreover, patients may describe disturbances in swallowing and speech. The non-specific symptoms may also include those involving in other chronic pain symptomatology, such as faintness, chest or lower back pain pain, poor appetite, etc. [2]. Pathological changes in the teeth, periodontium or oral mucosa may also be connected with TMD [1]. Several local and generalized factors exist in the background of TMD. This chapter reviews the literature concerning the epidemiology, etiology and treatment of TMD, focussing on the connection between TMD and psychosocial factors, especially depression.

Diagnosis of TMD

The diagnosis of TMD is based on anamnestic data and clinical examination. Clinical examination includes measurement of movements of the mandible, registration of deviations and pain during mandibular movements, auscultation of TMJ sounds, and palpation of the masticatory muscles and the TMJs. At present, TMD are considered as comprising several diseases of varying etiology and pathology.

Over the years, many classification schemes for TMD have been offered. Helkimo's indices were the first to be developed mainly for epidemiologic purposes in the diagnosis of TMD [3]. The American Academy of Orofacial Pain (AAOP) published an updated diagnostic classification for TMD in 1996 [1]. The TMD are subclassified into two primary diagnostic categories: arthrogenous and myogenous. The myogenous category is further subdivided into muscular hyperarousal due to stress and muscular abnormality associated with parafunctional oral habits (e.g., bruxism), while the arthrogenous category is subdivided on the basis of specific structural abnormalities (e.g. internal derangement of the temporomandibular joint or degenerative disease).

The Research Diagnostic Criteria (RDC) developed by Dworkin and LeResche [2] established a dual diagnosis for TMD. The axis I of the RDC assesses the physical conditions, including muscle disorders, disc displacements and other types of joint conditions that may contribute to the pain disorder. The axis II recognizes also the psychosocial issues that contribute to the suffering, pain behavior and disability associated with the patient's pain experience. The axis II assesses and classifies the global severity of the pain condition in terms of pain intensity, pain-related disability, depression, and non-specific symptoms.

In measuring depression, a number of self-report approaches have been shown to be reliable and valid, including the Centre for Epidemiological Studies Depression Scale (CES-D), the Beck Depression Scale, the Symptoms Checklist 90 (SCL-90), and others. Because the SCL-90 provides both a depression scale and scale measuring the severity of non-specific physical symptoms (the somatisation subscale), it is included in the Axis II assessment of the RDC/TMD criteria [2].

Analyses of data from TMD clinical centres has revealed good to excellent reliability, validity, and clinical utility for the Axis II measures of depression, somatization, and graded chronic pain. The study by Dworkin et al [4] compared the RDC/TMD depression scale to the Beck Depression Inventory and the Center for Epidemiologic Studies Depression Scale. Their data supported concurrent validity of the RDC/TMD measure and its use as a depression screening tool. Its clinical utility is based on its demonstrated usefulness for alerting TMD clinicians to potentially noteworthy depressive symptomatology in TMD patients.

Epidemiology of TMD

Signs and symptoms of TMD appear relatively frequently in populations. Clicking of the TMJ is the most common TMD symptom in the population, with prevalence levels of up to 30 % [5,6]. Instead, mouth-opening limitations are relatively rare, occurring in 5% or less of the population [7,8]. The prevalence of facial pain has been reported to vary between 5 and 20% in adult population [6, 9-15].

Women have shown to suffer from TMD more frequently than men [5, 6, 8, 11, 12, 16, 17]. Further, women have noted to suffer from TMD-related pain symptoms more than men, usually at a ratio of 2:1 or 1.5:1 [6, 9-13, 18]. Studies with patient samples have shown even higher predominance of TMD among women [10, 12, 19, 20]. The study by Velly et al [21] found that female gender has almost three times the risk of chronic masticatory myofascial pain than males. Further, it has been shown that women need treatment for their TMD problems two to three times as often as men [22].

Subjective symptoms of TMD are more common among young and middle-aged adults than among children or elderly [11-13, 23], while clinical signs seem to be more prevalent in the elderly [16, 24]. Additionally, Salonen et al [16] have found that reported symptoms of TMD decrease with age, while clinical signs increase.

Etiology of TMD

The etiology and pathology of TMD varies and is partly controversial [2, 20]. General factors, such as impaired health, general joint and muscle diseases, psychological and psychosocial factors, and local influences such as occlusal disturbances and traumas, can exist in the background of TMD [1]. TMD may be also be related to oral parafunctional activity, such as nocturnal tooth grinding and clenching as well as habitual clenching during daytime [15, 17, 25].

Traditionally, disturbances in dental occlusion have been considered to have a role in the initiation, aggravation or acceleration of TMD [20]. The most common theory of occlusal factors in the etiology of TMD is the "neuromuscular theory" [26] According to this theory, occlusal interferences induce imbalance in the neuromuscular structure via proprioceptive feedback, leading to pain and dysfunction. Occlusion has been regarded as one of the major influences on TMD, and treatment of occlusion as an important strategy in the treatment of TMD [27]. There is, however, considerable evidence that occlusal factors alone are poor correlates to explain TMD etiology, and their clinical relevance still requires further study [1, 2, 20, 28].

Besides local condition, it has been proposed that TMD may be part of a generalized pain condition. Several studies have found a significant overlap between TMD-related pain and pain in other parts of the body [6, 29-32]. Further, comorbidity between TMD and fibromyalgia has been noted in several studies [32-34]. Especially patients with myogenous TMD may have complaints and diffuse muscle tenderness beyond the masticatory muscles [29, 35]. As the TMD include in the category of musculoskeletal diseases, many of the risk factors for TMD are similar to risk factors for other pain problems [13]. Widespread pain has been shown to associate with risk of developing TMD pain-related disability especially among women, though without having TMD at baseline [36].

The Role of Psychological Factors in TMD

Findings by several studies have noted that TMD resemble musculoskeletal disorders and chronic pain disorders in general [37], and the role of psychological and psychosocial factors has been emphasized in TMD [37-39]. As the TMD comprise the most common cause of chronic facial pain conditions, they are often associated with somatic and psychological complaints including fatigue, sleep disturbances, anxiety, and depression [40, 41].

The psychological factors are thought to have a role in the cause or maintenance of TMD, and they may predispose the condition to chronicity [42]. Despite the association found between psychosocial factors and TMD, there is less evidence that these factors are etiologic [37]. On the other hand, it has been stated that psychological disturbances may be a consequence of pain in TMD patients [43]. Subcategorization of patients into diagnostic subgroups of TMD suggests that myogenous patients may have more psychological difficulties than patients with arthrogenous TMD[44-46].

The role of psychological stressors in TMD has been examined in a number of studies [22, 25, 47, 48], supposing that stress is a predisposing factor for TMD, especially for masticatory muscle pain [49, 50]. Studies have also shown that anxiety and depression influence the occurrence of TMD symptoms and their severity [51-56, 40]. Further, it has been noted that beliefs, catastrophising and coping strategies [57-59] as well as optimism [60] are related to the experience of TMD. Moreover, subjects with TMD have been found to have increased scores in somatization, a tendency to report non-specific physical symptoms as noxious or troublesome [13, 61-63].

In terms of personality profiles, it has been shown that TMD correlate with personality characteristics in a similar way to those of other chronic pain patients [64, 65]. On the other hand, there are studies that have found no evidence of a connection between personality and TMD [66, 67]. Alexithymia means literally "no words for feelings". It denotes a deficit in the ability to differentiate emotional states from physical ones and to identify and describe one's feelings, as well as a preference for externally oriented, utilitarian thinking rather than fantasy or introspection [68]. Alexithymia has been noted to associate with somatization [69] as well as with certain symptoms of TMD and pain in the orofacial area [70-72].

TMD and Depression

Epidemiological studies show that depression is a common mental disorder in population, affecting at least 20% of women and 10% of men at some time during their life time [73]. It has been shown that chronic pain conditions and depressive disorders have some pathophysiologic characteristics in common [74]. Therefore it is understandable that an association between depression and chronic pain syndromes has been shown in several studies [9, 10, 75].

Depression has been noted to associate with TMD according to several clinical and epidemiological studies (Table 1). High rates of depression have been shown in patients with TMD [21, 41, 44, 45, 53-55, 61, 63, 76-78]. In a study of Korszun et al [53] involving 72 facial pain patients, 53 % fulfilled criteria for a diagnosis of major and minor depression, and 22% reported depressive symptoms. It has been shown that especially pain-related TMD are connected with depression. Using the RDC/TMD criteria, Celic et al [63] investigated differences in the prevalence of depression and somatization scores in 154 TMD patients. They found that patients with myofascial pain and arthralgia psychologically differed from those with disc displacement, concerning levels of depression and somatization. Additionally, the study by Yap et al [61] examined the relationship between depression, somatization and masticatory muscle and TMJ pain on palpation in 196 patients with TMD, and found an association between severe depression and masticatory muscle pain. Instead, no significant difference in TMJ pain scores was observed for depression and somatization scales. Strong associations between depression and especially muscle-related TMD have also been found by Kino et al [46].

Table 1. Studies that investigated the relationship between depression and temporomandibular disorders (TMD)

Author, year	No. of individuals	No. of women/men	Age/years	Population	Measure of TMD	Measure of depression	Main results
Von Korff et al, 1988 (9)	1,016	82% women, 78% men	18-75	adults	self-report of facial pain	SCL-90 revised	Persons with pain had higher levels of anxiety, depression, and non-pain somatic symptoms than those without pain
McCreary et al, 1991 (44)	112	86% women	mean 39	TMD patients	clinical examination	Beck's Depression Inventory	Patients with primary myalgia had the highest scores on the pain and distress measures
Gallagher et al, 1991 (76)	136	136 women	mean 38	TMD patients	TMPDS criteria	DSM-III-R	41 % of patients showed major depression
Vimpari et al, 1995 (52)	780	435 women, 345 men	55	Finnish adults	Helkimo´s dysfunction index	Zung´s depression scale	connection between depression and TMD symptoms
Gatchel et al, 1996 (42)	101		mean 38	51 patients with acute TMD and 50 patients with chronic TMD	Diagnostic criteria by Laskin	Interview DSM-III-R	A significant psychological comorbidity in both groups of patients
Korszun et al, 1996 (53)	72		18-66	facial pain patients	University of Washington criteria for myofascial pain dysfunction, objective signs for joint diseases	Psychiatric evaluation DSM-IV	53% had major/minor depression, 22% depressive symptoms
Carlson et al, 1998 (54)	70	33 women/group	mean 30	35 masticatory muscle pain patients (MMP)/ 35 matched controls	RDC/TMD	CES-D self-report scale	persons with MMP reported more depression than matched controls
Raphael et al, 2000 (83)	162	162 women	Patients with regional TMD: mean 44 (SD 11); patients with widespread pain mean mean 42 (SD 1.7	subjects who had histories of myofascial face pain (MFP)	diagnostic criteria established by the International Association for the Study of Pain	psychiatric Interview DSM-III-R	Patients with MFP and a history of widespread pain were more likely to have higher rates of depression than those with no history of widespread pain.

Study	N	Sex	Age	Population	self-reported TMD symptoms	reported depression	Depression associated with pain-related TMD symptoms.
Sipilä et al, 2001 (56)	5,696	2,978 women, 2,819 men	31	adults		(diagnosed by a doctor), the Symptom Checklist (SCL)-25 depression subscale	Depression associated with pain-related TMD symptoms.
Yap et al, 2002 (45)	117	28 men, 89 women	mean age 33.3 +/- 10.3 years	TMD patients	RDC/TMD	SCL-90 depression scale	39% of patients were clinically depressed. Patients with myofascial pain and other joint conditions had significantly higher levels of depression than patients diagnosed with only disk displacements
Rantala et al, 2003 (79)	1,339	656 women, 683 men	30-55 (mean 35, SD 7)	working adults	A self-administered postal questionnaire	SCL-90 depression scale	Frequent pain and TMJ-related symptoms were associated with self-reported depression
Velly et al, 2003 (21)	183	72% women	18-60	83 patients with masticatory myofascial (MFP)/100 controls	RDC/TMD	SCL-90 depression scale	Depression associated with MFP
Yap et al, 2003 (78)	191	53 men, 138 women	mean age 33.6 +/- 9.3	TMD patients	RDC/TMD	SCL-90 depression scale	40 % of patients had moderate to severe depression
Yap et al, 2004 (61)	255	68 men, 187 women	a mean age of 33.0	TMD patients	RDC/TMD history questionnaire	SCL-90 depression scale	43 % of patients had moderate/severe depression. A positive correlation between depression and non-specific symptoms
Bonjardim et al, 2005 (80)	217	120 girls, 97 boys	12-18	adolescents	a self-report questionnaire, the Craniomandibular Index, the Dysfunction Index, the Palpation Index	The Hospital Anxiety (HADSa) and Depression Scale (HADSd)	HADSd associated with increasing number of TMD subjective symptoms but not with clinical signs of TMD

Table 1. (Continued)

Kino et al, 2005 (46)	511	Women accounted for more than 70% in each group	median 29-49 (depending on the subtype of TMD)	TMD patients	RDC/TMD	the Hospital Anxiety and Depression Scale	Those with myofascial pain group had higher depression scores than those in disc displacement group
Le Resche et al, 2005 (81)	3,101	1548 girls, 1553 boys	11-17	adolescents	report on TMD pain in the prior 3 months	SCL-90 depression scale	Rates of somatization, depression and probability of experiencing multiple pains increased with pubertal development in girls
Sipilä et al, 2006 (82)	5,696	2,978 women, 2,819 men	31	adults	self-report of facial pain	SCL-25 depression subscale	Comorbidity between facial pain, widespread pain, and depressiveness was found to be particularly prevalent among women
Celić et al, 2006 (63)	154	117 women, 37 men	mean 39 +/-14.5	TMD patients	RDC/TMD	SCL-90 depression scale	20 % of patients had severe depression. Patients with myofascial pain and arthralgia psychologically differed from those with disc displacement.
Selaimen et al, 2006 (41)	102	102 women	15-45	72 muscle-related TMD patients/ 30 pain-free controls	RDC/TMD	Beck Depression Inventory	TMD patients had statistically significantly higher sleep and depression scores than controls

Depression has been shown to associate with TMD also according to epidemiological studies [9, 52, 56, 79-82]. In the study from 5,696 young adults [56] questionnaire information concerning TMD symptoms was collected. Depression was measured with a question about reported depression (diagnosed by a doctor), and with the Symptom Checklist-25 depression subscale (SCL-25 DS). The results showed that depression associated with TMD symptoms, especially those related to pain.

The results showed a stronger connection of facial pain symptoms and reported depression (diagnosed by a doctor) among women than men, suggesting that these pain conditions may have a connection to psychopathology more commonly among women than among men. On the other hand, the gender differences may be due to differences in the care-seeking behaviour between the genders.

The results of the epidemiologic study by Von Korff et al [9] involving 1,016 subjects showed that subjects with facial pain had a prevalence of 10% of major depression (measured with the SCL-90 revised scale), which was five times higher than in non-pain subjects. Another population-based study of Vimpari et al [52] also found a connection between depression (according to Zung's self-rating depression scale) and subjective symptoms of TMD in 780 55-year-old subjects.

The connection between depression and TMD has also been found among adolescents. The study by Bonjardim et al [80] investigated the relationship of anxiety and depression with signs and symptoms of TMD among 217 non-patient adolescents. Both anxiety and depression were associated with an increasing number of TMD subjective symptoms. However, only anxiety was correlated with clinical signs of TMD, primarily muscle tenderness.

It has been found that depressive symptomatology is associated with reporting of multiple non-specific physical symptoms [61, 83], especially multiple chronic pain symptoms [10]. The study by Yap et al [61] examined the prevalence of depressive symptoms and their association with report of non-specific physical symptoms (NPSs) in 154 TMD patients, using the RDC. They found that 43 and 51% of the patients scored moderate-to-severe on the depression and NPS scales, respectively. Further, a significant and positive correlation was observed between depression and NPS scores. In their clinical study Raphael and colleagues [83] found that women with myofascial face pain and a history of widespread pain were more likely to have a history of major depression, compared with women with myofascial face pain but not widespread pain. In a study by Yap et al [84], 16% of the 202 TMD patients studied experienced more than three pain items. They observed significant correlations between the number of pain items experienced and depression (measured using the SCL-90 depression score). Further, in a study by Velly et al [85], of 162 outpatients with TMD, a cluster analysis classified the subjects into subgroups of localised and generalised disorder, of which the latter was found to relate to depression.

The comorbidity between TMD, multiple pain conditions and depressiveness has also shown in epidemiological studies. The study by LeResche et al [81] assessed the relationship of TMD pain and multiple pain conditions to gender and pubertal development a cross-sectional, population-based survey of 3,101 adolescents. The found that rates of somatization, depression and probability of experiencing multiple pains increased with pubertal development in girls. In another population-based study from 5,696 young adults [82], data on facial pain, pain in other areas of the body and depressiveness (measured using the SCL-25 depression subscale) were gathered using questionnaires. It was found that half of the subjects with facial pain also experienced simultaneously pain in 6 or more areas of the body (51% among women and 44% among men). The prevalence of depressiveness was about 30% among subjects with facial pain and simultaneously pain in 6 or more areas of the body. Comorbidity between facial pain, generalised pain and depressiveness was more clearly seen among women than men.

Pathophysiological Connections in TMD and Depression

Depressive disorders are chronic conditions that produce both emotional and physical symptoms. Increasing evidence suggests that in some patients with depressive disorders a neurodegenerative process may occur, highlighting the importance of early and aggressive intervention. Serotonin and norepinephrine neurotransmitter systems influence neuroplasticity in the brain, and both are involved in mediating the therapeutic effects of most currently available antidepressants [86]. A dysfunction at the level of the serotonergic and noradrenergic neurons can thus affect both the ascending and descending pathways resulting in the psychological and somatic symptoms of depression but also in physical painful symptoms [87].

As a consequence of the common pathophysiological characteristics between pain and depression, it is understandable that an association between depression and TMD has been found in several studies. Especially muscular TMD has been regarded as a common stress-related condition showing marked comorbidity with depression and fibromyalgia, both of which are associated with dysregulation of cortisol secretion in the hypothalamic- pituitary-adrenal (HPA) axis [88] The HPA axis has a wide range of central and peripheral functions [89, 90]. High levels of cortisol, indicating HPA hyperactivity, have been noted to occur in depression and facial pain [90] as well as in fibromyalgia [91, 92]. Thus individuals who have an underlying abnormality of the stress hormone response resulting in high cortisol levels may be prone to overlapping symptoms of TMD related pain, generalised pain and depression [90]. The comorbidity between multiple pain conditions and depressiveness found especially among women could be explained by biological mechanisms. In both animal and human studies, it has been demonstrated that females are more susceptible than males to stress-induced HPA axis dysregulation, related to the pathophysiology of pain and depression [93].

Treatment of TMD

The aim of the treatment of TMD is mostly to manage pain [2]. The treatment of TMD includes occlusal, behavioral, physical and pharmacological treatments [1]. Conservative treatment of TMD consists of interocclusal orthopedic appliances (also referred to as occlusal splints), occlusal rehabilitation and exercises of masticatory muscles [1]. Based on systematic reviews of randomized controlled trials on splint therapy, it has been concluded that the use of occlusal splints may be beneficial in the treatment of TMD, but the evidence is scarce [94, 95]. At present, there is still insufficient evidence regarding the treatment response of splint therapy, and there exists a need for well-conducted RCTs that pay attention to the method of allocation, blind outcome assessment, sample size and the duration of follow-up.

Controlled clinical trials suggest an effect for the occlusal adjustment on TMD [96], on chronic headaches [97, 98] as well as on neck and shoulder pain [99]. However, the use of occlusal adjustment as a treatment for TMD has been questioned because of the lack of evidence regarding the effect [94, 95, 100]. At present, it is recommended that occlusal adjustment should not be used as a prophylactic method [100]. However, the occlusal treatments are still used in combination with other treatments, such as occlusal splint therapy and physiotherapy [27].

Pharmacologic intervention in the management of TMD is usually considered in conjunction with other treatments, especially when pain is poorly controlled by other treatments [101]. The pharmacologic agents used in the treatment of TMD include analgesics, anti-inflammatory agents, corticosteroids, anxiolytics, muscle relaxants and antidepressants. Non-opiate analgesics are effective for mild to moderate acute TMD pain, and opioids are considered for short-term use in controlling acute severe pain [20]. Tricyclic antidepressants appear to be effective in the control of chronic orofacial pain of non-inflammatory origin, independent of their effects on mood [102], with daily doses smaller than those typically used in the treatment of depression [103] Further, combined therapy, i.e. a combination of occlusal splint and antidepressant therapy, has shown to be more effective in pain relief, compared with single therapies [104]. In severe cases of chronic facial pain associated with masticatory hyperactivity, botulinum toxin has shown to be relatively safe and effective [105].

When TMD coexist with depression, patients respond best to therapies that address both the TMD and depression [104]. The effect of biospsychosocial interventions in the treatment of TMD has been examined in recent studies. Gatchel et al [77] evaluated the effect of comorbid depression and pain on an early biopsychosocial intervention for acute TMD patients. They found that with appropriate biopsychosocial intervention, acute TMD patients, regardless of the presence or absence of vulnerability to depression symptomatology, can be effectively treated. A cognitive-behavioral therapy intervention for TMD patients with heightened psychologic and psychosocial disability has also been shown to be effective, especially in improving pain-related symptoms, in conjunction with usual treatment [106].

Dworkin et al [107] has presented a tailored self-care treatment program in the treatment of TMD, comparing it with the usual treatment. They showed that the tailored self-care treatment program significantly decreased TMD pain, pain-related interference in activity, reduced the number of masticatory muscle pain as well as lowered the additional visits for TMD treatment. The self-care program was associated with consistent, although non-statistically significant, trends towards lower levels of depression and somatization. Ability to cope with TMD, knowledge concerning TMD and patient satisfaction was significantly enhanced for the self-care group. The authors concluded that the use of RDC/TMD psychosocial assessment criteria can contribute to successful clinical decision-making for the management of TMD.

Conclusion

Based on the present knowledge, it can be concluded that depression is associated with self-reported TMD- symptoms, especially those related to pain. However, additional examinations are needed to indicate the association of depression with clinical signs of TMD. In addition, the cross-sectional designs of the present studies give no information of the causality between TMD and depression. Although depression can take part in the etiology of pain, it has been argued that depression may also develop as a consequence of the physical suffering [108].

The heterogeneity of the patient samples should be taken into account when estimating the effectiveness of therapies. Despite the uncertainty about the causal relationships between TMD and depression, the comorbidity should be considered in the treatment strategies. The connection of TMD, generalised pain condition and depression may make diagnosis and treatment of TMD complicated. It should be noted that depression may have an effect on the outcome of the treatment of TMD. When treating patients with TMD, dentists should consider the possible presence of psychopathology and, if necessary, consult appropriate mental health professionals. In clinical practice, besides conservative treatment of TMD, a multidisciplinary approach is needed, especially for patients with complex pain conditions.

Although depression is a common disorder, it is particularly evident in treatment settings; more than 20 percent of patients seen in primary care clinics have clinically significant depressive symptoms [109]. The diagnosis of depression is missed in 50% of primary care cases, and appropriate treatment is rendered in less than 10% of cases [110]. The diagnosis and treatment of depression should be especially relevant to dentists because they are often the primary health care personnel who treat patients with facial pain. Dentists can provide an important contribution to health care by identifying depression in patients and referring them for treatment.

References

[1]   Okeson, JP. Management of temporomandibular disorders and occlusion. 6th edition. St. Louis: Mosby; 2008.

[2]   Dworkin SF, LeResche L. Research diagnostic criteria for temporomandibular disorders: review, criteria, examinations and specifications, criteria. *J. Craniomand Disord. Facial Oral Pain* 1992; 6, 301-355.

[3]   Helkimo M. Studies on function and dysfunction of the masticatory system. II. Index for anamnestic and clinical dysfunction and occlusal state. *Swed. Dent. J.* 1974; 67: 101-121.

[4]   Dworkin SF, Sherman J, Mancl L, Ohrbach R, LeResche L, Truelove E. Reliability, validity, and clinical utility of the research diagnostic criteria for Temporomandibular Disorders Axis II Scales: depression, non-specific physical symptoms, and graded chronic pain. *J. Orofac. Pain* 2002; 16: 207-220.

[5]   Magnusson T, Egermark I, Carlsson G.E. A longitudinal epidemiologic study of signs and symptoms of temporomandibular disorders from 15 to 35 years of age. *J. Orofac. Pain* 2000; 14: 310-319.

[6]   Rauhala K, Oikarinen KS, Järvelin MR, Raustia AM. Facial pain and temporomandibular disorders- an epidemiological study of the Northern Finland 1966 Birth Cohort. *J. Craniomand Pract* 2000; 18: 40-46.

[7]   Huber MA, Hall EH. A comparison of the signs of temporomandibular joint dysfunction and occlusal discrepancies in a symptom-free population of men and women. *Oral Surg Oral Med. Oral. Pathol.* 1990; 70: 180-183.

[8]   De Kanter RJ, Truin G.J, Burgersdijk RC, Van't Hof MA, Battistuzzi PG., Kalsbeek, H, Käyser AF. Prevalence in the Dutch adult population and a meta-analysis of signs and symptoms of temporomandibular disorder. *J. Dent. Res 1993*; 72: 1509-1518.

[9]   VonKorff M, Dworkin SF, LeResche L, Kruger A. An epidemiologic comparison of pain complaints. *Pain* 1988; 32: 173-183.

[10]   Dworkin SF, VonKorff MR, LeResche L. Multiple pains and psychiatric disturbance: An epidemiologic investigation. *Arch. Gen. Psychiatr.* 1990; 47: 239-244.

[11]   Lipton JA, Ship JA, Larach-Robinson D. Estimated prevalence and distribution of reported orofacial pain in the United States. *J. Am. Dent. Assoc.* 1993; 124: 115-121.

[12]   Goulet JP, Lavigne G.J, Lund, JP. Jaw pain prevalence among French-speaking Canadians in Quebec and related symptoms of temporomandibular disorders. *J. Dent. Res.* 1995; 74: 1738-1744.

[13]   LeResche L. Epidemiology of temporomandibular disorders: implications for the investigation for etiologic factors. *Crit. Rev. Oral. Biol. Med.* 1997; 8: 291-305.

[14]   Riley III JL, Gilbert G.H. Orofacial pain symptoms: an interaction between age and sex. *Pain* 2001; 90: 245-256.

[15]   Ahlberg, K, Ahlberg, J, Könönen, M, Alakuijala, A, Partinen, M, Savolainen, A. Peceived orofacial pain and its associations with reported bruxism and insomnia symptoms in media personnel with or without irregular shift work. *Acta Odontol. Scand.* 2005; 63: 213-217.

[16]   Salonen L, Hellden L, Carlsson GE. Prevalence of signs and symptoms of dysfunction in the masticatory system: an epidemiologic study in an adult Swedish population. *J. Craniomandib. Disord. Facial Oral Pain* 1990; 4: 241-250.

[17]   Johansson A, Unell L, Carlsson GE, Soderfelt B, Halling A. Gender difference in symptoms related to temporomandibular disorders in a population of 50-year-old subjects. *J. Orofac. Pain* 2003; 17: 29-35.

[18]   Kamisaka M, Yatani H, Kuboki T, Matsuka Y, Minakuchi H. Four-year longitudinal course of TMD symptoms in an adult population and the estimation of risk factors in relation to symptoms. *J. Orofac. Pain* 2000; 14: 224-232.

[19]   Bush FM, Harkins SW, Harrington WG., Price DD. Analysis of gender effects on pain perception and symptom presentation in temporomandibular pain. *Pain* 1993; 53: 73-80.

[20]   McNeill C. Management of temporomandibular disorders: concept and controversies. *J. Prosth. Dent.* 1997; 77, 510-522.

[21] Velly AM, Gornitsky M, Philippe P. Contributing factors to chronic myofascial pain: a case-control study. *Pain* 2003; 104: 491-499.

[22] Kuttila M, Kuttila S, Niemi PM, Alanen P, LeBell Y. Fluctuation of treatment need in relation to age, gender, stress, and diagnostic subgroups. *Acta Odontol. Scand.* 1997; 55: 350-355.

[23] Glass EG, McFlynn FD, Glaros AG., Melton K, Romans K. Prevalence of temporomandibular disorder symptoms in a major metropolitan area. *J. Craniomand Pract.* 1993; 11: 217-220.

[24] Rutkiewicz T, Könönen M, Suominen-Taipale L, Nordblad A, Alanen P. Occurence of clinical signs of temporomandibular diorders in adult Finns. *J. Orofac. Pain.* 2006; 20: 208-216.

[25] Glaros AG, Williams K, Lausten L. The role of parafunctions, emotions and stress in predicting facial pain. *J. Am. Dent. Assoc.* 2005; 136: 451-458.

[26] De Boever JA. Functional disturbances of the temporomandibular joint. In: Zarb GA, Carlsson GE, editors. The temporomandibular joint: function and dysfunction. Copenhagen: Munksgaard; 1979; 193-214.

[27] De Boever JA, Carlsson G.E, Klineberg IJ. Need for occlusal therapy and prosthodontic treatment in the management of temporomandibular disorders. Part I. Occlusal interferences and occlusal adjustment. *J. Oral Rehabil.* 2000; 27: 367-379.

[28] Pullinger, AG, Seligman DA. Quantification and validation of predictive values of occlusal variables in temporomandibular disorders using a multifactorial analysis. *J. Prosthet. Dent* .2000; 83: 66-75.

[29] Hagberg C, Hagberg M, Kopp S. Musculoskeletal symptoms and psychosocial factors among patients with craniomandibular disorders. *Acta Odontol. Scand.* 1994; 52: 170-177.

[30] Turp JC, Kowalski CJ, O´Leary N, Stohler CS. Pain maps from facial pain patients indicate a broad pain geopraphy. *J. Dent. Res* 1998; 77: 1465-1472.

[31] Sipilä K, Zitting P, Siira P, Niinimaa A, Raustia AM. Generalized pain in community subjects with facial pain- a case-control study. *J. Orofac Pain* 2005; 19: 127-132.

[32] Marbach JJ. Is myofascial face pain a regional expression of fibromyalgia? *J. Musculoskeletal Pain* 1995; 3: 93-97.

[33] Plesh O, Wolfe F, Lane N. The relationship between fibromyalgia and temporomandibular disorders: prevalence and symptoms severity. *J. Rheumatol.* 1996; 23: 1948-1952.

[34] Hedenberg-Magnusson B, Ernberg M, Kopp S. Presence of orofacial pain and temporomandibular disorder in fibromyalgia. A study by questionnaire. *Swed. Dent. J.* 1999; 23: 185-192.

[35] Dao TTT, Reynolds WJ, Tenenbaum HC. Comorbidity between myofascial pain of masticatory muscles and fibromyalgia. *J. Orofac Pain* 1997; 11: 232-241.

[36] John MT, Miglioretti DL, LeResche L, Von Korff M, Critchlow CW. Widespread pain as a risk factor for dysfunctional temporomandibular disorder pain. *Pain* 2003; 102: 257-263.

[37] Suvinen TI, Reade PC, Kemppainen P, Könönen M, Dworkin SF Review of aetiological concepts of temporomandibular pain disorders: towards a biopsychosocial

model for integration of physical disorder factors with psychological and psychosocial illness impact factors. *Eur. J. Pain* 2005; 9: 613-633.

[38] Rollman GB, Gillespie JM. The role of psychosocial factors in temporomandibular disorders. *Curr. Rev. Pain* 2000; 4: 71-81.

[39] List T, Wahlund K, Larsson B. Psychosocial functioning and dental factors in adolescents with temporomandibular disorders: a case-control study. *J. Orofac Pain* 2001; 15: 218-227.

[40] Yatani H, Studts J, Cordova M, Carlson CR, Okeson JP. Comparison of sleep quality and clinical and psychologic characteristics in patients with temporomandibular disorders. *J. Orofac Pain* 2002; 16: 221-228.

[41] Selaimen CM, Jeronyomo JC, Brilhante DP, Grossi ML. Sleep and depression as risk indicators for temporomandibular disorders in a cross-cultural perspective: a case-control study. *Int. J. Prosthodont* 2006; 19: 154-161.

[42] Gatchel R, Garofalo J, Ellis E, Holt C. Major psychological disorders in acute and chronic TMD: an initial examination. *J. Am. Dent .Assoc* .1996; 127: 1365-1374.

[43] Murray,H, Locker D, Mock D, Tenenbaum HC. Pain and the quality of life in patients referred to a craniofacial unit. *J. Orofac Pain* 1996; 10: 316-323.

[44] McCreary CP, Clark GT, Merril RL, Flack V, Oakley ME. Psychological distress and diagnostic subgroups of temporomandibular disorder patients. *Pain* 1991; 44: 29-34.

[45] Yap Au, Tan KB, Chua FK, Tan HH. Depression and somatization in patients with temporomandibular disorders. *J. Prosthet. Dent* .2002; 88: 479-484.

[46] Kino K, Sugisaki M, Haketa T, Amemori Y, Ishikawa T, Shibuya T, Sato F, Amagasa T, Shibuya T, Tanabe H, Yoda T, Sakamoto I, Omura K, Miyaoka H. The comparison between pains, difficulties in function, and associating factors of patients in subtypes of temporomandibular disorders. *J. Oral Rehabil* .2005; 32: 315-325.

[47] Uhac I, Kovac Z, Valentic-Peruzovic M, Juretic M, Moro LiJ, Grzic R. The influence of war stress on the prevalence of signs and symptoms temporomandibular disorders. *J. Oral Rehabil.* 2003; 30: 211-217.

[48] De Leeuw R, Bertoli E, Schmidt JE, Carlson CR. Prevalence of post-traumatic stress disorder symptoms in orofacial pain patients. *Oral Surg. Oral Med. Oral Pathol. Oral Radiol. Endod* .2005; 99: 558-568.

[49] Akhter R, Hassan NM, Aida J, Kanehira T, Zaman KU, Morita M. Association between experience of stressful life events and muscle-related temporomandibular disorders in patients seeking free treatment in a dental hospital. *Eur. J. Med. Res.* 2007; 12: 535-540.

[50] Bertoli E, De Leeuw R, Schmidt JE, Okeson JP, Carlson CR. Prevalence and impact of post-traumatic stress disorder symptoms in patients with masticatory muscle or temporomandibular joint pain: differences and similarities. *J. Orofac Pain* 2007; 21:107-119.

[51] Vassend O, Krogstad BS, Dahl BL. Negative affectivity, somatic complaints, and symptoms of temporomandibular disorders. *J. Psychosom. Res.* 1995; 39: 889-899.

[52] Vimpari SS, Knuuttila MLE, Sakki TK, Kivelä S-L. Depressive symptoms associated with symptoms of the temporomandibular joint pain and dysfunction syndrome. *Psyhosom Med.* 1995; 57: 439-444.

[53] Korszun A, Hinderstein B, Wong M. Comorbidity of depression with chronic facial pain and temporomandibular disorders. *Oral Surg. Oral Med. Oral Pathol. Oral Radiol. Endod* .1996; 82: 496-500.

[54] Carlson CR. Psychological and physiological parameters of masticatory muscle pain. *Pain* 1998; 76: 297-307.

[55] Madland G, Feinmann C, Newman S. Factors associated with anxiety and depression in facial arthromyalgia. *Pain* 2000; 84: 225-232.

[56] Sipilä K, Veijola J, Jokelainen J, Järvelin MR, Oikarinen KS, Raustia AM, Joukamaa M. Association between facial pain, temporomandibular disorders and depression- an epidemiological study of the Northern Finland 1966 Birth Cohort. *J. Craniomandib. Pract* .2001; 19: 183-187.

[57] Epker J, Gatchel RJ. Coping profile differences in the biopsychosocial functioning of patients with temporomandibular disorders. *Psychosom. Med* .2000; 62: 69-75.

[58] Turner JA, Dworkin SF, Mancl L, Huggins KH, Truelove EL. The roles of beliefs, catasrophizing, and coping in the functioning of patients with temporomandibular disorders. *Pain* 2001; 92: 41-51.

[59] Niemi PM, Le Bell Y, Kylmälä M, Jämsä T, Alanen P. Psychological factors and responses to artificial interferences in subjects with and without a history of temporomandibular disorders. *Acta Odontol. Scand.* 2006; 64: 300-305.

[60] Sipilä K, Ylöstalo PV, Ek E, Knuuttila ML. Association between optimism and self-reported facial pain. *Acta Odontol. Scand* .2006; 64: 177-182.

[61] Yap AU, Chua FK, Tan KB. Depressive symptoms in Asian TMD patients and their association with non-specific physical symptoms reporting. *J. Oral Pathol. Med* .2004; 33: 305-310.

[62] Rantala MA, Ahlberg J, Suvinen TI, Savolainen A, Könönen M. Chronic myofascial pain, disk displacement with reduction and psychosocial factors in Finnish non-patients. *Acta Odontol. Scand* .2004; 62: 293-297.

[63] Celić R, Panduríć J, Dulcić N. Psychologic status in patients with temporomandibular disorders. *Int. J. Prosthodont* .2006; 19: 28-29.

[64] Michelotti A, Martina R, Russo M, Romeo R. Personality characteristics of temporomandibular disorder patients using M.M.P.I. *J. Craniomand. Pract* .1998; 16: 119-125.

[65] Mongini F, Ciccone G, Ibertis F, Negro C. Personality characteristics and accompanying symptoms in temporomandibular joint dysfunction, headache, and facial pain. *J. Orofac Pain* 2000; 14: 52-28.

[66] Parker MW, Holmes EK, Terezhalmy GT. Personality characteristics of patients with temporomandibular disorders: diagnostic and therapeutic implications. *J. Orofac Pain* 1993; 7: 337-344.

[67] Marbach JJ. Is there a myofascial, temporomandibular disorder personality? *J. Mass Dent. Soc.* 1995; 44: 12-15, 36-37.

[68] Taylor GJ, Bagby RM, Parker JDA. The alexithymia construct: a potential paradigm for psychosomatic medicine. *Psychosomatics* 1991; 32: 153-164.

[69] Taylor GJ. Somatoform disorders. In: Taylor GJ, Babgy RM, Parker JDA, editors. Disorders of affect regulation: alexithymia in medical and psychiatric illness. Cambridge: Cambridge University Press; 1997; 114-137.

[70] Sipilä K, Veijola J, Jokelainen J, Järvelin MR, Oikarinen KS, Raustia AM, Joukamaa M. Association of symptoms of TMD and orofacial pain with alexithymia: an epidemiological study of the Northern Finland 1966 Birth Cohort. *J. Craniomandib. Pract* .2001; 19; 246-251.

[71] Ahlberg J, Nikkilä H, Könönen M, Partinen M, Lindholm H, Sarna S, Savolainen A. Associations of perceived pain and painless TMD-related symptoms with alexithymia and depressive mood in media personnel with or without irregular shift work. *Acta Odontol. Scand* 2004; 62: 119-123.

[72] Glaros, AG, Lumley MA. Alexithymia and pain in temporomandibular disorder. *J. Psychosom. Res* .2005; 9: 85-88.

[73] Kessler RC, McGonagle KA, Zhao S, Nelson CB, Hughes M, Eshleman S, Wittchen HU, Kendler KS. Lifetime and 12-month prevalence of DSM-III-R psychiatric disorders in the United States. Results from the National Comorbidity Survey. *Arch. Gen. Psychiatry* 1994; 51: 8-19.

[74] Magni G. On the relationship between chronic pain and depression when there is no organic lesion. *Pain* 1987; 31: 1-21.

[75] Lautenbacher S, Spernal J, Schreiber W, Krieg JC. Relationship between clinical pain complaints and pain sensitivity in patients with depression and panic disorders. *Psychosom. Med.* 1999; 61: 822-827.

[76] Gallagher RM, Marbach JJ, Raphael KG, Dohrenwend BP, Cloitre M. Is major depression comorbid with temporomandibular pain and dysfunction syndrome? A pilot study. *Clin. J. Pain* 1991; 7: 219-225.

[77] Gatchel RJ, Stoell AW, Bushang P. The relationships among depression, pain, and masticatory functioning in temporomandibular disorder patients. *J. Orofac Pain* 2006; 20: 288-296.

[78] Yap Au, Dworkin SF, Chua FK, List T, Tan KB, Tan HH. Prevalence of temporomandibular disorder subtypes, psychologic distress, and psychosocial dysfunction in Asian patients. *J. Orofac Pain* 2003; 17: 21-28.

[79] Rantala MA, Ahlberg J, Suvinen TI, Nissinen M, Lindholm H, Savolainen A, Könönen M. Temporomandibular joint related painless symptoms, orofacial pain, neck pain, headache, and psychosocial factors among non-patients. *Acta Odontol. Scand* 2003; 61: 217-222.

[80] Bonjardim LR, Gavião MB, Pereira LJ, Castelo PM. Anxiety and depression in adolescents and their relationship with signs and symptoms of temporomandibular disorders. *Int. J. Prosthodont.* 2006; 18: 347-352.

[81] LeResche L, Mancl LA, Drangsholt MT, Saunders K, Korff MV. Relationship of pain and symptoms to pubertal development in adolescents. *Pain* 2005; 118: 201-209.

[82] Sipilä K, Ylöstalo PV, Joukamaa M, Knuuttila ML. Comorbidity between facial pain, generalized pain and depressiveness in young adults. *J. Orofac Pain* 2006; 20: 24-30.

[83] Raphael KG, Marbach JJ, Klausner J. Myofascial face pain. Clinical characteristics of those with regional vs. widespread pain. *J. Am. Dent. Assoc* .2000; 131: 161-171.

[84] Yap AU, Chua EK, Dworkin SF, Tan HH, Tan KB. Multiple pains and psychosocial functioning/ psychologic distress in TMD patients. *Int. J. Prosthod.* 2002; 15: 461-466.

[85] Velly AM, Philippe P, Gornitsky M. Heterogeneity of temporomandibular disorders: cluster and case-control analyses. *J. Oral Rehabil* 2002; 29: 969-979.

[86] Delgado PL. Common pathways of depression and pain. *J. Clin. Psychiatry* 2004; 65 Suppl. 12:16-19.

[87] Stahl S, Briley M. Understanding pain in depression. *Hum Psychopharmacol* 2004; 19 Suppl 1: 9-13.

[88] Korszun A, Young EA, Singer K, Carlson NE, Brown MB, Crofford L. Basal circadian cortisol secretion in women with temporomandibular disorders. *J. Dent. Res.* 2002; 81: 279-283.

[89] Korszun A, Papadopoulos E, Demitrack M, Engleberg C, Crofford L. The relationship between temporomandibular disorders and stress-associated syndromes. *Oral Surg Oral Med. Oral Pathol. Oral Radiol. Endod* .1998; 86: 416-420.

[90] Korszun A. Facial pain, depression and stress- connections and directions. *J. Oral Pathol.. Med* 2002; 31: 615-619.

[91] Demitrack MA. Chronic fatigue syndrome and fibromyalgia. *Psychiatr. Clin. North Am.* 1998; 21: 671-693.

[92] Crofford LJ. Neuroendocrine abnormalities in fibromyalgia and related disorders. *Am. J. Med Sci* 1998; 315: 359-366.

[93] Young EA. Sex differences and the HPA axis: implications for psychiatric disease. *J. Gend. Specif. Med.* 1998; 1: 21-27.

[94] Forssell H, Kalso E, Koskela P, Vehmanen R, Puukka P, Alanen P. Occlusal treatments in temporomandibular disorders: a qualitative systematic review of randomized controlled trials. *Pain* 1999; 83: 549-560.

[95] Tsukiyama Y, Baba K, Clark GT. An evidence-based assessment of occlusal adjustment for temporomandibular disorders. *J. Prosthet. Dent* .2001; 86: 57-66.

[96] Forssell H, Kirveskari P, Kangasniemi P. Effect of occlusal adjustment on mandibular dysfunction. A double-blind study. *Acta Odontol. Scand.* 1986; 44: 63-69.

[97] Forssell H, Kirveskari P, Kangasniemi P. Changes in headache after treatment of mandibular dysfunction. *Cephalalgia* 1985; 5: 229-236.

[98] Vallon D, Ekberg E, Nilner M, Kopp S. Occlusal adjustment in patients with craniomandibular disorders including headaches. A 3- and 6-month follow-up. *Acta Odontol. Scand* 1995; 53: 55-59.

[99] Karppinen K, Eklund S, Suoninen E, Eskelin M, Kirveskari P. Adjustment of dental occlusion in treatment of chronic cervicobrachial pain and headache. *J. Oral Rehabil.* 1999; 26: 715-721.

[100] Koh H, Robinson PG. Occlusal adjustment for treating and preventing temporomandibular joint disorders. *J. Oral Rehabil* .2004; 31: 287-292.

[101] Dionne RA. Pharmacologic treatments for temporomandibular disorders. *Oral Surg Oral Med Oral. Pathol. Oral Radiol. Endod* 1997; 83: 134-142.

[102] Plesh O, Curtis D, Levine J, McCall WD, Jr. Amitriptyline treatment of chronic pain patients with temporomandibular disorders. *J. Oral Rehabil.* 2000; 27: 834-841.

[103] Pettengill CA, Reisner-Keller L. The use of tricyclic antidepressants for the control of chronic orofacial pain. *J. Craniomand Pract.* 1997; 15: 53-56.

[104] Tversky J, Reade PC, Berschman, Holeill BJ, Wright J. Role of depressive illness in the outcome of treatment of temporomandibular joint pain-dysfunction syndrome. *Oral Surg. Oral Med. Oral Pathol.* 1991; 71: 696-699.

[105] Ihde SK, Konstantinovic VS. The therapeutic use of botulinum toxin in cervical and maxillofacial conditions: an evidence-based review. *Oral Surg, Oral Med, Oral Pathol, Radiol. Endod,* 2007; 104: 1-11.

[106] Dworkin SF, Turner JA, Mancl L, Wilson L, Massoth D, Huggins KH, LeResche L, Truelove E. A randomized clinical trial of a tailored comprehensive care treatment program for temporomandibular disorders. *J, Orofac Pain* 2002; 16:259-276.

[107] Dworkin SF, Huggins KH, Wilson L, Mancl L, Turner JA, Massoth D, LeResche L, Truelove E. A randomized clinical trial using research diagnostic criteria for temporomandibular disorders-axis II to target clinic cases for a tailored self-care TMD treatment program. *J. Orofac Pain* 2002; 16: 48-63.

[108] Dohrenwend BP, Raphael KG, Marbach JJ, Gallagher RM. Why is depression comorbid with chronic myofascial face pain? A family study test of alternative hypoteses. *Pain* 1999; 83: 183-192.

[109] Kaplan HI, Sadock BJ. Comprehensive textbook of psychiatry. Baltimore: Williams andWilkins; 1995.

[110] Montano CB. Recognition and treatment of depression in a primary care setting. *J. Clin. Psychiatry* 1994; 55 (Suppl.): 18-34.

In: Women and Depression
Editors: Paula Hernandez and Sara Alonso

ISBN 978-1-60456-647-5
© 2009 Nova Science Publishers, Inc.

Chapter 15

Why Does Depression Develop in Complicated Osteoporosis? (Clinical study)

J. Wendlova[9]

Osteological Centre, University Hospital and Policlinic, Bratislava, Slovakia

Abstract

Patients and methods. In a prospective study we observed which female patients developed depression following an acute and painful vertebral fracture. On the day of diagnosing the vertebral fracture the patients filled the questionnaires 1 and 2. The depression developed in some patients was diagnosed by means of the DSM – IV questionnaire. For the statistical evaluation of questionnaires we chose randomly 32 patients with depression (out of 33 patients) aged 51-73, and 32 patients without depression (out of 44 patients) aged 52-70.

The aim of the study: To verify the hypothesis that the patients with more traumatic experience in the anamnesis (Questionnaire No. 1) are more depression prone following the osteoporotic vertebrae fractures and their character features are typical for subjects with higher emotional vulnerability (Questionnaire No. 2).

Statistical analysis: 1. Questionnaires 1 and 2 were evaluated by two statistical methods: a) automatization of mathematical and statistical estimates and tests based on binomial distribution; b) ADALINE Programme.

2. Assessment of relative risk for developing depression.

Results: Questionnaire No. 1 completed by depressed patients contained statistically significant higher number of positive answers to questions defining experienced stress situations (differences in values of weights of questionnaire parameters expressed in percentages within linear combination of the whole group).

---

[9] Correspondence to author: Jaroslava Wendlova Doc., MD., PhD, Osteological Centre, University Hospital and Policlinic, Limbova 5, 835 05 Bratislava, Slovak Republic, jwendlova@chello.sk

Questionnaire No. 2 completed by depressed patients contained statistically significant higher number of positive answers by more depression prone subjects in comparison with non-depressed patients (differences in values of weights of questionnaire parameters.

1. Patients lapsed into depression most often on the 32nd day following the vertebra fracture.
2. Proposed questionnaires are according to validity criteria (sensitivity, specificity, prediction value of positive test, prediction values of negative test, test effectiveness) indicated for identification of persons risking the onset of depression following the osteoporotic fracture of vertebrae.
3. Relative risk (RR) for developing depression in patients with osteoporotic fracture, which answered in Questionnaire No. 1 eight and more questions positive is *7,0 time* higher than in patiens with osteoporotic fracture, which answered in Questionnaire No. 1 less than eight guestions positive. For Questionnaire No. 2 it is *8,5 time* higher.

Conclusion: We recommend to use questionnaires No. 1 and 2 in female patients with acute painful vertebrae fractures to select patients with the risk of depression development. These patients should be followed more frequently as outpatients and in case of first clinical symptoms of depression should be recommended for special psychiatric care. Early therapy of depression enables to accelerate the mobilisation, rehabilitation and resocialisation of patients, to improve the quality of their lives and to reduce the costs of analgetic treatment of pain, sedatives and rehabilitation.

Key words: Aetiology – depression – osteoporosis – post menopause – vertebrae fracture

Introduction

Fractures as complications of osteoporosis represent an important social and economic problem, because they increase the costs of treatment and complex care of patients. Risk factors for osteoporotic fractures are: female sex, premature menopause, age, primary or secondary amenorrhoea, primary and secondary hypogonadism in man, Asian or white ethnic origin, previous fragility fracture, low bone mineral density, glucocorticoid therapy, high bone turnover, family history of hip fracture, low bodyweight, neuromuscular disorders, smoking, excessive alcohol consumption, long-term immobilisation, low dietary calcium intake, vitamin D deficiency (1). According to Cummings et al. cohort study (2) a 50-year-old Caucasian woman has a 32% chance of a vertebral fracture occurring in her remaining lifetime. Even more striking, women with prevalent vertebral deformities have a risk of sustaining a subsequent vertebral fracture that is five times that of women without prevalent vertebral deformities (3,4).

Vertebral fractures lead to deformations of the chest – kyphosis, conditioning biomechanical changes in the musculoskeletal system with subsequent clinical symptomatology:

➤   discopathies, pseudoradicular or radicular syndrome, muscular dysbalance of the trunk musculature (chronic backache)

- ➢ ileocostal-friction syndrome (friction of costal arches with ala ossis ilii during the trunk movement)
- ➢ increase of intraabdominal pressure (loss of appetite, dyspeptic problems, diffused pain in the abdomen and under the right costal arch, obstipation)
- ➢ growth of pressure forces on pulmonary parenchyma (the disposition to infection of upper respiratory tract and lungs, the reduction of maximal breathing capacity, and the decrease of right ventricular systolic ejection fraction in combination with the increased diastolic content of the right ventricle represent a risk for the development of cor pulmonale chronicum)
- ➢ disposition to falls mainly in leaning forward (deviating the body's centre of gravity from its normal position, disruption of skeletal statics)

Osteoporotic fracture represents for a patient a long-term stress situation, as it brings about a lifestyle change with the limitation of everyday activities and the loss of total independence. The success of the vertebral fracture therapy is often complicated by the development of depression, which is frequently diagnosed late or not at all; sometimes it is treated by sedatives as a neurasthenic syndrome, without the effect of such a treatment.

In the osteological department we were able to observe in some patients with osteoporotic vertebral fractures a very slow and unsuccessful mobilisation, rehabilitation and reconvalescence in comparison with other patients whose mobilisation was relatively quick, and they could return to their original lifestyle with some limitations. In the group of unsuccessfully mobilised patients persisted a marked vertebrogenic algic syndrome, aversion to cooperation with the physician and physiotherapist, and inability to live a normal life. These patients were prevailingly diagnosed as depressive.

The above-mentioned clinical experience brought us to the annotation of a prospective study to answer this question: Why did some women, following the clinical vertebral fracture, despite a standard therapy, develop depression and some women did not.

The Aim of the Study

1. To find out the confidence interval (C.I.) and median ($\tilde{x}$) for time interval of the onset of clinical symptoms of depression from the onset of osteoporotic fracture of vertebra.
2. To set up Questionnaire No.1 focused on the anamnesis of experienced mental stress situations.
3. To compare anamnestic data (positive or negative answer) focused on experienced mental traumas, obtained by means of *Questionnaire No. 1* in the group of depressed female patients with osteoporotic vertebrae fractures, with the group of female patients with osteoporotic vertebrae fractures, but without depression.
4. To compare the differences in positive and negative answers in completed *Questionnaire No. 2* (characteristics of depression prone personality - according F.Flach) between the groups of depressed and non-depressed patients.
5. To evaluate validity criteria for Questionnaires No. 1 and 2:

- sensitivity
- specificity
- prediction values of the positive test
- prediction value of the negative test
- test effectiveness

6. To calculate the relative risk (RR) for developing depression in patients with osteoporotic fracture.

Questionnaire No. 1

For every life situation you experienced in the past insert the plus sign (+),
or the minus sign (-) if such an event did not happen to you during your lifetime.

	D	NonD
1. Wrong lifestyle – disorganised lifestyle		
1.1. Long-term lack of sleep	18	6
1.2. Repeated overwork and exhaustion by excessive work	26	14
1.3 Lack of regular exercise	29	30
2. Previous diseases, long-term care of gravely ill person close to you		
2.1. Post-natal depression	6	2
2.2. Operations (give number, e.g.: 3)	12	7
2.3. Personal experience of serious illness	25	12
2.4. Long-term care of gravely ill close person who died	16	4
3. Experience of failure or sin feeling		
3.1. I failed in a serious situation and I still blame myself for it	15	10
3.2. I have a feeling that I sinned and I cannot come to terms with it	16	9
4. Difficult life trials I experienced:		
4.1. Death of a family member (give number)	28	29
4.2. Divorce	10	7
4.3. Disintegration of the family	11	3
4.4. Job loss	5	6
4.5. Serious financial difficulties	21	24
4.6. Loneliness, desertedness	26	7

4.7. Repeated failures in activities I felt very strongly about	23	7
4.8. Long-term conflict relations in the workplace	22	4
4.9. Nursing of physically or mentally handicapped child	1	0
4.10.I experienced an alcohol addiction	0	0

Questionnaire No. 2

Depression Prone Personality Profile

If you identify with a feature fitting you in the past, insert the plus sign (+), if not, insert the minus sign (-).

	D	NonD
1. I took things very seriously, I had a feeling of a high moral responsibility for everything I did	29	14
2. I was very ambitious, I always tried to perform well	19	10
3. I was definitely a competitive person	27	22
4. I always had a feeling of having a lot of energy, that I am indefatigable, that I can work myself "into the ground"	27	4
5. I always cared too much how other people feel	18	4
6. I never wanted to hurt other people's feelings	17	5
7. I was always too much dependent on people I loved	27	19
8. I reacted too emotionally to anything that could even in a smallest way possible reduce the feeling of my self-esteem	29	13
9. Any tactlessness from other people hurt me too deeply (every humiliation or insult)	18	2
10. I was at a loss what to do in confrontation with a hostile attitude of other people, I was often helpless against attacks by other people	22	3
11. If I was verbally attacked I had troubles to pull myself together and defend myself – even in case when the defence was really justified	23	6

Characteristics of the Cohort of Examined Female Patients and Methods Applied

During the period of six years the study gradually included patients with one newly sustained (painful) clinical vertebral fracture, who in the past had none or at most two vertebral fractures. The patients were diagnosed with a primary or secondary osteoporosis (condition after a hysterectomy and bilateral adnexectomy, malabsorption syndrome – asymptomatic coeliacia, chronical atrophic gastritis with achlorhydria, M. Crohn). The study did not include patients with osteoporosis, induced by glucocorticoids. On the very day when the acute vertebral fracture was diagnosed, each patient filled a questionnaire No. 1 and 2.

Questionnaire 1 was set up to include the most frequent model situations of stress and mental trauma in people' s lives. Questionnaire 2 was set up according to Frederic Flach (5), including character features of persons inclined to develop depression following stressful life situations.

All patients, both in acute and chronical stage of vertebral fracture, received a standard treatment by analgesics, nonsteroid antirheumatics, myorelaxants and physical therapy:

1) in the acute stage: local application of cold, electrotherapy, tender relaxing back massage;
2) in the chronical stage: kinesitherapy directed at the removal of muscular dysbalance in the area of trunk muscles.

The choice of analgesic drug and its dosage were on individual basis, aimed at removing or minimising backache.

Depression in patients was diagnosed by means of the DSM-IV questionnaire (6).

Depressive patients were adequately treated by antidepressants. For the final evaluation of comparison of questionnaires we chose at random 32 (D) depressive patients (from the overall number of 33) and 32 (nonD) nondepressive patients (from the overall number of 44). We chose the same number of patients in both groups (observation and control) to meet the criteria for proper evaluation of qualitative features by means of questionnaires. In the depressive patients group (D) there were four patients who had already sustained one clinical vertebral fracture in the past. In the non-depressive patients group (nonD) there were four patients who had overcome a vertebral fracture and one patient had overcome two vertebral fractures. From all patients with vertebral fractures (n = 64) 5 were treated with bisphosphonates (1 – 3 years), 4 with calcitonin (2 – 3 years), 6 with selective estrogen receptor modulators (1 – 2 years). In 49 patients were established the diagnosis of osteoporosis, when they suffered from osteoporotic vertebral fracture. These patients were not treated in the past. The age of patients in the D group ranged from 51 to 73 years, in the nonD group from 52 to 70 years.

Statistical Analysis

1. Time for Developing Depression Following Osteoporotic Fracture

We calculated the confidence interval (95% C.I.) and median ($\tilde{x}$) for time interval (given as the number of days from the onset of vertebra fracture) characteristic for the onset of clinical signs of depression

2. Evaluation of Questionnaires

In the completed questionnaires we compared:

a)   presence or absence in the anamnesis of experienced stress situation
b)   presence or absence of character feature for a depression prone personality (DPP)

in the cohort of depressed and non-depressed female patients with osteoporotic vertebrae fractures.

In statistical evaluation we used two methods for the comparison of qualitative signs:

2.1. Automatization of Mathematical and Statistical Estimates and Tests Based on Binomial Distribution (7,8)

According to this statistical method the number of positive answers (x) to all·questions (n) in Questionnaires No. 1 and 2 is given as a percentage of positive answers (P) from the total number of questioned patients in the D or NonD groups (n = 32).

$$P = \frac{x}{n} \cdot 100\%$$

Differences between percentage values of positive answers in Questionnaires No 1 and 2 for D and NonD groups were evaluated by χ^2 (chi – square test) Statistically significant difference between answers was achieved when the following condition was met:

$$\chi^2 > 3.841$$

2.2. ADALINE, PC software (9)

Using ADALINE program we calculated absolute values of parameter weights in Questionnaires No 1 and 2 and their percentage expression within linear combination of the whole group. Absolute values of weights of individual parameters are given in bar diagrams. We evaluated also validity parameters of the questionnaires (sensitivity, specificity, prediction value of positive test, prediction value of negative test, effectiveness). The ADALINE program includes also the production of a recognition patterns matrix.

Recognition Patterns

Every questionnaire item has a binary character (positive or negative answer). Positive answer (the presence of experience in the anamnesis, presence of DPP character feature) was indicated by the plus sign ($y = +1$), negative answer by the minus sign ($y = -1$). Recognition patterns in the form of a matrix show graphically the differences in answers to every question by every investigated patient.

3. Calculation of Relative Risk (RR)

We calculated relative risk (10, 11) for developing depression in patients with acute vertebrae fractures by means of binary association – contingency tables (Tab K1, K2).

The risk (R_1) is a ratio of the number of patients with depression exposed to risk factors (a) to the total number of observed patients exposed to risk factors (a + b). The risk (R_2) is a ratio of the number of patients with depression without exposure to risk factors to the total number of patients not exposed to risk factors. Relative risk (RR) is the ratio of the risk for depression by patients with the risk factors to the risk for depression by patients without the risk factors.

$$R_1 = \frac{a}{a+b} \qquad R_2 = \frac{c}{c+d}$$

$$RR = \frac{R_1}{R_2} = \frac{\dfrac{a}{a+b}}{\dfrac{c}{c+d}}$$

Table K1. Contingency table for Questionaire No.1

	Depression	
Questionaire No. 1	Yes	No
Positive	28 (a)	4 (b)
Negative	4 (c)	28 (d)

Table K2. Contingency table for Questionaire No.2

	Depression	
Questionaire No. 2	Yes	No
Positive	29 (a)	5 (b)
Negative	3 (c)	27 (d)

a, b, c, d - frequencies

Results

1.

Median for developing depression was the 32nd day following the onset of the osteoporotic vertebra fracture. Patients developed depression at the least after 7 days, at the most after 52 days.

$\tilde{x}$ (median) for 95% C.I = 32 days   95% C.I. :   -upper limit 38 days

- lower limit 24 days

2.

Evaluation of Questionnaire No.1

Questionnaires completed by depressed patients included statistically significant higher number of positive answers to questions defining experienced stress situation in life (Table 1).

Table 1a

Z – score (SD) ROI$_1$	T – score (SD) ROI$_1$		Total count in row
	> - 2,5 (count)	≤ - 2,.5 (count)	
> - 1,0	474 d	4 c	478
≤ - 1,0	15 b	5 a	20
Total count in column	489	9	498

a, b, c, d, - frequencies

Table 1b

Coeficient of assotiation	Intensity of assotiation	Approximate significance
Phi	0,35613	*
Cramer´s V	0,35613	*
Pearson´s	0,33549	*

$\alpha = 0,05$ $p > 0,05$ * statistical significance

Differences in weights values of questionnaire parameters expressed in percentages within linear combination of the whole group are given in Table 2 (questions are numbered) . Table 2 contains those questions, statistically significant for diagnosing risk patients, where the weights of answers reached positive numbers (in % or in absolute numbers) in the D group and negative numbers in the NonD group. The number of questions meeting these criteria is, at the same time, a minimum number of questions to which the patient has to give a positive answer to be included into the depression development risk group. For Questionnaire No. 1 it is a minimum of eight positive answers.

According to validity criteria (Table 3) we consider Questionnaire No 1 indicated for the recognition of depression development risk patients following an acute painful vertebra fracture.

Fig 1. brings differences in answers of depressed and non-depressed patients to individual questions by means of recognition patterns (positive answer – black field, negative answer – white field).

Questionnaire No.1

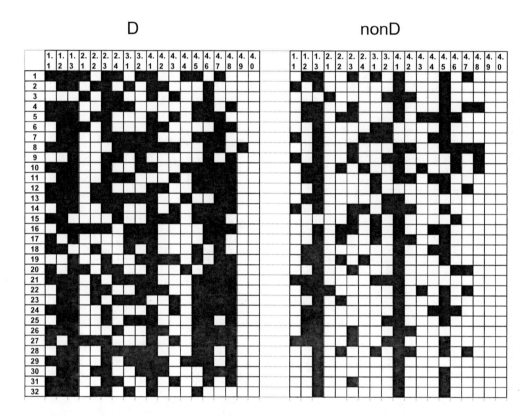

Figure 1. Discrimination analysis of recognition patters for Questionnaire No. 1. (Columns are numbered by questions numbers in Questionnaire No. 1, the lines are numbered by serial numbers of individual patients n = 32, positive answer –black field, negative answer – white field).

Questionnaire No. 2

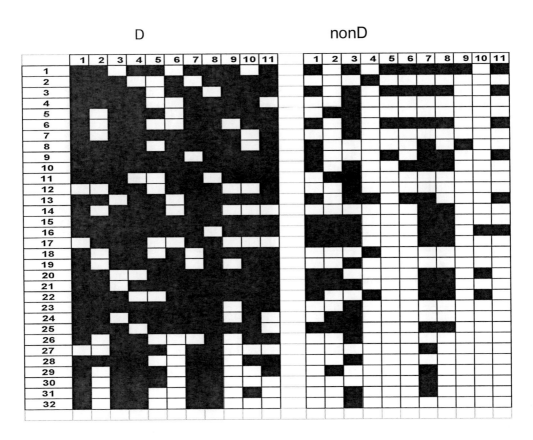

Figure 2. Discrimination analysis of recognition patters for Questionnaire No. 2. (Columns are numbered by numbers of questions about character features of depression prone persons in Questionnaire No. 2, the lines are numbered by serial numbers of individual patients n = 32, positive answer – black field, negative answer – white field).

Table 2. Comparison of the number of positive answers (expressed in percentage % from the overall number of questioned patients n = 32) in *Questionnaire No. 1* for every question in the group of depressed patients (D) and non-depressed patients (NonD) by means of χ^2 .($\alpha = 0,05$)

Question No.	D n = 32 (%)	NonD n = 32 (%)	χ^2 (chi – square test)
1.1.	56	19	**10,252**
1.2.	84	44	**12,485**
1.3.	88	94	0,756
2.1.	22	6	3,505
2.2.	38	22	1, 01
2.3.	78	38	**11,562**

Table 2. (Continued)

2.4.	50	16	**9,194**
3.1.	44	31	1,074
3.2.	50	28	3,281
4.1.	88	88	0,000
4.2.	34	23	1,086
4.3.	34	9	**6,363**
4.4.	16	19	0,075
4.5.	66	75	0,677
4.6.	78	22	**22,841**
4.7.	72	22	**17,647**
4.8.	72	13	**27,077**
4.9.	3	0	0,178
4.0.	0	0	0,000

Table 3. Validity criteria of Questionnaire No. 1 ($\alpha = 0,05$)

group	TN	FP	FN	TP	sensitivity	specificity	Prediction values of the positive test	Prediction values of the negative test	Test effectivness
D	25	7	1	31	96,88	78,13	81,58	96,15	87,50
NonD	31	1	7	25	78,13	96,88	96,15	81,58	87,50

TP – true positives
TN – true negatives
FP – false positives
FN – false negatives

Table 3a

Z – score (SD) ROI$_3$ (count)	T – score (SD) ROI$_3$		Total count in row
	> - 2,5 (count)	≤ - 2,.5 (count)	
> - 1,0	430 d	25 c	455
≤ - 1,0	31 b	12 a	43
Total count in column	461	37	498

Table 3b

Coeficient of assotiation	Intensity of assotiation	Approximate significance
Phi	0,24004	*
Cramer's V	0,24004	*
Pearson's	0,23341	*

$\alpha = 0,05$ $p > 0,05$

Evaluation of Questionnaire No. 2

Questionnaires completed by depressed patients included statistically significant higher number of positive answers for character features of depression prone persons in comparison with non-depressed patients (Table 4).

Table 4. Percentage representation of parameters weights in Questionnaire No. 2 within linear combination of the whole group. ($\alpha = 0,05$)

Question No.	Weights of parameters of questionnaire (in %)	
	D	**NonD**
1	12,48	6,85
2	5,17	- 13,64
3	19,26	4,53
4	11,08	- 10,86
5	0,35	- 9,45
6	- 0,55	- 7,98
7	18,80	8,75
8	19,00	3,83
9	1,51	- 13,44
10	4,81	- 16,65
11	7,00	- 4,00

Differences in weights values of questionnaire parameters expressed in percentages within linear combination of the whole group are given in Table 5.

Table 5 contains the questions, statistically significant for diagnosing risk patients, where the weights of answers reached positive numbers (in % or in absolute numbers) in the D group and negative numbers in the NonD group. The number of questions meeting these criteria is, at the same time, a minimum number of questions to which the patient has to give a positive answer to be included into the depression prone person risk group. For Questionnaire No. 2 it is a minimum of six positive answers.

**Table 5. Comparison of the number of positive answers (expressed in percentage %
from the overall number of questioned patients n = 32) in Questionnaire No. 2 for
every question in the group of depressed patients (D) and non-depressed patients
(NonD) by means of χ^2 . ($\alpha = 0,05$)**

Question No.	D n = 32 (%)	NonD n = 32 (%)	χ^2 (chi square – test)
1.	91	44	18,447
2.	59	31	5,254
3.	84	69	2,234
4.	84	13	41,273
5.	56	13	15,160
6.	53	16	10,774
7.	84	59	5,188
8.	91	41	20,686
9.	56	6	22,687
10.	69	9	28,423
11.	72	19	20,356

According to validity criteria we consider Questionnaire No. 2 indicated for diagnosing
depression prone persons (Table 6).

**Table 6. Validity criteria of Questionnaire No. 2 for evaluation of character features of
depression prone persons (DPP). ($\alpha = 0,05$)**

group	TN	FP	FN	TP	senzitivity	specificity	Prediction values of the positive test	Prediction values of the negative test	Test effectiveness
					Validity criteria (in %)				
D	30	2	4	28	87,50	93,75	93,33	88,24	90,63
NonD	28	4	2	30	93,75	87,50	88,24	93,33	90,63

Fig 2 brings differences in character features of depressed and non-depressed patients by
means of recognition patterns (positive answer – black field, negative answer – white field).

3.

Calculation of Relative Risk for Questionnaire No. 1 (Tab K1)

$$RR = \frac{R_1}{R_2} = \frac{\dfrac{a}{a+b}}{\dfrac{c}{c+d}} = \frac{\dfrac{28}{28+4}}{\dfrac{4}{4+28}} = \frac{0,875}{0,125} = 7.0 \qquad \text{95\% CI (6. 4; 8. 1)}$$

RR for developing depression in patients with osteoporotic vertebrae fractures is 7,0 time higher for patients, which answered in Questionnaire No. 1 eight and more questions positive then in patients with osteoporotic fractures, which answered in Questionnaire No. 1 less than eight questions positive

Calculation of Relative Risk for Questionnaire No. 2 (Tab K2)

$$RR = \frac{R_1}{R_2} = \frac{\dfrac{a}{a+b}}{\dfrac{c}{c+d}} = \frac{\dfrac{29}{29+5}}{\dfrac{3}{3+27}} = \frac{0,8529}{0,1000} = 8.529 \qquad \text{95\% CI (7.6 ; 9.2)}$$

RR for developing depression in patients with osteoporotic vertebrae fractures is 8,5 time higher for patients, which answered in Questionnaire No. 2 six and more questions positive, then in patients with osteoporotic fractures, which answered in Questionnaire No. 2 less than six questions positive.

Discussion

We have not met a similar study in literature to compare our results with. Several studies, whose authors investigated clinical symptomatology accompanying osteoporotic vertebrae fractures, present also the reactive depression as one of the symptoms (12 - 17), but do not examine its reasons.

In our study we have been dealing with the reasons of the development of reactive depression in female patients in acute or chronically stage of painful osteoporotic vertebra fractures. We found out that those patients developed depression who had in their anamnesis more frequent incidence of traumatic experiences and a long-term overexertion on the job or at home. The onset of osteoporotic vertebra fracture with following vertebrogenic pain syndrome, disruption of sleep regime, limited mobility, loss of physical performance and independence represented for the patients a long-term stress situation. The median for developing depression was the 32nd day after the osteoporotic vertebra fracture. In this study we did not point out only that female patients with osteoporotic vertebrae fractures in acute or chronically stage of the illness may develop reactive depression, but we tried to answer the question: Why do only some female patients develop depression? We see the contribution of our study in the finding that depression is developed more frequently in those women who have in their anamnesis a number of traumatic experiences and their character features are typical for depression prone persons (DPP).

Conclusion

Based on the result of our study we recommend the use of Questionnaires No. 1 and 2 in patients with acute painful vertebrae fractures for detecting risk patients for depression development. These patients should be followed more frequently within ambulatory care and in case of first clinical symptoms of depression should be recommended for special psychiatric care. Early anti-depression treatment by antidepressants of the 3rd and 4th generation (selective serotonine reuptake inhibitors - SSRI, serotonine and noradrenaline reuptake inhibitors – SNRI, noradrenergic and specific serotonergic antidepressants - NaSSA) could accelerates the mobilisation, rehabilitation and resocialisation of patients, could improves quality of their lives and reduces the costs of analgetic pain treatment, sedatives and rehabilitation. It has to be investigated in future studies.

References

[1]   Kanis JA : Diagnosis of osteoporosis and assessment of fracture risk.Lancet 2002, 359, 1929 – 1936

[2]   Cummings SR, Black DM, Rubin SM: Lifetime risks of hip, Colle´s, or vertebral fractures nad coronary heart disease among Caucasian postmenopausal women.*Arch Intern Med 1989*, 148, 2445 – 2448

[3]   Black DM, Arden NK, PalermoI, Pearson J, Cummings SR.: Prevalent veretebral deformities predict hip fractures and new vertebral deformities *but not wrist fracture: Study of osteoporotic fractures research group.*J Bone Miner Res 1999, 14, 821 – 828

[4]   Klotzbuecher CM, Ross PD, Lansman PB, Abbot TA, Berger M : Patients with prior fracture have an increased risk of future fractures: a summary of the literature and statistical synthesis.*J Bone Miner Res 2000*, 15, 721 - 739

[5]   Flach FF: *The secret strength of depression. 2nd ed*, Philadelphia, Lippincott, 1974 26 – 28

[6]   American Psychiatric Association. *Diagnostic and Statistical Manual of Mental Disorders, 1994 , 4 th ed.,* Washington DC, American Psychiatric Association

[7]   Mikulecky M, Komornik J, Ondrejka P : Automatizacia matematicko – statistickych odhadov a testov na zaklade binomickeho rozdelenia. PC software, Comtel, 1997

[8]   Mikulecky M   Quantifying the probabilities in the process of medical diagnosis. *Eurorehab 2003,* 4, 211 – 216

[9]   Widrow B, Smith FW. Pattern recognizing control systems. In: Tou JT., Wilcox RH.: *Computer and Information science. Collected papers on learning adaptation and control in information systems. 2nd ed,* Washington, 1964 Sparten Books, 40 – 47

[10]   Mikulecky M: Asociacia kvalitativnych znakov – kontingencne tabulky.*Euro Rehab* 2003, 13,88 - 96

[11]   Mc Nutt LA, Wu CH, Xue X, Hafner JP: Estimating the *relative risk in cohort studies and clinical trials of common outcomes. Am* J Epidemiol 2003, 157, 940 – 943

[12]   Cizza G, Ravn P, Chrousos GP, Golg PW: Depression a major unrecognised   risk factor for osteoporosis ? Trends Endocrinol Metab 2001, 12, 198 – 203

[13]   Papaioannon A, Watts NB, Kendler DL, Yuen ChK et al. : Diagnosis and management of vertebral fractures in elderly adults. *Am J Med 2002,* 113, 220 – 228

[14]   Greendale GA, Barret – Connor E, Ingles S, Haile R: Late physical and functional effects of osteoporosis fracture in women. The Rancho Bernardo study. *J Am Geriatr Soc 1995,* 48, 546 – 549

[15]   Greendale GA, De Amicis TA, Bucur A et al.: A prospective study of the effect of fracture on measured physical performance : results from the Mac Arthur Study – MAC. J Am Geriatr Soc 2000, 43, 955 – 961

[16]   Cook DJ, Guyatt GH, Adachi JD et al. : *Quality of life issues in women with vertebral fractures due to osteoporosis. Arthritis* Rheum 1993, 36, 750 – 756

[17]   Rapado A: General management of vertebral fractures. *Bone 1996,* 18, 191 - 196

In: Women and Depression
Editors: Paula Hernandez and Sara Alonso
ISBN 978-1-60456-647-5
© 2009 Nova Science Publishers, Inc.

Chapter 16

Depression in Women Physicians and Nurses: A View from Athens, Greece

Athanasios Tselebis [1], Dionysios Bratis[1] and Ioannis Ilias [2]
1. Sotiria Hospital, Athens, Greece,
2. Klimax Support Foundation, Athens, Greece

Abstract

Depression is more prevalent in adult women than men; the etiology of this difference is elusive. Differences in the hormonal milieu of the sexes may play a role, but societal factors may also take their toll. Women physicians and nurses are no exception regarding depression. In the USA although the lifetime prevalence of depression is 12-13% for male and 18-20% for female physicians (the latter being equal to that of the general population), their completed suicide rate is 1.4-2.3 times higher than that of the general population.

Greek society is characterized by close-knit relationships that may also provide a more supportive environment. In the same country the healthcare sector is profoundly iatrocentric and the number of nurses compared to that of physicians is disproportionately low.

Bearing these Greek particularities in mind, we have assessed depression and anxiety in medical and nursing personnel and found no overall differences among subjects. However, age and depression scores were positively correlated in female nurses only. Furthermore, in other studies, we noted that smoking behavior of physicians (regardless of gender) was more anxiety- than depression-driven. In another study we discovered that in nurses their degree of sense of coherence renders them either resistant or vulnerable to depression and burnout.

In conclusion, stress management interventions should be sought in the healthcare workplace, but they should be equally focused on medical and nursing personnel, and particularly women.

Introduction

The first descriptions of melancholic syndromes are found in Sumerian and Egyptian texts around 2600 BCE. However, Hippocrates (460-370 BCE) was the one that introduced the terms "melancholy" and "mania". It appears that "mania", corresponded generally to psychoses, whilst "melancholy" was used to describe chronic mental disturbances and not depression *per se*, according to current definitions. The Hippocratic perception of melancholy and mania was maintained for long; Pinel (1745-1826 CE) used a classification system that corresponded to that of Hippocrates.

The first indirect reports, on the predominance of women regarding depressive symptoms are found in the Greek mythology, where women outnumber men that commit suicide (Tselebis, Georgakopoulou, Katsadoros, and Ilias, 1999). Self-destructive behaviour in Greek mythology is linked to life events that cause shame, guilt and disappointment (Preti and Miotto, 2005). Interestingly, Homer, in the "Odyssey", gives women (Helen in particular) possession of a medicament that cures the pain of sorrow (Homer, 1996).

Epidemiology of Depression: Greek Data

Depression, encompasses a wide spectrum of mood states, that extend from mild dysthymia to overt clinical syndromes, according to the diagnostic criteria of DSM and ICD-10 (Sadock and Sadock, 2007). Even if depression's prevalence varies from population to population, it is calculated that 5.8% of men and 9.5% of women will suffer an episode of depression within a 12-month period. In the United States the lifetime incidence of depression exceeds 12% and 20% for men and women, respectively (Belmaker and Agam, 2008). The etiology of depression remains obscure (Belmaker and Agam, 2008); there may be hormonal influences (in particular from the hypothalamic-pituitary-gonadal/-adrenal axes) that lead to its preponderance in women (Abel and Kulkarni, 2006). According to the World Health Organization (WHO), depression as a clinical syndrome, is a mental disturbance with increasing prevalence. Depression is an important public health burden, being the fourth most prevalent disease. Furthermore, according to WHO, if current demographic and epidemiologic tendencies persist, by the year 2020 depression will account for 5.7% of the total disease burden (WHO, 2001b).

Epidemiologic research leads to the conclusion that an important percentage of women (in the 18 - 64 year-old range) in the general population in Greece suffer occasionally from depressive symptoms (with a prevalence of 8.1%-20.1% and showing an increasing tendency)(Madianos, 1997). A comparison of patients with depression shows that that in the same age group more women suffer from it (60%) than men (40%) (Karkanias et al., 2007).

Other studies in Greece evaluate the coexistence of depressive symptomatology in patients with somatic diseases. In this line of research the usual tool for assessing depressive symptomatology is the Beck Depression Inventory (BDI) that has been translated and adapted in Greek (Beck, Ward, Mendelson, Mock, and Erbaugh, 1961; Donias and Demertzis, 1983) Women that were hospitalized for chronic obstructive pulmonary disease as well as women scheduled to undergo elective surgery have shown higher BDI scores compared to men

(Chrona et al., 2006; Tselebis et al., 2006). It is common knowledge that depression is the most frequent mental disturbance that leads to destructive behavior and suicide (WHO, 2001a).

In Greece attempts of self-destruction remain low compared to the rest of Europe: for most age groups more women attempt suicide compared to men. In particular it is female subjects, with minor psychopathology and using less violent methods that attempt suicide. On the contrary, individuals that complete suicide are usually men, of older age, with major psychopathology; they usually use violent and more dangerous methods (Kontaxakis, 1997). The problem of suicide is important under the age of 22 for women, as this group represents approximately 25% of all suicide behaviors. In this group the ratio of women to men is one to three, whereas in the general population this ratio is one to two.

Depression in Greek Health Professionals

The quality of care that is offered to sick people is influenced by the perceived pressure and the mental burden of health professionals. Health care equipment and instruments are checked and maintained systematically to ensure reliability and effectiveness; the patients' survival depends on them. In sharp contrast to this, humans working in the health care sector do not appear to receive such attention. Health professionals are exposed to a harmful environment, with serious short- or long-term consequences at a somatic and psychological level. Furthermore, within a unique professional culture, they fail to recognize that they require care and deny a patient role for themselves.

The appearance of depression in health professionals is usually examined vis-à-vis factors that affect its development, burden or co-morbidity (such as stress, burnout, or substance abuse). By focusing on these parameters research excluded factors such as the sense of perceived family support or the degree of sense of coherence, which could have a protective or even therapeutic function against the development of depression.

Exhaustion Depression or Professional Burnout?

In 1962 Kielholz and Beck described a particular form of depression, termed *exhaustion depression*. In this form of depression somatic and psychosomatic disturbances play a primordial role (Kielholz and Beck, 1962). Kielholz described exhaustion depression as a situation that presents after a latency of years, during which emotional pressure, repeated traumatic experiences and low intensity (and self-containing in time) mood crises prevail, leading, finally, to the development of an overt episode of depression. Causative factors for this syndrome include financial hardships, professional conflicts or increased obligations and responsibilities in the workplace and the family environment (lacking a supporting network that would offer the individual a feeling of acceptance). Early symptoms according to Kielholz include hypersensitivity, irritability, fatigue and sleep disturbance. Under conditions of intense emotional stress, these symptoms can mutate into a psychosomatic disorder, in which symptoms from the autonomous nervous system dominate. At this stage subjects may show alcohol or substance abuse in a vain effort to repress the symptoms. If the symptoms are not recognized at this stage and no suitable psychological support is offered subjects proceed to the development of depression. Actually, exhaustion depression is not used as a term in clinical practice, but authors, such as Pöldinger indicate that the description of this particular syndrome is identical to what is currently reported in the literature as the syndrome of (professional) burnout (Poldinger, 1998).

The term burnout was introduced in 1974, when Freudenberger described group of symptoms from overstrain that he observed in mental health professionals and volunteers (Freudenberger, 1974). Of all the proposed definitions of burnout the one that is widely accepted was formulated by Maslach who described the phenomenon as a syndrome of mental and bodily exhaustion, which professionals develop because the nature of their work compels them to extensive and continuous professional relation with other persons (C. Maslach, 1982). Burnout does not present suddenly and is not attributed to a single stressful event. On the contrary it is considered to be the result of chronic stress that "floods" the worker, who feels that his/her mental reserves do not suffice to cope with the pressure of his/her workplace. According to Maslach, the three main factors that delineate professional burnout are sentimental exhaustion, depersonalization and lack of personal achievement. These three factors presented successively as the degree of burnout increases progressively (C. Maslach and Jackson, 1986; Ongle, 1983). Regarding health professionals, the first clues are seen with the sentimental exhaustion the worker feels, as he/she does not have the mental energy to invest in his/her work. In the second stage a distant attitude opposite the patients develops, while in the final stage comes the resignation of the worker from any effort to change the existing situation. The worker loses interest and any positive sentiments for patients or customers; this contributes to the development of a negative self-image.

In this theoretical frame, with depressive symptoms overlapping those of professional burnout, researchers that focus on the mental health of health professionals often chose to examine simultaneously these two clinical entities using the appropriate tools.

The first relevant study regarding the Greek workplace was presented relatively recently and dealt with the process of translating in Greek and adapting the Maslach questionnaire (Anagnostopoulos and Papadatou, 1992). In a subsequent study the researchers tried to determine the likely individual and environmental factors that contribute to the appearance of burnout in nurses working in oncologic and general hospitals in Athens, Greece (Papadatou, Anagnostopoulos, and Monos, 1994). Using a sample of 443 women nurses, they did not observe a difference in the degree of burnout between those that worked in oncologic hospitals compared to those that worked in general hospitals. They concluded that psychological factors contribute more than demographic factors and work conditions to developing burnout. In a similar study in a sample of 368 workers, the researchers' protocol included Maslach's questionnaire as well as Eysenck's Personality Questionnaire (EPQ) (Iacovides, Foudulakis, Moysidou, and Ierodiakonou, 1997). It appears that multidimensional interaction exists among the characteristics of subjects and burnout. The authors concluded that development of burnout is not an expected reaction to workplace conditions and nor is it associated with stress. Burnout resembles a clinical syndrome that includes neurotic personality characteristics. Subjects with depressive characteristics show increased vulnerability to burnout because of their innate weakness to draw satisfaction from their work. To further evaluate the issues raised, the same authors followed after a few years with a new study that included, in addition to the tools mentioned above, Zung's Self-Rating Depression Scale; a statistically significant correlation was seen between depression and burnout (Iacovides, Fountoulakis, Moysidou, and Ierodiakonou, 1999). In all the studies the effect of gender on burnout was not assessed, probably because until very recently, the presence of male nurses in Greek hospitals was disproportionately small and, consequently, any conclusions that took gender into account would be precarious.

More recent studies begin to take into consideration the factor of gender, as progressively more men enter the nursing profession in Greece. We reported a likely statistical preponderance of women against men in the development of burnout; this appears to be related to women's low values in personal accomplishment compared to their male colleagues. Interestingly a significant correlation was observed between depressive symptoms and professional burnout, particularly in women (Tselebis, Moulou, and Ilias, 2001).

Co-Morbidity with Depression

Anxiety and Depression in Greek Nurses and Doctors

Anxiety represents a basic human experience and is observed worldwide. Epictetus (55-135 CE) characterizes anxiety as being not fear of illness, pain, or death, but as fear of fear. Kierkegaard (1844 CE) attributes anxiety to the conscience of freedom and guilt, to the fear of emptiness and non-existence, which leads to feelings of despair and inaptitude and eventually depression (Alevizos, 1997). Anxiety, in normal situations, serves as a signal of vigilance and warning for imminent danger, ensuring prompt action and preparedness to face or evade a dangerous situation. Anxiety is a generalized reaction towards unknown/vague threats or internal conflicts and can become chronic, thus morphing into a constant model of reaction to the environment and a relatively immutable personality characteristic. When anxiety is very intense and extended, it ceases to play its adaptive role and becomes pathological. This pathological dimension of anxiety includes mental and somatic symptoms. Psychological symptoms of anxiety include intense concern, feeling of imminent danger, distress, difficulty of concentration and feeling of decreased perception faculty (Hatzimanolis, 1997).The coexistence of anxiety and depression is one of the more frequent and difficult to solve problems in daily clinical psychiatric practice. Even with the aid of modern diagnostic systems, symptoms of anxiety overlap with those of other clinical conditions, such as generalized anxiety disorder, dysthymic disorder or food intake disorder. Epidemiologic data show that mood and anxiety disorders have a high probability of coexisting. In large epidemiologic studies in the USA, 3.6% of the population had a history of co-morbidity from mood and anxiety disorder. Forty three percent of patients with mood disorder also have a history of anxiety disorder, whereas in 25% of individuals with diagnosed anxiety disorder – during the course of their disease – a mood disorder is also diagnosed (Regier, Burke, and Burke, 1990). Researchers in Canada and Europe show that depression coexists with anxiety disorder in 33% to 75% of cases (Rabavilas, 1996).

The coexistence of symptoms of anxiety and depression was also confirmed in studies on Greek health professionals, since a high correlation of BDI scores with the scores in the Greek version of the Spielberger State Trait Anxiety Scale was observed (Spielberger, Gorush, and Lushene, 1970). Overall, 16% of doctors and nurses – men and women combined - presented pathological scores in both tools; the corresponding percentage for women exceeded 19%. More in detail, 18% of women doctors and 20% of female nurses had pathological scores in both tools (Tselebis, Gournas, Tzitzanidou, Panaghiotou, and Ilias, 2006). In the same study, mean anxiety and depression scores for doctors and nurses were considerably higher than the corresponding mean scores in the general Greek population; the highest scores were observed in female nurses.

Stress, Depression and Smoking

Studies in nursing personnel show that stress contributes to the maintenance of the smoking habit; however likely coexistence of depression and smoking was not assessed (Tselebis, Panaghiotou, Theotoka, and Ilias, 2001). In a further study we examined the relationship of depression, anxiety and smoking habit in a sample of Greek doctors (Tselebis, Papaleftheris, Balis, Theotoka, and Ilias, 2003). Doctors that stopped smoking showed low anxiety scores compared not only to smokers but also to non-smokers. We can speculate that trait anxiety, which constitutes a relatively stable mental characteristic, participates actively in the maintenance or in the interruption of the smoking habit. Smokers did not show any correlation between the number of cigarettes consumed per day, depression or anxiety. Re-examining the data of that particular study vis-à-vis gender, we observed that almost 50% of female doctors presenting depressive symptoms were smoking. However, since more than 50% of female doctors with high anxiety sores were smoking, we believe that smoking behavior in medical personnel is linked to the presence of anxiety disorder regardless of depressive symptoms. Assessment of the relationship of smoking behavior with the individual's mentality is important to implement interventions by health services for smoking cessation (Karkanias et al., 2006).

Protective Factors

Sense of Coherence Versus Depression

In the theoretical framework for the Sense of Coherence (SOC) concept, Aaron Antonovsky tried to explain why certain individuals manage successfully to deal with painful, external or unknown events/stimuli (that potentially cause anxiety), with no negative consequences to their bodily and/or mental health (Antonovsky, 1996). According to Antonovsky's theory, a strong SOC helps the individual to conceive the world as structured and foreseeable, with any ensuing problems that result as being manageable and the requirements of life as being interesting challenges. Antonovsky's theory contributes to a change of viewpoint from "why is an individual sick" to "why is an individual healthy". In

Antonovsky's SOC questionnaire, high scores indicate a high degree of coherence and, hence, a lower probability for the individual to be prone to illness (Antonovsky, 1993). Since SOC scores do not appear to vary with age, Antonovsky concluded that SOC is a personality characteristic that is shaped at a relatively young age and remains stable in time. SOC has been used in research focused on health psychology and has been linked to somatic disease. In a sample of Greek nurses, mean SOC scores were statistically higher from the mean Greek population SOC score (63.6 versus 59.9). No difference in SOC was seen between men and women; interestingly, a strong negative correlation of SOC was observed with burnout and BDI scores. (Karalis et al., 2004; Kataki, Anagnostopoulou, and Kioseoglou, 2002; Tselebis, Moulou, and Ilias, 2001). The available data do not permit any further interpretations such as whether high SOC is related in some way with the choice of profession or if this is a chance finding. It appears that high SOC has a protective function against the development of depressive symptoms and professional burnout. This protective effect may also apply against anxiety but this has not been sufficiently studied in Greek doctors and nurses.

Family Support against Depression

Greek society and family are characterized by tight bonds among their members. The Greek family is often, for an individual, the basic source to receive support and provide feedback. Taking this into consideration, we studied the relation of family support with depression in a sample of Greek nurses, using the BDI questionnaire along with Julkunen's Family Support Scale questionnaire (FSS) [Julkunen, J.,and Greenglass, E.R. (1989) The Family Support Scale; Unpublished manuscript, York University; the validated Greek version of FSS was used, courtesy of Dr T Anagnostopoulou](Tselebis, Karkanias, Gournas, Bratis, and Perissaki, 2004). Depressive symptoms were found in 13.7% of subjects, with women showing statistically higher levels. An interesting finding was a significant negative correlation between perceived family support and depression. In a similar study we examined the effect of family support on the probability of developing burnout; family support showed a positive correlation with personal achievement and a negative correlation with sentimental exhaustion. Thus, increased engagement in family support acts protectively against the development of burnout (Tselebis, Moulou, Bratis, and Gournas, 2005).

Conclusion

Depression in women health professionals parallels the corresponding depression statistics of women in the general population. The increased presence of depression symptoms in this particular population appears to be related to complex and interacting factors that include biological and biochemical effects, and the multifaceted roles that women are called to undertake in their effort to cope with the continuously increasing requirements of a competitive work environment (such as the healthcare field) along with family care. Thus, at first sight, it appears that the burden of women regarding the danger of developing depression, is related to or is the result of conflict between the need for professional-scientific achievement and family responsibilities and obligations. Relevant studies that have been undertaken in Greece are few and they indicate the co-existence of factors that potentially have a protective effect vis-à-vis the risk of developing depressive symptoms. More systematic studies are needed, that will include a larger number of factors - demographic, social, psychological, biological – to determine with higher precision their individual role and their interaction; the objective is more effective prevention and management of depression in this particularly sensitive population group.

References

Abel, K. M., and Kulkarni, J. (2006). Depression in women: Hormonal influences. In D. Castle, J. Kulkarni and K. M. Abel (Eds.), *Mood and anxiety disorders in women* (pp. 116-135). Cambridge, UK: Cambridge University Press.

Alevizos, B. (1997). Introduction. In *Anxiety and anxiety disorders [in Greek]* (pp. 11-14). Athens, GR: Athens Medical Society.

Anagnostopoulos, F., and Papadatou, D. (1992). Factor analysis of the burnout inventory questionnaire in a sample of nurses [in Greek]. *Psychologika Themata, 183*, 202.

Antonovsky, A. (1993). The structure and properties of the sense of coherence scale. *Social Science and Medicine, 36*, 725-733.

Antonovsky, A. (1996). The sense of coherence. An historical and future perspective. *Isr J Med Sci, 32*, 170-178.

Beck, A. T., Ward, C. H., Mendelson, M., Mock, T., and Erbaugh, J. (1961). An inventory for measuring depression. *Archives of General Psychiatry, 4*, 561-571.

Belmaker, R. H., and Agam, G. (2008). Major depressive disorder. *New Engl J Medicine, 358*, 55-68.

Chrona, H., Daras, P., Papanastassiou, S., Tselebis, A., Bratis, D., Moussas, G., et al. (2006). The prevalence of depression prior an elective surgery. *European Journal of Anaesthesiology, 23*, 3.

Donias, S., and Demertzis, I. (1983). *Evaluation of depressive symptoms with Beck's depression questionnaire [in Greek].* Paper presented at the 10th Hellenic Congress of Neurology and Psychiatry, Athens, GR.

Freudenberger, H. J. (1974). Staff burnout. *J Soc Issues 30*, 159-165.

Hatzimanolis, I. (1997). Diagnosis and classification of anxiety disorders. In *Anxiety and anxiety disorders [in Greek]* (pp. 15-31). Athens, GR: Athens Medical Society.

Homer. (1996). Book 4 (R. Fagles, Trans.). In *The Odyssey* (pp. 219-230). London: Penguin Classics.

Iacovides, A., Foudulakis, K., Moysidou, C., and Ierodiakonou, C. (1997). Burnout in Nursing Staff: A clinical syndrome rather than a psychological reaction? . *Gen Hosp Psychiatry, 19*, 419-428.

Iacovides, A., Fountoulakis, K. N., Moysidou, C., and Ierodiakonou, C. (1999). Burnout in nursing staff: is there a relationship between depression and burnout? *Int J Psychiatry Med, 29*, 421-433.

Karalis, I., Langius, A., Tsirogianni, M., Faresjo, T., Nettelbladt, P., and Lionis, X. (2004). The translation-validation of the sense of coherence scale into Greek and its use in primary health care. *Archives of Hellenic Medicine, 21*, 195-203.

Karkanias , A., Moussas, G., Giotakis, K., Tselebis, A., Bratis, D., and Toubis, M. (2006). Psychopathology in women seeking medical support in order to quit smoking. *European Psychiatry, 21 Suppl 1,* S 211.

Karkanias, A., Moussas, G., Pachi, A., Vassila-Demi, K., Bratis, D., and Tselebis, A. (2007). Seasonal hospitalization in patients with mood disorders. *Annals of General Psychiatry, 7 Suppl 1*, 192.

Kataki, H., Anagnostopoulou, T., and Kioseoglou, G. (2002). The translation-adaptation of the sense of coherence scale into Greek In A. Stalikas, S. Triliva and P. Roussi (Eds.), *Psychometric tools in Greece [in Greek]* (pp. 291-292). Athens, GR: Ellinika Grammata.

Kielholz, P., and Beck, D. (1962). Diagnosis, autonomic tests, treatment and prognosis of exhaustion depressions. *Compr Psychiatry, 3*, 8-14.

Kontaxakis, B. P. (1997). Depression and suicide [in Greek]. In *Depression* (pp. 121-128). Athens, GR: Athens Medical Society.

Madianos, M. G. (1997). Epidemiology of depression [in Greek]. In *Depression* (pp. 20-32). Athens, GR: Athens Medical Society.

Maslach, C. (1982). *Burnout: The Cost of Caring.* Upper Saddle River, NJ: Prentice-Hall.

Maslach, C., and Jackson, S. E. (1986). *Maslach Burnout Inventory Manual* (2 ed.). Palo Alto, CA: Consulting Psychologists Press.

Ongle, M. (1983). Stages of Burnout among oncology nurses in the hospital setting. *Oncology Nursing Forum 10*, 31-34.

Papadatou, D., Anagnostopoulos, F., and Monos, D. (1994). Factors contributing to the development of burnout in oncology nursing. *British Journal of Medical Psychology, 67*, 187-199.

Poldinger, W. (1998). Masked Depression, Exhaustion Depression and the Burn-Out Syndrome. In B. Luban-Plozza and S. Sharma (Eds.), *Psychosomatic Disorders in General Practice* (pp. 357-383). Basel, CH: Schwabe.

Preti, A., and Miotto, P. (2005). Suicide in classical mythology: cues for prevention. *Acta Psychiatrica Scandinavica, 111* 384-391.

Rabavilas, A. D. (1996). Comorbidity of depression with anxiety disorders. In *Depression [in Greek]* (pp. 102-109). Athens, GR: Athens Medical Society.

Regier, D. A., Burke, J. D., and Burke, K. C. (1990). Comorbidity of affective and anxiety disorders in the NIMH epidemiological Catchment Area Program. In J. D. Maser and C. R. Cloninger (Eds.), *Comorbidity of mood and anxiety disorders* (pp. 113-122). Washington, DC: American Psychiatric Press.

Sadock, B. J., and Sadock, V. A. (2007). Depression and Bipolar Disorder. In *Kaplan and Sadock's Synopsis of Psychiatry* (10 ed., pp. 527-562). Philadelphia, PA.

Spielberger, G. D., Gorush, R. L., and Lushene, R. E. (1970). *The State-Trait Anxiety Inventory*. Palo Alto, CA: Consulting Psychologists Press.

Tselebis, A., Bratis, D., Moussas, G., Pantou, I., Harikiopoulou, M., Vey, H., et al. (2006). Anxiety and depression assessment in patients with chronic obstructive pulmonary disease. *European Respiratory Journal, 8 Suppl 50*, 62.

Tselebis, A., Georgakopoulou, A., Katsadoros, K., and Ilias, I. (1999, November 6-10). *Suicide and self -destruction in the Greek mythology.* Paper presented at the 20th Congress of the International Association for Suicide Prevention, Athens, Greece.

Tselebis, A., Gournas, G., Tzitzanidou, G., Panaghiotou, A., and Ilias, I. (2006). Anxiety and Depression in Greek nursing and medical personnel. *Psychological Reports, 99,* 93-96.

Tselebis, A., Karkanias, A., Gournas, G., Bratis, D., and Perissaki, K. (2004). Depression and perception of family support in nursing staff [in Greek]. *Psychiatriki, 15 Suppl 1,* 257.

Tselebis, A., Moulou, A., Bratis, D., and Gournas, G. (2005, October 21-25). *Study of family support and burnout [in Greek]* Paper presented at the Third Hellenic Congress of Systemic Therapy, Iraklion, GR.

Tselebis, A., Moulou, A., and Ilias, I. (2001). Burnout versus depression and sense of coherence: A study in Greek nursing staff. *Nursing and Health Sciences, 3,* 69-71.

Tselebis, A., Panaghiotou, A., Theotoka, I., and Ilias, I. (2001). Nursing staff anxiety versus smoking habits. *International Journal of Nursing Practice, 7,* 221-223.

Tselebis, A., Papaleftheris, E., Balis, E., Theotoka, I., and Ilias, I. (2003). Smoking related to anxiety and depression in Greek medical staff. *Psychological Reports, 92,* 529-532.

WHO. (2001a). In *World Health Report 2001. Mental Health - New Understanding, New Hope [Greek Edition]* (pp. 39-41). Athens, GR: Hellenic Ministry of Health and Welfare.

WHO. (2001b). In *World Health Report 2001. Mental Health - New Understanding, New Hope [Greek Edition]* (pp. 21-31). Athens, GR: Hellenic Ministry of Health and Welfare.

In: Women and Depression

Editors: Paula Hernandez and Sara Alonso

ISBN 978-1-60456-647-5

© 2009 Nova Science Publishers, Inc.

Chapter 17

Comparing the Profile and Presence of Depression among Nursing Students from Diurnal and Afternoon Courses

Antonia Regina Ferreira Furegato[10], Edilaine Cristina da Silva[1],Jair Licio Ferreira Santos[2] and Gabriela Carrion Degrande Moreira[3]

[1] Department of Pyschiatric Nursing and Human Sciences – University of São Paulo at Ribeirão Preto College of Nursing, WHO Collaborating Centre for Nursing Research Development, Brazil

[2] Department of Social Medicine, University of São Paulo at Ribeirão Preto College of Medicine, Brazil

[3] Scientific Initiation of NUPRI – CNPq.

Abstract

This study aimed to identify the profile of students from two Nursing courses (Bachelor - diurnal and Teaching Diploma – afternoon) verifying signs of depression and self-esteem levels, comparing these variables. A total of 114 students, properly informed, from the diurnal and afternoon courses at the College of Nursing at Ribeirão Preto participated in the study. The data search was obtained on known, valid and largely used instruments: Brazilian Economic Classification Criteria – CEB; Beck's Depression Inventory –BDI; Janis and Field's Self-Esteem Scale. The data were submitted to analysis of correlation with significance level at 5%. The results show prevalence of 94 women (82,4%), 63% between 20 and 24 years old; 32.06% (Teaching Diploma) are older than 25 years and 32% (Bachelor) are younger than 20 years old; 69.6% (Bachelor) do not work, and 86.1% belong to classes A2 and B; 75.8% (Teaching Diploma) work and 67.4% from the total belong to classes B2 and C. The data show 15.4% (Bachelor) and 28.6% (Teaching Diploma) with signs indicative of depression (three severe cases in the afternoon courses). The self-esteem levels were classified in 97.4% as medium and high. None of the cases indicative of moderate and severe depression presented low self-

10. furegato@eerp.usp.br.

esteem. The conclusion is that there are significant differences between the profiles of the two groups of subjects especially the higher incidence of depression among the Teaching Diploma students. It is possible that the prestige perceived in the academic context is a resilient factor, positively influencing the students' self evaluation.

Keywords: *Mental health, Psychiatric Nursing, Adjustment disorders, Self-concept.*

I – Introduction

Historically, professional development in nursing has been directed by positivist science, valuing objectivity, imposing neutrality and indifference as the condition for day-to-day performance [1]. In this rationalist condition, the focus is on the biological aspect and technicality. However, new trends in nursing education lead to a more humanistic and critical model, emphasized on bio-psycho-social care. The propositions for humanized teaching and professional performance consider the subjectivity and emotions of nursing professionals. These propositions value the nurse as a therapeutic tool that cares for people who suffer [2-5].

From this perspective, nurses have a participative role in the process of transformation in the many interdisciplinary environments of action, decision, and development. Therefore, there is a need to look after this professional's health.

Over the last decades, in every sector of society, there has been a growing concern regarding human integrality, ensuring life conditions and quality, valuing people who were once an object of discrimination, segregation, or exploitation. Furthermore, this concern has also addressed environmental protection.

The concepts of disease and mental health have also been objects of these transformations, which reflect on the relationships between health people and mental patients, as well as on health system organizations.

Despite these changes, worldwide mental disease rates remain a matter of concern. The World Health Organization (WHO) has reported that 450 million people in the world are affected by mental problems at some point of their lives, both neurological and behavioral; and over 80 thousand suicides occur every year [6].

Depression affects millions of people. It poses harms to their lives, like reducing their performance at school, at work, and performing everyday activities. Depression also affects personal relationships, and is responsible for high suicide rates [7-11].

People with depression find it difficult to perform everyday activities because of the changes to their ability to concentrate and to their disposition, since they also present sleepiness, weakness, lack of energy, and little enthusiasm to face day-to-day tasks. Studies on self-esteem have reported that depression is among the main causes of failure at school, at work, and in personal relationships.

Self-esteem refers to the level of consideration and respect that individuals have for themselves; it is a self mental portrait. There have been studies on whether high levels of self-esteem could cause better performance, success, happiness, and a healthy lifestyle [12-15].

Individuals unaffected by depression and with a positive self-evaluation present a fair rate of emotions and feelings, work independently, take on daily responsibilities, are proud of their personal achievements, tolerate frustrations, and have good relationships with the people around them.

Despite the lack of clear evidence, studies have shown that there must be some relation between depression and self-esteem, i.e., whenever depression exists, there is a low level of self-esteem or higher self-depreciation [10,16-18]. Hence, nursing students and professionals merit special attention, since they work directly with people who need their care. Nursing is a job that takes up 24 hours in a day, and is performed with other health professionals (teams) as well as managing teams of auxiliaries. The level of attention and dedication required in the job, in addition to the daily stressful situations and proximity to human suffering can affect the individual's wellbeing and quality of life. Certainly, a good mental and physical health would benefit the nurse's professional performance.

These considerations have been the motivation to study depression among women at different phases of their life, as well as among nursing students and professionals. Furthermore, we have sought to provide guidance to these individuals and refer them to specialized care. This attitude is supported by the international literature, which evaluates the cost-effectiveness of informational programs and therapies as well as training for health professionals, due to its positive impact [19].

II – Objectives

1. to identify the profile of second-year nursing undergraduates of the bachelor degree and teaching bachelor degree courses;
2. to verify the presence of indicative signs of depression and the subjects' level of self-esteem;
3. to compare the differences and particularities of both groups.

III – Method

The full project regarding this research was approved by the Research Ethics Committee of the University of Sao Paulo at Ribeirao Preto College of Nursing, and is supported by the CNPq (Brazilian Scientific and Technological Development Council). The project also addresses other variables, such as the individuals' knowledge and opinion regarding depression and quality of life. The analyses concerning this aspect of the project will be published in a further article.

In the health area, the scientific method implies managing the interface of qualitative and quantitative techniques, which often requires a historical and analytical analysis to contextualize the findings. This is a qualitative study using quantitative data, through psychometric measures (scales) and semi-structured evaluations (questionnaires).

Scale measurements are one of the many forms of psychometric measurement, including psychological tests, inventories, questionnaires, and scales with the minimum parameters to be considered legitimate and valid instruments [20].

Location and Subjects

This study was performed at the Ribeirão Preto College of Nursing, in 2007, with second-year students of the Nursing Undergraduate Course, of both the bachelor degree and teaching bachelor degree courses.

Every year, 80 students enter the diurnal Nursing course (bachelor degree), and this is the 53rd class. The teaching bachelor degree course (nocturnal) was established in 2006, and receives 50 new students every year. Therefore, this is the 1st class, in the second college year. The undergraduate courses last four (diurnal) and five (nocturnal) years.

The sample was limited to second-year students because there were no more advanced classes in the teaching bachelor degree course that would allow comparing classes, since there is only one diurnal (bachelor degree) and one nocturnal (teaching bachelor degree) course.

Of the 85 students enrolled in the discipline that offered the opportunity for data collection, 65 subjects participated (76.5%). Three students refused to participate and the others did not attend class on the day the tests were administered.

In the teaching bachelor degree course, all subjects participated, i.e., all 49 students enrolled answered the tests. It should be stressed that the researcher of this study was the professor of the class selected for data collection in this group.

Instruments

The study used well-known instruments, validated and widely used in the scientific community: CEB, BDI, and SES.

- CEB – Brazil Criteria of Economic Classification (in Portuguese: *Critérios de Classificação Econômica Brasil*)

The CEB was designed to define large classes that answer the needs of segmentation (purchasing power), using statistical techniques based on collectivity. Thus, it was expected that the studied group would show a low probability of classification error [21].

Students received this instrument and were asked to inform how many of the 10 items listed they had at home (in case they lived in dorms, they should answer considering their family home). In addition, they were asked to inform the educational level of the head of the family.

- BDI - Beck Depression Inventory

The BDI is a 21-item scale, with intensity ranging from 0 to 3 and representing symptoms and attitudes such as sadness, pessimism, sense of failure, dissatisfaction, feelings of guilt and expectations of punishment, dislike of self, social withdrawal, indecisiveness, change in body image, work inhibition, sleep disorders, fatigability, loss of appetite and weight, somatic preoccupation, and decreased libido [22].

The psychometric features of the Portuguese version were tested by Gorenstein and Andrade [18].These authors evaluated factorial differences in the dimensions: cognition – affectivity, somatic dislike of self, and prejudice against depression in young people. Based on its theoretical framework, this test values the cognitive symptoms and is self-administered, especially among subjects with good education levels, as in the case of university students.

BDI classifications are different in case it is administered in a unsuspected population (such as the case with nursing students), searching for symptoms indicating depression, or when it is administered at a clinical setting, for purposes of diagnosis and treatment. Scores for screening: >15=no depression; 15 to 19 = dysphoria (mild depression); 20 to 29 = moderate depression; above 30 = severe depression.

This inventory has a heading where the subject provides some personal and socio-demographic information.

      – SES – Janis and Field Self-Esteem Scale

This is a Likert scale consisting of 23 items, translated from French and adjusted to the Brazilian context [23].

The scale allows the evaluation of one's self-esteem levels and feelings of social adequacy/inadequacy, i.e., the subject's thoughts and feelings about personal and social issues.

On the scale, subjects choose the frequency of their thoughts and feelings regarding each item. Answers are given in a scale from 1 to 5 (Always/Often/Sometimes/Rarely/Never). Questions 3, 7, 8, 9, and 10 have inverted values. The maximum score is 115 divided in thirds, and allows for the classification of subjects' self-esteem levels as low (0-38), aveagre (39-76), and high (77-115).

Data Collection

Nursing undergraduates (diurnal and nocturnal) answered the set of tests (scales and questionnaires) after being properly informed about the ethical aspects, the importance of their participation, and about how to proceed with answering the tests. Students were given the free choice of participation. It was also assured that they would have a quick reply regarding the results, especially regarding depression. All participants provided written consent.

After the explanations, the set of tests was handed out. Students were asked to remain silent for better concentration. Three researchers and one Scientific-Initiation student of the Center for Studies on Interpersonal Relations (*Núcleo de Estudos das Relações Interpessoais – NUPRI*) were present and available to solve any doubts individually as well as to check the answered tests so as to avoid any failures.

Observation: *students identified with signs for moderate and severe depression were seen individually and forwarded to appropriate support.*

Procedures and Analysis of the Results

Data were inserted in a MS Excel database, and later analyzed using STATA. Correlation analysis and significance tests were carried out. Fisher's exact test was used to compare sociodemographic and self-esteem variables with depression [24]. The level of significance was 5%.

IV-Results

Of the 120 students enrolled in the second year of the Nursing Undergraduate course, 114 participated, which corresponded to all 49 students of the nocturnal course (teaching bachelor degree), and 81% (65) of those enrolled in the diurnal course (bachelor degree).

As expected, most (82.4%) students were females. Nonetheless, the number of male students exceeds previous reports in the literature [25]. The studied group showed a considerable number of men (17.5%), who were most in the age group of 20-24 years (50%). Eighteen students were older than 25 years, of which 7 were men (Table 1).

It is worth stressing that 88.3% of the women were younger than 24 years, and 85% of the men were above 20. In the group, 62.3% of students were in the age group 20-24 years, of which 32.6% in the teaching bachelor degree course were above 25 and 32% of those in the bachelor degree course were under 20.

Another interesting data is the participants' marital status. Of the total, 104 subjects (91.3%) were single, eight were married, and two women were divorced.

Regarding employment, an inverse relation was observed between subjects in both courses. In the bachelor degree course, 69.9% did not work, whereas in the teaching bachelor degree course, 75.8% did. This result is compatible with the courses' hours, i.e., the nocturnal (teaching bachelor degree) course offers a chance for people who were already employed to attend university and keep their jobs (Table 1).

Table 1. Sociodemographic variables of students enrolled in the Bachelor and Teaching Bachelor degree courses, Ribeirão Preto, 2007

VARIABLE	Bachelor		Teaching Bachelor		Total	
(n=114)	f	%	f	%	f	%
Gender						
Male	7	10.8	13	26.5	20	17.5
Female	58	89.2	36	73.5	94	82.5
Age group						
<20	21	32.3	4	8.2	25	21.9
20 to 24	42	64.6	29	59.2	71	62.3
25 or more	2	3.1	16	32.6	18	15.8

VARIABLE	Bachelor		Teaching Bachelor		Total	
Occupation Employed						
Yes	8	24.2	25	51.0	33	29.5
No	55	75.8	24	49.0	79	70.6
Social Class						
A1	-	-	-	-	-	-
A2	17	26.1	6	12.2	23	20.2
B1	21	32.3	7	14.3	28	24.5
B2	18	27.7	17	34.7	35	30.7
C	7	10.8	16	32.6	23	20.2
D	2	3.1	3	6.2	5	4.4
E	-	-	-	-	-	-

The data regarding the economic classification of the 114 subjects show that there were no cases, neither in class A1 nor class E. Therefore, subjects were neither very rich nor very poor. In the teaching bachelor degree course, the largest concentrations were in classes B2 and C, totaling 67.3%. In the bachelor course, on the other hand, only 13.9% are in classes C and D, i.e., 86.1% are in classes A2 and B, as shown in Table 1.

In the teaching bachelor degree course, 38.8% are in classes C and D. Class A2 comprises 26.1% of bachelor degree students and 12.2% of teaching bachelor degree students. These results, regarding the two groups, are above the Brazil rate for Class A2. In the bachelor degree course, classes B1 and B2 total 60%, whereas the Brazil rate would be 14%. Even in the teaching bachelor degree course, the rate is superior, i.e., 49%.

Depression and Self-Esteem

The results found in the nursing students' answers to the Beck inventory reveal that 15.4% of bachelor degree students and 28.6% of teaching bachelor degree students show signs of depression (mild, moderate, and severe), as shown in Table 2.

It is worth to stress that there was one case of moderate depression was among the bachelor degree course and six cases in the teaching bachelor degree, in addition to one and three sever cases, respectively. The four cases of severe depression occurred in women. Gender differences in the other levels were insignificant.

Fisher's exact test revealed significant results, especially comparing depression with age and social class in both groups. There were differences and similarities regarding the presence of these symptoms in the two groups. Students under 20 years showed similar symptom proportions. However, for the age group the age group 20-24, the incidence was greater in teaching bachelor degree students, and very common among 25-year-old students in this course (5 out of 11), but none in the bachelor degree course.

In the bachelor course, most depression cases were in class B1, of which almost 30% showed symptoms. An interesting proportion was found in the teaching bachelor degree course. The lower the purchasing power, the greater the presence of depression, ranging from 16.7% to 33.4%, from class A2 to D, but present in all classes. It should be remembered that no students, in either group, were ranked in classes A1 or E.

Table 2. Results for the depression and self-esteem tests in nursing students, per course Bacharelado Ribeirão Preto, 2007

TEST	Bachelor Degree		Teaching Bachelor Degree	
	f	%	f	%
Depression				
No Depression	55	84.5	35	71.4
Dysphoria	8	12.3	5	10.2
Moderate depression	1	1.6	6	12.2
Severe depression	1	1.6	3	6.2
Self-Esteem				
Low	1	1.6	2	4.1
Average	57	87.7	36	73.5
High	7	10.7	11	22.4
Total	65	100.0	49	100.0

Table 3. Levels of depression according to the levels of self-esteem in nursing students. Ribeirão Preto, 2007

Level of Depression	Level of Self-Esteem			
	Low	Average	High	Total
No Depression	3	82	5	90
Dysphoria	0	9	4	13
Moderate Depression	0	1	6	7
Severe Depression	0	1	3	4
Total	3	93	18	114

Regarding self-esteem, considering the 114 nursing undergraduates, it was found that the overall self-esteem is considered between average and high (98.4%). Only three students (with no signs of depression) presented low self-esteem (Table 2).

Interestingly, of the 11 students in the teaching bachelor degree course who presented high levels of self-esteem, 10 showed signs for depression. Both groups showed a mode balanced rate for average self-esteem levels.

Crossing information between classes with depression and self-esteem levels, the results for Fisher's exact test show that 79% of the students did not present depression and the average level of self-esteem stood out, since only three students showed low self-esteem. In general, of those presenting signs for depression, four were classified as severe depression, of which three showed high self-esteem and one showed average self-esteem. None of the four cases of severe depression reported low levels of self-esteem (Table 3).

The same thing occurred with students classified as having moderate depression. None of them presented low self-esteem, in fact six presented self-esteem levels above average (85.7%). Thus, is is observed that, in this group, 16% had high levels of self-esteem, which disagrees with studies that associate depression to low self-esteem levels.

V – Discussion

Previous studies have been carried out to research characteristics of students enrolled in the Ribeirão Preto College of Nursing. One study had the purpose to indetify the sociodemographic profile of the nursing students enrolled in the course from 1999 to 2003, and found that 92.3% were 21 years old or younger [25]. Another study, performed less than ten years ago, showed that 90% of the freshmen were younger than 20 years [26]. A study performed in 2006 reported an average age of 21.5 years [27].

Studies have also addressed other features besides age. A recent study reported that the male presence in the nursing course was between 2.6 and 10.8% in the studied 5-year period. The authors state there is an ongoing change in men's interest, as there has been an increase in their search for the nursing course. Regarding another feature, the study also shows that 96.3% of the sample was single and that 95.4% did not work [25]. It is also observed that the sample of the present study shows some agreement with the profile of bachelor degree students reported in previous studies. However, ther is a clear disagreement compared to the teaching bachelor degree course, i.e., more men, and with more students above 25 years of age, and with most keeping a job while attending the nursing course.

Regarding the main findings in this study, the indicative signs of depression among nursing students are above average when a binary relationship is considered (having depression or not, including mild depression in this group), i.e., 15.4% and 28.6% respectively in the bachelor degree and the teaching bachelor degree courses. This rate is more present in the teaching bachelor degree course, for all age groups, and more marked on those above the age of 25.

A study performed in Maringá (Paraná State) found that 18.3% of Medicine Students had depression (with cutting scores between 10 and 30 in the Beck Inventory). The authors state a study performed in Chicago (USA), which reported that 12% of Medical students showed signs for depression, using 14 as the cutting score in the same sacale [28].

Depression in the general population has been reported to be around 10-12% [7,8,9,11,29,30].

The overall result of this study, including for mild depression, are above average rates stated in the literature. However, if only moderate and severe depression were considered, the findings for nursing undergraduates would be below those rates.

In this study, the subjects' distribution according to their self-esteem is quite interesting. Even before having finished creating the database, we worried about checking the results for the Beck Inventory with the purpose to call all students ranking moderate and severe depression for counceling. We heard their stories and personal situation. It was surprising that the student who needed clinical intervention were already being followed by a professional, some, in fact, were taking appropriate medication, or undergoing psychotherapy. It was possible to clear out doubts and, in general, these students felt that they had our support in case they needed. Some of the reported life contexts are stressful and adverse. The literature points out that such factors can strengthen or even induce cases of depression [7,31]. However, we were surprised by the positive attitude the subjects had regarding themselves. Though this does not exempt them from further risk, it shows they have some resilient factor that maintains them in their current condition. Resilience is the individual's ability to have healthy behaviors despite being in an adverse context.

The Fisher's test showed there is an inverse relationship between depression and self-esteem. The initial reaction was to think there was an error in the information. The data were reviewed and the results confirmed that there was no direct relationship between depression and self-esteem.

One of the most respected researchers on self-esteem states that, in clinical observations, depression is accompanied by low self-esteem. Studies performed in the United States found a significant association between self-esteem levels and depression among nurses [12].

A study carried out by the Center for Studies on Interpersonal Relations (*Núcleo de Estudos das Relações Interpessoais – NUPRI*) observed that though students of the diurnal nursing course had normal depression rates, the group's levels of self-esteem were either average or low [16].

Questionnaires are useful screening tools, but objective symptoms are particularly unstable. Therefore, a high score on the test does not always correspond to a precise diagnosis for depression in young people. It is known that the evaluation for the presence of depression should take into consideration the overlap of factors. On the other hand, there is evidence that success in school, the youth's ability to deal with difficult situations, and family support can protect young people from the effect of depression [32].

Self-concept depends on personal features, but it is linked to the values of the society in which the individual lives, such as intellectual competence, attraction and physical skills, sexual identification, leadership, mood, and moral features. Similarly, social benefits and achievements make people believe they are more worthy or more important than others.

Based on information in the literature, a reflection was done on the results of the present study. It was observed that the profile evidences a group of university students, predominantly of classes B and C, who are pursuing their dream – to study nursing, in a public university, and with the perspective to soon be part of the working world. Of the third part that is older than 25 years, especially in the teaching bachelor degree course, many already work in the field and some already have their own families. The students are filled with hope for better economic and social conditions by obtaining their bachelor or teaching bachelor degrees. These are considered resilient factors that help students to deal with adversities.

It is also worth stressing that this group counts with a significant male participation (17.5%), and only 22% are under 20 years of age. This suggests that most students made a conscientious professional choice and value this achievement very much.

One of the clearest aspects of personal identity is expressed through one's professional choice. If self-concepts depend on both personal features and social values, the prestige felt by nursing students, in the context of the University of Sao Paulo, can have a positive affect on their self-evaluation.

VI – Conclusion

The profile found among students of the bachelor and teaching bachelor degree courses in nursing show significant differences that could affect or favor the presence of depression among them, or even be a resilient element in this context, with special emphasis on the following points:

- A significant rate of male students, especially in the nocturnal course (teaching bachelor degree);
- One forth of students are older than 25 years, especially in the nocturnal course; a similar rate was found in the diurnal course for students younger than 20 years;
- There is an inverse relationship between employment and course (diurnal and nocturnal); i.e., most students in the teaching bachelor degree course work, whereas most in the bachelor degree course do not.
- Regarding economic classification, in the teaching bachelor degree course, most students are in classes B2 and C, whereas in the bachelor degree course most are in classes A2 and B. Both results are above the Brazil rate.
- There was a significant correlation in the comparison of signs of depression and self-esteem levels between the two groups. The depression cases found in both groups were above the average rates for the general population when mild depression cases were included, but those rates were below average if only moderate and severe cases are considered.
- Self-esteem results were distributed in three levels, with most being rated as average and high. However, there was no direct correlation between depression and self-esteem levels, which disagrees with previous studies. There is a significant correlation between the variables, but without a direct relationship.

This study suggests the presence of positive stigma levels activated by resilient factors, minimizing the possible consequences of depression, related to school achievements as a factor of social prestige and their further insertion into the work market.

VII – References

[1]   Prado ML, Reibnitz KS, Gelbcke FL. Aprendendo a cuidar: a sensibilidade como elemento plasmático na formação da profissional crítico-criativa em enfermagem. Texto and Contexto Enfermagem, 2006 15(2): 296-302.

[2]   Travelbee J. Intervention en enfermeria psiquiátria. Colômbia, Carvajal, 1982.

[3]   Furegato ARF. Relações interpessoais terapêuticas na enfermagem. Ribeirão Preto (SP): SCALA; 1999.

[4]   Waldow VR. Cuidado humano – o resgate necessário. Porto Alegre(RS): Sagra/Luzzatto, 1999.

[5]   Silva MJP. Comunicação tem remédio – a comunicação nas relações interpessoais em saúde. São Paulo (SP): Gente; 1996.

[6] OMS - Organização Mundial da Saúde (OMS). Relatório Mundial da Saúde. Saúde mental: nova concepção, nova esperança. Lisboa (PO): Ministério da Saúde; 2002.

[7] Lafer B, Almeida OP, Fraguas Jr G, Miguel EC. Depressão no ciclo da vida. Porto Alegre (RS): Artes Médicas; 2000.

[8] Dalgalarrondo P. Psicopatologia e semiologia dos transtornos mentais. Porto Alegre(RS): Artes Médicas; 2007.

[9] Montgomery S. Confrontando la depression. Guia del médico. New York (NY): Pfizer International; 1997.

[10] OPAS/OMS - Organización Panamericana de la Salud/ Organización Mundial de la Salud. Programa de Salud Mental, División de Promoción de la Salud: Modelo para la capacitación de la enfermera general en la identificación y manejo de los transtornos afectivos. Generalista I, Washington (DC): OPAS/OMS; 1999.

[11] Maj M, Sartorius N. Transtornos depressivos. Porto Alegre (RS): ARTMED; 2005.

[12] Rosenberg M. Society and adolescent self-image. New Jersey (USA). Princeton University Press, 1965.

[13] Tousend DC. Enfermagem Psiquiátrica: conceitos de cuidado. Rio de Janeiro (RJ): Guanabara Koogan, 2002.

[14] Fundichely OM, Zaldwar RI. Auto-estima en el personal de enfermería. Rev Enf. Cuba. 1999 15(3): 184-9.

[15] Baumeinster RF, Campbell JD, Krueger JI, Wohs KD. Does hight self-esteem cause better performance, interpersonal success, happiness, or healthier lifestyles? Psychol Scien Publ Inter, 2003 4(1): 1-43.

[16] Furegato ARF, Silva EC, Campos MC, Cassiano RPT. Depressão e auto-estima entre estudantes de enfermagem. Rev Psiq Clínica, 2006 33(5): 239-44.

[17] Apostolo JLA, Rodrigues MA, Olivera JP. Evaluación de los estados emocionales de estudiantes de enfermería. INDEX de Enfermería (ES), 2007 26(56): 26-9.

[18] Gorenstein C, Andrade L. Inventário de depressão de Beck: propriedades psicométricas da versão em português. Revista Psiq Clinica, 1998 25(5): 245-50.

[19] Rosenbaum JF, Hylan TR. O custo dos transtornos depressivos: uma revisão. In Maj M, Sartorius N. Transtornos depressivos. Porto Alegre(RS): ARTMED, 2005.

[20] Pasquali L. Instrumentos psicológicos: manual pratico de elaboração. Brasília (DF): UNB/Prática Gráfica, 1999.

[21] ABEP - Associação Brasileira de Empresas de Pesquisa– Critério de Classificação Econômica Brasil, 2005. www.abep.org. Acesso em 15/11/2007

[22] Beck AT, Ward CH, Mendelson M, Mock J, Erbaugh J. An inventory for measuring depression. Archives of General Psychiatry, 1961 4: 551-71.

[23] Cardoso SES. Auto-estima e crise: base para o nexo entre delinqüência juvenil e aspectos da personalidade. 1979. Dissertação (Mestrado) PUC. Rio de Janeiro.

[24] Siegel S, Castellan Jr NJ. Estatística não paramétrica para ciências do comportamento. Porto Alegre (RS); ARTMED, 2006.

[25] Wetterich NC, Melo MRAC. Sociodemographic profile of undergraduate nursing students. Rev Latino americana Enfermagem, 2007 15(3): 404-10.

[26] UNIVERSIDADE DE SÃO PAULO – Prefeitura do Campus de Ribeirão Preto. Acessória de Comunicação Social e Impressa. Perfil do Calouro Ribeirão 1993-1998. Jornal USP, 2005.

[27] Shinyashiki GT, Mendes IAC, Trevizan MA, Day RA. Socialização profissional: estudantes tornado-se enfermeiros. Rev. Latinoamericana Enfermagem, 2006 14(4): 601-7.

[28] Porcu M, Fritzen CV, Helber C. Sintomas depressivos nos estudantes de medicina da Universidade Estadual de Maringá. Psiquiatria na Prática Médica, v. 34: março de 2001. http://www.unifesp.br/dpsiq/polbr/ppm/index05.htm. Acesso em 03/12/2007.

[29] Organización Panamericana de la Salud/Organización Mundial de la Salud – Manual de recursos sobre salud mental, derechos humanos y legislación de la OMS. Genebra, 2006.

[30] Sadock B., Sadock VA. Compêndio de Psiquiatria. Porto Alegre (RS): ARTMED, 2007.

[31] Olié JP, Marcher JP, Costa e Silva JA. Neuroplasticity: a new approach to the path o physiology of depression. London UK: Current Medicine Group, 2005.

[32] Harrington R. Transtornos depressivos em crianças e adolescentes: uma revisão. In Maj M, Sartorius N. Transtornos depressivos. Porto Alegre (RS). ARTMED, 2005.

In: Women and Depression   ISBN 978-1-60456-647-5
Editors: Paula Hernandez and Sara Alonso   © 2009 Nova Science Publishers, Inc.

Chapter 18

Women, Depression, and Cardiovascular Disease

Ryan Thibodeau[11,] and Randall S. Jorgensen[+]*

[*]Psychology Department, St. John Fisher College, Rochester, New York, USA
[+]Syracuse University, Syracuse, New York, USA

Abstract

Compared to men, women are disproportionately subject to both depression and certain adverse cardiovascular outcomes. In this chapter, we review a large body of data on women, depression, and cardiovascular disease (CVD). First, we highlight epidemiologic data related to women's higher prevalence of depression, and discuss possible explanations thereof. Second, we explore findings on the nature and scope of CVD among women. Next, we summarize data regarding the status of depression as a risk factor for future CVD and a prognostic indicator for established CVD, emphasizing findings pertinent to women. We then examine possible mechanisms underlying the depression-CVD relationship and conclude by exploring a host of treatment issues. Throughout the chapter, we offer a variety of recommendations and directions for future research. The present chapter, in its integration of large and diverse research literatures, should serve as a useful resource for professionals interested in the links between women, depression, and CVD.

Can personality traits, psychiatric disorder, or other psychological factors make a person physically sick? Relationships between psychosocial factors and various markers of physical health and illness have long captured the attention of health professionals. Identification of psychosocial variables that might reliably predict both the onset of physical illnesses and their course remains a top priority for health psychologists and professionals in allied fields.

---

11 Address correspondence to: Ryan Thibodeau; Pioch 103A, Psychology Department, St. John Fisher College, Rochester, NY 14618; Email: rthibodeau@sjfc.edu, phone: 585-899-3749

Sustained inquiry into the psychosocial predictors of cardiovascular disease (CVD), in particular, has yielded an impressive accumulation of data (see Smith and Ruiz, 2002, for a review). Among the psychosocial variables most rigorously studied in the context of CVD are the Type A behavior pattern (Friedman and Rosenman, 1959) and its constituent elements (e.g., hostility; Jorgensen et al., 2001; Williams and Barefoot, 1988), perceived or actual social isolation (Berkman, 1995), a toxic work environment (Landsbergis et al., 2001), and vital exhaustion, a depression-like state marked by fatigue, feelings of demoralization, and irritability (e.g., Appels and Mulder, 1989). Research on psychosocial predictors of CVD is particularly important in view of the finding that traditional risk factors (e.g., poor diet, sedentary lifestyle, smoking, hypertension) provide an incomplete account of variance in CVD morbidity and mortality (Feldman, Makuc, Kleinman, and Cornoni-Huntley, 1989).

In addition to the psychosocial variables noted above, depression has emerged as a robust indicator of CVD onset and prognosis, independent of other risk factors (see Hemingway and Marmot, 1999, for a review). In fact, some have argued that depression surpasses all other psychosocial risk factors in the prediction of CVD outcomes (but see Suls and Bunde, 2005). Data regarding the depression-CVD link may be particularly salient for women, who are approximately twice as likely as men to become depressed (Bourdon, Rae, Locke, Narrow, and Regier, 1992; Kessler et al., 1994).

The purpose of the present chapter is to provide an up-to-date review of research and theory concerning women, depression, and CVD. First, we summarize data on the epidemiology of depression, focusing on sex differences in prevalence and proposed explanations thereof. Second, we dismiss the persistent notion that CVD is a "man's disease" by providing evidence that women, compared to men, are disproportionately subject to a variety of adverse cardiac outcomes. The third section offers an in-depth analysis of the depression-CVD link, especially as it pertains to women. Fourth, we explore the possible mechanisms through which depression "gets under the skin" to increase risk for adverse cardiac outcomes. Finally, we consider a host of issues relevant to the treatment of both depression and CVD, paying particular attention to research most applicable to women. Throughout the chapter, we offer recommendations and highlight areas ripe for additional study.

Before launching our discussion, two terminological issues merit attention. First, we should note that *cardiovascular disease* is a generic term that encompasses a variety of specific conditions, such as *coronary heart disease* (accumulation of plaque in the arteries that supply the heart, causing restricted blood flow), *stroke* (interruption of blood flow to one or more areas of the brain), *hypertension* (chronically elevated blood pressure), and *congestive heart failure* (inadequate blood flow from the heart to the body's tissues and organs). An overwhelming majority of available theory and research illuminates the relationship between depression and coronary heart disease, so the present chapter reflects this state of affairs. However, we highlight findings related to other cardiovascular conditions (most notably stroke) when they are available. Hereafter, we use the term *cardiovascular disease* (or *CVD*) when we discuss cardiac disease in general terms, and we invoke the terms corresponding to specific cardiac conditions when such a strategy is appropriate. Second, we use the term *depression* to refer to both *Diagnostic and Statistical Manual* (DSM; American Psychiatric Association, 1994) depressive disorders and individual differences in the experience of self-reported depressive symptoms. The research evidence indicates that both are meaningfully related to certain aspects of CVD onset and prognosis.

Women and Depression – Sex Differences in Prevalence and Possible Explanations

Across studies, there is great variability in estimates of the prevalence of depression. To illustrate, two large, methodologically rigorous epidemiologic surveys arrived at dramatically different conclusions regarding the lifetime prevalence of a Major Depressive Episode among adults in the United States. In the Epidemiologic Catchment Area (ECA) study (Bourdon et al., 1992), the lifetime prevalence of a Major Depressive Episode was estimated to be 5.9%. In contrast, data from the National Comorbidity Study (NCS; Kessler et al., 1994) suggest a lifetime prevalence of 17.1%, nearly three times the ECA-derived estimate. Differences in methodological characteristics and/or diagnostic schemes (DSM-III in ECA versus DSM-III-R in NCS), among other factors, may be responsible for the divergent estimates (see Kessler et al., 1994, for a more extended discussion). Of note, however, the ECA and NCS data are more consistent with respect to sex differences in the lifetime prevalence of depression. In both studies, women were far more likely to report experiencing a lifetime Major Depressive Episode than men (2.4 and 1.7 times more likely in ECA and NCS, respectively). Across psychiatric epidemiologic studies, women are typically 1.5 to 3 times more likely to report a previous Major Depressive Episode (Kessler, McGonagle, Swartz, Blazer, and Nelson, 1993; see Nolen-Hoeksema, 1987, for a review). Moreover, this sex difference appears cross-culturally robust. Weissman and her colleagues (1996) studied the prevalence of Major Depressive Disorder and Bipolar Disorder among men and women in 10 countries. They reported that across all 10 countries, women had a higher prevalence of lifetime depression than men (see also Angst et al., 2002; but see Levav, Kohn, Golding, and Weissman, 1997). The sex difference in the prevalence of depression is not attributable to a greater tendency for women to disclose depressive difficulties (Bogner and Gallo, 2004; King and Buchwald, 1982) or to biases on the part of diagnosticians (Amenson and Lewinsohn, 1981). Likewise, it is not an artifact of sex differences in socioeconomic indicators, as statistically controlling for such variables does not markedly alter the relationship between sex and self-reported depressive symptoms (Ensel, 1982). The sex difference in the prevalence of depression, undoubtedly one of the most consistent findings in all of psychiatric epidemiology, appears impervious to numerous alternative explanations.

What accounts for this difference? Why is the prevalence of depression greater among women than men? Nolen-Hoeksema and her colleagues (Nolen-Hoeksema, 1987; Nolen-Hoeksema, 2002; Nolen-Hoeksema and Girgus, 1994; Nolen-Hoeksema, Larson, and Grayson, 1999) have been active in the construction and empirical evaluation of theory aimed at accounting for sex differences in depression. The most prominent accounts of the sex difference have invoked biological factors, psychosocial factors, or some combination of both.

Biological explanations of the sex difference in depression posit that there is something intrinsic to the female sex that increases risk for depression. Genetic explanations (e.g., a mutated gene on the X chromosome that contributes to the pathogenesis of depression; Winokur and Tanna, 1969) have generally not been borne out in the data. In addition, the female gonadal hormones have long been implicated as a potential mechanism linking the female sex with an increased prevalence of depression. In particular, researchers have explored whether periods of substantial fluctuation in female gonadal hormones are associated with increased rates of depression. Several pieces of data bear on this possibility. First, sex differences in depression first emerge at around the onset of puberty (Nolen-Hoeksema and Girgus, 1994), when estrogen levels rise sharply (Steiner, Dunn, and Born, 2003). Second, approximately three quarters of women experience some degree of mood change during the premenstrual period (American Psychiatric Association, 1994); for a small number of women, this change is sufficiently large to justify a diagnosis of Premenstrual Dysphoric Disorder. Third, many women experience mood disturbances in the postpartum period (Stein, Marsh, and Morton, 1981), another phase known to be marked by hormonal fluctuation. Some women experience markedly altered mood in the perimenopausal and menopausal periods, during which time estrogen levels decline, but most women do not (Steiner et al., 2003).

There are some problems with applying these data to answer the question of why there are sex differences in the prevalence of depression. First, note that the above data address questions related to *phasic, within-person* changes (e.g., Do women experience temporary increases in depressed mood during the premenstrual period?), whereas the question of *stable* sex differences in depression requires a *between-person* account. Second, why do sex differences in depression persist between these critical periods of fluctuation, when female gonadal hormones are presumably more stable? Any viable hormonal account must address why the female gonadal hormones confer risk for depression that is stable, enduring, and not limited to any particular time period. As one example of such an account, Seeman (1997) speculated that the cyclicity of estrogen renders women chronically more sensitive to stress and, in turn, depression and anxiety. Overall, however, the balance of the evidence suggests that female biology, per se, provides an incomplete account of sex differences in depression (Nolen-Hoeksema, 2002).

A number of psychosocial explanations of the sex difference in depression have been posited and evaluated. Among the psychosocial variables most thoroughly investigated in this context are interpersonal dependency and greater involvement in interpersonal relationships than men (McBride and Bagby, 2006), ruminative coping (the tendency to excessively dwell on emotional distress; e.g., Lyubomirsky and Nolen-Hoeksema, 1993), several varieties of depressogenic cognitive styles (Abramson, Metalsky, and Alloy, 1989; Beck, 1963; Hankin and Abramson, 2001; Peterson and Seligman, 1984), greater experience of stressful and traumatic events (Weiss, Longhurst, and Mazure, 1999), and chronic strain (a multifaceted construct which involves numerous domestic stressors, role burden, and unsatisfactory relationships). Many of these psychosocial explanations have received more consistent support than the biological accounts noted previously. For instance, Nolen-Hoeksema and colleagues (1999) found that a combination of ruminative coping, chronic strain, and low mastery of the environment fully mediated sex differences in self-reported depressive symptoms. In addition, an estimated one third of the gender difference in depression has been attributed to greater physical violence against girls than boys (Cutler and Nolen-Hoeksema,

1991). In short, psychosocial explanations of the sex difference in depression have proven viable and merit continued research attention.

Finally, a number of investigators have suggested that a more complete understanding is likely to emerge only from integrative models which assume that biological and psychosocial influences interact in complex ways over time to yield sex differences in the prevalence of depression (Hankin and Abramson, 2001; Kessler, 2003; Nolen-Hoeksema and Girgus, 1994; Nolen-Hoeksema et al., 1999).

Regardless of the causal mechanism underlying the sex difference, the deleterious impact of depression on women, their relationships, their families, and their communities is undeniable. First, depression exerts a powerful impact on morbidity and functional status. The Global Burden of Disease study rated depression the most burdensome disease afflicting middle-aged people worldwide, as indexed by disability adjusted life years (DALYs), a composite measure of years lost to premature death and to suboptimal physical health (Murray and Lopez, 1996). Consistent with the epidemiologic data cited previously, the study also concluded that the burden of depression is greater for women than men. Second, the economic consequences of depression are also damaging. Depression-related productivity losses at work cost American employers billions of dollars annually (Greenberg et al., 2003). Third, depression predicts poor interpersonal relationships and marital difficulties (Joiner and Coyne, 1999). Fourth, depressed women who have children are at risk of transmitting their mood problems to their offspring through biological, psychosocial, or other mechanisms (Goodman and Gotlib, 1999). Finally, depression is problematic in its own right, irrespective of its negative impact on other life domains. It is associated with enormous emotional pain, personal struggle, and a dramatically diminished quality of life.

Women and Cardiovascular Disease

Just as women are more likely to become depressed than men, research increasingly demonstrates that they are also disproportionately subject to a variety of untoward cardiac outcomes. This fact stands in stark opposition to the traditional view that CVD is a "man's disease." Data indicate that this misguided view is endorsed by the lay public (Emslie, Hunt, and Watt 2001), CVD patients (Ruston, Clayton, and Calnan, 1998), and even health professionals (Jacobs and Eckel, 2005; Richards, McConnachie, Morrison, Murray, and Watt, 2000). Abundant evidence suggests that CVD is a serious and growing health problem for women. We present a small sampling of this evidence to highlight the nature and scope of the problem of women and CVD.

CVD is the number one killer of women in the United States and in many places around the world (World Health Organization, 2007). In 2004, 460,000 American women died of CVD compared to 410,000 American men (American Heart Association, 2007). One in two women will eventually die of CHD or stroke (Brown, 1997). To compound the problem, women grossly underestimate their risk of CVD (Hart, 2005; but see Mosca, Ferris, Fabunmi, and Robertson, 2004) and mistakenly believe that other health threats are more salient. For instance, women are likely to report that breast cancer is the leading cause of death among women (Pilote and Hlatky, 1995). In reality, however, women are over 11 times more likely to die of CVD than of breast cancer (American Heart Association, 2007). This pervasive underestimation of the CVD threat is likely to have serious consequences. First, it delays or even precludes intervention. Because of their lowered perception of risk, women who experience cardiac symptoms may be unlikely to attribute them to cardiac causes (Miller and Kollauf, 2002). Compounding this problem is the fact that women and men frequently present with different cardiac symptoms (e.g., Mosca et al., 1997). Thus, women who have knowledge only of the typical male clinical presentation may be particularly prone to symptom misattribution (Schoenberg, Peters, and Drew, 2003). Second, women may be unlikely to undertake preventative measures or engage in health behaviors to moderate a risk that is erroneously viewed as minimally important. Third, women respond with greater negative affect (including depression) upon a diagnosis of CVD or after an acute cardiac event (e.g., Carney, Freedland, and Jaffe, 1990; Frasure-Smith, Lespérance, Juneau, Talajic, and Bourassa, 1999; Grace, Abbey, et al., 2005) such as myocardial infarction (MI; more commonly referred to as heart attack). This is troublesome because negative affect predicts a poor prognosis (see Januzzi, Stern, Pasternak, and DeSanctis, 2000, for a review). Fourth, underestimation of women's cardiac risk by health professionals may result in less aggressive or otherwise ineffective CVD intervention (e.g., Tobin et al., 1987), which, in turn, would predict greater morbidity and mortality. It is clear that continued educational efforts are needed to increase women's awareness of CVD risk and to combat the persistent and mistaken view that men have a monopoly on cardiac problems.

Women are also subject to poorer outcomes than men once the presence of CVD is established. A wealth of data suggests that women have a poorer prognosis than men in the aftermath of acute myocardial infarction (AMI; Dittrich et al., 1988; Greenland, Reicher-Reiss, Goldbourt, and Behar, 1991). Data from the American Heart Association (2001) reveal that 38% of women compared to 25% of men die within one year of AMI. Women experience a greater incidence of cardiac events in the aftermath of congestive heart failure (Johnson, 1994). Women are also subject to greater disability and more severe functional/role impairments following a cardiac event (see P.M. Davidson et al., 2003, for a review). Women have a poorer prognosis (i.e., slower improvement, higher hospital readmission rates, greater mortality) than men undergoing coronary bypass surgery (Connerney, Shapiro, McLaughlin, Bagiella, and Sloan, 2001; Phillips Bute et al., 2003; Vaccarino et al., 2003; Weintraub, Wenger, Jones, Craver, and Guyton, 1993).

Why do women fare worse than men upon diagnosis of CVD, after acute cardiac events such as MI, and after surgery? In the next section, we explore whether women's greater prevalence of depression may explain some of the sex difference in CVD prognosis (see, e.g., Carney, Freedland, Smith, Lustman, and Jaffe, 1991). For now, however, we explore a variety of demographic, biological, and treatment-related variables that may mediate the difference.

First, the onset of CVD occurs approximately 10 years later in women compared to men (e.g., Lerner and Kannel, 1986). Indeed, women typically start to manifest CVD symptoms after levels of estrogen (with its cardio-protective effects) drop in menopause. Women's more advanced age may, in turn, be associated with greater CVD severity and increased medical comorbidity that complicates prognosis. Consistent with this explanation, female CVD patients are more likely than their male counterparts to present with hypertension, diabetes mellitus, and a history of congestive heart failure (e.g., Fiebach, Viscoli, and Horwitz, 1990). Second, there is evidence that female CVD patients receive less aggressive treatments (e.g., Tobin et al., 1987), which may predict a difficult course of illness and a poorer prognosis following an acute cardiac event. Systematic bias on the part of physicians may be partly to blame for this trend (Jacobs and Eckel, 2005; Richards et al., 2000). Alternatively, women may be referred for treatment later in the disease process, when aggressive intervention would be considered too risky or judged to be ineffective. Third, some have speculated that diagnostic procedures may be more accurate for men than for women (Heston and Lewis, 1992). If so, reduced diagnostic accuracy may lead to suboptimal intervention and, in turn, a poor prognosis. Fourth, there is evidence that nonparticipation in cardiac rehabilitation programming, poorer treatment adherence, and dropout are more salient problems for women than for men (P.M. Davidson et al., 2003).

In some studies, statistical adjustment for one or more of these factors significantly reduces or eliminates the sex difference in CVD prognosis (see Vaccarino, Krumholz, Berkman, and Horwitz, 1995, for a review). For instance, Fiebach and colleagues (1990) found that sex differences in post-MI survival were attenuated after statistical adjustment for differences in age, comorbid medical conditions, and several markers of clinical severity. Likewise, Dittrich and colleagues (1988) found that after statistical adjustment for congestive heart failure and age, sex did not independently predict in-hospital mortality post-MI. In other studies, however, sex differences in post-MI prognosis persist even after statistical adjustment for age, medical history, and other relevant variables (e.g., Greenland et al., 1991; Jenkins et al., 1994). These data merit exploration of whether psychosocial variables such as depression explain some portion of the sex difference in CVD prognosis not accounted for by traditional risk factors.

Women, Depression, and Cardiovascular Disease

Having established that women are more subject to both depression and certain CVD-related outcomes, we now review research related to depression's status as an indicator of CVD onset and prognosis, underscoring findings most relevant to women. This section reviews data pertinent to the following questions: (1) Is depression an independent risk factor for the onset of CVD among initially healthy persons of both sexes? (2) Is depression an independent risk factor for poor prognosis among known CVD patients of both sexes? (3) Is the relationship between depression and CVD-related outcomes stronger for women than men? (4) Do sex differences in depression explain, in part or in whole, why there are sex differences in certain CVD-related outcomes? (5) Is depression more of a problem for women compared to men after an acute cardiac event?

Depression as a risk factor for CVD onset. Before undertaking a selective review of the evidence concerning depression as a risk factor the onset of CVD, a few methodological and conceptual issues are worth noting. First, that research participants naturally vary with respect to depression precludes experimental manipulation of this variable. As such, studies examining the link between depression and CVD are necessarily observational in nature. In order to confidently draw inferences regarding the effect of depression, investigators must control for a potentially wide array of variables that may be related to both depression and CVD (e.g., smoking, exercise, body mass). However, distinguishing between confounding variables and mediating variables is often an unclear exercise informed largely by the idiosyncratic views of individual researchers. Put another way, which variables should be regarded as confounding the depression-CVD relationship, and which variables should be regarded as lying along the causal pathway linking depression and CVD (cf., Frasure-Smith and Lesperance, 2005a)? For many investigators, this judgment is rendered by considering the extent to which a variable is intrinsic to the essence of depression. Application of this criterion would lead to the treatment of smoking as a confounding variable, but systemic inflammation (for instance) as a mediating variable. Only statistical elimination of confounding variables is key to internal validity and interpretive clarity. Second, given the overlap between symptoms of CVD and somatic symptoms of depression (e.g., fatigue, weakness), one might question whether evidence as to their causal link reflects only one underlying pathology. Of course, the strategy of recruiting only individuals who are free of CVD symptoms at study outset assuages this concern. In addition, documenting relationships between early depression and an acute cardiac event years later strengthens arguments related to the independence of depression and CVD (Dimsdale, 1993; Barefoot and Schroll, 1996). Third, Barefoot and Schroll (1996) also highlight the importance of evaluating effects of psychosocial variables on "hard" cardiac outcomes (i.e., cases of documented disease). It is well known that personality variables such as neuroticism (Costa et al., 1985) predict complaints of chest pain even in the absence of CVD. Thus, depression may predict a "soft" outcome such as angina pectoris because of a hypervigilance to physical symptoms, a bias toward increased symptom reporting, or some other factor. The studies reviewed here boast a high degree of interpretive clarity because of methodologically rigorous designs characterized by adequate controls and prospective examination of "hard" cardiac outcomes.

Numerous studies in the United States and elsewhere have concluded that depression is an independent risk factor for the development of coronary heart disease. A study by Anda and colleagues (1993) is illustrative of this large research literature. In this study, 2,832 American adults (aged 45-77 years) who were healthy at study baseline completed a general well-being scale that included several items tapping depressive symptoms. Follow-up (mean = 12.4 years) assessments of fatal and nonfatal coronary heart disease were carried out by examining death records and hospital discharge records, respectively. After controlling for the potential confounding effects of sociodemographic (age, sex, race, educational attainment, marital status) and traditional cardiac risk factors (smoking, physical activity, alcohol use, total cholesterol, systolic blood pressure, body mass index), the relative risk ratios associated with depression were 1.5 and 1.6 for fatal and nonfatal coronary heart disease, respectively. Thus, independent of sociodemographic and traditional cardiac risk factors, depressed individuals were approximately 1.5 times more likely to experience fatal or nonfatal coronary heart disease than their nondepressed counterparts. This finding is broadly consistent with an abundance of other data (e.g., Aromaa et al., 1994; Barefoot and Schroll, 1996; Ferketich, Schwartzbaum, Frid, and Moeschberger, 2000; Hällström, Lapidus, Bengtsson, and Edström, 1986; Wassertheil-Smoller et al., 1996; see Frasure-Smith, 2005; Hemingway and Marmot, 1999; and Rugulies, 2002, for reviews).

A smaller accumulation of studies on depression as a risk factor for incident stroke complements the data on coronary heart disease. In one prospective study of 6,676 initially stroke-free adults, depression was a robust predictor of stroke mortality independent of age, sex, education, alcohol consumption, smoking, body mass index, hypertension, and diabetes (Everson, Roberts, Goldberg, and Kaplan, 1998). Similar findings from other investigators are further suggestive of a depression-stroke relationship (e.g., Gump, Matthews, Eberly, and Chang, 2005; Jonas and Mussolino, 2000). Another study demonstrated that vital exhaustion (a depression-like state marked by fatigue, feelings of demoralization, and irritability) prospectively predicted first strokes, after controlling for a host of traditional risk factors, among a cohort of 2,432 Dutch participants (Schuitemaker, Dinant, van der Pol, Verhelst, and Appels, 2004). Overall, the data suggest that the damaging effects of depression are not limited to the coronary arteries, but also to the cerebral vasculature implicated in stroke.

Interestingly, although researchers have generally assumed that depression affects cardiac health via processes that gradually unfold over a long period of time, there is also suggestive evidence that episodes of acute depression may directly trigger acute cardiac events. In one study (Steptoe, Strike, Perkins-Porras, McEwan, and Whitehead, 2006), periods of acute depression were associated with a substantially increased risk of experiencing an acute cardiac event in the following two hours. Conclusions from this study were limited, in part, by its retrospective reliance on patients' self-reported mood prior to the cardiac event. However, these provocative findings warrant further investigation in subsequent studies.

Overall, the weight of the evidence has led some researchers to conclude that depression is the psychosocial risk factor that is most strongly and consistently related to the onset of CVD, surpassing even the Type A behavior pattern, which has garnered a glut of empirical attention. However, the well-documented role of depression in the development of CVD continues to be underestimated in some circles. Frasure-Smith and Lespérance (2005a) noted that depression was absent among CVD risk factors listed in a recent report of the American College of Cardiology (Benjamin, Smith, Cooper, Hill, and Luepker, 2002). To be sure, the medical establishment has been slow to warm to notions of the so-called "mind-body" connection (see, e.g., Angel, 1985).

Depression as a risk factor for poor CVD prognosis. Not only does depression play a causal role in the onset of CVD, but it also independently predicts poor prognosis after an acute cardiac event. Frasure-Smith and her colleagues (Frasure-Smith and Lespérance, 2003; Frasure-Smith, Lespérance, and Talajic, 1995; Frasure-Smith et al., 1999; Lespérance, Frasure-Smith, and Talajic, 1996) have been pivotal in the accumulation of data in this important area.

Previously, we stated that adequate controls for confounding variables were key to establishing internal validity in studies of depression and CVD onset. In studies evaluating the prognostic impact of depression in cases of established CVD, one such confounding variable is particularly noteworthy: CVD severity. As an example, consider post-MI patients. It stands to reason that individuals who sustain greater cardiac damage during MI will be both (1) more depressed and (2) more likely to endure a worse prognosis. Without adequate controls, then, it would be unclear whether depression exerts any prognostic influence independent of extent of cardiac damage. Several studies have shown that depression does, in fact, predict poor post-MI prognosis independent of CVD severity. In one study (Frasure-Smith and Lespérance, 2003), 896 men and women completed the Beck Depression Inventory (BDI; Beck, Ward, Mendelson, Mock, and Erbaugh, 1961) during a hospital admission for MI and were followed up for cardiac mortality for five years. Results showed that BDI scores predicted five-year cardiac mortality after adjustment for age, sex, education, smoking, previous MI, diabetes, and several indexes of cardiac dysfunction. Anxiety, anger, general negative affectivity, and social support were not predictive after adjustment for the full set of covariates. Other studies have yielded similar findings (Ahern et al., 1990; Barefoot et al., 1996; Frasure-Smith et al., 1995; Frasure-Smith et al., 1999; Grace, Abbey, et al., 2005; Horsten, Mittleman, Wamala, Schenck-Gustafsson, and Orth-Gomér, 2000; Ladwig, Kieser, König, Breithardt, and Borggrefe, 1991; Lespérance et al., 1996; Rutledge et al., 2006; see Januzzi et al., 2000, for a review). Another study showed that even minimal levels of depressive symptoms (i.e., BDI scores between 4 and 9) predicted all-cause mortality among 285 post-MI men and women (Bush et al., 2001). In addition, Major Depressive Disorder is a significant independent predictor of acute cardiac events after coronary bypass surgery (Connerney et al., 2001). Overall, the evidence indicates that depression is an independent risk factor for poor prognosis in the aftermath of an acute cardiac event or cardiac surgery.

Is the relationship between depression and CVD-related outcomes stronger for women? Up to this point, our discussion of depression's negative impact on CVD onset and prognosis has proceeded without making reference to possible sex differences. Research has established, however, that the importance of some risk factors does indeed vary by sex. For instance, diabetes is a more robust risk factor for the development of CVD for women compared to men (Barrett-Connor and Wingard, 1983). Likewise, a high triglyceride count is a more potent predictor of coronary heart disease for women compared to men (Nguyen and McGlaughlin, 2002). Organic risk factors aside, there is also evidence of differential importance of psychosocial risk factors. For example, hostility has been shown to predict post-MI mortality among men (e.g., Everson et al., 1997; Matthews, Gump, Harris, Haney, and Barefoot, 2004), but not women (Powell et al., 1993). On the basis of these and other data, Chesney (1993) argued that the importance of psychosocial risk factors is likely to vary substantially as a function of sex. In light of this assertion and available data, is it possible that depression is an especially potent predictor of CVD onset or prognosis for women?

It has been speculated that depression is, in fact, a more robust CVD risk factor for women compared to men. For example, Jacobs and Sherwood (1996) rightly asserted that depression plays a role in the development of coronary heart disease, but further stated that this "may be especially true for women..." (p. 204). Similarly, Dimsdale (1993) wondered whether "depression may be a substantial cardiovascular risk factor affecting women in particular" (p. 122). These possibilities are difficult to fully evaluate because very few studies conduct, or report results of, formal statistical tests designed to evaluate a sex by depression interaction effect on cardiac outcomes (noteworthy exceptions are detailed later). In some cases, investigators report that depression is a statistically significant risk factor for one sex but not the other. Although this is not necessarily indicative of a statistical interaction, this evidence does bear on the question of the relative importance of depression in predicting cardiac outcomes for women versus men. Consequently, such evidence is considered here.

In short, the data are mixed. Some research is consistent with the hypothesis that depression is a more potent predictor of CVD onset or prognosis for women compared to men. One study found that depressive symptoms predicted coronary heart disease for diabetic women but not diabetic men (Lloyd et al., 1996). One study of 4,508 community-dwelling men and women in the United States found that an increase in depressive symptoms over time predicted stroke and MI among women but not men (Wassertheil-Smoller et al., 1996). Other research supports the opposite conclusion. For instance, one study (Aromaa et al., 1994) found that covariate-adjusted associations between depressive symptoms and numerous cardiac outcomes (MI, angina pectoris, coronary heart disease, congestive heart failure, and hypertension) were consistently larger for men compared to women. In another study, depression predicted first strokes among men but not women after adjustment for several traditional cardiac risk factors (Jonas and Mussolino, 2000). In spite of findings suggestive of apparent sex differences, most of the research seems to suggest that there is little difference in the impact of depression on cardiac outcomes for women versus men. Put another way, depressive symptoms, when present, seem to be equally damaging to cardiac health for both sexes. Support for this view comes from a study in which a primary aim was to evaluate possible sex moderation of the depression-CVD link (Frasure-Smith et al., 1999). In this study, sex did not moderate the link between BDI depression scores and one-year cardiac mortality among a sample of 896 post-MI participants. Similarly, Barefoot and Schroll (1996) found no evidence that sex moderated the link between depression and either MI or total mortality.

In sum, it would be unwise to draw firm conclusion on the basis of the limited data just presented. Additional research is needed to fully evaluate hypotheses regarding the relative importance of depression in predicting cardiac outcomes for women versus men. The lack of data on this topic is at least partly attributable to the fact that, until recently, women were largely ignored in research regarding CVD and its risk factors. In other cases, the data are available, but investigators either neglect to test for sex by depression interaction effects or fail to report results of such analyses. We strongly encourage researchers in this area to (1) continue recruiting large numbers of women in studies of CVD risk and (2) begin to more intensively explore possible sex differences in the depression-CVD link.

Do sex differences in depression explain, in part or in whole, why there are sex differences in certain CVD-related outcomes? Recall that women, compared to men, are disproportionately subject to a variety of adverse cardiac outcomes. These include greater morbidity and mortality post-MI, greater disability and more severe functional/role impairments following an acute cardiac event, and a poorer prognosis following coronary bypass surgery. Some have speculated that women's greater prevalence of depression may explain part of the sex difference in these cardiac outcomes. For instance, Carney and colleagues (1991) suggested that "the higher prevalence of depression in women after myocardial infarction could help to explain their increased mortality risk" (p. 1877).

We are aware of only two studies, both by Frasure-Smith and her colleagues, which reported results of mediational analyses required to optimally address this question. The first study examined demographic, psychosocial, and cardiac predictors of prognosis in the first year post-MI. Results showed that adding anxiety and history of depression to a model in which sex predicted acute cardiac events resulted in a significantly improved model fit. In contrast, adding sex to a model in which anxiety and history of depression predicted acute cardiac events failed to yield a significantly improved model fit. Thus, although formal mediational analyses (see Baron and Kenny, 1986) were not reported, these data suggest that the combination of anxiety and previous history of depression at least partially mediated sex differences in post-MI prognosis. It is unclear whether depression, alone, would have similarly mediated such sex differences. On the basis of their findings, Frasure-Smith and colleagues (1995) wrote: "It appears that women's greater tendency to express depression and anxiety... may place them at increased risk for the thrombogenic events represented by recurrent acute coronary syndromes following MI" (p. 395). In the second study, Frasure-Smith and colleagues (1999) examined gender differences in a number of post-MI outcomes, including cardiac mortality, MI recurrence, and need for additional cardiac procedures. Significant sex differences emerged for only one of these outcomes, MI recurrence (9.2% of women compared to 4.9% of men experienced a subsequent MI). Although accounting for baseline BDI depression scores slightly diminished this sex difference, it remained significant even after this adjustment ($p = .036$). Thus, depression did not mediate the sex difference in MI recurrence in this dataset.

As with sex moderation of the depression-CVD link, much more data are needed to draw meaningful conclusions regarding possible depression mediation of sex differences in cardiac outcomes. Investigators in this area should more consistently conduct and report results of formal mediational analyses. In the end, it may prove difficult to obtain a robust mediational effect of depression. Recall that a variety of mediators of sex differences in cardiac outcomes have already been established. These include age, comorbid medical conditions (e.g., congestive heart failure), and CVD severity (e.g., Dittrich et al., 1988; Fiebach et al., 1990). As such, there may be very little variance in the sex difference for depression to explain after accounting for these established factors.

Among individuals with CVD, is depression more of a problem for women compared to men? Since depression is a more salient problem for women compared to men even in the absence of cardiac disease (e.g., Kessler et al., 1993; Nolen-Hoeksema, 1987) it stands to reason that a similar sex difference should emerge in the context of CVD. Indeed, a considerable body of evidence suggests that depression is more problematic among women, compared to men, with CVD. Women with chronic cardiac illness score higher on a measure of depressive symptoms than men with similar cardiac disease (Holahan, Moos, Holahan, and Brennan, 1995). Likewise, among patients with coronary heart disease, women have a higher prevalence of Major Depressive Disorder than men (Carney et al., 1987). Women also experience greater problems with Major Depressive Disorder, and score higher on measures of depressive symptoms, than men post-MI (Arthur, 2006; Balog et al., 2003; Carney et al., 1990; Frasure-Smith et al., 1999; Grace, Abbey, et al., 2005; Schwartzman and Glaus, 2000; Westin, Carlsson, Erhardt, Cantor-Graae, and McNeil, 1999; Wiklund et al., 1993). Limited data demonstrate that sex differences in post-MI anxiety are also robust. For instance, Moser and her colleagues (2003) found that post-MI women scored higher on a measure of anxiety symptoms compared to post-MI men across five countries. Of note, not all studies reveal sex differences in psychosocial distress in the post-MI period. In one study, women were not more depressed, anxious, or angry either one month or four months after MI (Riegel and Gocka, 1995). These discrepant results may be attributable to significantly greater social support reported by women compared to men in the Riegel and Gocka study. In any event, the balance of the evidence points to a reliable association between female sex and greater distress post-MI. Moreover, the anxiety data reveal that sex differences in psychosocial distress in the post-MI period may not be limited to depression.

Data regarding sex differences in depression subsequent to coronary bypass surgery mirror the post-MI data highlighted previously. Compared to men, women have a greater prevalence of Major Depressive Disorder, and more severe depressive symptoms, after undergoing coronary bypass surgery (Ai et al., 1997; Czajkowski et al., 1997; Lindquist et al., 2003; Naqvi, Naqvi, and Merz, 2005). In another study, although both women and men showed significant improvement from baseline on a number of psychosocial variables, sex differences in depression and anxiety were still present one year after coronary bypass surgery (Phillips Bute et al., 2003). Other data paint a more optimistic picture of women's post-surgery adjustment. In two separate studies (Duits et al., 1998; Mitchell et al., 2005), women showed greater improvement in depressive symptoms compared to men in the postoperative period. These findings may, in part, reflect the possibility that women stood to improve more because of a higher level of initial symptoms.

Explaining the Depression-CVD Link

With prospective associations between depression and CVD onset and prognosis firmly established, we now focus our attention on explaining this link. How does depression "get under the skin" to affect cardiac outcomes? The explanatory factors most often studied in this context fall into one of two broad categories: social/behavioral and biological. This distinction, although imperfect (e.g., social/behavioral mechanisms themselves promote disease by affecting biological functioning), provides a framework for our discussion of the variables proposed to explain the depression-CVD link.

Social/behavioral explanations. First, depressed individuals are likely to engage in a variety of unhealthy behaviors that are known to increase risk for adverse cardiac outcomes. These behaviors include smoking, excessive alcohol consumption or illicit drug use, poor diet, poor sleep habits, and decreased physical activity (Bonnet et al., 2005; Glassman et al., 1990; Leas and McCabe, 2007). However, such health behavior variables do not fully explain the link between depression and CVD. As noted previously, relationships between depression and CVD typically persist even after accounting for health behaviors. Second, there is abundant evidence that depression is associated with poor adherence to medical treatment (see DiMatteo, Lepper, and Croghan, 2000, for a review). In one study, individuals with Major Depressive Disorder were significantly less likely to take cardiac medications as prescribed, more likely to forget to take cardiac medications, and more likely to skip a dose, compared to nondepressed individuals (Gehi, Haas, Pipkin, and Whooley, 2005; see also Carney, Freedland, Eisen, Rich, and Jaffe, 1995). Post-MI depressed individuals are less likely to implement lifestyle changes (e.g., low fat diet, regular exercise) to ameliorate risk for future cardiac events (Ziegelstein et al., 2000). Depression also predicts nonparticipation in, and premature termination of, cardiac rehabilitation programming (Ades, Waldmann, McCann, and Weaver, 1992; Caulin-Glaser, Maciejewski, Snow, LaLonde, and Mazure,

2007; Sanderson and Bittner, 2005). Third, research has demonstrated that depressed individuals are more likely than nondepressed individuals to generate stressful life circumstances that may confer risk for adverse cardiac outcomes (e.g., Harkness and Luther, 2001).

Biological explanations. In recent years, there has been an explosion of research concerning biological pathways linking depression and CVD. First, among healthy individuals, there is considerable beat-to-beat variation in heart rate, (called *heart rate variability)* reflecting a predominance of parasympathetic control over the heart (Santerre and Allen, 2007). Depressed individuals, compared to their nondepressed counterparts, exhibit decreased heart rate variability at rest (Carney et al., 2001; Guinjoan et al., 2004; Hughes and Stoney, 2000; Stein et al., 2000). This decreased heart rate variability is thought to reflect increased sympathetic activation, decreased parasympathetic activation, or a combination of both. In turn, disruptions in the autonomic control of the heart are widely thought to confer increased risk for cardiac morbidity (see Carney, Freedland, and Veith, 2005, for a review). Second, depression has been linked to higher plasma levels of norepinephrine and higher resting heart rate (Lake et al., 1982; Rudorfer, Ross, Linnoila, Sherer, and Potter, 1985; Wyatt, Portnoy, Kupfer, Snyder, and Engelman, 1971), both presumably reflecting an overactive autonomic nervous system. Consistent with the heart rate variability data, these findings may be further indicative of impaired autonomic function in depression, and may provide additional clues as to the depression-CVD link. Third, it is possible that depressed individuals evidence greater autonomically-mediated cardiovascular reactivity to psychological stress, which may, in turn, damage the heart and/or its vasculature (Gerin et al., 2000), yielding enhanced risk for cardiac disease. Data regarding depression and cardiovascular reactivity are mixed. One recent meta-analysis concluded that depression is indeed associated with exaggerated cardiovascular reactivity to stress (Kibler and Ma, 2004), but several studies report null findings (e.g., Carroll, Phillips, Hunt, and Der, 2006). Fourth, links between depression and impairments in critical parameters of immune function have received a great deal of research attention. For instance, numerous studies have shown that depression facilitates the production and activity of proinflammatory cytokines, most notably interleukin 6 (IL-6; see Kiecolt-Glaser and Glaser, 2002). Chronically high levels of IL-6 and other proinflammatory agents encourage the accumulation of plaque in blood vessels, causing narrowing and subsequently increasing risk for adverse cardiac outcomes. IL-6 also increases production of C-reactive protein (CRP), which is itself correlated with depressive severity (Suarez, 2004; Penninx et al., 2003; but see Douglas, Taylor, and O'Malley, 2004) and predictive of cardiac dysfunction (Papanicolaou, Wilder, Manolagas, and Chrousos, 1998). Inflammatory processes are now widely implicated as playing a central role in the pathogenesis of CVD. Fifth, recent data show that depression is related to dysfunction in the vascular endothelium, a layer of cells that lines the interior of blood vessels (Sherwood, Hinderliter, Watkins, Waugh, and Blumenthal, 2005). Endothelial dysfunction, in turn, predicts the occurrence of acute cardiac events among individuals with CVD (Mancini, 2004). Sixth, depression has been linked to increased platelet aggregation (e.g., Mikuni, Kagaya, Takahashi, and Meltzer, 1992; Musselman et al., 1996; Pollock, Laghrissi-Thode, and Wagner, 2000), a process that can promote thrombus formation, atherosclerosis, and acute cardiac events (see Markovitz and Matthews, 1991). Finally, there is evidence that the baroreflex, a homeostatic mechanism that controls blood pressure, is disrupted among individuals with Major Depressive Disorder (Davydov, Shapiro, Cook, and Goldstein, 2007).

In sum, a variety of social/behavioral and biological explanations of the depression-CVD link have been advanced. At present, no data are available which permit the evaluation of the relative importance of each proposed mechanism. Moreover, a rather large amount of conflicting data has frustrated attempts to render judgments regarding the importance of one proposed mechanism versus another. Additional rigorous tests of mechanistic hypotheses are needed to address this critical issue.

Treatment Considerations

With respect to treatment, we highlight three areas of inquiry that are germane to our discussion: (1) treatment of depression, in its own right, among individuals with CVD, (2) treatment of depression for the explicit purpose of modifying cardiac outcomes (with an emphasis on female issues), and (3) treatment of CVD among women.

Treatment of depression among individuals with CVD. The possibility that improvements in psychosocial functioning might modify cardiac outcomes among at-risk individuals has captured the attention of researchers and health professionals for several years. Although insights derived from this work are both theoretically informative and practically useful, we should emphasize that effective treatment of depression is desirable irrespective of its possible cardiac benefits. As noted previously, depression powerfully diminishes quality of life in affected individuals and exerts a pervasive, negative influence in numerous spheres of functioning. At present, pharmacologic intervention is the dominant approach to the treatment of depression. This begs two questions: Is antidepressant medication (1) safe and (2) effective for patients with CVD?

The potentially dangerous cardiovascular effects of the tricyclic antidepressants (TCAs) are widely known. TCAs are associated with significantly increased heart rate, increased risk for arrhythmic activity, and decreased heart rate variability (see Roose and Miyazaki, 2005, for a review). For these and other reasons, TCAs are generally contraindicated for individuals with cardiac disease. The newer class of antidepressants, the selective serotonin reuptake inhibitors (SSRIs), appears to have a much more favorable safety profile. Data from two randomized controlled trials of SSRI treatment of depression among cardiac patients support this view. The Canadian Cardiac Randomized Evaluation of Antidepressant and Psychotherapy Efficacy Trial (CREATE; Lespérance et al., 2007) established the safety of citalopram in treating depression among individuals with coronary heart disease. Likewise, in the Sertraline Antidepressant Heart Attack Randomized Trial (SADHART; Glassman et al., 2002), no significant differences in several cardiac safety measures were found between the sertraline and placebo group. In fact, sertraline has been shown to reduce platelet activity among men and women with a history of acute cardiac events (Serebruany et al., 2003). Thus, an added advantage of SSRI treatment is its apparently beneficial effects on one mechanism thought to play a key role in the pathogenesis of CVD. Interestingly, suggestive evidence from SADHART indicated that patients treated with sertraline experienced a slightly (and nonsignificantly) lower incidence of cardiac events. With respect to the efficacy question, both the SADHART and CREATE data show that SSRIs offer some advantage over placebo in reducing depressive symptoms among cardiac patients.

Among depressed CVD patients unwilling to take medication or unable to tolerate side effects, alternative treatments should be considered. Of course, psychotherapy is effective in reducing depressive symptoms among individuals without CVD (Lambert and Ogles, 2004). However, very few data concerning the efficacy of psychotherapy in treating depression in CVD patients are available. The CREATE trial showed that interpersonal psychotherapy provided no benefit over standard clinical management (Lespérance et al., 2007). In the Enhancing Recovery in Coronary Heart Disease Patients (ENRICHD) trial, cognitive-behavioral therapy yielded a statistically significant but modest improvement in depression scores over usual care among depressed or socially isolated post-MI patients (ENRICHD Investigators, 2003). Thus, the limited data that are available offer a mixed view of the efficacy of psychotherapy in treating depression among CVD patients. It is possible, of course, that certain psychotherapies will prove effective whereas others will not. This question awaits further study.

A small body of data suggests that exercise may be effective in treating depression among post-MI patients (see Lett, Davidson, and Blumenthal, 2005, for a review). Two controlled studies provided encouraging results regarding the superiority of exercise over control conditions in yielding reductions in depressive symptoms (Stern, Gorman, and Kaslow, 1983; Taylor, Houston-Miller, Ahn, Haskell, and DeBusk, 1986). Given that regular exercise is also known to ameliorate cardiac risk among CVD and non-CVD populations (Albert et al. 2000), this particular intervention may be viewed as especially attractive for individuals who seek to, at once, reduce depressive symptoms and improve cardiac outcomes. However, vigorous exercise may be contraindicated for certain CVD patients (e.g., those with severe impairment), and physicians must carefully consider a patient's particular clinical presentation prior to offering treatment recommendations.

In sum, additional research is clearly needed to identify pharmacologic and nonpharmacologic interventions that are both safe and effective in treating depression among individuals with CVD. In view of sex differences in various phenomena related to depression and CVD, testing of treatment by sex interactions could offer a better understanding of whether certain treatments are more or less effective for females versus males.

Treatment of depression as a means modifying cardiac outcomes. The idea that successful treatment of depression might improve cardiac prognosis among CVD patients is not universally embraced. Nor does it boast substantial empirical support, as will soon be evident. It is noteworthy, then, that several sets of published guidelines for the treatment or prevention of cardiac disease mention evaluation and treatment of depression as an important component of intervention. Examples are guidelines by the National Heart, Lung, and Blood Institute (K.W. Davidson et al., 2006), The American Heart Association (Mieres, 2006), and a joint task force of the American College of Cardiology and the American Heart Association (Antman et al., 2004).

There is a reasonable basis for speculating that successful treatment of depression should improve cardiac outcomes. First, if indeed early depression is both causally *and* independently related to some later CVD outcome, then it stands to reason that reducing depressive symptoms might meaningfully impact the cardiac endpoint. Second, successful psychotherapeutic treatment of depression is associated with improvements on select measures of cardiac function, including resting heart rate and heart rate variability (Carney et al., 2000); these improvements may, in turn, reduce the risk of acute cardiac events. Third, pharmacological treatment may improve both depressive symptoms and cardiac prognosis via separate mechanisms. For instance, sertraline reduces platelet activity (Serebruany et al., 2003) and sympathetic nervous system activity (Shores, Pascualy, Lewis, Flatness, and Veith, 2001) irrespective of its effects on depressive symptoms.

A large number of studies have evaluated whether psychosocial interventions (targeting risks other than depression) improve cardiac outcomes. Of these studies, some have yielded encouraging findings, whereas others have not (see Dusseldorp, van Elderen, Maes, Meulman, and Kraaij, 1999; and Linden, Stossel, and Maurice, 1996, for reviews). One large trial found that a program designed to reduce Type A behavior among men yielded reductions in fatal and non-fatal MI (Friedman et al., 1984). In another study, a combination of monthly telephone calls to address psychological distress and home visits led to significant reductions in cardiac mortality compared to a usual care control group (Frasure-Smith and Prince, 1985). In contrast to these positive results, Jones and West (1996) found that a combination of counseling, education, relaxation training, and stress management training was not superior to a usual care control group with respect to a variety of clinical outcomes. Similarly, Frasure-Smith and colleagues (1997) failed to find any significant cardiac benefit of an intervention composed of emotional support, reassurance, and education. Of note, the Jones and West (1996) and Frasure-Smith et al. (1997) studies were not specifically designed to reduce depressive symptoms, but rather psychological distress, broadly construed. In fact, both studies found no significant effect of treatment on measures of depressive symptoms. If depression, specifically, were targeted for intervention, would a clear cardiac benefit emerge?

In the ENRICHD trial, 2,481 post-MI men and women with a DSM depressive disorder or low perceived social support were randomized to an intervention and a control group. The intervention consisted primarily of six months (mean = 11 sessions) of individual cognitive-behavioral therapy, a well-validated treatment for depression in medically well populations (Butler, Chapman, Forman, and Beck, 2006). Intervention group participants who were seriously depressed at study outset or who failed to show significant improvement in depressive symptoms after five weeks were additionally given antidepressant medication. Results showed that after an average follow-up of 29 months, participants in the intervention group did not significantly differ from the control group on the primary study outcomes, MI recurrence and death. Thus, the ENRICHD intervention failed to significantly improve CVD morbidity and mortality. A closer look at the ENRICHD study may offer clues as to why.

First, although the intervention group was statistically superior to the control group with respect to change in depression scores from baseline, this difference was rather small. The mean change on the Hamilton Rating Scale for Depression was 10.1 points for the intervention group and 8.4 points for the control group. Because both groups showed a similar, substantial improvement from baseline in depressive symptoms, differentiation on the cardiac outcomes may have been unlikely. Moreover, Frasure-Smith and Lespérance (2005b) pointed out that by study end, 20.6% of control participants versus 28.0% intervention participants had been treated with antidepressant medication. This ostensible blurring of the intervention across groups may help explain both the similar declines in depression from baseline and the similar rates of MI recurrence and death. Second, Frasure-Smith and Lespérance (2005b) also noted that if depression and cardiac disease share a common underlying cause, treating one is unlikely to effect meaningful change in the other. Rutledge and colleagues (2006) made a related argument: It may be that intervention efforts might best be directed toward the causal mechanisms that link depression and CVD, not depression itself. Third, treatment of depression may be unlikely to yield reduction in cardiac risk above and beyond that already offered by aggressive pharmacologic, antiplatelet, and revascularization treatments (Naqvi et al., 2005). Of course, the most straightforward explanation for the ENRICHD failure is that depression treatment may simply be ineffective in markedly altering cardiac outcomes.

Post hoc sex by ethnicity subgroup analyses of the ENRICHD data revealed some interesting and potentially useful findings (Schneiderman et al., 2004). The treatment appeared to be effective in reducing cardiac death and nonfatal MI among White men only (p = .004); no such effect emerged for White women or minority (i.e., Black, Hispanic, Asian, American Indian) men or women. Post hoc analyses also revealed that women fared worst in treatment. White and minority women in the intervention group actually showed a slightly (and nonsignificantly) higher risk of all-cause mortality, cardiac mortality, and nonfatal MI compared to women in the usual care control condition. This pattern of data is reminiscent of findings from another trial aimed at evaluating the effects of a psychosocial intervention on cardiac measures. Frasure-Smith and colleagues (1997) found that women who received a psychosocial intervention to address emotional distress were nearly twice as likely to die in the following year compared to women in the usual care control condition (10.3% versus 5.4%, p = 0.051). These data, combined with the ENRICHD findings, underscore (1) the distinct possibility that men and women respond very differently to similar cardiac rehabilitation programming, and (2) the challenges inherent in formulating rehabilitative strategies from which women can profit. The design and implementation of sex-specific programming should be considered an important priority. What are some key ingredients of cardiac rehabilitation programming for women? We offer insights related to this question next.

Treatment of CVD among women. It is becoming increasingly clear that women and men have divergent needs in the context of cardiac rehabilitation programming. In light of data suggesting that women bring a unique set of strengths, vulnerabilities, beliefs, attitudes, and treatment aims into the rehabilitative setting, a one-size-fits-all approach that fails to account for these factors is unlikely to yield meaningful gains. Our focus in this section is to highlight a variety of treatment strategies that facilitate optimally effective cardiac rehabilitation programming for women.

First, nonparticipation in cardiac rehabilitation programming is a serious problem for women. A number of factors appear to be responsible for this trend, including fewer referrals for women compared to men, elective nonparticipation, poor treatment adherence, difficulty traveling to and consistently attending sessions, and dropout (see P.M. Davidson et al., 2003). Clearly, strategies to increase women's levels of participation in cardiac rehabilitation are needed. Physicians and other health professionals should be encouraged to closely monitor their referral patterns and eliminate any sex biases that may be apparent. Physicians must also take an active role in educating their female cardiac patients as to the importance of rehabilitation programming as a means of encouraging timely initiation and maintenance of treatment. Important others in female patients' lives should be enlisted to provide transportation to and from rehabilitation sessions and other forms of instrumental support. Once in rehabilitation, strategies to discourage premature termination must be implemented. Such strategies may include consistent praise and other forms of positive reinforcement for attendance and treatment adherence, clear communication of the benefits of rehabilitation, tailoring of rehabilitation programming to meet the unique needs and concerns of individual patients, and elimination of potential barriers to continued participation. With respect to such barriers, research indicates that the attitudes of female cardiac patients and their family members are likely to be particularly strong obstacles to rehabilitation. In many cultures, the social milieu dictates that women are supposed to prioritize the needs of others over their own. This "otherness" orientation (Hawthorne, 1994) may lead female cardiac patients to minimize the importance of their condition, to decline the involvement of potential sources of emotional and instrumental support in their recovery, to refuse or substantially delay treatment, or to yield to family obligations which compete with treatment-related activities. Furthermore, friends or family members who embrace women's "otherness" orientation may be unlikely to perceive female cardiac patients' illness as serious and worthy of intensive intervention. Modification of beliefs and attitudes that preclude prioritization of the self and disrupt cardiac rehabilitation may prove to be an important component of a comprehensive approach to treating female cardiac patients.

Second, female cardiac patients are more likely than men to value the social and supportive aspects of cardiac rehabilitation programming (Johnson and Morse, 1990; King and Jensen, 1994). Thus, opportunities to provide support to, and receive support from, women with similar experiences may be perceived as an especially valuable aspect of cardiac rehabilitation for women. Additional research is needed to evaluate the possibility that women's cardiac rehabilitation programming requires a greater supportive emphasis in order to maximize benefit. Third, a large number of cardiac rehabilitation programs highlight the importance of physical activity as a key component of cardiovascular health. Women often report diminished perceptions of exercise self-efficacy (Schuster and Waldron, 1991), a finding that suggests that cardiac rehabilitation programming for women should teach only those exercise skills that female cardiac patients can reasonably acquire. In addition, to the extent that these perceptions are unfounded, modification of low exercise self-efficacy beliefs may be indicated for exercise-based programming to achieve its full impact. Similarly, women's greater tendencies to (1) attribute CVD to uncontrollable causes and (2) perceive their condition as untreatable (Grace, Krepostman, et al., 2005) are clearly ripe for corrective intervention.

Summary and Conclusions

Data consistently show that approximately twice as many women as men experience Major Depression. In addition, women generally score higher on self-report measures of depressive symptoms. A number of biological, psychosocial, and integrative explanations, many of which have been empirically supported, are available to account for these sex differences in depression. At the same time, women are disproportionately subject to a variety of adverse CVD-related outcomes, including greater morbidity and mortality post-MI, greater incidence of acute cardiac events in the aftermath of congestive heart failure, more severe functional/role impairments following a cardiac event, and poorer prognosis after coronary bypass surgery.

Available evidence demonstrates that depression and CVD are causally related. Both Major Depression and elevated levels of self-reported depressive symptoms are robust, independent predictors of CVD onset and prognosis. It is unclear whether depression is a more potent predictor of CVD-related outcomes for women versus men; the scant data that are available to address this possibility are mixed. Similarly, very few studies have explored whether sex differences in certain cardiac outcomes are explained by sex differences in depression. However, the limited available data suggest that depression does not fully explain sex differences in cardiac outcomes. More consistent (but not total) support has been found for the idea that women experience greater depressive difficulties following a diagnosis of CVD, an acute cardiac event, or cardiac surgery.

Several mechanistic explanations of the depression-CVD link have been advanced. Regarding social/behavioral explanations, data indicate that depressed individuals (1) engage in a variety of unhealthy behaviors that are known to increase risk for adverse cardiac outcomes (e.g., smoking, excessive alcohol consumption, poor sleep habits, decreased physical activity), (2) demonstrate poor adherence to medical treatment or cardiac rehabilitation programming, (3) are less likely to implement lifestyle changes (e.g., low fat diet, regular exercise) to ameliorate cardiac risk, and (4) frequently expose themselves to stressful life circumstances that confer cardiac risk. Biological explanations of the depression-CVD link invoke (1) dysfunction of the autonomic nervous system (e.g., decreased heart rate variability, higher plasma levels of norepinephrine, higher resting heart rate, greater cardiovascular reactivity to psychological stress), (2) disruptions in immune function (e.g., greater systemic inflammation), (3) endothelial dysfunction, (4) increased platelet aggregation, and (5) problems with the baroreflex. It is presently unclear which explanations are most important in accounting for the depression-CVD relationship.

Finally, SSRIs appear safe and reasonably effective in treating depression among patients with CVD. Cognitive-behavioral therapy has shown modest efficacy in one randomized control trial employing a post-MI sample, whereas interpersonal therapy yielded no gains in another. Until more data on cardiac populations are available, vast research literatures on the efficacy of different types of psychotherapy with medically well individuals should inform psychotherapeutic treatment decisions involving cardiac patients. In spite of the documented causal links between depression and CVD, there is presently no clear evidence that successful treatment of depression can improve cardiac outcomes or ameliorate cardiac risk. However, this provocative possibility merits additional study. Finally, cardiac rehabilitation programming for women should incorporate existing knowledge regarding women's unique strengths, vulnerabilities, beliefs, attitudes, and rehabilitative needs. Strategies to address female cardiac patients' (1) high rates of nonparticipation, (2) "otherness" orientation which involves prioritization of others' needs over their own, (3) low perceived exercise self-efficacy, and (4) faulty beliefs regarding the controllability and treatability of cardiac disease are especially warranted.

In conclusion, we hope that this chapter has provided a useful integration of the large research literatures concerning women, depression, and CVD. As indicated throughout, a number of the ideas explored here await further study. We feel that continued research in these areas holds enormous promise of evaluating and improving theory, clarifying mechanistic explanations, formulating more effective treatments, improving affected individuals' quality of life, informing public policy, and facilitating a greater fundamental understanding of the complex interrelationships between women, depression, and cardiac disease. We feel that this work is especially important in light of the increasing urgency of women's problems with depression, cardiac disease, and their point of intersection.

References

Abramson, L.Y., Metalsky, G.I., and Alloy, L.B. (1989). Hopelessness depression: A theory-based subtype of depression. *Psychological Review, 96,* 358-372.

Ades, P.A., Waldmann, M.L., McCann, W.J., and Weaver, S.O. (1992). Predictors of cardiac rehabilitation participation in older coronary patients. *Archives of Internal Medicine, 152,* 1033-1035.

Ahern, D.K., Gorkin, L., Anderson, J.L., Tierney, C., Hallstrom, A., Ewart, C., et al. (1990). Biobehavioral variables and mortality or cardiac arrest in the Cardiac Arrhythmia Pilot Study (CAPS). *American Journal of Cardiology, 66,* 59-62.

Ai, A.L., Peterson, C., Dunkle, R.E., Saunders, D.G., Bolling, S.F., and Buchtel, H.A. (1997). How gender affects psychological adjustment one year after coronary artery bypass graft surgery. *Women and Health, 26,* 45-65.

Albert, C.M., Mittleman, M.A., Chae, C.U., Lee, I.M., Hennekens, C.H., and Manson, J.E. (2000). Triggering of sudden death from cardiac causes by vigorous exertion. *New England Journal of Medicine, 343,* 1355-1361.

Amenson, C.S., and Lewinsohn, P.M. (1981). An investigation into the observed sex difference in prevalence of unipolar depression. *Journal of Abnormal Psychology, 90,* 1-13.

American Heart Association (2001). *2002 heart and stroke facts: Statistical update.* Dallas, TX: Author.

American Heart Association (2007). *Heart disease and stroke statistics: 2008 update at-a-glance.* Dallas, TX: Author.

American Psychiatric Association (1994). *Diagnostic and statistical manual of mental disorders* (4th ed.). Washington, DC: Author.

Anda, R., Williamson, D., Jones, D., Macera, C., Eaker, E., Glassman, A., et al. (1993). Depressed affect, hopelessness, and the risk of ischemic heart disease in a cohort of U.S. adults. *Epidemiology, 4,* 285-294.

Angel, M. (1985). Disease as a reflection of the psyche. *New England Journal of Medicine, 312,* 1570-1572.

Angst, J., Gamma, A., Gastpar, M., Lépine, J.P., Mendlewicz, J., and Tylee, A. (2002). Gender differences in depression: Epidemiological findings from the European DEPRES

I and II studies. *European Archives of Psychiatry and Clinical Neuroscience, 252,* 201-209.

Antman, E.M., Anbe, D.T., Armstrong, P.W., Bates, E.R., Green L.A., Hand, M., et al. (2004). ACC/AHA guidelines for the management of patients with ST-elevation myocardial infarction: A report of the American College of Cardiology/American Heart Association Task Force on Practice Guidelines. *Circulation, 110,* e82-e292.

Appels, A., and Mulder, P. (1989). Fatigue and heart disease: The association between 'vital exhaustion' and past, present and future coronary heart disease. *Journal of Psychosomatic Research, 33,* 727-738.

Aromaa, A., Raitasalo, R., Reunanen, A., Impivaara, O., Heliövaara, M., Knekt, P., et al. (1994). Depression and cardiovascular diseases. *Acta Psychiatrica Scandinavica, 377,* 77-82.

Arthur, H.M. (2006). Depression, isolation, social support, and cardiovascular disease in older adults. *Journal of Cardiovascular Nursing, 21,* 52-57.

Balog, P., Janszky, I., Leineweber, C., Blom, M., Wamala, S.P., and Orth-Gomér, K. (2003). Depressive symptoms in relation to marital and work stress in women with and without coronary heart disease: The Stockholm Female Coronary Risk Study. *Journal of Psychosomatic Research, 54,* 113-119.

Barefoot, J.C., Helms, M.J., Mark, D.B., Blumenthal, J.A., Califf, R.M., Haney, T.L., et al. (1996). Depression and long-term mortality risk in patients with coronary artery disease. *American Journal of Cardiology, 78,* 613-617.

Barefoot, J.C., and Schroll, M. (1996). Symptoms of depression, acute myocardial infarction, and total mortality in a community sample. *Circulation, 93,* 1976-1980.

Baron, R.M., and Kenny, D.A. (1986). The moderator-mediator variable distinction in social psychological research: Conceptual, strategic, and statistical considerations. *Journal of Personality and Social Psychology, 51,* 1173-1182.

Barrett-Connor, E., and Wingard, D.L. (1983). Sex differential in ischemic heart disease mortality in diabetics: A prospective population-based study. *American Journal of Epidemiology, 118,* 489-496.

Beck, A.T. (1963). Thinking and depression: I. Idiosyncratic content and cognitive distortions. *Archives of General Psychiatry, 9,* 324-333.

Beck, A.T., Ward, C.H., Mendelson, M., Mock, J.E., and Erbaugh, J. (1961). An inventory for measuring depression. *Archives of General Psychiatry, 4,* 561-571.

Benjamin, E.J., Smith, S.C., Jr., Cooper, R.S., Hill, M.N., and Luepker, R.V. (2002). Task force #1 – Magnitude of the prevention problem: Opportunities and challenges. *Journal of the American College of Cardiology, 40,* 588-603.

Berkman, L.F. (1995). The role of social relations in health promotion. *Psychosomatic Medicine, 57,* 245-254.

Bogner, H.R., and Gallo, J.J. (2004). Are higher rates of depression in women accounted for by differential symptom reporting? *Social Psychiatry and Psychiatric Epidemiology, 39,* 126-132.

Bonnet, F., Irving, K., Terra, J.L., Nony, P., Berthezène, F., and Moulin, P. (2005). Anxiety and depression are associated with unhealthy lifestyle in patients at risk of cardiovascular disease. *Atherosclerosis, 178,* 339-344.

Bourdon, K.H., Rae, D.S., Locke, B.Z., Narrow, W.E., and Regier, D.A. (1992). Estimating the prevalence of mental disorders in U.S. adults from the Epidemiologic Catchment Area Survey. *Public Health Reports, 107,* 663-668.

Brown, K.S. (1997). Heart disease: Women's unique risks demand attention. *Annals of Internal Medicine, 127,* 952-953.

Bush, D.E., Ziegelstein, R.C., Tayback, M., Richter, D., Stevens, S., Zahalsky, H., et al. (2001). Even minimal symptoms of depression increase mortality risk after acute myocardial infarction. *American Journal of Cardiology, 88,* 337-341.

Butler, A.C., Chapman, J.E., Forman, E.M., and Beck, A.T. (2006). The empirical status of cognitive-behavioral therapy: A review of meta-analyses. *Clinical Psychology Review, 26,* 17-31.

Carney, R.M., Blumenthal, J.A., Stein, P.K., Watkins, L., Catellier, D., Berkman, L.F., et al. (2001). Depression, heart rate variability, and acute myocardial infarction. *Circulation, 104,* 2024-2028.

Carney, R.M., Freedland, K.E., Eisen, S.A., Rich, M.W., and Jaffe, A.S. (1995). Major depression and medication adherence in elderly patients with coronary artery disease. *Health Psychology, 14,* 88-90.

Carney, R.M., Freedland, K.E., and Jaffe, A.S. (1990). Insomnia and depression prior to myocardial infarction. *Psychosomatic Medicine, 52,* 603-609.

Carney, R.M., Freedland, K.E., Smith, L., Lustman, P.J., and Jaffe, A.S. (1991). Relation of depression and mortality after myocardial infarction in women. *Circulation, 84,* 1876-1877.

Carney, R.M., Freedland, K.E., Stein, P.K., Skala, J.A., Hoffman, P., and Jaffe, A.S. (2000). Change in heart rate and heart rate variability during treatment for depression in patients with coronary heart disease. *Psychosomatic Medicine, 62,* 639-647.

Carney, R.M., Freedland, K.E., and Veith, R.C. (2005). Depression, the autonomic nervous system, and coronary heart disease. *Psychosomatic Medicine, 67 (Supp. 1),* S29-S33.

Carney, R.M., Rich, M.W., Tevelde, A., Saini, J., Clark, K., and Jaffe, A.S. (1987). Major depressive disorder in coronary artery disease. *American Journal of Cardiology, 60,* 1273-1275.

Carroll, D., Phillips, A.C., Hunt, K., and Der, G. (2007). Symptoms of depression and cardiovascular reactions to acute psychological distress: Evidence from a population study. *Biological Psychology, 75,* 68-74.

Caulin-Glaser, T., Maciejewski, P.K., Snow, R., LaLonde, M., and Mazure, C. (2007). Depressive symptoms and sex affect completion rates and clinical outcomes in cardiac rehabilitation. *Preventive Cardiology, 10,* 15-21.

Chesney, M.A. (1993). Social isolation, depression, and heart disease: Research on women broadens the agenda. *Psychosomatic Medicine,* 434-435.

Connerney, I., Shapiro, P.A., McLaughlin, J.S., Bagiella, E., and Sloan, R.P. (2001). Relation between depression after coronary artery bypass surgery and 12-month outcome: A prospective study. *Lancet, 358,* 1766-1771.

Costa, P.T., Zonderman, A.B., Engel, B.T., Baile, W.F., Brimlow, D.L., and Brinker, J. (1985). The relation of chest pain symptoms to angiographic findings of coronary artery stenosis and neuroticism. *Psychosomatic Medicine, 47,* 285-293.

Cutler, S.E., and Nolen-Hoeksema, S. (1991). Accounting for sex differences in depression through female victimization: Childhood sexual abuse. *Sex Roles, 24,* 425-438.

Czajkowski, S.M., Terrin, M., Lindquist, R., Hoogwerf, B., Dupuis, G., Shumaker, S.A., et al. (1997). Comparison of preoperative characteristics of men and women undergoing coronary artery bypass grafting (the Post Coronary Artery Bypass Graft [CABG] Biobehavioral Study). *American Journal of Cardiology, 79,* 1017-1024.

Davidson, K.W., Kupfer, D.J., Bigger, J.T., Califf, R.M., Carney, R.M., Coyne, J.C., et al. (2006). Assessment and treatment of depression in patients with cardiovascular disease: National Heart, Lung, and Blood Institute Working Group Report. *Psychosomatic Medicine, 68,* 645-650.

Davidson, P.M., Daly, J., Hancock, K., Moser, D., Chang, E., and Cockburn, J. (2003). Perceptions and experiences of heart disease: A literature review and identification of a research agenda in older women. *European Journal of Cardiovascular Nursing, 2,* 255-264.

Davydov, D.M., Shapiro, D., Cook, I.A., and Goldstein, I. (2007). Baroreflex mechanisms in major depression. *Progress in Neuro-Psychopharmacology and Biological Psychiatry, 31,* 164-177.

DiMatteo, M.R., Lepper, H.S., and Croghan, T.W. (2000). Depression is a risk factor for noncompliance with medical treatment: Meta-analysis of the effects of anxiety and depression on patient adherence. *Archives of Internal Medicine, 160,* 2101-2107.

Dimsdale, J.E. (1993). Coronary heart disease in women: Personality and stress-induced biological responses. *Annals of Behavioral Medicine, 15,* 119-123.

Dittrich, H., Gilpin, E., Nicod, P., Cali, G., Henning, H., and Ross, J., Jr. (1988). Acute myocardial infarction in women: influence of gender on mortality and prognostic variables. *American Journal of Cardiology, 62,* 1-7.

Douglas. K.M., Taylor, A.J., and O'Malley, P.G. (2004). Relationship between depression and C-reactive protein in a screening population. *Psychosomatic Medicine, 66,* 679-683.

Duits, A.A., Duivenvoorden, H.J., Boeke, S., Taams, M.A., Mochtar, B., Krauss, X.H., et al. (1998). The course of anxiety and depression in patients undergoing coronary artery bypass graft surgery. *Journal of Psychosomatic Research, 45,* 127-138.

Dusseldorp, E., van Elderen, T., Maes, S., Meulman, J., and Kraaij, V. (1999). A meta-analysis of psychoeducational programs for coronary heart disease patients. *Health Psychology, 18,* 506-519.

Emslie, C., Hunt, K., and Watt, G. (2001). Invisible women? The importance of gender in lay beliefs about heart problems. *Sociology of Health and Illness, 23,* 203-233.

ENRICHD Investigators (2003). Effects of treating depression and low perceived social support on clinical events after myocardial infarction: The Enhancing Recovery in Coronary Heart Disease Patients (ENRICHD) Randomized Trial. *Journal of the American Medical Association, 289,* 3106-3116.

Ensel, W.M. (1982). The role of age in the relationship of gender and marital status to depression. *Journal of Nervous and Mental Disease, 170,* 536-543.

Everson, S.A., Kauhanen, J., Kaplan, G.A., Goldberg, D.E., Julkunen, J., Tuomilehto, J., et al. (1997). Hostility and increased risk of mortality and acute myocardial infarction: The mediating role of behavioral risk factors. *American Journal of Epidemiology, 146,* 142-152.

Everson, S.A., Roberts, R.E., Goldberg, D.E., and Kaplan, G.A. (1998). Depressive symptoms and increased risk of stroke mortality over a 29-year period. *Archives of Internal Medicine, 158,* 1133-1138.

Feldman, J.J., Makuc, D.M., Kleinman, J.C., and Cornoni-Huntley, J. (1989). National trends in educational differentials in mortality. *American Journal of Epidemiology, 129,* 919-933.

Ferketich, A.K., Schwartzbaum, J.A., Frid, D.J., Moeschberger, M.L. (2000). Depression as an antecedent to heart disease among women and men in the NHANES I study. *Archives of Internal Medicine, 160,* 1261-1268.

Fiebach, N.H., Viscoli, C.M., and Horwitz, R.I. (1990). Differences between women and men in survival after myocardial infarction: Biology or methodology? *Journal of the American Medical Association, 263,* 1092-1096.

Frasure-Smith, N., and Lespérance, F. (2003). Depression and other psychological risks following myocardial infarction. *Archives of General Psychiatry, 60,* 627-636.

Frasure-Smith, N., and Lespérance, F. (2005a). Reflections on depression as a cardiac risk factor. *Psychosomatic Medicine, 67 (Supp. 1),* S19-S25.

Frasure-Smith, N., and Lespérance, F. (2005b). Depression and coronary heart disease: Complex synergism of mind, body, and environment. *Current Directions in Psychological Science, 14,* 39-43.

Frasure-Smith, N., and Lespérance, F., Juneau, M., Talajic, M., and Bourassa, M.G. (1999). Gender, depression, and one-year prognosis after myocardial infarction. *Psychosomatic Medicine, 61,* 26-37.

Frasure-Smith, N., and Lespérance, F., Prince, R.H., Verrier, P., Garber, R.A., Juneau, M., et al. (1997). Randomised trial of home-based psychosocial nursing intervention for patients recovering from myocardial infarction. *Lancet, 350,* 473-479.

Frasure-Smith, N., and Lespérance, F., and Talajic, M. (1995). The impact of negative emotions on prognosis following myocardial infarction: Is it more than depression? *Health Psychology, 14,* 388-398.

Frasure-Smith, N., and Prince, R. (1985). The ischemic heart disease life stress monitoring program: Impact on mortality. *Psychosomatic Medicine, 47,* 431-445.

Friedman, M., and Rosenman, R.H. (1959). Association of a specific overt behavior pattern with increases in blood cholesterol, blood clotting time, incidence of arcus senilis and clinical coronary artery disease. *Journal of the American Medical Association, 169,* 1286-1296.

Friedman, M., Thoresen, C.E., Gill, J.J., Powell, L.H., Ulmer, D., Thompson, L., et al. (1984). Alteration of type A behavior and reduction in cardiac recurrences in postmyocardial infarction patients. *American Heart Journal, 108,* 237-248.

Gehi, A., Haas, D., Pipkin, S., and Whooley, M.A. (2005). Depression and medication adherence in outpatients with coronary heart disease: Findings from the Heart and Soul Study. *Archives of Internal Medicine, 165,* 2508-2513.

Gerin, W., Pickering, T.G., Glynn, L., Christenfeld, N., Schwartz, A., Carroll, D., et al. (2000). An historic context for behavioral models of hypertension. *Journal of Psychosomatic Research, 48,* 369-377.

Glassman, A.H., Helzer, J.E., Covey, L.S., Cottler, L.B., Stetner, F., Tipp, J.E., et al. (1990). Smoking, smoking cessation, and major depression. *Journal of the American Medical Association, 264,* 1546-1549.

Glassman, A.H., O'Connor, C.M., Califf, R.M., Swedberg, K., Schwartz, P., Bigger, J.T., Jr., et al. (2002). Sertraline treatment of major depression in patients with acute MI or unstable angina. *Journal of the American Medical Association, 288,* 701-709.

Goodman, S.H., and Gotlib, I.H. (1999). Risk for psychopathology in the children of depressed mothers: A developmental model for understanding mechanisms of transmission. *Psychological Review, 106,* 458-490.

Grace, S.L., Abbey, S.E., Kapral, M.K., Fang, J., Nolan, R.P., and Stewart, D.E. (2005). Effect of depression on five-year mortality after an acute coronary syndrome. *American Journal of Cardiology, 96,* 1179-1185.

Grace, S.L., Krepostman, S., Brooks, D., Arthur, H., Scholey, P., Suskin, N., et al. (2005). Illness perceptions among cardiac patients: Relation to depressive symptomatology and sex. *Journal of Psychosomatic Research, 59,* 153-160.

Greenberg, P.E., Kessler, R.C., Birnbaum, H.G., Leong, S.A., Lowe, S.W., Berglund, P.A., et al. (2003). The economic burden of depression in the United States: How did it change between 1990 and 2000? *Journal of Clinical Psychiatry, 64,* 1465-1475.

Greenland, P., Reicher-Reiss, H., Goldbourt, U., and Behar, S. (1991). In-hospital and 1-year mortality in 1,524 women after myocardial infarction: Comparison with 4,315 men. *Circulation, 83,* 484-491.

Guinjoan, S.M., de Guevara, M.S., Correa, C., Schauffele, S.I., Nicola-Siri, L., Fahrer, R.D., et al. (2004). Cardiac parasympathetic dysfunction related to depression in older adults with acute coronary syndromes. *Journal of Psychosomatic Research, 56,* 83-88.

Gump, B.B., Matthews, K.A., Eberly, L.E., and Chang, Y.F. (2005). Depressive symptoms and mortality in men: Results from the Multiple Risk Factor Intervention Trial. *Stroke, 36,* 98-102.

Hällström, T., Lapidus, L., Bengtsson, C., and Edström, K. (1986). Psychosocial factors and risk of ischaemic heart disease and death in women: A twelve-year follow-up of participants in the population study of women in Gothenburg, Sweden. *Journal of Psychosomatic Research, 30,* 451-459.

Hankin, B.L., and Abramson, L.Y. (2001). Development of gender differences in depression: An elaborated cognitive vulnerability-transactional stress theory. *Psychological Bulletin, 127,* 773-796.

Harkness, K.L., and Luther, J. (2001). Clinical risk factors for the generation of life events in major depression. *Journal of Abnormal Psychology, 110,* 564-572.

Hart, P.L. (2005). Women's perceptions of coronary heart disease: An integrative review. *Journal of Cardiovascular Nursing, 20,* 170-176.

Hawthorne, M.H. (1994). Gender differences in recovery after coronary artery surgery. *Image – The Journal of Nursing Scholarship, 26,* 75-80.

Hemingway, H., and Marmot, M. (1999). Psychosocial factors in the aetiology and prognosis of coronary heart disease: Systematic review of prospective cohort studies. *British Medical Journal, 318,* 1460-1467.

Heston, T.F., and Lewis, L.M. (1992). Gender bias in the evaluation and management of acute nontraumatic chest pain. *The Family Practice Research Journal, 12,* 383-389.

Holahan, C.J., Moos, R.H., Holahan, C.K., and Brennan, P.L. (1995). Social support, coping, and depressive symptoms in a late-middle-aged sample of patients reporting cardiac illness. *Health Psychology, 14,* 152-163.

Horsten, M., Mittleman, M.A., Wamala, S.P., Schenck-Gustafsson, K., and Orth-Gomér, K. (2000). Depressive symptoms and lack of social integration in relation to prognosis of CHD in middle-aged women: The Stockholm Female Coronary Risk Study. *European Heart Journal, 21,* 1072-1080.

Hughes, J.W., and Stoney, C.M. (2000). Depressed mood is related to high-frequency heart rate variability during stressors. *Psychosomatic Medicine, 62,* 796-803.

Jacobs, A.K., and Eckel, R.H. (2005). Evaluating and managing cardiovascular disease in women: Understanding a woman's heart. *Circulation, 111,* 383-384.

Jacobs, S.C., and Sherwood, J.B. (1996). The cardiac psychology of women and coronary heart disease. In R. Allan and S.S. Scheidt (Eds.), *Heart and mind: The practice of cardiac psychology* (pp. 197-218). Washington, DC: American Psychological Association.

Januzzi, J.L., Jr., Stern, T.A., Pasternak, R.C., and DeSanctis, R.W. (2000). The influence of anxiety and depression on outcomes of patients with coronary artery disease. *Archives of Internal Medicine, 160,* 1913-1921.

Jenkins, J.S., Flaker, G.C., Nolte, B., Prince, L.A., Morris, D., Kurz, J., et al. (1994). Causes of higher in-hospital mortality in women than in men after acute myocardial infarction. *American Journal of Cardiology, 73,* 319-322.

Johnson, J.L., and Morse, J.M. (1990). Regaining control: The process of adjustment after myocardial infarction. *Heart and Lung, 19,* 126-135.

Johnson, M. (1994). Heart failure in women: A special approach? *Journal of Heart and Lung Transplantation, 13,* 130-134.

Joiner, T., and Coyne, J.C. (Eds.) (1999). *The interactional nature of depression: Advances in interpersonal approaches.* Washington, DC: American Psychological Association.

Jonas, B.S., and Mussolino, M.E. (2000). Symptoms of depression as a prospective risk factor for stroke. *Psychosomatic Medicine, 62,* 463-471.

Jones, D.A., and West, R.R. (1996). Psychological rehabilitation after myocardial infarction: Multicentre randomised controlled trial. *British Medical Journal, 313,* 1517-1521.

Jorgensen, R.S., Frankowski, J.J., Lantiga, L.J., Phadke, K., Sprafkin, R.P., and Abdul-Karim, K.W. (2001). Defensive hostility and coronary heart disease: A preliminary investigation of male veterans. *Psychosomatic Medicine, 63,* 463-469.

Kessler, R.C. (2003). Epidemiology of women and depression. *Journal of Affective Disorders, 74,* 5-13.

Kessler, R.C., McGonagle, K.A., Swartz, M., Blazer, D.G., and Nelson, C.B. (1993). Sex and depression in the National Comorbidity Survey I: Lifetime prevalence, chronicity and recurrence. *Journal of Affective Disorders, 29,* 85-96.

Kessler, R.C., McGonagle, K.A., Zhao, S., Nelson, C.B., Hughes, M., Eshleman, S., et al. (1994). Lifetime and 12-month prevalence of DSM-III-R psychiatric disorders in the United States: Results from the National Comorbidity Survey. *Archives of General Psychiatry, 51,* 8-19.

Kibler, J.L., and Ma, M. (2004). Depressive symptoms and cardiovascular reactivity to laboratory behavioral stress. *International Journal of Behavioral Medicine, 11,* 81-87.

Kiecolt-Glaser, J.K., and Glaser, R. (2002). Depression and immune function: Central pathways to morbidity and mortality. *Journal of Psychosomatic Research, 53,* 873-876.

King, D.A., and Buchwald, A.M. (1982). Sex differences in subclinical depression: Administration of the Beck Depression Inventory in public and private disclosure situations. *Journal of Personality and Social Psychology, 42,* 963-969.

King, K.M., and Jensen, L. (1994). Preserving the self: Women having cardiac surgery. *Heart and Lung, 23,* 99-105.

Ladwig, K.H., Kieser, M., König, J., Breithardt, G., and Borggrefe, M. (1991). Affective disorders and survival after acute myocardial infarction: Results from the post-infarction late potential study. *European Heart Journal, 12,* 959-964.

Lake, C.R., Pickar, D., Ziegler, M.G., Lipper, S., Slater, S., and Murphy, D.L. (1982). High plasma norepinephrine levels in patients with major affective disorder. *American Journal of Psychiatry, 139,* 1315-1318.

Lambert, M.J., and Ogles, B.M. (2004). The efficacy and effectiveness of psychotherapy. In M.J. Lambert (Ed.), *Bergin and Garfield's handbook of psychotherapy and behavior change* (5th ed., pp. 139-193). New York: Wiley.

Landsbergis, P.A., Schnall, P.L., Belkic, K.L., Schwartz, J., Pickering, T.G., and Baker, D. (2001). Work stressors and cardiovascular disease. *Work: Journal of Prevention, Assessment, and Rehabilitation, 17,* 191-208.

Leas, L., and McCabe, M. (2007). Health behaviors among individuals with schizophrenia and depression. *Journal of Health Psychology, 12,* 563-579.

Lerner, D.J., and Kannel, W.B. (1986). Patterns of coronary heart disease morbidity and mortality in the sexes: A 26-year follow-up of the Framingham population. *American Heart Journal, 111,* 383-390.

Lespérance, F., Frasure-Smith, N., Koszycki, D., Laliberté, M.A., van Zyl, L.T., Baker, B., et al. (2007). Effects of citalopram and interpersonal psychotherapy on depression in patients with coronary artery disease: The Canadian Cardiac Randomized Evaluation of Antidepressant and Psychotherapy Efficacy (CREATE) trial. *Journal of the American Medical Association, 297,* 367-379.

Lespérance, F., Frasure-Smith, N., and Talajic, M. (1996). Major depression before and after myocardial infarction: Its nature and consequences. *Psychosomatic Medicine, 58,* 99-110.

Lett, H.S., Davidson, J., and Blumenthal, J.A. (2005). Nonpharmacologic treatments for depression in patients with coronary heart disease. *Psychosomatic Medicine, 67 (Supp. 1),* S58-S62.

Levav, I., Kohn, R., Golding, J.M., and Weissman, M.M. (1997). Vulnerability of Jews to affective disorders. *American Journal of Psychiatry, 154,* 941-947.

Linden, W., Stossel, C., Maurice, J. (1996). Psychosocial interventions for patients with coronary artery disease: a meta-analysis. *Archives of Internal Medicine, 156,* 745-752.

Lindquist, R., Dupuis, G., Terrin, M.L., Hoogwerf, B., Czajkowski, S., Herd, J.A., et al. (2003). Comparison of health-related quality-of-life outcomes of men and women after coronary artery bypass surgery through 1 year: findings from the POST CABG Biobehavioral Study. *American Heart Journal, 146,* 1038-1044.

Lloyd, C.E., Kuller, L.H., Ellis, D., Becker, D.J., Wing, R.R., and Orchard, T.J. (1996). Coronary artery disease in IDDM: Gender differences in risk factors but not risk. *Arteriosclerosis, Thrombosis, and Vascular Biology, 16,* 720-726.

Lyubomirsky, S., and Nolen-Hoeksema, S. (1993). Self-perpetuating properties of dysphoric rumination. *Journal of Personality and Social Psychology, 65,* 339-349.

Mancini, G.B. (2004). Vascular structure versus function: Is endothelial dysfunction of independent prognostic importance or not? *Journal of the American College of Cardiology, 43,* 624-628.

Markovitz, J.H., and Matthews, K.A. (1991). Platelets and coronary heart disease: Potential psychophysiologic mechanisms. *Psychosomatic Medicine, 53,* 643-668.

Matthews, K.A., Gump, B.B., Harris, K.F., Haney, T.L., and Barefoot, J.C. (2004). Hostile behaviors predict cardiovascular mortality among men enrolled in the Multiple Risk Factor Intervention Trial. *Circulation, 109,* 66-70.

McBride, C., and Bagby, R.M. (2006). Rumination and interpersonal dependency: Explaining women's vulnerability to depression. *Canadian Psychology, 47,* 184-194.

Mieres, J.H. (2006). Review of the American Heart Association's guidelines for cardiovascular disease prevention in women. *Heart, 92 (Supp. 3),* iii10-iii13.

Mikuni, M., Kagaya, A., Takahashi, K., and Meltzer, H.Y. (1992). Serotonin but not norepinephrine-induced calcium mobilization of platelets is enhanced in affective disorders. *Psychopharmacology, 106,* 311-314.

Miller, C.L., and Kollauf, C.R. (2002). Evolution of information on women and heart disease 1957-2000: A review of archival records and secular literature. *Heart and Lung, 31,* 253-261.

Mitchell, R.H., Robertson, E., Harvey, P.J., Nolan, R., Rodin, G., Romans, S., et al. (2005). Sex differences in depression after coronary artery bypass graft surgery. *American Heart Journal, 150,* 1017-1025.

Mosca, L., Ferris, A., Fabunmi, R., and Robertson, R.M. (2004). Tracking women's awareness of heart disease: An American Heart Association national study. *Circulation, 109,* 573-579.

Mosca, L., Manson, J.E., Sutherland, S.E., Langer, R.D., Manolio, T., Barrett-Connor, E. (1997). Cardiovascular disease in women: A statement for healthcare professionals from the American Heart Association. *Circulation, 96,* 2468-2482.

Moser, D.K., Dracup, K., McKinley, S., Yamasaki, K., Kim, C.J., Riegel, B., et al. (2003). An international perspective on gender differences in anxiety early after acute myocardial infarction. *Psychosomatic Medicine, 65,* 511-516.

Murray, C.J.L., and Lopez, A.D. (Eds.). (1996). *The global burden of disease: A comprehensive assessment of mortality and disability from diseases, injuries, and risk factors in 1990 and projected to 2020.* Cambridge, MA: Harvard University Press.

Musselman, D.L., Tomer, A., Manatunga, A.K., Knight, B.T., Porter, M.R., Kasey, S., et al. (1996). Exaggerated platelet reactivity in major depression. *American Journal of Psychiatry, 153,* 1313-1317.

Naqvi, T.Z., Naqvi, S.S., and Merz, C.N. (2005). Gender differences in the link between depression and cardiovascular disease. *Psychosomatic Medicine, 67 (Supp. 1),* S15-S18.

Nguyen, V.H., and McLaughlin, M.A. (2002). Coronary artery disease in women: A review of emerging cardiovascular risk factors. *Mount Sinai Journal of Medicine, 69,* 338-349.

Nolen-Hoeksema, S. (1987). Sex differences in unipolar depression: Evidence and theory. *Psychological Bulletin, 101,* 259-282.

Nolen-Hoeksma, S. (2002). Gender differences in depression. In I.H. Gotlib and C.L. Hammen (Eds.), *Handbook of depression* (pp. 492-509). New York: Guilford Press.

Nolen-Hoeksema, S., and Girgus, J.S. (1994). The emergence of gender differences in depression during adolescence. *Psychological Bulletin, 115,* 424-443.

Nolen-Hoeksema, S., Larson, J., and Grayson, C. (1999). Explaining the gender difference in depressive symptoms. *Journal of Personality and Social Psychology, 77,* 1061-1072.

Papanicolaou, D.A., Wilder, R.L., Manolagas, S.C., and Chrousos, G.P. (1998). The pathophysiologic roles of interleukin-6 in human disease. *Annals of Internal Medicine, 128,* 127-137.

Penninx, B.W., Kritchevsky, S.B., Yaffe, K., Newman, A.B., Simonsick, E.M., Rubin, S., et al. (2003). Inflammatory markers and depressed mood in older persons: Results from the Health, Aging and Body Composition study. *Biological Psychiatry, 54,* 566-572.

Peterson, C., and Seligman, M.E. (1984). Causal explanations as a risk factor for depression: Theory and evidence. *Psychological Review, 91,* 347-374.

Phillips Bute, B., Mathew, J., Blumenthal, J.A., Welsh-Bohmer, K., White, W.D., Mark, D., et al. (2003). Female gender is associated with impaired quality of life 1 year after coronary artery bypass surgery. *Psychosomatic Medicine, 65,* 944-951.

Pilote, L., and Hlatky, M.A. (1995). Attitudes of women toward hormone therapy and prevention of heart disease. *American Heart Journal, 129,* 1237-1238.

Pollock, B.G., Laghrissi-Thode, F., Wagner, W.R. (2000). Evaluation of platelet activation in depressed patients with ischemic heart disease after paroxetine or nortriptyline treatment. *Journal of Clinical Psychopharmacology, 20,* 137-140.

Powell, L.H., Shaker, L.A., Jones, B.A., Vaccarino, L.V., Thoresen, C.E., and Pattillo, J.R. (1993). Psychosocial predictors of mortality in 83 women with premature acute myocardial infarction. *Psychosomatic Medicine, 55,* 426-433.

Richards, H., McConnachie, A., Morrison, C., Murray, K., and Watt, G. (2000). Social and gender variation in the prevalence, presentation and general practitioner provisional diagnosis of chest pain. *Journal of Epidemiology and Community Health, 54,* 714-718.

Riegel, B., and Gocka, I. (1995). Gender differences in adjustment to acute myocardial infarction. *Heart and Lung, 24,* 457-466.

Roose, S.P., and Miyazaki, M. (2005). Pharmacologic treatment of depression in patients with heart disease. *Psychosomatic Medicine, 67 (Supp. 1),* S54-S57.

Rudorfer, M.V., Ross, R.J., Linnoila, M., Sherer, M.A., and Potter, W.Z. (1985). Exaggerated orthostatic responsivity of plasma norepinephrine in depression. *Archives of General Psychiatry, 42,* 1186-1192.

Rugulies, R. (2002). Depression as a predictor for coronary heart disease. a review and meta-analysis. *American Journal of Preventative Medicine, 23,* 51-61.

Ruston, A., Clayton, J., and Calnan, M. (1998). Patients' action during their cardiac event: Qualitative study exploring differences and modifiable factors. *British Medical Journal, 316,* 1060-1064.

Rutledge, T., Reis, S.E., Olson, M., Owens, J., Kelsey, S.F., Pepine, C.J., et al. (2006). Depression is associated with cardiac symptoms, mortality risk, and hospitalization among women with suspected coronary disease: The NHLBI-sponsored WISE study. *Psychosomatic Medicine, 68,* 217-223.

Sanderson, B.K., and Bittner, V. (2005). Women in cardiac rehabilitation: Outcomes and identifying risk for dropout. *American Heart Journal, 150,* 1052-1058.

Santerre, C., and Allen, J.J.B. (2007). Methods for studying the psychophysiology of emotion. In J. Rottenberg and S.L. Johnson (Eds.), *Emotion and psychopathology: Bridging affective and clinical science* (pp. 53-79). Washington, DC: American Psychological Association.

Schneiderman, N., Saab, P.G., Catellier, D.J., Powell, L.H., DeBusk, R.F., Williams, R.B., et al. (2004). Psychosocial treatment within sex by ethnicity subgroups in the Enhancing Recovery in Coronary Heart Disease clinical trial. *Psychosomatic Medicine, 66,* 475-483.

Schoenberg, N.E., Peters, J.C., and Drew, E.M. (2003). Unraveling the mysteries of timing: Women's perceptions about time to treatment for cardiac symptoms. *Social Science and Medicine, 56,* 271-284.

Schuitemaker, G.E., Dinant, G.J., van der Pol, G.A., Verhelst, A.F., and Appels, A. (2004). Vital exhaustion as a risk indicator for first stroke. *Psychosomatics, 45,* 114-118.

Schuster, P.M., and Waldron, J. (1991). Gender differences in cardiac rehabilitation patients. *Rehabilitation Nursing, 16,* 248-253.

Schwartzman, J.B., and Glaus, K.D. (2000). Depression and coronary heart disease in women: Implications for clinical practice and research. *Professional Psychology: Research and Practice, 31,* 48-57.

Seeman, M.V. (1997). Psychopathology in women and men: Focus on female hormones. *American Journal of Psychiatry, 154,* 1641-1647.

Serebruany, V.L., Glassman, A.H., Malinin, A.I., Nemeroff, C.B., Musselman, D.L., van Zyl, L.T., et al. (2003). Platelet/endothelial biomarkers in depressed patients treated with the selective serotonin reuptake inhibitor sertraline after acute coronary events: The Sertraline AntiDepressant Heart Attack Randomized Trial (SADHART) Platelet Substudy. *Circulation, 108,* 939-944.

Sherwood, A., Hinderliter, A.L., Watkins, L.L., Waugh, R.A., and Blumenthal, J.A. (2005). Impaired endothelial function in coronary heart disease patients with depressive symptomatology. *Journal of the American College of Cardiology, 46,* 656-659.

Shores, M.M., Pascualy, M., Lewis, N.L., Flatness, D., and Veith, R.C. (2001). Short-term sertraline treatment suppresses sympathetic nervous system activity in healthy human subjects. *Psychoneuroendocrinology, 26,* 433-439.

Smith, T.W., and Ruiz, J.M. (2002). Psychosocial influences on the development and course of coronary heart disease: Current status and implications for research and practice. *Journal of Consulting and Clinical Psychology, 70,* 548-568.

Stein, G., Marsh, A., and Morton, J. (1981). Mental symptoms, weight changes, and electrolyte excretion in the first post partum week. *Journal of Psychosomatic Research, 25,* 395-408.

Stein, P.K., Carney, R.M., Freedland, K.E., Skala, J.A., Jaffe, A.S., Kleiger, R.E., et al. (2000). Severe depression is associated with markedly reduced heart rate variability in patients with stable coronary heart disease. *Journal of Psychosomatic Research, 48,* 493-500.

Steiner, M., Dunn, E., and Born, L. (2003). Hormones and mood: From menarche to menopause and beyond. *Journal of Affective Disorders, 74,* 67-83.

Steptoe, A., Strike, P.C., Perkins-Porras, L., McEwan, J.R., and Whitehead, D.L. (2006). Acute depressed mood as a trigger of acute coronary syndromes. *Biological Psychiatry, 60,* 837-842.

Stern, M.J., Gorman, P.A., and Kaslow, L. (1983). The group counseling v exercise therapy study: A controlled intervention with subjects following myocardial infarction. *Archives of Internal Medicine, 143,* 1719-1725.

Suarez, E.C. (2004). C-reactive protein is associated with psychological risk factors of cardiovascular disease in apparently healthy adults. *Psychosomatic Medicine, 66,* 684-691.

Suls, J., and Bunde, J. (2005). Anger, anxiety, and depression as risk factors for cardiovascular disease: The problems and implications of overlapping affective dispositions. *Psychological Bulletin, 131,* 260-300.

Taylor, C.B., Houston-Miller, N., Ahn, D.K., Haskell, W., and DeBusk, R.F. (1986). The effects of exercise training programs on psychosocial improvement in uncomplicated postmyocardial infarction patients. *Journal of Psychosomatic Research, 30,* 581-587.

Tobin, J.N., Wassertheil-Smoller, S., Wexler, J.P., Steingart, R.M., Budner, N., Lense, L., et al. (1987). Sex bias in considering coronary bypass surgery. *Annals of Internal Medicine, 107,* 19-25.

Vaccarino, V., Krumholz, H.M., Berkman, L.F., and Horwitz, R.I. (1995). Sex differences in mortality after myocardial infarction: Is there evidence for an increased risk for women? *Circulation, 91,* 1861-1871.

Vaccarino, V., Lin, Z.Q., Kasl, S.V., Mattera, J.A., Roumanis, S.A., Abramson, J.L., et al. (2003). Sex differences in health status after coronary artery bypass surgery. *Circulation, 108,* 2642-2647.

Wassertheil-Smoller, S., Applegate, W.B., Berge, K., Chang, C.J., Davis, B.R., Grimm, R., Jr., et al. (1996). Change in depression as a precursor of cardiovascular events: SHEP Cooperative Research Group (Systoloc Hypertension in the elderly). *Archives of Internal Medicine, 156,* 553-561.

Weintraub, W.S., Wenger, N.K., Jones, E.L., Craver, J.M., and Guyton, R.A. (1993). Changing clinical characteristics of coronary surgery patients: Differences between men and women. *Circulation, 88,* 1179-1186.

Weiss, E.L., Longhurst, J.G., and Mazure, C.M. (1999). Childhood sexual abuse as a risk factor for depression in women: Psychosocial and neurobiological correlates. *American Journal of Psychiatry, 156,* 816-828.

Weissman, M.M., Bland, R.C., Canino, G.J., Faravelli, C., Greenwald, S., Hwu, H.G., et al. (1996). Cross-national epidemiology of major depression and bipolar disorder. *Journal of the American Medical Association, 276,* 293-299.

Westin, L., Carlsson, R., Erhardt, L., Cantor-Graae, E., and McNeil, T. (1999). Differences in quality of life in men and women with ischemic heart disease: A prospective controlled study. *Scandinavian Cardiovascular Journal, 33,* 160-165.

Wiklund, I., Herlitz, J., Johansson, S., Bengtson, A., Karlson, B.W., and Persson, N.G. (1993). Subjective symptoms and well-being differ in women and men after myocardial infarction. *European Heart Journal, 14,* 1315-1319.

Williams, R., Jr., and Barefoot, J.C. (1988). Coronary-prone behavior: The emerging role of the hostility complex. In B.K. Houston and C.R. Snyder (Eds.), *Type A behavior pattern: Research, theory, and intervention* (pp. 189-211). Oxford, England: Wiley.

Winokur, G., and Tanna, V.L. (1969). Possible role of X-linked dominant factor in manic-depressive disease. *Diseases of the Nervous System, 30,* 89-93.

World Health Organization (2007). *Cardiovascular diseases fact sheet.* Retrieved November 15, 2007, from http://www.who.int/mediacentre/factsheets/fs317/en/print.html

Wyatt, R.J., Portnoy, B., Kupfer, D.J., Snyder, F., and Engelman, K. (1971). Resting plasma catecholamine concentrations in patients with depression and anxiety. *Archives of General Psychiatry, 24,* 65-70.

Ziegelstein, R.C., Fauerbach, J.A., Stevens, S.S., Romanelli, J., Richter, D.P., and Bush, D.E. (2000). Patients with depression are less likely to follow recommendations to reduce cardiac risk during recovery from a myocardial infarction. *Archives of Internal Medicine, 160,* 1818-1823.

In: Women and Depression
Editors: Paula Hernandez and Sara Alonso

ISBN 978-1-60456-647-5
© 2009 Nova Science Publishers, Inc.

Chapter 19

Right Vestibular Hypo Activity in Depression, the Theory of Suprachiasmatic-Raphe-Vestibular Nuclei System Asymmetry

Ana María Soza Ried
Chilean Aerospace Medicine Center, Chile

Abstract

Depression patients characterized by chronobiologic alterations as diminution of locomotor activity, altered sleep architecture, changes in the cyclic pattern of cortisol, growth, and thyroid hormones secretion, all governed by the Suprachiasmatic Nuclei in the hypothalamus. Several previous studies in animals confirmed anatomical and functional relationships between Suprachiasmatic Nuclei and Vestibular Nuclei through Raphe Nuclei in the brain stem. In our research we demonstrated that vestibular activity is diminished at the right side in Major Depression and Bipolar Disease patients during the Depression phase of the illness. It is hypothesized that the right Vestibular hypo activity is induced by ipsilateral dysfunction of Raphe Nuclei or Suprachiasmatic Nuclei, two neuronal nuclei that modulate vestibular function. To support this idea we analyze, in this chapter, the multiple evidences of anatomical and functional alterations of the serotoninergic Raphe Nuclei and of chronobiologic-suprachiasmatic disturbances in depressed patients, and we discuss the importance of studying the right–left asymmetry of activity of both nuclei in the future. The study of the bilateral distribution of cortisol, leptin, orexin and estrogen receptors in Raphe Nuclei is also proposed in order to investigate the possible contribution of those depression-associated hormones in right–left asymmetric Raphe Nuclei activity. In summary, the possibility of an asymmetric modulating effect of Raphe Nuclei on Suprachiasmatic Nuclei could contribute to the development of chronobiologic symptoms including depressed mood, and on the other side, Raphe Nuclei modulating effects on Vestibular Nuclei, could explain the asymmetric vestibular response.

Introduction

Depression syndrome is a well established entity characterized by depressed mood and negative feelings accompanied by a variety of symptoms and signs usually poor studied with objective methods. The unknown etiology of this syndrome is an intriguing question that pushes us to investigate new possibilities explaining the mechanism that produces it. Depression can be considered a syndrome like fever, in which the high temperature can be triggered by many different primary causes, even though the final mechanism that produces fever is always the same. I am not referring to the different negative circumstances of life that can lead to a depression, but I am referring to different neuro-phatophysiological mechanisms that finish in a common final pathway producing depression. According to this idea the monoaminergic theory is an interesting starting point of study, but in my opinion it is only one part of a more complex pathophysiologic mechanism. Affirming that the actual treatment with antidepressants is the cure for depression is analogous to saying that the aspirin is the cure for all the diseases that causes a fever. Antidepressants are just symptomatic medication, that's why people need chronic treatments. Now is the time to add a new complementary hypothesis in order to explain this syndrome better and to do it urgently for therapeutic proposes.

The Register of the Brain Stem Activity in Depression Showed Asymmetry of Vestibular Function

At the start of my medical career attending othorhynolaryngology, I notice that many patients with symptoms of dizziness or vertigo, shared anxiety, depressed mood or both. So when it was time to propose a thesis for my Neurobiology and Behavioral Sciences Master Degree, I decided to study the vestibule-ocular reflex in depressed subjects. The original hypothesis was very simple: if depression develops secondary to alterations in neurotransmitters, we also would find alterations in the vestibule-ocular reflex if this brain stem integrated reflex uses those neurotransmitters that are misfunctioning in depression.

The study of this reflex was ideal for our purposes because we could have an objective measurement of the brain stem activity that does not respond to voluntary control and is impossible to simulate. Other advantages were the low cost and not being an invasive exam. In this first study I probed objectively that it was an asymmetry of the vestibular function in a hundred per cent of the depressed subjects studied. Then in a second study, I reconfirmed these results in a larger group of depressed people with different degrees of depression.

For Measuring the Brain Stem Activity In Depression Subjects, We Used Two Different Techniques

Caloric Technique in the First Experiment

For the first experiment I recruited 8 subjects (4 males and 4 females) who had the actual diagnosis of Major Depression, 1 left handed and 7 right handed. The control group was formed by 10 healthy subjects (3 males and 7 females), 2 left handed and 8 right handed.

The exam consisted of stimulating the vestibular receptors of the inner ear with hot water (44°C) irrigation in the external ear conduct or to inhibit them with cold water (30°C). The vestibular information travels through the vestibular nerve to the correspondent vestibular nuclei in the brain stem, which integrates the information and initiates the correspondent ocular movements called nystagmus. The stimulation of the right ear with hot water stimulates the horizontal semicircular channel receptors, producing a slow movement of the eyes (slow phase component) to the right side controlled by right vestibular nuclei, and a compensatory saccadic rapid movement to the left (fast phase component), controlled by the Paramedian Pontine reticular Formation. The stimulation of the same ear with cold water generates the eyes movement to the contralateral side because of the inhibition of right vestibular nuclei. We then registered the velocities of the eye movements during the fast and slow phase of the nystagmus and compared both sides, right and left, corresponding to the activity of Vestibular Nuclei and Paramedian Pontine Reticular Formation respectively.

Because of the depression state of the experimental subjects, the main difficulty was on patients coming to the hospital on time. Even though people wanted to participate, it was very difficult for them to awake in the morning or just to dress up or to decide to go. This study was published in Neuroscience volume 144, 2007

Results of the First Experiment

Slow Phase velocity We detected a statistically significant decrease in the velocity of the slow phase of the nystagmus in patients. At 30°C stimulation of the right ear, the depression group's mean was 12.71 ± 4.78 °/sec of angular velocity, significantly lower than 43.5 ± 14.27 °/sec of the control group ($p < 0.01$). At 30°C left ear stimulation, depression group showed a mean of 24.38 ± 11.39 °/sec, significantly lower than $41.6 + 14.32$ °/sec of the control group ($p < 0.05$). Stimulation at 44°C also showed lower slow phase velocities in the depression group. Right ear at 44°C in the depression group was 15.43 ± 7.41, and in the control group it was 48.34 ± 20.31 ($p < 0.01$). Left ear stimulation at 44°C showed 14.71 ± 8.04 °/sec in depression group that was significantly different from 41.64 ± 16.16 °/sec of the control group ($p < 0.01$).

The magnitude of asymmetry was measured by calculating an angular velocity ratio from the right to the left ear (RE/LE) in each subject. The slow phase velocity ratio at 30°C stimulation was 0.56 ± 0.19 in depression group and 1.18 ± 0.57 in control group ($p < 0.01$). No significant variation in the slow phase velocity ratio was detected in the depression group,

1.16± 0.32, and the control group, 1.22±0.55 at 44°C stimulation. We didn't find any relation between hand preference or sex and the asymmetries of the vestibular ocular reflex. Also we didn't find any relation between age and velocities or asymmetry of the reflex.

Fast Phase Velocity The fast phase velocity (FPV) was significantly lower in patients at 30°C in the right ear with a mean of the angular velocity of 126.3±52.1 compared to 202.7+68.9 of the controls (p<0.05). No significant differences were found in 30°C left ear and 44°C right and left ear stimulation. There were not significant differences in the groups' fast phase velocities ratios at 30°C and 44°C stimulation.

Dissymmetry and Disrhythmic nystagmus: Saccadic arc decomposition during calibration was found in 4 of the depressed people, and dysrhythmic nystagmus was detected in 5 of the patients in that group. The members of the control group did not present dysrhythmic nystagmus and calibration was normal.

Rotating Chair Technique in the Second Experiment

In the second experiment the idea was to repeat the first experiment in a larger group of patients. For this purpose a group of 16 depressed patients was studied. In this opportunity we didn't use the caloric test, instead we used the rotating chair for stimulating the vestibular system. We didn't know if this different technique for evaluation of vestibular function would give the same results of the first experiment, but the idea was to probe this different technique because it was more comfortable for patients and also more physiological.

Depression Group: This group consisted of 16 subjects, 8 males and 8 females, with an average age of 39.83±11.59 (mean ± SD). Fourteen of them were right-handed and two left-handed. The group consisted of patients presenting with major depression or bipolar disease (I and II) who had been diagnosed by a psychiatrist using Diagnostic and Statistical Manual of Mental Disorders (DSM-IV; American Psychiatric Association, 1994) criteria. Each subject in this group presented a recent Hamilton Rating Scale for Depression 21 item score of >10. All of the patients were taking the medication prescribed by their health care provider, when applicable. Benzodiazepines were suspended 24 hours before the exam.

Control Group: This group consisted of 20 subjects, 7 males and 13 females, with an average age of 40.7±14.55. All of the subjects were right-handed. This group was composed of office workers from the Aerospace Medical Center and university students who presented a Hamilton Rating Scale for Depression (HAM-D) score of <6 and had no history of psychiatric illness or other major diseases.

All subjects were interviewed by the same person using a standard questionnaire about their general health. The magnitude of depression was scored using the HAM-D-21 item scale.

Vestibule-ocular reflexes were measured at the Chilean Air Force's Aerospace Medical Center. All measurements were taken between 8 and 11 a.m. using the same equipment (including a Tonnies Optokinetik rotating chair). Subjects were asked to sit in the chair with their head at a thirty degree angle. Three silver electrodes were attached to the skin using conducting gel and tape (one at each external angle of the eyes and the third in the center of the forehead).

In order to calibrate eye movement in the polygraph, the subject was asked to look at two points of light at ten degree angles to the left and right of his or her eyes. Eye movement to the right side is seen as upwards displacement of the polygraph registration needle and left displacements as downwards

Rotations to the right side of the patient stimulate the right horizontal semicircular channel because of the ampullipetus current of the endolymphatic liquid and inhibit the contra lateral one, and vice versa. Semicircular channels sense changes in velocity or the acceleration of the movement. The acceleration of the rotating chair is $25°/s^2$ for four seconds. Normally, semicircular channel sensory neurons stimulate the ipsilateral vestibular nuclei in the brain stem. Motor ocular nuclei are controlled by vestibular nuclei, which make the eyes move at the same velocity but in the opposite direction of the chair in order to stabilize the gaze. This is the slow phase of nystagmus. A rapid compensatory movement in the contra lateral direction is controlled by paramedian pontine reticular formation. This is the fast phase of nystagmus.

While the chair is rotating, the patient's eyes are closed and the room is dark (in order to ensure that the subject's eyes do not fixate). Measures of nystagmus during the rotation of the chair were called per-rotatory nystagmus. When the chair stops, the horizontal channel receives an ampullifugal inhibitory endolymphatic current, which is contrary to the previous current and corresponds to the post-rotatory nystagmus.

Millimetric record paper runs at 10 mm/s. In order to quantify the velocity of the slow phase, the pendent of 4 or 5 representative nystagmus in each stimulus was measured. The ratio between right and left per and post-rotatory slow phase of the nystagmus was used to quantify the magnitude of per and post rotatory asymmetry of the vestibule-ocular reflex and the mean between per and post-rotatory asymmetry, which we called general asymmetry, was used.

The significance of the differences observed was tested using Mann-Whitney test.

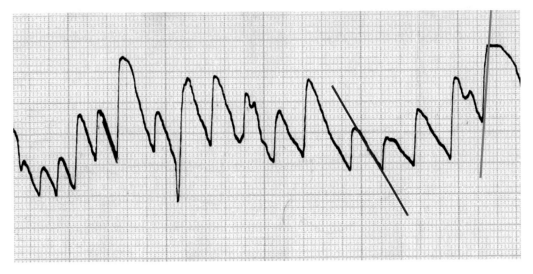

Figure1. Electronystagmographic register. Red line corresponds to the Slow Phase of nystagmus and the green one to the Fast Phase.

Table1. Depression and control subjects characteristics DGS: Depression Group Subject CGS: Control Group Subject; HAM-D: Hamilton scale score; Right/Left PER: Right/Left Per rotatory SPV ratio; Right/Left POST: Right/Left Post rotatory SPV ratio; General Asymmetry: Mean between Per and Post asymmetry.

Subject	Sex	Age	Handedness	HAM-D Score	Right/Left PER	Right/Left POST	General Asymmery	Psichiatric Diagnostic
DS1	Male	30	Right	28	0.7	0.6	0.7	Major Depression
DS2	Male	47	Right	25	0.7	0.7	0.7	Bipolar I Disease
DS2	Male	47	Right	25	0.6	0.5	0.5	Bipolar I Disease
DS3	Male	39	Right	25	0.9	0.7	0.8	Major Depression
DS4	Female	31	Left	24	0.8	0.5	0.7	Bipolar I Disease
DS5	Male	43	Right	24	0.9	0,6	0.7	Major Depression
DS6	Male	52	Right	22	0.7	0.7	0.7	Major Depression
DS7	Female	40	Right	21	0.7	1.0	0.8	Bipolar II Disease
DS8	Female	45	Right	19	1.6	0.5	1.1	Major Depression
DS9	Female	23	Right	15	0.6	1.1	0.8	Major Depression
DS10	Female	44	Right	14	0.8	1.0	0.9	Major Depression
DS11	Female	23	Right	11	0.7	0.8	0.7	Major Depression
DS12	Male	25	Left	11	1.1	0.7	0.9	Bipolar I Disease
DS13	Male	34	Right	11	0.7	1.0	0.8	Bipolar I Disease
DS14	Female	26	Right	10	0.8	0.9	0.9	Major Depression
DS15	Male	54	Right	10	0.9	0.6	0.7	Major Depression
DS16	Female	57	Right	10	0.4	0.5	0.4	Major Depression
DS16	Female	57	Right	10	1.3	0.4	0.8	Major Depression
CS1	Female	63	Right	6	1.1	1.1	1.1	Healthy
CS2	Female	58	Right	5	1.1	0.9	1	Healthy
CS3	Female	19	Right	4	1.3	1.1	1.2	Healthy
CS4	Female	38	Right	3	1.1	0.9	1	Healthy
CS5	Female	48	Right	3	1.1	0.9	1	Healthy
CS6	Male	22	Right	2	0.8	1.1	1	Healthy
CS7	Female	30	Right	2	1.6	1.1	1.4	Healthy
CS8	Female	51	Right	2	0.9	1.1	1	Healthy
CS9	Male	37	Right	1	1.3	0.9	1.1	Healthy
CS10	Female	50	Right	1	1	0.9	0.9	Healthy
CS11	Female	22	Right	0	1	1.1	1.1	Healthy
CS12	Female	42	Right	0	1.1	1.1	1.1	Healthy
CS13	Female	20	Right	0	0.9	0.8	0.9	Healthy
CS14	Male	45	Right	0	1.1	1.1	1.1	Healthy
CS15	Male	48	Right	0	1.2	1.1	1.1	Healthy
CS16	Male	56	Right	0	1.3	1.3	1.3	Healthy
CS17	Female	24	Right	0	1	1	1	Healthy
CS18	Male	28	Right	0	1.2	1.6	1.4	Healthy
CS19	Female	57	Right	0	1	0.8	0.9	Healthy
CS20	Male	56	Right	0	1.1	1	1	Healthy

Results of the Second Experiment

Slow Phase Velocity

We detected that Right Per (38.5 ± 1.76 of Control Group vs 29.86 ± 3.42 of Depression Group, P=0.01) and Post rotatory (37.07 ± 2.76 of Control vs 28.01 ± 2.08 of Depression

Group, P=0.015) slow phase velocity was significantly lower in the members of the Depression Group as compared to the Control Group, while Left Per (35.09±1.43 of Control vs 36.05±2.78 of Depression Group) and Left Post rotatory (36.84±3.22 of Control Group vs 40.89±2.83 of Depression Group) vestibular response were not significantly different between Depression and Control Group (mean±SEM) (Figure 2).

Per-Rotatory Asymmetry

The per rotatory asymmetry for the members of the Depression Group was 0.83±0.06 (mean+SEM). This was significantly lower than the 1.11±0.03 found in members of the Control Group (P=0.0002 two-tailed, Mann-Whitney test).

Post-Rotatory Asymmetry

Post-rotatory asymmetry was 0.71±0.04 in the depression group. This result is significantly lower than the 1.05±0.04(mean±SEM) presented by the healthy control group (P<0.0001 two-tailed, Mann-Whitney test).

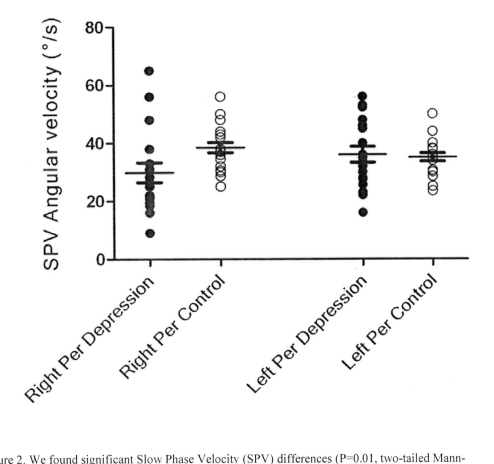

Figure 2. We found significant Slow Phase Velocity (SPV) differences (P=0.01, two-tailed Mann-Whitney test) between depression and control subjects when the reflex is controlled by the right vestibular nuclei, such difference doesn't appear in the left side controlled reflex. (Bars show mean±SEM) .

General Asymmetry

No significant differences were found between per and post-rotatory asymmetry in the two groups. This led us to take the mean of per and post- asymmetry for each subject in order to calculate the General Asymmetry. The result of 0.75±0.03 found in the depression group was significantly lower than the 1.08±0.03(mean±SEM) found in the healthy group (P<0.0001 two-tailed, Mann-Whitney test) (Figure 3).

Dissymmetry of Eyes Movements

During the calibration of the eyes movements for starting the recording, dissymmetry was found in three subjects of the Depression Group and in one in the Control Group (Figure 4). The analysis of smooth pursuit ocular movements to the pendulum stimulus showed type III pattern of response (characteristic of cerebella dysfunction) in four subjects of the Depression Group and in one subject in the Control Group (Figure 5).

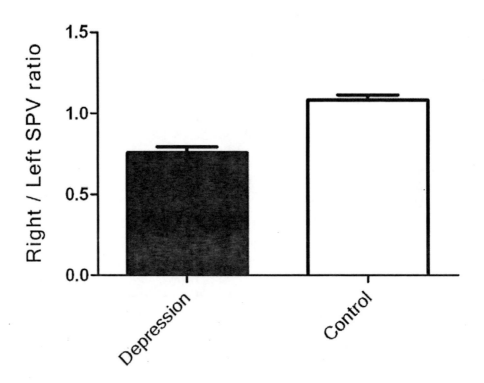

Figure 3. Clear asymmetry differences between Depression group patients and Controls (P<0.0001 two-tailed, Mann-Whitney test) (Bars show mean±SEM)

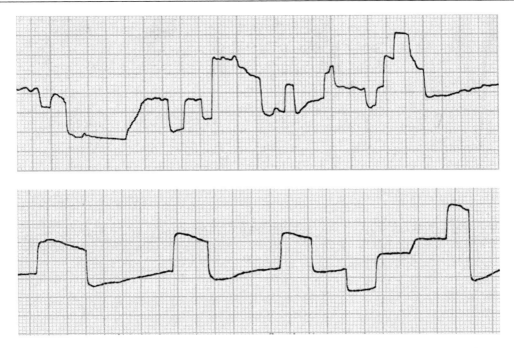

Figure 4 . Registers of eyes movements during the calibration in a depressed patient (upper) and in a control subject (lower register). Subjects were asked to look at a light point at 10° to the right and 10° to the left. Note the dissymmetry of the eyes movement in the depressive patient compared with the clean register of control subject.

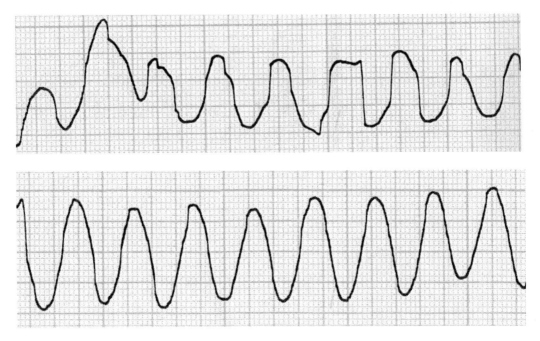

Figure5. Smooth ocular movement register when subjects are looking at a pendulum. Note the dissymmetry of eyes movements in the upper register that corresponds to a depressive patient, the lower register show normal characteristics.

Vestibulo-Ocular Reflex Study Allows Demonstrating Dysfunction of Specific Brain Stem Structures in Depression

Right Slow Phase Velocity Diminution is Indicative of Right Vestibular Nuclei Hypo Function in Depression

When we analyze Right and Left Vestibular Nuclei Slow phase velocity, within each depressed subject, we found nearly the half of activity of right side compared to the left side in the first experiment. In the second one, using the rotation chair, we found a less important diminution of the right side activity but still very significant, with an average right/left ratio of 0.75 for the depression group subjects. As the Slow phase velocity is controlled by the ipsilateral vestibular nuclei we can conclude that Right vestibular nuclei is hypo active in depression. In all the depressed subjects the slow phase velocity was diminished at the right side with no relation to the handedness or the sex. The meaning of this finding has to be studied searching what is the relation between vestibular nuclei and the neuronal circuitry involved in mood control and specifically what is the relation between the right side vestibular activity and mood.

Previous Studies about Abnormal Asymmetries in Depression

For many time scientists have been searching abnormal asymmetries in brain structures that could explain depression and other psychiatric diseases. As during the evolution of the species and also during the ontogeny, each hemisphere develops different specialized functions, this theory supports the idea that some specific lateralized brain areas that commands mood are dysfunctional. As mood is highly related with superior cerebral functions, it wasn't estrange to start studying frontal lobe bilateral differences of volume, thickness, EEG waves, metabolic activity etc. The amygdale, caudate nucleus or the thalamus also has been studied. But until now, nobody thought that brain stem functions could be involved in this disease, and probably it sounded not very interesting to study, because as I said previously, mood states seem to be related with superior cerebral functions and not with primitive ones. However, now looking again with new eyes, depression seems to be a very old emerged reaction that humans share with many other less evolved animals, and probably brain stem, is involved, at least in part, in its pathophysiology and responds to an adaptive behavior.

Reading the literature we can find controversial information about different brain asymmetries in depression, and a not exhaustive analysis can give us evidence of right and left abnormalities indistinct.

Vakili showed right hippocampal volume diminution in females with depression using Magnetic Resonance Imaging (Vakili K, 2000) and Mervaala demonstrated that left hippocampus is significantly smaller in severe depression and showed that right amygdalar volumes are smaller than left. (Mervaala E, 2000) Also Stewart showed evidence of right hemisphere dysfunction in depression measured by dichotic tests (Stewart JW, 1999) and Deldin gave evidence of right posterior brain anomaly reduction of N200 component of the event-related brain potential to faces in depressed subjects. (Deldin PJ, 2000) EEG registers showed right parietotemporal hypoactivation in depression (Kentgen LM, 2000) Also evidence of decreased right frontal lobe volume in depression (Kumar A,2000) and perinatal anoxia or hypoxia that leads to a blunted stress-induced dopamine release and an increase of DA transporter in right prefrontal cortex but not in the left, goes in the same direction demonstrating right side brain involvement (Brake WG, 2000) However other investigations show the contrary, as decreased left frontal resting cortical alpha band EEG (Harmon-Jones E, 1997), smaller left hippocampal volume in patients with depression without smaller volumes of amygdale, caudate, frontal and temporal lobe or whole brain volume found by Bremner (Bremner JD, 2000) and the greater relative right frontal activation of depressed subjects compared with nondepressed subjects with no differences in parietal asymmetry. (Schaffer CE, 1983)

Finally other studies neither find right nor left alterations as the increased variability of frontal EEG asymmetry in depression compared to healthy controls. (Debaner S, 2000) and Pillay investigation shows no anatomical alterations in basal ganglia (caudate and lenticular nucleus) (Pillay SS, 1998)

Absence of Fast Phase Velocity Asymmetries is Indicative of Symmetry of Pontine Reticular Formation Activity in Depression Subjects

Fast Phase Velocity depends on Reticular Pontine Reticular Formation witch is not asymmetric in depression. It means that certain nuclei and functions are specifically abnormal in depression and there isn't a whole brain lateralized dysfunction, furthermore they are remitted only to neuronal centers that are functionally related with mood regulation.

We didn't find other literature about fast phase bilateral (right versus left side) comparison in depressed patients.

Dysrhythmic Nystagmus and Decomposition of the Saccadic Arc are Indicative of Cerebellar Disturbances in Depression

Analyzing the electronystagmographic ocular movement's registers we found signs of cerebellar functional alterations in depression. The main finding was dysrrhythmic nystagmus and dissymmetric saccadic movements visible in the decomposition of the saccadic arc during the calibration.

Other previous study showed that depressed patients demonstrated increased rates of response suppression errors on an antisaccade task, less accurate memory for special location information in a special delayed response task, dissymmetric visually guided saccades and increased rates of saccadic intrusions during visual fixation providing quantitative documentation of significant disturbances in neurophysiological processes subserved by prefrontal cortex and cerebellar vermis. (Sweeney JA, 1998)

In summary: The main finding of our study is the asymmetry of the vestibulo-ocular reflex specifically right vestibular hypo activity in depression. What is the mechanism that origins this alteration? With the purpose of explaining better the possible theories I will begin talking about chronobiology and depression.

Depression Characterizes by Chronobiologic Alterations

Depression characterizes by clear chronobiologic abnormalities, although different or similar chronobiologic alterations are common to other mental health diseases as schizophrenia, ADHD and bipolar disease for example.

Chronobiologic functions are governed by the Suprachiasmatic Nuclei in the hypothalamus. This paired structure controls the activity of different brain areas that modulates hormonal secretion, mood, sleep-wake cycles and motor activity. The exact neuronal or humoral relation between SCN and the different brain areas involved in chronobiologic functions are not very clear, but experiments have shown that bilateral extirpation of SCN leads to dysrhythmic pattern of hormonal secretion, sleep, motor activity and finally to the cancers and death.

Light and Depression

Light that we receive in the melanopsin containing photoreceptors in the retina stimulates suprachiasmatic cells. This photic stimulus is capable of modulating the rhythmic chronobiologic activities including mood. It is known that enhancing the light stimulus in some depressive subjects can cure depression symptoms. This evidence allows us to propose that the SCN (suprachiasmatic nucleus) is an important nucleus on modulating mood states, and we could propose that the SCN is the main controller of mood states. But if it is the case, we wonder, witch mechanism leads to the development of other kinds of depression that doesn't respond to light treatment. Theoretically dysfunctions of any of the other neural afferents to SCN or in the SCN itself could origin depression.

Sleep Chronobiologic Alterations in Depression

One of the main chronobiologic alterations in depression is sleep abnormalities including insomnia or hypersomnia. Polisomnogram studies show sleep architecture abnormalities with reduced slow-wave sleep, shortened rapid eye movement (REM) latency and increased REM density in depression (Emslie GJ, 2001). The therapeutic role of sleep deprivation in some depressed subjects also suggests the relation between chronobiology and mood diseases.

Hormonal Chronobiologic Abnormalities in Depression

The altered pattern of cortisol secretion, with an hyper secretion that don't suppress with dexamethasone in DST (dexamethasone test) and loss of the physiological circadian pattern of secretion, has been described largely in the literature. Antonijevic showed enhanced secretion of ACTH and cortisol, a reduction in slow wave sleep, a blunted nocturnal grow hormone surge and elevation of CRH (Antonijevic I A, 2000) and Beck-Friis showed melatonin diminution, enhanced CRH, abnormal dexamethasone suppression test in severe depression (Beck-Friis J, 1985)

Hypothyroidism with a lower TSH and enhanced vasopressin are also frequent findings in depression.

Motor Activity Alterations In Depression

One of the external visible signs of suprachiasmatic function is locomotor activity, and wheel running counters are used frequently in hamsters experimental animals for studying the suprachiasmatic rhythmicity. In depression we can see different patterns of activity, being the motor retardation one of the most frequent findings in severe depression. Other altered states as motor agitation also is found. The way how the suprachiasmatic nuclei controls the motor activity is unknown, but experiments have shown that the extirpation of suprachiasmatic nuclei leads to a lose of in the normal pattern of motor activity in hamsters that recovers with an implantation of suprachiasmatic nuclei (Silver R, 1990; Meyer–Bernstein ER,1999; Harrington ME 1990; Pickard GE,1982;Pickard GE, 1983; Donaldson JA,1982)

The Suprachiasmatic-Raphe-Vestibular Nuclei System

The Relation between Suprachiasmatic Activity and Vestibular Function

As the Suprachiasmatic Nuclei controls motor activity and the vestibular nuclei receive motion information, we suggest that there is a feed back relation between both nuclei. Even thought, until the moment, the exact relationship between suprachiasmatic and vestibular nuclei is unknown, there are many studies that show anatomical and functional relationships between both structures. Researchers also have demonstrated that vestibular activity regulates circadian system (Murakami DM et al., 2002) and specifically medial vestibular nucleus, polysynaptically project to suprachiasmatic nuclei and monosynaptically to intergeniculate leaflet (Horowitz SS et al., 2004).

Evidence of Relationships between Suprachiasmatic Nuclei and Raphe Nuclei

It is widely accepted that raphe nuclei are one of the most important non-photic inputs to suprachiasmatic nuclei. Retrograde labeling techniques could confirm projections from raphe nuclei to SCN in rats, which would allow us to confirm that it receives inputs from dorsal raphe nuclei, median raphe nuclei and raphe magnus (Hay-Schmidt et al., 2003). Functional regulation of SCN by raphe nuclei also has been demonstrated in the literature (Muscat L et al., 2005; Ehlen JC et al., 2001; Glass JD et al., 2003; Dudley TE et al., 1999) (Meyer-Bernstein EL and Morin LP., 1996; Mintz EM et al., 1997; Colbron S et al., 2002; Collin M et al., 2000; Blasiak T and Lewandowski MH., 2003; Greenwood BN et al., 2005; Mrosovvsky N., 1996; Hastings MH et al., 1998; Meyer-Bernstein EL and Morin LP., 1999).

The Role of Raphe Nuclei in Depression; Previous Evidence

Clinical studies in humans suggest that raphe nuclei could play an important role in regulating SCN activity. Antidepressants known as selective serotonin reuptake inhibitors diminish depressive symptoms, including circadian alterations. Post mortem studies have revealed structural anomalies in raphe nuclei (Becker G et al., 1994; Becker G et al., 1995), a decrease in the number of neurons in the raphe nuclei in depressed patients (Baumann B et al., 2002) and increased tryptophan hydroxylase in dorsal raphe nuclei in depressed people who committed suicide (Boldrini M et al., 2005). Reduced brain serotonin transporter also has been described in living depressed patients (Malison TR et al., 1998).

In short, there is evidence to suggest a dysfunction of raphe nuclei in depression that can induce the circadian alterations characteristic of depression. On the other hand, raphe nuclei dysfunction could be a manifestation of SCN dysfunction and not it origin.

Evidence of Relationships between Raphe Nuclei and Vestibular Nuclei

Studies in animals indicate there are anatomical (Halberstadt AL and Balaban CD., 2003; Horowitz SS et al., 2004) and functional (Licata F et al., 1995; Kishimoto et al., 1991) relationships between vestibular nuclei and raphe nuclei.

The theory: Right versus left SCN-Raphe-Vestibular Nuclei System is symmetric in healthy state, in depression there is an asymmetry that consists in right side hypo activity and normal left function.

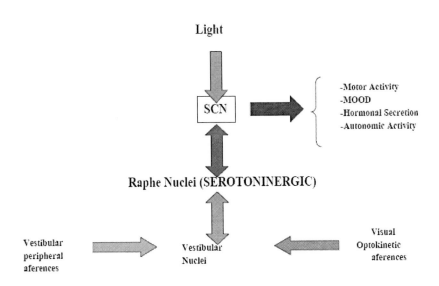

Figure 6 . Schematic representation of Suprachiasmatic Nuclei functioning SCN: Suprachiasmatic Nuclei. In healthy state, right and left side of SCN-Raphe Nuclei-Vestibular Nuclei system is symmetric. In depression we detected right side vestibular hypo activity that could have it origin in right SCN dysfunction, in right raphe nuclei dysfunction or in both.

Conclusion

Right vestibular hypo activity previously reported in depressive patients, using caloric tests (0.56 asymmetry ratio) (Soza AM and Aviles M, 2007), was confirmed in the second investigation we are presenting now, using rotatory tests (0.76 asymmetry ratio).

The dissymmetry of eye movements during the calibration and of smooth eye movements during pendular visual stimulus, gives new support for the theory of cerebellar disturbances addressed in the same previously mentioned article.

The anatomic and functional relationship between SCN-Raphe Nuclei and Vestibular Nuclei, suggests that the lateralized vestibular dysfunction found in depression could have its origin in ipsilateral SCN or Raphe Nuclei dysfunction.

Previous evidence in hamsters has shown that suprachiasmatic nuclei lateralize into right or left side activity following exposure to constant light (De la Iglesia HO, 2000). Given that stress is cause-effect related with mood diseases (Nemeroff CB, Vale WW, 2005 ; Bale TL and Vale WW, 2003; Neigh GN, Nemeroff CB, 2006) and constant light seems to be a stressful condition (Vernikos-Daniellis J, 1970), we wonder if stress might act the same way in humans and cause SCN activity to be asymmetric. If this is in fact the case, we must investigate why the asymmetry appears on one side (right hypo activity in depression) and not in the contra lateral side. There also is a need to study anatomical and functional asymmetries of raphe nuclei structures, especially the bilateral distribution of hormone receptors as leptin (Finn P D, 2001; Collin, 2000), orexin and estrogens that could affect SCN and vestibular function in an asymmetric way.

Fernandez-Galaz (2002) observed that leptin can be selectively accumulated by serotonergic neurones in the Raphe Nuclei and that this mechanism is gender specific. He demonstrates that after 6 hours of leptin administration, all male and female rats showed massive leptin binding in the dorsal raphe, while 30 min after leptin treatment, only 10% of male rats exhibited leptin-labeled cells in contrast to 50% of females. These findings support the idea that the midbrain serotoninergic system is an important mediator of the effects of leptin on brain function and may provide an explanation for gender differences in metabolism regulation and its coordination with higher functions of the brain. But the right-left side symmetry of leptin activity hasn't been studied in raphe nuclei.

Several previous studies suggests asymmetries in cortisol and CRH receptor distribution in brain structures in depressed people (Sullivan RM, Gratton A,1999; Tops M, 2005; Buss KA, 2003; Field T, 2002; Diego MA, 2001), supporting the pathophysiologic importance of this idea, but right-left asymmetries of CRH receptors in raphe nuclei is still not studied. In the other hand wheel running have been probed to alter raphe nuclei activity (Greenwood BN, 2005), although right or left side differences on raphe nuclei activity have not been reported in animal models of depression

The relationship between vestibular-raphe nuclei-SCN asymmetry and mental disorders introduces a new approach for the neural mechanisms involved in depression physiopathology. The role of SCN on mood states also must be addressed, especially in view of the fact that circadian alterations have been demonstrated clearly in depression. It is possible that the current monoaminergic theory must be included in an approach that considers all of the afferents that influence SCN function, including light, raphe nuclei-serotonin, vestibular, and probably other functions. It would therefore be of interest to analyze which afferent is failing in each patient.

In view of all of this, there is a need to discuss and re-analyze the meaningfulness of vestibular exams in vestibular symptomatic otorhinolaryngologic patients. Questions remain as to whether they only reflect vestibular dysfunctions or are also indicative of chronobiologic bilateral desynchronization.

Finally, it is important to note that given that vestibular activity probably reflects SCN activity, the idea of an in vivo appreciation of right and left SCN activity could be interesting.

Acknowledgment

I acknowledge to the Medical Technicians Brigita Certanec and Joel Reyes. To the Commandants Dr. Gustavo Hein and Dr. Polanco for approving the investigation.

References

Antonijevic IA, Murck H, Frieboes RM, Barthelmes J, Steiger A. (2000) Sexually dimorphic effects of GHRH on sleep-endocrine activity in patients with depression and normal controls - part I: the sleep eeg. *Sleep Res. Online*, *3*:5-13

Bale TL and Vale WW (2003).CRF and CRF receptors: role in stress responsivity and other behaviors. *Annual Review of Pharmacology and Toxicology.* *44*:525-557

Baumann B, Bielau H, Krell D,Agelink MW, Diekmann S, Wurthmann C, Truner K, Bernstein HG, Danos P, Bogerts B(2002). Circumscribed numerical deficit of dorsal raphe neurons in mood disorders. *Psychol. Med. 32*: 93-103

Beck-Friis J, Ljunggren JG, Thoren M, von Rosen D, Kjeliman BF, Wetterberg L(1985). Melatonin, cortisol and ACTH in patients with major depressive disorder and healthy humans with special reference to the outcome of the dexamethasone suppression. *Psychoneuroendocrinology.10*: 173-86.

Becker G, Becker T,Struck M (1995). Reduced echogenicity of brainstem raphe specific to unipolar depression: a transcranial color-coded real-time sonography study. *Biol. Psychiatry 38*:180-184

Becker G, Stuck M, Bogdahn U, Becker T (1994). Echogenicity of the brainstem raphe in patients with mayor depression. *Psychiatry Res. 55*: 75-84

Blasiak T, Lewandowski MH. (2003). Dorsal raphe nucleus modulates neuronal activity in rat intergeniculate leaflet. *Behav. Brain Res. 138*:179-185

Boldrini M,Underwood MD, Mann JJ, Arango V. (2005) .More tryptophan hydroxylase in the brainstem dorsal raphe nucleus in depressed suicides. *Brain Res .1041*:19-28

Brake WG, Sullivan RM, Gratton A.(2000) Perinatal distress leads to lateralized medial prefrontal cortical dopamine hypofunction in adult rats *The Journal of Neuroscience, 20*:5538:5543

Bremner JD, Narayan M, Anderson ER, Staib LH, Miller HL, Charney DS. (2000) Hippocampal volume reduction in major depression *Am. J .Psychiatry, 157*:115-118

Buss KA, Schumacher JR, Dolski I, Kalin NH, Goldsmith HH, Davidson RJ (2003)Right frontal brain activity, cortisol, and withdrawal behavior in 6-month-old infants. *Behav. Neurosci. 117*:11-20

Colbron S, Jones M, Biello SM. (2002). MDMA alters the response of the circadian clock to a photic and non-photic stimulus. *Brain Res ..956*:45-52

Collin M, Hakansson-Ovesjo ML, Misane I, Ogren SO,Meister B. (2000).Decreased 5-HT transporter mRNA in neurons of the dorsal raphe nucleus and behavioral depression in obese leptin-deficeint ob-ob mouse. *Brain Res. Mol. Brain Res. 81*:51-61

Debener S, Beauducel A, Nessler D, Brocke B, Heilemann H, Kayser J (2000) Is resting anterior EEG alpha asymmetry a trait marker for depression? Findings for healthy adults and clinically depressed patients. *Neuropsychobiology, 41*:31-37

De la Iglesia HO, Meyer Jennifer, Carpino A, Schwartz WJ (2000) Antiphase oscilation of the left and right suprachiasmatic nuclei. *Science, 290*:799-801

Deldin PJ, Keller J, Gergen JA, Miller GA (2000) Right-posterior face processing anomaly in depression. *J. Abnorm. Psychol. 109*:116-21

Diego MA, Field T, Hernandez-Reif M. (2001) CES-D depression scores are correlated with frontal EEG alpha asymmetry.*Depress Anxiety.13*:32-7

Donaldson JA, Stephan FK. (1982) Entrainment of circadian rhythms: retinofugal pathways and unilateral suprachiasmatic nucleus lesions. *Physiol. Behav. 29*:1161-9

Dudley TE, DiNardo La, Glass JD (1999). In vivo assessment of the midbrain raphe nuclear regulation of serotonin release in the hamster suprachiasmatic nucleus. *J. Neurophysiol. 81*:1469-1477

Ehlen JC ,Grossman GH, Glass JD. (2001).In vivo resetting of the hamster circadian clock by 5-HT7 receptors in the suprachiasmatic nucleus. *J. Neurosci. 21*:5351-5357

Emslie GJ, Armitage R, Weinberg WA, Rush AJ, Mayes TL, Hoffmann RF.(2001) Sleep polysomnography as a predictor of recurrence in children and adolescents with major depressive disorder *Int. J. Neuropsychopharmacol., 4*:159-68

Field T, Diego M, Hernandez-Reif M, Schanberg S, Kuhn C. (2002) Relative right versus left EEG in neonates. *Dev. Psychobiol .41*:147-155

Finn P. D, Cunningham M. J., Rickard D. G., Clifton D. K, Steiner R. A.(2001) Serotonergic Neurons Are Targets for Leptin in the Monkey *The Journal of Clinical Endocrinology and Metabolism 86*: 422-426

Fernández-Galaz M. C., Diano S., T. L. Horvath (2002)Leptin. Uptake by Serotonergic Neurones of the Dorsal Raphe. *Journal of Neuroendocrinology;14*:429-434

Glass JD, Grossman GH, Farnbauch L, Di Nardo L (2003). Midbrain raphe modulation of nonphotic circadian clock resetting and 5-HT release in the mammalian suprachiasmatic nucleus. *J. Neurosci. 23*:7451-7460

Greenwood BN, Foley TE, Day HE, Burhans D, Brooks L, Campeau S, Fleshner M (2005). Wheel running alters serotonin (5-HT) transporter, 5-HT1A, 5-HT1B, and alpha 1b-adrenergic receptor mRNA in the rat raphe nuclei. *Biol. Psychiatry 57*:559-568

Halberstadt AL, Balaban CD (2003). Organization of projections from raphe nuclei to the vestibular nuclei in rats. *Neuroscience 120*:573-594

Harmon-Jones E, Allen JJ (1997) Behavioral activation sensitivity and resting frontal EEG asymmetry: covariation of putative indicators related to risk for mood disorders; *J. Abnorm. Psychol., 106*:159-63

Harrington ME, Eskes GA, Dickson P, Rusak B(1990) Lesions dorsal to the suprachiasmatic nuclei abolish split activity rhythms of hamsters. *Brain Res. Bull. 24*:593-7.

Hastings MH, Duffield GE, Smith EJD, Maywood ES, Ebling FJP. (1998). Entrainment of the circadian system of mammals by non-photic cues. *Chronobiol. Int;15*:425-445

Hay-Schmidt A, Vrang N, Larsen PJ, Mikkelsen JD (2003). Projections from the raphe nuclei to the suprachiasmatic nucleus of the rat. *J. Chem. Neuroanat. 25*:293-310

Horowitz SS, Blanchard JH, Morin LP (2004). Intergeniculate leaflet and ventral lateral geniculate nucleus afferent connections: An anatomical substrate for functional input from vestibulo-visuomotor system. *.J Comp Neurol 474*:227-245

Horowitz SS, Blanchard JH, Morin LP (2004). Intergeniculate leaflet and ventral lateral geniculate nucleus afferent connections: An anatomical substrate for functional input from vestibulo-visuomotor system. *J. Comp. Neurol. 474*:227-245

Kentgen LM, Tenke CE, Pine DS, Fong R, Klein RG, Bruder GE. (2000) Electroencephalographic asymmetries in adolescents with major depression: influence of comorbidity with anxiety disorders *J. Abnorm. Psychol.*, *109*:797-802

Kishimoto T, Sasa M, Takahori S (1991). Inhibition of lateral vestibular nucleus neurons by 5-hydroxytriptamine derived from the dorsal raphe nucleus. *Brain Res.* *553*:229-237

Kumar A, Bilker W, Lavretsky H, Gottlieb G. (2000)Volumetric asymmetries in late-onset mood disorders: an attenuation of frontal asymmetry with depression severity *Psychiatry Res.*, *100*:41-7

Licata F, Li Volsi G, Maugeri G,Santangelo F (1995). Neuronal responses in vestibular nuclei to dorsal raphe electrical activation. *J. Vestib. Res* .*5*:137-145

Neigh GN, Nemeroff CB (2006). Reduced glucocorticoid receptors: consequence or cause of depression? *Trends Endocrinol. Metab.*, *17*:124-125

Nemeroff CB, Vale WW (2005). The neurobiology of depression: inroads to treatment and new drug discovery. *J. Clin. Psychiatry*, *66*:5-13

Malison TR, Price LH, Berman R, van Dick CH, Pelton GH, Carpenter L, Sanacora G (1998). Reduced brain serotonin transporter availability in mayor depression as measured by [123I]-2 beta-carbomethoxi-3 beta (4-iodophenyl) tropane and single photon emission computed tomography. *Biol. Psychiatry 44*:1090-1098

Martinot M, Bragulat V, Artiges E, Dolle F, Hinnen F, Jouvent R, Martinot J(2001) Decreased presynaptic dopamine function in the left caudate of depressed patients with affective flattening and psychomotor retardation. *Am. J. Psychiatry*, *158*:314-6

Mervaala E, Fohr J, Kononen M, Valkonen-Korhonen M, Vaino P, Partanen K, Partanen J, Tiihonen J Viinamaki H, Karjalainen AK, Lehtonen J. (2000) Quantitative MRI of the hippocampus and amygdala in severe depression *Psychol Med.*, *30*:117-25

Meyer-Bernstein EL, Morin LP (1996). Differencial serotonergic innervation of the suprachiasmatic nucleus and the intergeniculate leaflet and its role in circadian rhythm modulation. *J. Neurosci. 16*: 2097-2111

Meyer-Bernstein EL, Morin LP (1999). Electrical stimulation of the median or dorsal raphe nuclei reduces light induced FOS protein in the suprachiasmatic nucleus and causes circadian activity rhythm phase shifts. *Neuroscience 92*: 267-279

Mintz EM, Guillespie CF, Marvel CL, Hurhman KL, Albers HE. (1997). Serotonergic regulation of circadian rhythms in Syrian hamsters. *Neuroscience 79*:563-569

Murakami DM, Erkman L, Hermanson O, Rosenfeld MG, Fuller CA (2002). Evidence for vestibular regulation of autonomic functions in a mouse genetic model. *Proc. Natl .Acad. Sci* .USA *99*:17078-17082

Muscat L, Tischler RC, Morin LP (2005). Functional analysis of the role of the median raphe as a regulator of hamster circadian system sensitivity to light. *Brain Res.1044*:59-66.

Mrosovvsky N (1996). Locomotor activity and non-photic influences on circadian clocks. *Biol. Rev. Camb. Philos. Soc. 71*:343-372

Pickard GE, Turek FW The suprachiasmatic nuclei: two circadian clocks?(1983) *Brain Res. 268*:201-10.

Pickard GE, Turek FW. (1982) Splitting of the circadian rhythm of activity is abolished by unilateral lesions of the suprachiasmatic nuclei. *Science 215*:1119-21

Pillay SS, Renshaw PF, Bonello CM, Lafer BC, Fava M, Yurgelun-Todd D. (1998) A quantitative magnetic resonance imaging study of caudate and lenticular nucleus gray matter volume in primary unipolar major depression: relationship to treatment response and clinical severity *Psychiatry Res*, *84*:61-74

Perreau-Lenz S.,Pevet P,Buijs RM, Kalsbeek A (2004)The biological Clock: the bodyguard of Temporal Homeostasis. *Chronobiology International 21*:1-25

Schaffer CE, Davidson RJ, Saron C, (1983) Frontal and parietal electroencephalogram asymmetry in depressed and nondepressed subjects. *Biol. Psychiatry*, *18*:753-62

Silver R, Lehman MN, Gibson M, Gladstone WR, Bittman EL. (1990) Dispersed cell suspensions of fetal SCN restore circadian rhythmicity in SCN-lesioned adult hamsters. *Brain Res. 525*:45-58.

Soza Ried AM, Aviles M(2007) Asymmetries of vestibular dysfunction in Major Depression. *Neurosci 144*:128-134

Stewart JW, Quitkin FM, McGrath PJ, Bruder GE. (1999)Do tricyclic responders have different brain laterality? *J. Abnorm. Psychol .108*:707-10

Sullivan RM, Gratton A(1999)Lateralized effects of medial prefrontal cortex lesions on neuroendocrine and autonomic stress responses in rats. *J. Neurosci. 19*:2834-2840

Sweeney JA, Strojwas MH, Mann JJ,Thase ME(1998).Prefrontal and cerebellar abnormalities in major depression: evidence from oculomotor studies.*Biol. Psychiatry*, *43*:584-94

Tops M at als. (2005) Acute cortisol administration modulates EEG alpha asymmetry in volunteers: relevance to depression. *Biol. Psychol. 69*:181-193

Vakili K, Pillay SS, Lafer B, Fava M, Renshaw PF, Bonello-Cintron CM, Yurgelun-Todd DA (2000) Hippocampal volume in primary unipolar major depression: a magnetic resonance imaging study. *Biol. Psychiatry, 15*: 1087-90

Vernikos-Daniellis J, Winget CM, Hetherington NW (1970) Diurnal rhythm of the pituitary-adrenocortical response to stress:effect of constant light and constant darkness. *Life Sci. Space Res. 8*:240-246

In: Women and Depression
Editors: Paula Hernandez and Sara Alonso

ISBN 978-1-60456-647-5
© 2009 Nova Science Publishers, Inc.

Chapter 20

Depression as a Risk Factor for Coronary Heart Disease in Women

Antonio Del Pino,[12] [13]*Maria Teresa Gaos*[14] *and Francisco Bosa*[15]
University of La Laguna, Spain

Introduction

The study of depression as a possible risk factor in the incidence of coronary heart disease (CHD) and for recurring coronary episodes or death in previously ill people has a certain tradition in the literature, but publications on this possible relation increased greatly after the appearance of a meta-analysis by Booth-Kewley and Friedman (1987). These authors reviewed 87 studies on the relationship between psychosocial risk factors, especially Type A Behavior (TAB) and its components, and cardiac disease (CD). Among their results referring to the relation between these factors and all types of CD is that greater effect size is produced on analysis of results from studies using TAB measured by the Structured Interview, with depression as a risk factor of considerable weight. Booth-Kewley and Friedman noted that although depression seemed to be reliably associated with CD, it had largely been underestimated. As from the 1980s, and particularly during the 1990s, the number of publications on this as a possible risk factor for CD increased, with a corresponding decline in the number of studies on TAB. Thus Scheidt (2000), in his editorial for a special edition of the Journal of Psychosomatic Research devoted to research on psychosocial factors implicated in cardiovascular diseases, expressed surprise about the absence of contributions to the special edition on TAB as a risk factor for CD.

The importance of depression is particularly great if we consider the results of the meta-analysis by Booth-Kewley and Friedman (1987) who found an effect size expressed in **z**

---

[12] Correspondence concerning this contribution should be addressed to first author. E-mail: apino@ull.es.
13 Department of Personality, Evaluation and Psychological Treatment. La Laguna University
14 Department of Psychobiology and Methodology of Behavioral Sciences. La Laguna University.
15 Head of Hemodynamic and Interventional Cardiology Section. University Hospital of the Canary Islands.

score of 6.44 for the relationship between depression and all types of CD. Effect size was 5.24 for the relationship between depression and myocardial infarction (MI) and 4.29 for the relationship between depression and angina pectoris as an indicator of CHD. Thus it was not unexpected when Lespérance and Frasure-Smith (2000) suggested that it was time to replace TAB with depression as a psychological priority for cardiologists because depression: a) is the fourth most frequent cause of mortality and early invalidity and the second in industrialized countries, only preceded by CHD; b) clearly plays a large part in medical prescription non-adherence and failure to follow recommendations on life-style changes; c) may interfere with and reduce the efficacy of other treatment aimed at ensuring that cardiovascular patients lead active and productive lives. Further weight is added to this issue by the fact that the rate of CHD has increased more rapidly in women than in men since 1984. In addition, estimated mortality for the period 1990-2020 indicates that ischemic cardiopathy and depression are leading factors contributing to world wide mortality (Murray and Lopez, 1997a; 1997b). Thus we are dealing with a major health issue, albeit controversial; in spite of the evidence in favor of its association with CHD, depression is not considered a risk factor, as became clear at the annual meeting of the American College of Cardiology held in Bethesda, 2002. The final report listed ten risk factors for CHD, and depression was not included.

Evidence for the Relation between Depression and Coronary Heart Disease

The possible weight of depression in the incidence and recurrence of CHD is mainly analyzed in prospective studies and the available evidence is usually presented in two types of evaluation – qualitative reviews and quantitative reviews or meta-analyses. Both types usually provide evaluation of two categories of results: those obtained from people without manifest CHD, therefore not diagnosed or detected, and those obtained from people diagnosed with CHD. Studies included in the first category are usually called etiologic since they aim to determine the effect of depression on the incidence of CHD, and those included in the second category aim to determine the contribution made by depression on the recurrence of CHD events or death by this disease in previously ill people. The development of the topic will be treated differently. For studies included in the first category, we will present a meta-analysis, while for those in the second category we can only present some data and comments. The reason for this difference is that, despite certain limitations, the literature contains a sufficient number of etiologic studies to be able to perform a meta-analysis, while the body of published prognostic research on depression and CD is too limited in quantity and quality to justify performing a meta-analysis (Wulsin, 2004), and even more so if, as is our objective, we focus only on CHD in women.

Studies on People without Coronary Heart Disease

Research in this category began with analysis of the incidence of CHD and CD deaths in people with psychiatric or serious psychological disorders (Malzberg, 1937; Weeke, 1979). Most of this research consisted of retrospective or case-control studies compared with general population data (Norton and Whalley, 1984; Rabins, Harvis and Koven, 1985; Tsuang, Woolson and Fleming, 1980). In addition, these studies presented the problem of having to elucidate whether CHD and death due to CD were a consequence of depression or due to the effect of the drugs used to treat the depression (Weeke, Juel and Vaeth, 1987). Although work with psychiatric patients has continued to be published (Angst, Stassen and Angst, 2002; Sharma and Markar, 1994; Vestergaard and Aagaard, 1991), problems of this type have meant that most research on depression and CHD has focused on theoretically healthy people i.e. study samples of people not diagnosed with CHD and not treated for depression over prolonged periods of time. Of particular relevance to the topic at hand is one study performed on people with psychiatric disorder that found higher risk of death due to CHD in depressed women but not in depressed men (Black, Warrack and Winokur, 1985).

We have mentioned these initial studies testimonially, without wishing to establish an artificial division between depression as a psychiatric disorder and depressive mood. We consider depression to be a depressive mood that is expressed on a continuum of lesser to greater degree and not a dichotomous disorder that is either present or absent.

Etiological Evidence for the Relation between Depression and Coronary Heart Disease in the General Population

The study of the relation between depression and CHD using samples of people who live in the community and who do not have CHD or psychiatric disorder eliminates the possible effect of both pharmacological treatment and the effect of institutional internment. The use of this type of sample causes a significant shift in focus from the most severe cases of depression to those with less severe or symptomatic depression. With this type of study, the question arises as to whether the processes responsible for the development of CHD or for increased mortality in people with severe depression, i.e. psychiatric cases or patients treated for depression, are sufficiently forceful to produce measurable effects in people with only slight or symptomatic depression.

The relationship between depression and CHD in men and women of the general population has been reported in several qualitative reviews. Concentrating only on those published as from the year 2000, we have that of Kubzansky, and Kawachi (2000) who analyzed studies published up to mid-1998. Kuper, Marmor, and Hemingway (2002) reviewed work published up to mid-2001: their objective was to evaluate the strength of causal relations between psychosocial factors and the incidence of CHD. Rudisch, and Nemeroff (2003) reviewed 14 studies published before 2002. Lett et al. (2004), on the basis of etiological studies published before 2003, quantified Risk Ratio (RR) with values ranging from 1.5 to 2.0. Wulsin (2004) also reviewed studies published before 2002 and presented specific questions as to the criteria whereby a particular risk factor should be considered as such. Suls, and Bunde (2005) presented a review of studies published before 2003 on anger, anxiety and depression as risk factors for cardiovascular disease. This review by Suls and Bunde used particularly lax inclusion criteria which favors over-inclusion, but they raised the interesting point as to whether it makes sense to talk about a particular emotional state (anger, anxiety, depression) as a determinant factor in CD or whether we should be talking more about a complex of emotional states, as they also propose. Lastly, mention must be made of the reviews by Frasure-Smith, and Lespérance (2005, 2006). The first covers studies published from mid-2001 to 15 December 2003, while the second deals with those published from 15 December 2003 to 15 December 2005.

As can be seen from the above list of reviews cited, the problem of evaluating study results is not the lack of information, but rather the choice of selection criteria for correct evaluation of the available publications. We believe that this is best achieved using meta-analyses and, based on their results, we propose to present and evaluate the evidence available on the relation between depression and CHD in the general population of men and women.

In this respect we have found four meta-analyses. Rugulies (2002) reviewed the literature up to May 2000 and included 11 studies in his meta-analysis, which resulted in an adjusted RR for CHD associated with depression of 1.64 [95% confidence interval (CI) : 1.29 - 2.08; p <.001]. A sensitivity analysis showed that clinical depression was a stronger predictor, RR = 2.69 (95% CI : 1.63 - 4.43; p <.001), than depressive mood, RR = 1.49 (95% CI : 1.16 – 1.92; p = .002) and controlling for the presence of CHD prior to initiating the study showed an RR of 1.51 (95% CI : 1.03 - 2.20; p = .03), slightly lower than that of studies not controlling for previous CHD: RR = 1.77 (95% CI : 1.27-2.45; p = .001). Crude or only age adjusted RR did not produce significant change in the adjusted RR. Crude RR for all the studies was 1.75 (95% CI : 1.37 - 2.25; p <.001), RR for studies evaluating clinical depression was 2.74 (95% CI : 1.57 - 4.76; p <.001), and RR for studies evaluating depressive mood was 1.59 (95% CI : 1.22 – 2.08; p =.001). According to Rugulies, this slight difference between the adjusted and unadjusted RR indicates that depression had a specific weight in the association with CHD independently of what are considered traditional risk factors for CHD.

Wulsin, and Singal (2003), like Rugulies (2002), limited their meta-analysis to CHD and depression considered in two ways: as a disorder and as a set of depressive symptoms. They reviewed the literature up to the end of the year 2000 and include only ten studies, giving a total RR for CHD associated with depression of 1.64 (95% CI : 1.41- 1.90).

To highlight the independent nature of the two meta-analyses cited above, it is noteworthy that their authors considered the same studies in only seven cases, despite having practically the same objectives and with only one year difference in publication date. The meta-analysis by Rugulies (2002) included eleven studies while that by Wulsin, and Singal (2003) included ten studies. Despite these differences, the most adjusted RR obtained was the same, namely 1.64. They only differed in the 95% CI.

Nicholson, Kuper, and Hemingway (2006) reviewed etiological and prognostic studies up to December 2003. They selected 21 etiological studies involving 124.509 participants followed for a mean 10.8 years. A total of 4.016 artery-coronary events occurred, giving an unadjusted RR of 1.81 (95% CI : 1.53 - 2.15). Of these 21 studies, eleven included results adjusted for other risk factors. Such adjustment had the effect of reducing the unadjusted RR of 2.08 (95% CI : 1.69 - 2.55; p <.001) to an adjusted RR of 1.90 (95% CI : 1.48 - 2.42).

The meta-analysis by Van der Kooy et al. (2007) aimed to estimate the risk associated with depression of suffering diverse cardiovascular diseases. This objective was broader than ours, with its focus on CHD alone. They reviewed 28 studies published up to January 2005. The effect size for all these studies was 1.46 (95% CI : 1.37 - 2.08), although the heterogeneity was substantial except for women, depressive disorders and MI. The effect of depression in women on different cardiovascular endpoints evaluated from nine studies was an effect size of 1.38 (95% CI : 1.22 - 1.55). Another noteworthy finding was that the group of four studies evaluating major depression not only obtained more homogenous results than the 21 studies evaluating depressive symptoms but also strongly predicted cardiovascular disease with RR = 2.54 (95% CI : 2.07 - 3.10) for major depression and RR = 1.39 (95% CI : 1.26-1.54) for symptomatic depression.

Conclusions

The etiological meta-analyses available allow us to affirm that healthy people with major depression or depressive symptoms show a clear risk of suffering CHD. The effect size alter adjusting for the possible contribution of other risk factors or variables explaining the possible relation between depression and CHD oscillates between 1.46 in the meta-analysis by Van der Kooy et al. (2007) and 1.90 in that performed by Nicholson, Kuper, and Hemingway (2006). In our opinion, these two meta-analyses employ wider inclusion criteria for both the evaluation of depression and the endpoint taken as a reference of cardiac disease. They included cardiovascular diseases instead of only CHD as did Rugulies (2002), Wulsin, and Singal (2003) and as we do. The magnitude of effect size obtained in the latter two meta-analyses, 1.64 in both cases, fall within the limits indicated so that a clear and significant relation can be affirmed between depression and CHD. This magnitude is similar to that of other risk factors for CHD such as smoking, with effect size of 1.25 for passive smokers and 2.5 for active smokers (He et al., 1999 and Wulsin, and Singal, 2003).

Etiological Evidence for the Relation between Depression and Coronary Heart Disease in Women: A Meta-Analysis

To date no meta-analysis has been published with the objective of evaluating the effect of depression on the incidence of CHD (objectively proven angina pectoris, MI and cardiac-related death) in healthy women with depression, using prospective studies with samples taken from the general population. The present meta-analysis is an attempt to achieve this objective.

Methods

Inclusion Criteria

The criteria used to include published studies on this topic were: 1) Prospective methodology, so that cross-sectional case control and retrospective studies were excluded. 2) Inclusion of women living in the community who were initially healthy or did not present apparent CHD at baseline. 3) Use as reference of CHD death due to this cause, MI resulting in death or not, and objectively proven angina pectoris due to CHD. 4) Depression considered as a disorder and/or a set of depressive symptoms. Studies on patients with bipolar disorder were excluded because most professionals agree that depression associated with unipolar and bipolar disorder differ substantially in etiology and clinical characteristics. 5) Evaluation of depression by means of a standard questionnaire, a diagnostic interview, a specialist medical diagnosis, taking anti-depressive medication by medical prescription or self-reporting of such diagnosis and treatment. 6) Follow-up of at least four years from baseline date. 7) Present a value of RR (or data allowing the calculation of RR) of developing CHD in the group of women with depression. 8) Selection, between publications referring to the same population cohort, of that which documented longer follow-up period.

Literature Search

From the meta-analyses and qualitative reviews cited, we obtained information on the topic up to 15 December 2006. From these we extracted those providing results referring only to women. For later dates we performed a search from December 2005 to October 2.007 using the data bases MEDLINE and PsycINFO. For MEDLINE we crossed 'depression' and the expanded term 'depressive disorder' with 'coronary heart disease'. For PsychInfo we crossed 'depression emotion' and 'affective disturbances' with 'coronary artery disease' and 'myocardial ischemia'.

Selecting Studies

We found 293 references, of which we selected 64 that seemed of probable interest judged by their published abstracts. These 64 articles were read by the first author. After a meeting with the other authors of the present study, it was decided to include only the study by Ahto, Isoaho, Puolijoki, Vahlberg, and Kivela (2007) in the list of eleven studies also included after reviewing the references cited in reviews or meta-analyses previously performed by other authors.

Among the studies that met our inclusion criteria were four that shared state health programs carried out in USA. We included the four since we considered them to be different. The study by Chang, Hahn, Teutsch, and Hutwagner (2001) and that by Ferketich, Schwartzbaum, Frid, and Moeschberger (2000) appear referred to the first National Health and Nutrition Examination Survey (NHANES-I) and its Epidemiologic Follow-Up Study (NHEFS) of the United States population. The NHANES 1 was a national study carried out in USA from 1971 to 1974, excluding Alaska, Hawaii and American Indian reserves. Data on around 32,000 people were collected. The longitudinal NHEFS followed a sub-sample of 14,407 adults aged 25–74 years who received a detailed medical examination and participated in the follow-up study, which included four follow-up surveys, the last conducted in 1992. The studies were published by researchers working in different states, Chang et al. in Georgia and Ferketich et al. in Ohio, without mutual citation. We therefore considered that these two studies, with different objectives, did not work with the same samples. The studies by Mendes de Leon et al. (1998) and Penninx et al. (1998) obtained their respective samples from the Established Populations for the Epidemiologic Studies of the Elderly (EPESE), a survey conducted between 1982 and 1983 on the population aged $\geq$ 65 years. Penninx et al. used data from 3 communities living in East Boston, Massachusetts, and data from the population of 2 counties in Iowa, and from a random sample of the population living in New Haven, Connecticut, stratified by housing type and sex. The study by Mendes de Leon et al. (1998) used a sample of people, especially men, living in New Haven, one of the cities from which Penninx et al. also collected part of their sample. Some sample overlap is therefore possible, although the endpoint chosen in each study was different.

Data Abstraction

After selecting the relevant studies, it was necessary to choose the endpoints to be included in the analysis of studies presenting results with more than one endpoint appropriate for our study. The guiding principle was to perform a first analysis including the most general or shared data. For example, the study by Chang et al. (2001) analyzed black and white women separately. As most women participants in the other studies were white, we only included in our meta-analysis those results pertaining to white women. In the study by Wassertheil-Smoller et al. (2004) we opted to include CAD as the endpoint because the authors defined it more strictly than CHD, the latter including cardiovascular disorders such as stroke, pulmonary embolism, and other or unknown types of cardiovascular disease. In other cases we made use of the most reliable data, as in the study by Ferketich et al. (2000) which provided results referring to fatal and non-fatal CHD. We chose the latter because it is easier to prove or verify CHD events in live people than in those who have died. When two adjustment models were presented, as in the studies by Aromaa et al. (1994), Ferketich et al. (2000) and Mendes de Leon et al. (1998), we included in our analysis those obtained using the greater number of adjusted variables. In accordance with this logic, from the study by Aromaa et al (1994) we included in the analysis of crude results the value referring to CHD, given that the CHD category is wider than that of MI or AP, and in the analysis of adjusted results we included the values referring to MI and to the adjustment model that included the greatest number of variables.

Statistical Analyses

Since the majority of the studies in the review had analyzed depression as a dichotomous variable, the meta-analyses were performed with RRs from dichotomous comparisons.

For the studies that failed to report the exact p value, the CI, or the standard error, we calculated, so that they could be included in the analyses, an approximate standard error by dividing the natural logarithm of the RR value by 1.96, which is the value of a unit-normal test statistic corresponding to a p value of 0.05.

In combining the individual RR estimates, we used a random-effects model because this model assumes heterogeneity across studies, and to determine the size of the effect of the modulating variable "follow-up", we performed a comparative meta-analysis of the studies by grouping them in intervals according to years of follow-up. The importance of the follow-up factor to appreciate inter-study heterogeneity was assessed by subtracting the total Q-statistic from the subgroup models from the Q-value in the un-stratified model.

The meta-analyses were performed with the Statistic Program: "*Comprehensive Meta-Analysis Version 2*" by BIOSTAT, INC.

Results

The most relevant characteristics of the twelve studies included in the meta-analysis are presented in TABLE 1 and the results obtained in them are shown in TABLE 2.

The twelve studies evaluated depression and the state of health of some 126,000 women who were followed for a period ranging from 4 to 26 years on average. The number of participants in each study ranged from 378 women in the study by Ahto et al. (2007) to 93.376 women in the study by Wassertheil-Smoller et al. (2004). The studies present the N at initiation, regardless of the number lost to follow-up or those not providing certain relevant data for the analysis. In cases where there was a notable difference between initial N and the women included in the analysis, as in the studies by Aromaa et al (1994) and Whooley, and Browner (1998), we have inserted in Table 2 the number of women included in the analyses.

The studies included in the meta-analyses relate the risk of depression to different endpoints. We only include in Table 2 those endpoints referring to CHD and its different manifestations. For this reason, adjusted results in the study by Marzari et al. (2005) and unadjusted results in that by Whooley, and Browner (1998) do not appear. These authors relate the risk associated with depression to 'all cause mortality'. In other cases, results are not given in the corresponding boxes simply because they did not appear in the publications, as in those by Chang et al (2001) or Wassertheil-Smoller et al. (1996) for example.

The endpoints included in the analyses of crude and adjusted results are marked in Table 2 with the sign †. The results obtained in the meta-analyses are presented in Table 3.

As can be seen, when the least-adjusted RRs (crude or age-adjusted) were entered in the meta-analysis the overall effect was 1.47 (95% CI: 1.25-1.74, p <.0001) with substantially significant heterogeneity (Q = 70.83, 9 df, p <.0001). For the most-adjusted results the overall effect declined strongly, RR = 1.14 (95% CI: 1.04-1.25, p =.004). Heterogeneity was also significant (Q = 27.19, 8 df, p = .001). A sensitivity analysis was performed to evaluate the overall effect of the meta-analyses carried out with the unadjusted and adjusted RRs of the same studies, i.e., eliminating the studies that failed to present any results. In this case the overall unadjusted RR was 1.72 (95% CI: 1.30-2.29, p <.0001) and the adjusted RR 1.12 (95% CI: 1.02-1.23, p =.01). We also wished to evaluate the overall effect of the twelve studies meeting our inclusion criteria based on adjusted results and, in those cases not providing adjusted results, the crude or least adjusted results. Using this same procedure, we analyzed the effect of different follow-up times grouping the studies in three ranges: less than 6 years of follow-up, 6 to 12 years, and 12 or more years. The results are shown in TABLE 4.

The RR for the overall effect of all studies was 1.19 (95% CI: 1.08-1.32, p = .001). Significant RRs were also found for the studies included in the first and second group of follow-up. The first group was homogeneous (Q = 8.35, 4 df, p = .08), but not the second (Q = 12.78, 3 df, p <.01).

Table 1. Summary of etiological studies included in meta-analysis

STUDIES	N. AGE: Range (Mean)	MEASUREMENT Follow-Up: Range (Mean)	END POINT
Ahto et al. (2007) Finland Population-based.	N = 378. Age 64-74: 269. ≥ 75: 109.	ZSRDS. Cutoff: ≥ 45; F-up = 12 y.	CHD and MI mortality
Aromaa et al. (1994) Mini-Finland Health S.	N = 2935. Age= 40-64: 1986 ≥ 65: 949	GHQ-36 (SF) & PSE (SF). F-up = ¿ - 8 y. (6.6 y.)	MI, AP and CHD
Barefoot & Schroll (1996) Denish Population-based	N = 321 Age = n.a. (77).	MMPI-D Subscale OBS. F-up. = 17-27 (26.2 y.)	CHD
Chang et al. (2001). NHANES & NHEFS.	N: WW = 5143; BW = 1000. Age: 35-74. (n.a)	GWBS. Cutoff: ≥ 13. F-up = 21. (!)	IHDE
Cohen el al. (2001) Hypertension control Program. New York City,	N = 2023. Age: 25-65 (54)	Are you now or are you been treated for depression? (Yes/no) F-up: 6 m- 5.0 y. (n.a.)	MI CE IHDE
Ferketich et al. (2000) NHANES & NHEFS	N = 5007. Age ≥ 30; (53.7)	CES-D. Cutoff: ≥23; F-up = 0.02-11.1 (8.3 y.)	Fatal CHD Nonfatal CHD
Marzari et al. (2005). ILSA.	N = 1.380. Age = 65-84 (73.6).	GDS. Cutoff: ≥ 10. F-up = 4 y.	CHD Events
Mendes de Leon et al. (1998). EPESE.	N = 1446. Age = 65-99 (n.a.)	CES-D. Cutoff: ≥21 F-up = ¿-10 (7.4 y.)	CHD Mortality Total CHD
Penninx et al. (1998) EPESE.	N = 2450. Age = 70-103 (78.3)	CES-D. Cutoff: ≥ 20. F-up = n.a. (4 y.)	CHD Events
Wassertheil-Smoller et al. (1996) SHEP	N = 2572. Age ≥ 60 (72).	CES-D. Cutoff: ≥16 F-up = n.a. (5 y.)	MI fatal and non fatal.
Wassertheil- Smoller et al. (2004) WHI-OS	N = 93.676. Age = 50-79 (n.a.)	CES-D (SF): Cutoff: ≥ 5. DIS· 2 items. F-up = n.a. (4.1 y)	CAD CHD.
Whooley & Browner (1998). Ambulatory Women.	N = 7518. Age ≥ 67 (n.a.).	GDS. (SF). Cutoff: ≥ 6. F-up = ¿-7 (6 y.)	CHD Mortality.

STUDIES: EPESE: Established Populations for the Epidemiologic Studies of the Elderly. ILSA: Italian Longitudinal Study on Aging. NHANES & NHEFS: National Health and Nutrition Examination Survey (1971–1974) and National Health epidemiologic Follow-up Study . SHEP: Systolic Hypertension in the Elderly Program. WHI-OS : Women's Health Initiative Observational Study.

DATA: N: Total number of participants. WW : White Women. BW : Black Women. n.a.: no available; F-up: Follow-up. y: years. SF : Short Form.

MEASUREMENT: Interviews: PSE= Present State Examination. Questionnaires: CES-D. Center for Epidemiological Studies-Depression Scale; DIS: Diagnostic Interview Schedule. GDS : Geriatric Depression Scale. GHQ-36 : General Health Questionnaire-36. GWBS: General Well-Being Schedule. MMPI: Minnesota Multifasic Personality Inventory. ZSRDS: Zung Self-Rating Depression Scale.

ENDPOINT: AP = Angina Pectoris; CAD = Coronary Artery Disease; CHD = Coronary Heart Disease; CE = Coronary Events; IHDE = Ischemic Heart Disease Events; MI = Myocardial Infarction.

Table 2. Results of the included studies on the association between depression and Coronary Heart Disease

STUDIES	CRUDE OR LEAST ADJUSTED	ADJUSTED RESULTS	ADJUSTED VARIABLES
Ahto et al. (2007)	RR = 3.80 (1.60-8.6)[1] Cardiac Mortal.	HR = 1.09 (1.03-1.16) Cardiac Mortal.	Age, marital status, social status and number of medicines
Aromaa et al. (1994)	RR = 2.59 (1.12-5.99): MI. AA	RR = 1.90 MI. RR = 3.11* AP (1)	(1): Age, education, traditional CHD factors.
	RR = 3.58 (2.21-5.76): AP, AA	RR = 1.56 MI †. RR = 2.84* AP (2)	(2): Age, education, any reported chronic disease.
	RR = 3.58 (2.22-5.76): CHD, AA †	n = 1986.	
Barefoot & Schroll (1996)	RR = 1.10 (1.00-1.21).[2] AA		
Chang et al. (2001)	RR = 1.3 (0.9, 1.8) WW †		
	RR = 0.8 (0.3, 2.0) BW		
Cohen el al. (2001)	RR = 2.14 (0.64-7.21) MI	HR = 2.42 (0.70-8.37) MI	Age, race, diabetes, smoking, history of CVD, left ventricular hypertrophy, cholesterol, education, hypertension, blood pressure, alcohol, BMI, blood sugar, and unmarried status
	RR = 2.46 (0.85-7.11) CE	HR = 2.69 (0.90-8.05) CE	
	RR = 2.54 (1.06-6.05) IHDE †	HR = 2.66 (1.10-6.46) IHDE †	
Ferketich et al. (2000)	RR = 1.02 (0.53-1.94) Fatal CHD	RR = 0.74 (0.40-1.48) Fatal. (1)	(1) Poverty index, smoking, diabetes, hypertension, BMI.
	RR = 2.09 (1.35-3.23). Nonfatal CHD †	RR = 1.73 (1.11-268) Nonfatal (2) †	(2) Poverty index, smoking, diabetes, hypertension, BMI.
Marzari et al. (2005)	RR = 1.80 (1.20-2.60)[1]		
Mendes de Leon et al. (1998)	CHD Mortality :	RR = 1.03 (1.01-1.05) (1). CHD Mortal	(1) Age, education, diabetes, smoking, blood pressure, angina pectoris.
	RR = 1.03 (1.01-1.05) : AA.	RR = 1.02 (0.99-1.05) (2). CHD Mortal	
	Total CHD:	RR = 1.02 (1.00-1.04) (1). Total CHD.	(2) Age, education, diabetes, smoking, blood pressure, angina pectoris., physical functioning.
	RR = 1.03 (1.01-1.04) : AA †	RR = 1.01 (0.99-1.03) (2). Total CHD†	
Penninx et al. (1998)	RR = 1.35 (0.92-1.97) Chronic Depres.	RR = 1.12 (0.76-1.65) Chronic Depres.	Smoking, alcohol, BMI, blood pressure, history of stroke, diabetes/cancer, physical disability.
	RR = 1.35 (0.92-1.98) New Depres. †	RR = 1.22 (0.83-1.80) New Depres. †	
Wassertheil-Smoller et al. (1996)		RR = 1.20 (0.97-1.48) MI.	Age, race, previous depression, education, history of stroke, MI, or diabetes, smoking, daily activity.
Wassertheil- Smoller et al. (2004)	RR = 1.26 (1.10-1.44) CAD †	RR = 1.12 (0.97-1.29) CAD †	Age, race, education, incomes, BMI, cholesterol, smoking, diabetes, hypertension, exercise, therapies.
	RR = 1.18 (0.95-1.46) CHD.	RR = 1.12 (0.89-1.41) CHD	
	Age and Race Adjusted		
Whooley & Browner (1998)		HR = 1.7 (1.0-3.0) CHD Mortality.	Age, history of MI, stroke, COPD, hypertension, diabetes, smoking, perceived health, and cognitive function.
		n. = 6176.	

Statistics: HR = Hazard Ratio; RR = Risk Ratio. In bracket, 95% Confidence Interval. † = Results included in our analyses. * Statistically significant (95% level).

Results: AA Age-adjusted. n = People in the analyses. Coronary problems: AP = Angina Pectoris; CAD = Coronary Artery Disease; CHD = Coronary Heart Disease; CE = Coronary Events; IHDE = Ischemic Heart Disease Events; MI, Myocardial Infarction. Risk Factor: BMI: Body Mass Index. COPD: Chronic Obstructive Pulmonary Disease. CVD: Cardiovascular Disease. 1 Calculated from data in the article. 2 Calculated from data out of the article.

Table 3. Forrest plot of the effect of depression on the incidence of coronary heart disease

Studies	Unadjusted RR (95% CI)	p	Adjusted RR (95% CI)	p
Ahte et al. (2007)	3.82 (1.68–8.68)	.001	1.09 (1.03–1.16)	.004
Aromaa et al. (1994)	3.58 (2.22–5.76)	<.0001	1.56 (1.00–2.43)	.050
Cohen et al. (2001)	2.54 (1.06–6.06)	.036	2.66 (1.09–6.44)	.030
Ferketich et al. (2000)	2.09 (1.35–3.23)	.001	1.73 (1.11–2.68)	.015
Mendes de Leon et al. (1998)	1.03 (1.01–1.05)	.02	1.01 (0.99–1.03)	.325
Penninx et al. (1998)	1.35 (0.92–1.98)	.125	1.22 (0.32–1.79)	.314
Wassertheil- Smeller et al. (2004)	1.26 (1.10–1.44)	.001	1.12 (0.97–1.29)	.119
Barefoot & Schroll (1996)	1.10 (1.00–1.20)	.045		
Chang et al. (2011)	1.30 (0.92–1.82)	.132		
Marzari et al. (2005)	1.82 (1.25–2.69)	.003		
Wassertheil-Smoller et al. (1995)			1.20 (0.97–1.48)	.058
Whooley & Browner (1998)			1.70 (0.98–2.94)	.091
Summary unadjusted	1.47 (1.25–1.74)	<.0001		
Summary adjusted			1.14 (1.04–1.25)	.004
Summary of the studies with adjusted and unadjusted results.	1.72 (1.30–2.29)	<.0001	1.12 (1.02–.23)	.018

Table 4. Overall effect of most adjusted results for all studies and for groups according to years of follow-up

Groups	Years F-up	Studies	RR	(95% CI)	p	RR and 95% CI
1	5.0	Cohen el al. (2001)	2.66	(1.09–6.44)	.030	
1	4.0	Marzari et al. (2005)	1.82	(1.23–2.69)	.003	
1	4.0	Pennix et al. (1998)	1.22	(0.82–1.79)	.314	
1	5.0	Wassertheil-Smoller et al. (1996)	1.20	(0.97–1.48)	.058	
1	4.1	Wassertheil-Smoller et al. (2004)	1.12	(0.97–1.29)	.119	
Summary group 1			1.27	(1.08–1.51)	.005	
2	6.6	Aromaa et al. (1994)	1.56	(1.00–2.43)	.050	
2	8.3	Ferketich et al. (2000)	1.73	(1.11–2.68)	.015	
2	7.4	Mendes de Leon et al. (1998)	1.01	(0.99–1.03)	.325	
2	6.0	Whooey & Browner (1998)	1.70	(0.98–2.94)	.091	
Summary group 2			1.21	(1.01–1.45)	.042	
3	12.0	Ahto et al. (2007)	1.09	(1.03–1.16)	.004	
3	26.2	Barefoot & Schroll (1996)	1.10	(1.00–1.20)	.046	
3	21.0	Chang et al. (2001)	1.30	(0.92–1.82)	.132	
Summary group 3			1.12	(0.96–1.31)	.145	
		Summary of all studies	1.19	(1.08–1.32)	.001	

Groups F-up	1	2	3	Overall
Q-value (df) P-value	8.35 (4) .079	12.78 (3) .005	1.10 (2) .667	39.50 (11) .000

Discussion

We believe this is the first analysis to quantify the risk posed by depression for the development of CHD across the available comparable community studies performed with women only. We consider it important to stress that this aspect was studied in women only because both depression and CHD present characteristics which are unique to women, as noted by Naqvi, Naqvi, and Merz (2005) and Wulsin et al. (2005) for example. Ferketich el al. (2000) previously studied these aspects and found that the most severe cases of depression in women were related with non-fatal CHD events, but not with fatal CHD events. In men, the most severe depressive symptoms were associated with both fatal and non-fatal events. Mendes de Leon et al. (1998) also investigated whether the relation between depression and CHD differed between men and women. For the men, there was no indication that the highest levels of symptoms of depression were associated with greater risk of CHD; in fact the men with the highest CES-D scores had the lowest risk. For the women, those with the highest scores in depressive symptoms had the highest risk, although this was especially for all types of coronary events.

We included 12 studies in our meta-analysis. Our inclusion criteria were restrictive enough to allow for comparability of studies and for valid application of the random effects model and sufficient breadth to include an adequate number of studies.

The unadjusted RR in our meta-analysis, 1.47 (95% CI: 1.25-1.74, $p <.0001$), for the overall effect is significant, although lower than the unadjusted RR presented by Rugulies (2002) for all the studies, RR = 1.75 (95% CI: 1.37-2.25), but very close to Rugulies' unadjusted RR for studies on depressive mood, 1.59 (95% CI: 1.22-2.08, $p = 0.001$), which is an appropriate classification of the depression suffered by most of the women participants in our study. The adjusted RR 1.14 (95% CI : 1.04-1.25, $p <.01$) for the overall effect obtained in our study is significant, but is clearly lower than that presented by Rugulies for all the studies with the most adjusted results [RR = 1.64 (95% CI: 1.29-2.08)], and by Wulsin, and Singal (2003) [RR = 1.64 (95% CI : 1.41-1.90)]. For the adjusted RRs obtained by the cited meta-analyses, the authors included results of some studies that only performed adjustment for age. For this reason the best comparative reference of these results is our most adjusted RR which was 1.19 (95% CI: 1.08-1.32). This is slightly lower than those obtained with mixed samples of men and women with greater numbers of participants which makes the occurrence of coronary events more probable.

Follow-up time does not explain our results because we established a minimum of four years follow-up as a criterion for inclusion, which is sufficient time for cardiac episodes to appear (Wulsin et al. 2005). We found that the highest RR was obtained in studies with least duration of follow-up times, from 4 to 6 years. In addition, the studies included many older and even hypertensive women, although without a history of CVD, as in studies by Cohen, Madhavan, and Alderman (2001) and Wassertheil-Smoller et al. (1996), which increases the likelihood of CHD events. On including this risk factor in our meta-analysis, we took care to ensure that this risk factor was under control in the study.

Our meta-analysis of the group of seven studies presenting both unadjusted and adjusted results showed that the unadjusted overall effect of these studies favored the relationship between depression and CHD to a greater extent than the unadjusted overall effect of all studies. This result supports the idea noted by Nicholson, Kuper, and Hemingway (2006) that authors who obtain relatively low unadjusted results do not publish adjusted results because they would possibly have to publish non-significant results.

This observation is an introduction to the issue of possible bias in publications. Wulsin, and Singal (2003) estimated that the relation they found between relative risk and variance supports the idea of bias in publications favoring studies with positive results, but they also observed that using the Rosenthal method, 572 studies with negative results would be necessary to negate the combined relative risk obtained in the meta-analysis. Nicholson, Kuper, and Hemingway (2006) interpreted the non-publication of adjusted results in some studies as an indicator of bias in the publication of results.

We wish to remark on the fact that eleven of the twelve studies included in our meta-analysis evaluated depression with a questionnaire, and only two also used an interview which moreover was in a short form. Therefore these studies mainly evaluated symptoms of depression. The CES-D was used in five of the 12 studies. It is measure with the best psychometric research background for epidemiologic studies and the broadest use in clinical research. In addition to the fact that the study by Wassertheil-Smoller et al. (2004) used a short form, the problem about its use that we faced was that none of the studies used the same cutoff to classify women participants as depressed or not depressed. This problem, together with the fact that ten of the twelve studies used different instruments or procedures to evaluate depression, illustrates the difficulty of rigorous study of the topic under consideration. However, as said by Wulsin, and Singal (2003), if an effect of depression shows up in multiple studies despite variations in methods, it is more likely to be a real effect than an artifact of shared study methods.

The question of measuring depression is not only how it is measured but also how often throughout the years of follow-up. If, as in most studies, depression is only measured at baseline, the fact that a relationship can be established with the incidence of a CHD event nine years later or more could be considered an extraordinary, almost miraculous fact. A single measurement in time also fails to answer an important question raised by Penninx et al. (1998) as to whether it is chronic or new-onset depression that exerts the greatest effect on CHD. Whooley, and Browner (1998) observed that the persistence of depression increases the risk of death HR = 2.53 (95% CI: 1.56-4.09) and that mortality rates in women with and without depression do not begin to diverge until approximately 16 months of follow-up.

We considered the existence of adjustment for the major confounders as important. To be able to affirm the relation between depression and the risk of CHD, it is especially important to consider the effect of age and impaired physical function. For this reason the study by Mendes de Leon et al. (1998) is of great interest; it seems to support the relation on the basis of findings in a subgroup of relatively healthy women defined as people surviving three or more years without any cardiac event or without impaired mobility.

Our meta-analysis has certain limitations, such as having used searches performed in previous meta-analyses. This has not, however, freed us from the task of having to decide on whether to include previous selections that we found difficult to justify, such as the inclusion of the study by Prat et al. (1996) in the meta-analysis of Rugulies (2002) and which we did not include. Another limitation is having wished to use very strict criteria regarding endpoints, eliminating all those studies that included death by all causes, but not so strict as to exclude the study by Wassertehil-Smoller et al. (1996) who worked with a clinical sample of hypertensive patients, not members of the community, or the study by Mendes de Leon et al. (1998) that presents RR for unit increments of depression. And, of course, having had to accept several sources of heterogeneity among the studies included in this meta-analysis, for example, different measures of depression, various definitions of CHD and a wide range of follow-up, from 4 to 27 years.

Studies on People with Coronary Heart Disease

Prevalence of Depression after a Coronary Heart Disease Event

Methodological problems inherent in the performance of any measurement in psychology and variability in the studies performed do not allow a single precise answer to this question. Mean values for the prevalence of *major depression* after a CHD event is estimated to range from 15% to 20%, and the prevalence of *depressive symptoms* is approximately 20% (Hance, Carney, Freedland, and Skala, 1996; Schleifer et al., 1989). According to Lespérance, and Frasure-Smith (2000), epidemiological survey data indicate that a typical cardiologist attending 25 hospital beds found four patients with *major depression* and five with some form of *minor depression*. Similar figures are estimated for cardiac outpatients. Recent reviews such as the meta-analysis by Melle et al. (2004) provide figures ranging from 8% to 47% for depressive symptoms and from 5% to 47% for depressive disorder, data which confirm the accuracy of previous estimates. These data have been corroborated by the University of Johns Hopkins Report on Depression After Myocardial Infarction (Bush et al. 2005)[16]. The report notes that major depression is found in about one of every five patients hospitalized for MI. This proportion is fairly consistent with the data from eight studies included in the report that used a structured clinical interview to establish this diagnosis. According to them, the prevalence of depressive symptoms varies more widely, range 10 to 47 percent.

This wide range of reported prevalence rates appears to be largely due to differences in measurement instruments used and for this reason the National Heart, Lung, and Blood Institute (NHLBI) on August 10 and 11, 2004, convened an interdisciplinary working group of experts in cardiology, psychology, psychiatry, nursing, epidemiology, clinical trial methodology, and biostatistics to develop recommendations concerning the assessment of depression in patients with CHD (Davidson et al. 2006). However, it is not only a question of using different measuring instruments. Another important consideration concerns threshold criteria. When the same instrument is used, differences in threshold criteria applied from study to study make it difficult to determine whether we are dealing with cases of symptomatic or more severe depression. Without going into fine details, one reason for the higher reported prevalence of potentially significant symptoms of depression is that instruments aiming to evaluate depression include among their items somatic symptoms that

---

16 Report prepared by the Johns Hopkins University Evidence-based Practice Center to the Agency for Healthcare Research and Quality of the U.S. Department of Health and Human Services.

may overlap with MI symptoms. This appears to happen more in the Beck Depression Inventory which uses as cutoff a score of 10 or higher and less in the Hamilton Anxiety and Depression Scale (HADS) which uses as cutoff a score of either 8 or higher or 11 or higher. The HADS does not include somatic symptoms and is designed for use in hospitalized patients.

The exact evaluation of the prevalence of depression in artery-coronary patients for both health care purposes and for the study of its possible relation with the recurrence of artery-coronary episodes also requires taking into consideration the time lapse between such an episode and the time when the depression is evaluated, the duration of the depressive mood and the recurrence or not of depressive moods over time. Differences in these parameters explain many discrepancies in research results.

The duration of depressive mood appears to be long. In the studies by Frasure-Smith, Lespérance, and Talajic (1993; 1995) major depression diagnosed after MI was re-diagnosed in 75% of the patients at 6 and 12 months of follow-up. These data and those of Hance et al. (1996), who reported that only half the patients diagnosed with depression just after an MI event were free of depression during follow-up, indicate that the diagnosis of depression made just after MI is fairly reliable.

Prognostic Evidence for Risk of Recurrence Associated with Depression after a Coronary Heart Disease Event

Despite the affirmation by Wulsin (2004) that the literature on depression and cardiovascular mortality is too limited in quantity and quality to be able to justify performing a meta-analysis, there are three such analyses of interest for this section: the meta-analyses by Barth, Schumacher, and Herrmann-Lingen (2004), Melle et al. (2004) and Nicholson, Kuper, and Hemingway (2006).

The meta-analysis by Barth, Schumacher, and Herrmann-Lingen (2004) includes studies published between 1980 and 2003. This meta-analysis includes the results of 20 studies, appearing in 29 publications, with an endpoint of mortality for different reasons. In the studies with medium and long-term follow-up periods, from three months to two years, the risk of cardiac-related death or for any other cause in artery-coronary patients with *depressive symptoms* was two times greater than in non-depressed patients, OR = 2.24 (95% CI: 1.37-3.60). This negative prognosis was maintained in studies with longer follow-up, more than two years, although with slightly reduced risk, OR = 1.78 (95% CI: 1.12-2.83). After adjusting for the possible effect of other cardiac risk factors, depressive symptoms still showed a significant impact on mortality in studies with follow-up periods of more than two years, HR = 1.76 (95% CI: 1.27-2.43). In most studies, the negative impact of *depressive disorders* is presented without adjustment for the effect of other risk factors. Clinical depression shows a non-significant short-term effect on mortality, OR = 2.07 (95% CI: 0.82-5.26), but this becomes significant after two years of follow-up, OR = 2.61 (95% CI: 1.53-4.47). Of these latter studies, only three present results after adjusting for the effect of possible risk factors.

The meta-analysis by Melle et al. (2004) presents the results of studies published up to January 2004 and covers the period 1975-2003. The inclusion criteria varied slightly from those applied in the meta-analysis by Barth, Schumacher, and Herrmann-Lingen (2004). The most notable is that, apart from death from any cause and cardiac mortality, they set cardiovascular episodes as an endpoint (MI, instable chest pain, the need for revascularization and arrhythmia) and they limited their meta-analysis to studies analyzing medium-term prognosis, i.e. follow-up periods of no more than 24 months. The meta-analysis included 22 studies describing follow-up of 16 different cohorts totalizing 6,367 patients with MI. After analyzing the data from nine studies and six cohorts of MI patients totalizing 3,343 cases, they found that depression was significantly associated with *cardiac mortality*, OR = 2.59 (95% CI: 1.77-3.77; p <.00001). A further nine studies with a total of 3,401 patients showed that depression in post-infarction patients was associated with a high risk of recurring *cardiac events*, OR = 1.95 (95% CI: 1.33-2.58; p <.001).

The meta-analysis by Nicholson, Kuper, and Hemingway (2006), who also included etiological studies, presents results of 34 prognostic studies published up to December 2003. They included 17,842 participants and placed special emphasis on analyzing, in addition to the effects of depression on the evolution of the disease and/or death, the possible weight of other risk factors, especially disease severity. The pooled and unadjusted estimate for the association between depression and prognosis of CHD in patients with the disease was 1.80 (95% CI: 1.50-2.15). Only 11 studies presented results adjusted for severity of CHD and the authors stressed that the unadjusted estimate of the association between depression and CHD was lower, 1.55 (95% CI : 1.23-1.96) in the studies not presenting results adjusted for CHD severity than in those did, 2.16 (95% CI: 1.67-2.80).

The authors, in agreement with Lane, Carrol, and Lip (2003; 2004), noted that eight studies presented results adjusted for the function of the left ventricle and that, although this attenuated the RR by 48%, from an unadjusted RR of 2.18 to an adjusted RR of 1.53 (95% CI: 1.11-2.10), this still proved significant.

Prognostic evidence for the risk of recurrence associated with depression after a CHD event has also been the subject of various qualitative reviews appearing after the year 2000, such as those by Frasure-Smith, and Lespérance (2005, 2006), Kuper, Marmot, and Hemingway (2002), and Lett et al. (2004). The latter review covered prognostic studies published up to 2003 and quantified RR with values from 1.5 to 2.5. Other reviews include those by Rudisch, and Nemeroff (2003), Suls, and Bunde (2005), and one by Wulsin (2004) covering a wide range of selected studies published up to December 2005 with more or less broad criteria.

It must be said that the reviews cited and the results of these meta-analyses do not specifically treat gender differences; the data refer to a mixed population of men and women, although they do focus on the relationship between depression and CHD. It may be concluded that *depressive symptoms* have a strong unfavorable impact on both short and long-term cardiac-related death. The impact of *major depression* on mortality, not significant at six months, manifests at two years as a twofold increase in risk of death in artery-coronary patients compared with patients not suffering depression. This result is in direct opposition to the hypothesis that the strength of the association between clinical depression and CHD death weakens as time passes. These meta-analyses also allow affirming that the association between depression after MI and cardiac mortality is consistent and differences in results are not dependent on whether the depression is evaluated by questionnaires or clinical interview. The strength of this association must, however, be tempered because the multivariate odds ratios were smaller than the bivariate odds ratios and this reduction suggests that the effect of depression on post-MI prognosis may be partly dependent on other factors. Nicholson, Kuper, and Hemingway (2006), interested in isolating the effect of risk factors for CHD and in controlling for the effect of the severity of CHD, actually affirm that incomplete and biased information for conventional risk factors and for severity of coronary disease mean that these estimates are likely to be inflated.

Prognostic Evidence for Risk of Recurrence Associated with Depression after a Coronary Heart Disease Event in Women

Our contribution to this section was to collect prognostic studies performed with men and women evaluating the relationship of depression with CHD death or events. Previous reviews covered the studies published up to 15 December 2005. We performed a search for the period between December 2005 and October 2007 in the databases MEDLINE and PSICINFO with the following selection criteria for the publications: 1) inclusion of more than 200 artery-coronary patients at baseline phase; 2) follow-up period of at least one year; 3) endpoint of CHD and its manifestations of death, non-fatal episodes of MI or angina pectoris with an objective test; 4) selection of the study with the longest follow-up when different results are published about the same cohort; 5) depression evaluated by interview or validated self report; 6) presentation of adjusted results analyzing the possible effect of other risk factors .

The results of our review, parts of which are available in del Pino, and Gaos (in press), indicate that there are an insufficient number of studies performed with women suffering from CHD to be able to quantitatively evaluate the effect of depression on the evolution of this disease or possible death due to CHD only in women.

As a summary of our search we can say that, of the studies analyzing this topic and using the *endpoint death*, only the study by Wassertheil-Smoller et al. (2004) provides results for women alone. The study was performed with 18,572 menopausal women aged 50 to 79 years. In the women with a history of cardiovascular disease and depression at baseline, the RR for death, adjusted for age and race, was 1.49 (95% CI: 1.16-1.92), and adjusted for age, race, education, income level and various CHD risk factors, was 1.22 (95% CI: 0.92-1.61). These data refer to death due to cardiovascular problems, which is a rather broader concept than death due to CHD. Judged from this single study, it cannot be said that depression after a CVD event is significantly associated with death due to cardiovascular problems because, when traditional risk factors are included in the model, the weight of depression ceases to be significant. The nine remaining publications included in our previous work had proportions of women ranging from 15% in the study by Herrmann, Brand-Driehorst, Buss, and Ruger (2000) to 40% in the study by Carney et al. (2003) performed with participants in the ENRICH study where racial diversity and both sexes were intentionally included. However, none of the other studies provide results exclusively pertaining to women.

With the endpoint of the study as *non-fatal artery-coronary events,* we found the study by Strick, Denollet, Lousberg, and Honig (2003), which was performed with men only, and a further ten studies with women participation ranging from 8% in the study by Denollet, Vaes, and Brutsaert (2000) to 40% in the study by Carney et al. (2003), which also provide results for this endpoint. Once again, only the study by Wassertheil-Smoller et al. (2004) provides results referring exclusively to women. In women with a history of cardiovascular disease and depression at baseline, the RR adjusted for age and race of suffering CHD episodes was 1.16 (95% CI: 0.94-1.42) and after adjusting for age, race, education, income level and various CHD risk factors, the RR was 0.94 (95% CI: 0.75-1.18). Both RR values proved non-significant. This study therefore does not support the relationship between depression and recurrence of cardiovascular episodes in women.

From this review it may be deduced that there is little information on the topic specifically referring to women, which has been noted by some researchers. Irvine et al. (1999), whose study used a medium sized sample for this type of study, openly indicated that the small number of women, n = 114, and the fact that only six suffered sudden cardiac death meant that they could not test the effects of the interaction between sex and the psychosocial variables on CHD. Welin, Lappas, and Wilhelmsen (2000) reported that there were too few women to enable multivariate analyses among them. In this respect some authors (Welin, Lappas, and Wilhelmsen, 2000; Denollet, Vaes, and Brutsaert, 2000) have complained of limitations for generalizing results given the greatly reduced number of women studied.

Prevalence of Depression after a Coronary Heart Disease Event in Women.

The University of Johns Hopkins Report (Bush et al., 2005) included 25 publications studying the question of the prevalence of depression in people who had suffered a coronary episode one month or more after discharge from hospital. Gender of participants was specified in 23 of them. Men only were studied in three studies and the remaining 20 report the prevalence of depression in a mixed population without providing separate results for each gender. Despite this, various publications provide some information on the topic of depression and CHD in women. Barefoot et al. (2000) reported, as expected, that a greater number of depressive symptoms at baseline and during follow-up were found in the women and were strongly associated with their functional status. Lauzon et al. (2003) also reported in their study that among the sample differences at baseline they found a greater proportion of women with depression, 25%, as compared to 19% in the men. Lane, Carroll, Ring, Beevers, and Lip (2002) reported that women more frequently than men obtained BDI scores above 10, which is the critical point indicating the presence of depressive symptoms. Along the same lines, Strik, Lousberg, Cheriex, and Honig (2004) noted that depressive patients in their sample were mainly women, a finding with a probability of error below 5%, and that their data showed a tendency for female gender to predict major cardiac events. Connerney, Shapiro, McLauglin, Bagiella, and Sloan (2001) reported that women were significantly more likely than men to have adverse cardiac outcomes after discharge from hospital. Multivariate analyses showed that their increased age, greater probability of living alone and longer stays in hospital after surgery did not account for their higher rate of cardiac events. Welin et al.

(2000) concluded that female gender and being depressed independently increased the risk of a fatal coronary event after an initial MI event.

Conclusions

From the available etiologic meta-analyses, it may be affirmed that there is a significant association between depression and CHD in the general population. We could also affirm a significant association between depression and CHD in women if we focus on the crude results of our meta-analysis performed with data obtained from women only. The evidence provided by prognostic studies about the relationship between depression and CHD in the general population is similar to that of etiologic studies, although the data for women only are scarce. The considerable reduction of RR values found using results adjusted for other factors means that the possible effect of depression is closely related with other risk factors for CHD. It is therefore necessary to determine the weight of each of these risk factors and the risk associated to their combination, as well as the type of association and the pathways whereby depression may contribute to the manifestation of CHD. Conclusions based on the results of meta-analyses should, however, be made with reservations due to the limitations of the prospective studies included in them and to the limitations of the meta-analyses themselves. The prevalence of depression after a CHD event seems higher in women than in men, although systematic studies are lacking in this respect. We believe that the correct evaluation of all these results is not to negate the possible role of depression in the incidence and recurrence of CHD, but rather to strive for more and better research into this topic.

References

Ahto, M., Isoaho, R., Puolijoki, H., Vahlberg, T., and Kivela, S.-L. (2007). Stronger symptoms of depression predict high coronary heart disease mortality in older men and women. *International Journal of Geriatric Psychiatry, 22,* 757-763.

Angst, F., Stassen, H.H., Clayton, P.J., and Angst, J. (2002) Mortality of patients with mood disorders: follow-up over 34–38 years. *Journal of Affective Disorders, 68,* 167-181.

Aromaa, A., Raitasalo, R., Reunanen, A., Impivaara, O., Heliovaara, M., Kneckt, P., Lehtinen, V., Joukama, M., and Maatela, J. (1994). Depression and cardiovascular diseases. *Acta Psychiatrica Scandinavica, 377,* 77-82.

Barefoot, J., Brummett, B., Helms, M., Mark, D., Siegler, I., and Williams, R. (2000). Depressive symptoms and survival of patients with coronary artery disease. *Psychosomatic Medicine, 62,* 790-795.

Barefoot, J., and Schroll, M. (1996). Symptoms of depression, acute myocardial infarction and total mortality in a community sample. *Circulation, 93,* 1976-1980.

Barth, J., Shumacher, M., and Herrmann-Lingen, C. (2004). Depression as a risk factor for mortality in patients with coronary heart disease: a meta-analysis. *Psychosomatic Medicine, 66,* 802-13.

Black, D.W., Warrack, G., and Winokur, G. (1985). Excess mortality among psychiatric patients. the Iowa record-linkage study. *Journal of the American Medical Association, 253*, 58-61.

Booth-Kewley, S., and Friedman, H. S. (1987). Psychological predictors of heart disease: A quantitative review. *Psychological Bulletin, 101*, 343-362.

Bush, D.E., Ziegelstein, R.C., Patel, U.V., Thombs, B.D., Ford, D.E., Fauerbach, J.A., McCann U.D., Stewart, K.J., Tsilidis, K.K., Patel, A.L, Feuerstein, C.J., Bass, E.B.. (2005). Post-Myocardial Infarction Depression. Evidence Report/Technology Assessment No. 123. (Prepared by the Johns Hopkins University Evidence-based Practice Center under Contract No. 290-02-0018.) AHRQ Publication No. 05-E018-1. Rockville, MD: Agency for Healthcare Research and Quality.

Carney, R., Blumenthal, J., Catellier, D., Freedland, K., Berkman, L., Watkins, L., Czajkowski, S., Hayano, J., and Jaffe, A. (2003). Depression as a risk factor for mortality after acute myocardial infarction. *American Journal of Cardiology, 92*, 1277-1281.

Chang, M., Hahn, R.A., Teutsch, S.M., and Hutwagner, L.C. (2001). Multiple risk factors and population attributable risk for ischemic heart disease mortality in the United States, 1971–1992. *Journal of Clinical Epidemiology, 54*, 634-644.

Cohen, H.W., Madhavan, S., and Alderman, M.H. (2001). History of Treatment for Depression: Risk Factor for Myocardial Infarction in Hypertensive Patients. *Psychosomatic Medicine, 63*, 203-209.

Connerney, I., Shapiro, P., McLauglin, J., Bagiella, E., and Sloan, R. (2001). Relation between depression after coronary artery bypass surgery and 12-month outcome: a prospective study. *Lancet, 358*, 1766-1771.

Davidson, K, Kupfer, K., Bigger, Th., Califf, R., Carney, R., Coyne, J., Czajkowski, S., Frank, E., Frasure-Smith, N., Freedland, K., Froelicher, E., Glassman, A., Katon, W., Kaufmann, P., Kessler, K., Kraemer, H., Krishnan, K., Lespérance, F., Rieckmann, N., Sheps, D., and Suls, J. (2005). Assessment and Treatment of Depression in Patients With Cardiovascular Disease: National Heart, Lung, and Blood Institute Working Group Report. *Annals of Behavioral Medicine, 32,*121-126.

Denollet, J., Vaes, J., and Brutsaert, D.L. (2000). Inadequate response to treatment in coronary heart disease: adverse effects of type D personality and younger age on 5-year prognosis and quality of life. *Circulation, 102* , 630-635.

Ferketich, A. K., Schwartzbaum, J. A., Frid, D. J., and Moeschberger, M. J. (2000). Depression as an antecedent to heart disease among women and men in the NHANES I study. National Health and Nutrition Examination Survey. *Archives of Internal Medicine, 160*, 1261-1268.

Frasure-Smith, N., and Lespérance, F. (2005). Reflections on depression as a cardiac risk factor. *Psychosomatic Medicine, 67*, Supp. 1, 19-25.

Frasure-Smith, N., and Lespérance, F. (2006). Recent Evidence Linking Coronary Heart Disease and Depression. *Canadian Journal of Psychiatry, 51*, 730-737.

Frasure-Smith, N., Lespérance, F., and Talajic, M. (1993). Depression following myocardial infarction: Impact on 6-month survival. *Journal of the American Medical Association, 270*, 1819-1825.

Frasure-Smith, N., Lespérance, F., and Talajic, M. (1995). The impact of negative emotions on prognosis following myocardial infarction: Is it more than just depression?. *Health Psychology, 14,* 388-398.

Hance, M., Carney, RM., Freedland, KE., and Skala, J. (1996) Depression in patients with coronary heart disease: a 12-month follow-up. *General Hospital Psychiatry, 18,* 61–65

He, J., Vupputuri, S., Allen, K., Prerost, M.R., Hughes, J., and Whelton, P.K. (1999) Passive smoking and the risk of coronary heart disease—a metaanalysis of epidemiologic studies. *New England Journal of Medicine, 340,* 920-926.

Herrmann, C., Brand-Driehorst, S., Buss, U., and Ruger, U. (2000). Effects of anxiety and depression on 5-year mortality in 5057 patients referred for exercise testing. *Journal of Psychosomatic Research, 48,* 455-462.

Irvine, J., Basinski, A., Baker, B., Jandciu, S., Paquette, M., Cairns, J., Connolly, S., Roberts, R., Gent, M., and Dorian, P. (1999). Depression and risk of sudden cardiac death after acute myocardial infarction: Testing for the confounding effects of fatigue. *Psychosomatic Medicine, 61,* 729-737.

Kubzansky, L. D., and Kawachi, I. (2000). Going to the heart of the matter: Do negative emotions cause coronary heart disease?. *Journal of Psychosomatic Research, 48,* 323-337.

Kuper, H., Marmot, M., and Hemingway, H. (2002) Systematic review of prospective cohort studies of psychosocial factors in the etiology and prognosis of coronary heart disease. *Seminar in Vascular Medicine, 2,* 267-314.

Lane, D., Carroll, D., and Lip, G.Y. (2003). Anxiety, depression and prognosis after myocardial infarction: is there a causal relationship?. *Journal of American College of Cardiology, 42,* 1801-1810.

Lane, D., Carroll, D., and Lip, G.Y. (2004). Reply. *Journal of American College of Cardiology, 44,* 473-474.

Lane, D., Carroll, D., Ring, C., Beevers, D.G., and Lip, G.Y.H. (2002). In-hospital symptoms of depression do not predict mortality 3 years after myocardial infarction. *International Journal of Epidemiology, 31,* 1179-1182.

Lauzon, C., Beck, C.A., Huynh, T., Dion, D., Racine, N., Carignan, S., Diodati, J.G., Charbonneau, F., Dupuis, R., and Pilote, L. (2003). Depression and prognosis following hospital admission because of acute myocardial infarction. *Canadian Medical Association Journal, 168,* 547-52.

Lespérance, F., and Frasure-Smith, N. (2000). Depression in patients with cardiac disease: A practical review. *Journal of Psychosomatic Research, 48,* 379-391.

Lett, H., Blumenthal, J., Babyak, M., Sherwood, A., Strauman, T., Robins, C., and Newman, M. (2004). Depression as a risk factor for coronary artery disease: Evidence, mechanisms, and treatment. *Psychosomatic Medicine, 66,* 305-315.

Malzberg, B. (1937). Mortality among patients with involution melancholia. *American Journal of Psychiatry, 93,* 1231-1238.

Marzari, Ch., Maggi, S., Manzato, E., Destro, C., Noale, M., Bianchi, D., Minicuci, N., Farci, G., Baldereschi, M., Di Carlo, A., Crepaldi, G., and the Italian Longitudinal Study on Aging Working Group. (2005) Depressive Symptoms and Development of Coronary

Heart Disease Events: The Italian Longitudinal study on Aging. *The Journals of Gerontology: MEDICAL SCIENCES, 60A,* 85-92.

Melle, J.P., de Jonge, P., Spijkerman, T.A., Tijssen, J.G.P., Ormel, J., van Veldhuisen, D.J., Brink, R.H.S., van den Kooy, K., and Berg, M.P. (2004). Prognostic association of depression following myocardial infarction with mortality and cardiovascular events: A meta-analysis. *Psychosomatic Medicine, 66,* 814-822.

Mendes de Leon, C.F., Krumholtz, H.M., Seeman, T.S., Vaccarino, V., Williams, C.S., Kasl, S. V., and Berkman, L. F. (1998). Depression and risk of coronary heart disease in elderly men and women: New Haven EPESE. *Archives of Internal Medicine, 158,* 2341-2348.

Murray, CJ., and Lopez, AD. (1997a). Global mortality, disability, and the contribution of risk factors: Global Burden of Disease Study. *Lancet, 349,* 1436-1442.

Murray, CJ., and Lopez, AD. (1997b). Alternative projections of mortality and disability by cause 1990-2020: Global burden of Disease Study. *Lancet, 349,* 1498-1504.

Naqvi, T.Z., Naqvi, S.S., and Merz, N.B. (2005). Gender differences in the link between depression and cardiovascular disease. *Psychosomatic Medicine, 67,* Sup. 1, 15-18.

Nicholson, A., Kuper, H., and Hemingway, H. (2006). Depression as an aetiologic and prognostic factor in coronary heart disease. *European Heart Journal 27,* 2763–2774

Norton, B., and Whalley, L.J. (1984). Mortality of a lithium-treated population. *British Journal of Psychiatry; 145,* 277-282.

Penninx, B.W., Guralnik, J.M., Mendes de Leon, C.F., Pahor, M., Visser, M., Corti, M-C., and Wallace, R.B. (1998). Cardiovascular events and mortality in newly and chronically depressed persons greater than 70 years of age. *American Journal of Cardiology, 81,* 988-994.

Pino, A. del, and Gaos, M. (En prensa). La depresión y la enfermedad cardiocoronaria: Una revisión. In: *Nuevas Aportaciones a la medicina psicosomática.* (Vol. II) Ciencia Biomédica. Servicio de publicaciones de la Universidad de Málaga. Serrano Noguera, V. (Coord).

Pratt, L.A., Ford, D.E., Crum, R.M., Armenian, H.K., Gallo, J.J., and Eaton, W.W. (1996). Depression, psychotropic medication, and risk of myocardial infarction: Prospective data from the Baltimore ECA follow-up. *Circulation, 94,* 3123-3129.

Rabins, P.V., Harvis, K., and Koven, S. (1985). High fatality rates of late-life depression associated with cardiovascular disease. *Journal of Affective Disorders, 9,* 165-167.

Rudisch, B., and Nemeroff, C.B. (2003). Epidemiology of comorbid coronary artery disease and depression. *Biological Psychiatry, 54,* 227-240.

Rugulies, R. (2002). Depression as a predictor for coronary heart disease: A review and meta-analysis. *American Journal of Preventive Medicine, 23,* 51-61.

Scheidt, S. (2000). The current status of heart-mind relationships. *Journal of Psychosomatic Research, 48,* 317-320.

Schleifer, S.J., Macari-Hinson, M.M., Coyle, D.A., Slater, W.R., Kahn, M., Gorlin, R., and Zucker, R. (1989). The nature and course of depression following myocardial infarction. *Archives of Internal Medicine, 149,* 1785-1789.

Sharma, R., and Markar, H.R. (1994). Mortality in affective disorder. *Journal of Affective Disorders, 31,* 91-96.

Strik, J.J., Denollet, J., Lousberg, R., and Honig, A., (2003). Comparing symptoms of depression and anxiety as predictors of cardiac events and increased health care consumption after myocardial infarction. *Journal of American College of Cardiology, 42,* 1801-1807.

Strik, J.J., Lousberg, R., Cheriex, E.C., and Honig, A. (2004). One year cumulative incidence of depression following myocardial infarction and impact on cardiac outcome. *Journal of Psychosomatic Research, 56,* 59-66.

Suls, J., and Bunde, J. (2005). Anger, anxiety, and depression as risk factors for cardiovascular disease: The problems and implications of overlapping affective dispositions. *Psychological Bulletin, 131,* 260-300.

Tsuang, M.T., Woolson, R.F., and Fleming, J.A. (1980). Premature deaths in schizophrenia and affective disorders: an analysis of survival and variables affecting the shortened survival. *Archives of General Psychiatry, 37,* 979-983.

Van der Kooy, K., Van Hout, H., Marwijk, H., Marten, H., Stehouwer, C., and Beekman, A. (2007). Depression and the risk for cardiovascular diseases: systematic review and meta-analysis. *International Journal of Geriatric Psychiatry, 22,* 613-626.

Vestergaard, P., and Aagaard, J. (1991). Five-year mortality in lithium-treated manic-depressive patients. *Journal of Affective Disorders, 21,* 33-38.

Wassertheil-Smoller, S., Applegate, W., Berge, K., Chang, C.J., Davis, B.R., Grimm, R., Kostis, J, Pressel, S., and Schron, E. (1996). Change in depression as a precursor of cardiovascular events (SHEP Study). *Archives of Internal Medicine, 156,* 553-561.

Wassertheil-Smoller, S., Shumaker, S., Ockene, J., Talavera, GA., Greenland, P., Cochrane, B., Robbins, J., Aragaki, A., and Dunbar-Jacob, J. (2004). Depression and cardiovascular sequelae in postmenopausal women: The Women's Health Initiative (WHI). *Archives of Internal Medicine, 164,* 289-298.

Weeke, A. (1979). Causes of death in manic depressives. En M. Schou, and E. Stromgren, (Ed). *Origin, prevention and treatment of affective disorders* (289-299). London: Academic Press.

Weeke, A., Juel, K., and Vaeth, M. (1987). Cardiovascular death and manic-depressive psychosis. *Journal of Affective Disorders, 13,* 287-292.

Welin, C., Lappas, G., and Wilhelmsen, L. (2000). Independent importance of psychosocial risk factors for prognosis after myocardial infarction. *Journal of Internal Medicine, 247,* 629-639.

Whooley, M. A., and Browner, W. S. (1998). Association between depressive symptoms and mortality in older women. *Archives of Internal Medicine, 158,* 2129-2135.

Wulsin, L.R. (2004). Is depression a major risk factor for coronary disease?. A systematic review of the epidemiologic evidence. *Harvard Review of Psychiatry, 12,* 79-93.

Wulsin, L.R., Evans, J.C., Vasan, R.S., Murabito, J.M., Kelly-Hayes, M., and Benjamin, E.J. (2005). Depressive symptoms, coronary heart disease, and overall mortality in the Framingham Heart Study. *Psychosomatic Medicine, 67,* 697-702.

Wulsin, L., and Singal, B. (2003). Do depressive symptoms increase the risk for the onset of coronary disease?. A systematic quantitative review. *Psychosomatic Medicine, 65,* 201-210.

In: Women and Depression

Editors: Paula Hernandez and Sara Alonso

ISBN 978-1-60456-647-5

© 2009 Nova Science Publishers, Inc.

Chapter 21

Neuroimaging of Major Depression in Women

Susanne Karch and Christoph Mulert

Department of Psychiatry and Psychotherapy, Ludwig-Maximilians-University
Munich, Germany

During the last few years our knowledge about disturbed brain function in major depression has been increased mainly due to new possibilities offered by neuroimaging methods like functional Magnetic Resonance Imaging (fMRI). Several key structures were identified to play an important role in major depression, such as the rostral and subgenual parts of the anterior cingulate cortex (ACC), the orbitofrontal cortex (OFC) and the dorsolateral prefrontal cortex (DLPFC). Subcortical regions like the amygdala, the thalamus and the nucleus accumbens also seem to play an important role. In comparison to the large number of studies investigating major depression with neuroimaging methods in general, only a few studies have directly addressed the question of gender-specific differences so far although there are hints that gender specific differences may exist. This review summarizes the most important findings related to neurobiological correlates of gender differences, neural responses in depression and particularly neuroimaging findings for depression in women suggesting new lines of research in this field.

Functional Imaging and Depression

Neuroimaging studies of mood disorder have primarily concentrated on prefrontal deficits, e.g. within the dorsolateral and dorsomedial PFC and subgenual ACC (Drevets 1998; Drevets et al. 1997; Mayberg et al. 1997). Decreased activity, for example, was found in brain regions including DLPFC, dorsomedial and dorsal anterolateral prefrontal cortex as well as dorsal ACC (Baxter et al. 1989; George et al. 1993). By contrast, increased responses could be shown in ventral regions and rostral areas, e.g. ventrolateral cortex, ventromedial cortex, orbitofrontal cortex, subgenual prefrontal cortex, amygdala, insular cortex and the rostral part of the ACC (Drevets et al. 1997; Liotti et al. 2000; Mayberg 1997). In addition, variations in basal ganglia and thalamic function have been reported (Drevets 2000; Mayberg 1997). Depression-related alterations in prefrontal, limbic and paralimbic brain regions seemed to normalize along with recovery from depression (Bench et al. 1995; Brody et al. 1999; Brody et al. 2001; Buchsbaum et al. 1997; Drevets et al. 2002; Kennedy et al. 2001; Mayberg et al. 2000; Mayberg et al. 1999), for instance a normalization of frontal hypoactivity in the DLPFC and ACC, increases in posterior cingulate and decreases in the prefrontal cortex, insula, amygdala, and hippocampus were shown (Davidson et al. 2003; Drevets et al. 2002; Kennedy et al. 2001).

A *limbic-cortical model of depression* was postulated, including dorsal, ventral and rostral brain regions (Mayberg et al. 1997; Mayberg et al. 2005): cognitive disturbances (e.g. attention, executive functioning) were primarily related to variations in dorsal brain regions including the DLPFC, dorsal ACC, posterior cingulate). Deficits in subcortical and paralimbic regions were suggested to be mainly associated to vegetative und somatic symptoms of depression, whereas the rostral part (e.g. rostral ACC) might serve as an important regulatory role (Deckersbach et al. 2006).

Some of the brain regions notably associated with affective disturbances is the *anterior cingulate cortex*: altered activation in major depression relative to controls has been repeatedly reported (Davidson et al. 2002). Neurobiological models of depression emphasized the importance of the ACC in the pathogenesis of depression (Davidson et al. 2002; Drevets 2001; Mayberg et al. 1997). It is postulated that (a) decreased activation in the dorsal ACC may be associated with impaired modulation of attention or deficits in executive functions; (b) hypoactivation in ventral parts of the ACC are assumed to be related to blunted conscious experience of affect, hypoarousal, anhedonia, reduced coping strategies in situations characterized by uncertainty, conflict, and expectancy violation between the environment and affective states (Davidson et al. 2002). In addition, neural responses of the ACC seemed to be related to treatment effect: Mayberg and colleagues (1997) demonstrated that enhanced responses of the rostral part of the ACC compared to nonresponders and healthy comparisons seemed to be characteristic for treatment responders. Similar results were found in other studies, for instance using EEG (Ebert et al. 1991; Pizzagalli et al. 2001). Deep brain stimulation of the subgenual cingulate region relieved symptoms of major depressive disorder in treatment-resistant depressed patients (Mayberg et al. 2005).

Hippocampal dysfunction is assumed to be related to inappropriate context regulation of affect that is often seen in depressed patients (Davidson et al. 2002). Structural alterations regarding the hippocampus were shown in various studies, e.g. a reduction in hippocampal volume (Videbech and Ravnkilde 2004); functional studies concerning this topic are rare. The hippocampus is suggested to be involved in learning and memory processes of healthy subjects. Functional imaging studies showed an involvement, for example, in perception of negative valenced and aversive information (Buchel et al. 1999; Lane et al. 1997) as well as pleasant autobiographical information (Fink et al. 1996).

Structural and functional abnormalities in the *amygdala* have also been reported. The amygdala is involved in processing of emotional stimuli and is primarily related to the strength of the pleasant or unpleasant stimulus (Davis and Whalen 2001). Depression seemed to be associated with an enlargement of the amygdala volume. Functionally, amygdala responses were reported to be enhanced in depressive patients (e.g. Drevets 2001). Functional variations seemed to reduce after remission (Drevets 2001). In general, the hyperactivation in the amygdala in major depression seemed to bias the initial evaluation of and the response to incoming information (Davidson et al. 2002).

Depression-related brain functions and deficits were examined by using cognitive or emotional tasks like processing and evaluation of emotional facial expressions or during resting states. Transient emotions, e.g. elicited by recalling sad autobiographical events and the presentation of pictures or films, led to an increase in BOLD responses in the subgenual prefrontal cortex, insula, and ventral prefrontal regions as well as the rostral ACC, whereas the responses of the DLPFC and the dorsal part of the ACC were decreased (Damasio et al. 2000; Drevets 2001; Mayberg et al. 1999). A review about *emotional information processing* in mood disorders revealed an attentional bias towards negative emotional cues, away from positive emotional cues indicated improved memory processes for negative emotional material (Leppanen 2006). Some of these alterations persisted after remission and were present in subjects with a high risk of developing of mood disorders (Leppanen 2006).

In healthy individuals, for example, expressions of increasing happiness were associated with linear increases of brain activity bilateral fusiform gyri and right putamen. Depressed individuals, by contrast, demonstrated responses in left putamen, left parahippocampal gyrus/amygdala, and right fusiform gyrus to expressions of increasing sadness (Surguladze et al. 2005). The authors concluded that these responses might indicate a potential neural basis for the negative cognitions and social dysfunction in major depression (Surguladze et al. 2005). Similar results were seen in a study by Elliott and colleagues (2002): the presentation of happy words led to enhanced activations in the anteromedial prefrontal cortex in healthy subjects, whereas comparable activations were seen during the presentation of sad words in depression (Elliott et al. 2002). Siegle et al (2002) found an enhanced reactivity of the amygdala to negative-emotional stimuli in depressed subjects; the prolonged physiological responses correlated with self-reported rehashing of negative information (Siegle et al. 2002). Beyond that, there is some evidence for lateralized dysfunctions in depression: the presentation of fearful faces, for example, revealed enhanced responses of the right amygdala and decreased responses of the left amygdala in depressive patients compared to healthy subjects (Thomas et al. 2001). The responsiveness of the right amygdala seemed to be stronger in healthy subjects whereas depressive subjects seemed to show reduced left-sided responses (Tomarken and Davidson 1994). Johnstone and colleagues (2007) suggested alterations in the lateralization in the prefrontal cortex: in healthy subjects, the left ventromedial prefrontal circuitry proved to be important for the downregulation of the amygdala response to negative stimuli. In depressed patients a counterproductive engagement of the right prefrontal cortex was shown (Johnstone et al. 2007). Altogether, these processes may contribute to the vulnerability for negative emotions and the onset of depressive episodes (Leppanen 2006).

The examination of *resting states* mostly revealed decreased activity in limbic areas as well as disturbed metabolism in prefrontal brain regions (Vasic et al. 2007), including the DLPFC (Baxter et al. 1989; Drevets et al. 2002; Mayberg et al. 1994; Sackeim et al. 1990) and the ACC (Buchsbaum et al. 1997; Galynker et al. 1998) which go back to their basic state along with the improvement of depressive symptoms.

Despite marked indicators for dysfunctional *cognitive functions* in depression, few neuroimaging studies exist addressing neurofunctional correlates of cognitive functions in mood disorders. Other reviews indicated pathological cortical activity in various brain regions especially the ACC (Audenaert et al. 2002; Matsuo et al. 2002; Wagner et al. 2006); findings about the DLPFC are less clear (Rogers et al. 2004). Some studies found increased (Wagner et al. 2006), some decreased responses during the presentation of tasks which are thought to measure executive functions (Audenaert et al. 2002; Matsuo et al. 2002). For example, during a planning task, decreased responses in patients with depression were elicited in the DLPFC and posterior cortical regions, as well as alterations in striatal and anterior cingulate activity could be shown (Elliott et al. 1997). Reduced dorsal ACC responses were seen during performance monitoring (Amaral et al. 1992). These findings suggested that dysfunctions in dorsal prefrontal brain structures might be responsible for attention and memory deficits in patients with mood disorders (Deckersbach et al. 2006).

Decreased responses in frontal brain regions were also demonstrated in studies about working memory capacities: BOLD responses of the lateral prefrontal cortex and the dorsal ACC were reduced in depressive patients compared to healthy controls (Harvey et al. 2005). Given that the performance did not differ significantly between groups, the authors suggested that cortical activity needs to be enhanced in depressed patients compared to healthy subjects in order to achieve the same results (Harvey et al. 2005). However, there are also contradictory results (Barch et al. 2003; Rose et al. 2006; Videbech et al. 2004).

In addition, the association of brain functions and therapy response was assessed in several studies: findings indicated that hypermetabolic responses of the rostral ACC have been found in depressed patients who later responded to antidepressant treatment. Whereas hypometabolism characterized non-responders when compared to controls (Mayberg et al. 1997; Mayberg et al. 1999; Rubin et al. 1995).

Regarding patients with brain lesions, there is some evidence that depression is prevalent in patients with lesions on the left side of the brain, e.g. stroke-patients with left prefrontal lesions show the most severe depression (Hama et al. 2007). These findings led to the assumption that the left prefrontal cortex is important for positive emotions and damage to this region may contribute to enhanced sadness and emotional dysfunctions.

Altogether, the findings suggest depression-related functional alterations in brain responses, especially in the amygdala-hippocampus complex and prefrontal brain regions (e.g. ACC, DLPFC). Variations appeared not only during processing of emotional information and the accomplishment of cognitive tasks, but also during rest. Neural activity of the rostral part of the ACC seemed to be characteristic for variations in treatment effect (Ebert et al. 1991; Mayberg et al. 1997; Pizzagalli et al. 2001).

Functional Imaging and Gender Differences

Gender-associated differences do exist in many aspects of perception and behavior, e.g. cognitive functioning, emotion, pain perception, vision, and hearing. Generally, it is suggested that women show improved abilities relating linguistic performance and performance in episodic memory tasks as well as enhanced emotionality. Men are assumed to show better visual-spatial and motoric capacities.

Regarding neural responses, differences in every brain lobe, including many 'cognitive' regions such as the hippocampus, amygdala and neocortex were found (Cahill 2006). Furthermore, alterations were found in insular and thalamic regions (Lee et al. 2005; Lee et al. 2002), occipital and cingulate regions (Fischer et al. 2004; Lee et al. 2002), frontal regions (Lee et al. 2002; Weiss et al. 2003), parietal regions (Weiss et al. 2003), and temporal regions (Ragland et al. 2000). In general, the global cerebral blood flow has demonstrated to be enhanced in women compared to men during rest (Gur et al. 1982) and cognitive activity (Esposito et al. 1996; Gur et al. 1982; Slosman et al. 2001).

Studies about processing of visual information as well as recognition of emotion in faces and cognitive abilities, e.g. working memory, showed significant differences between the sexes in their patterns of activation (Cowan et al. 2000; Fischer et al. 2004; Georgopoulos et al. 2001; Lee et al. 2005; Lee et al. 2002; Levin et al. 1998; Ragland et al. 2000; Speck et al. 2000). For instance, there is some evidence for hemispheric lateralization (Georgopoulos et al. 2001; Lee et al. 2002; Levin et al. 1998; Speck et al. 2000): processing of spatial information was associated with bilateral activations in men and a right-hemispheric dominance in women (Gur et al. 2000). Object recognition (Georgopoulos et al. 2001) and working memory tasks produced primarily left-sided activity in women and predominantly right-sided responses in men. However, not all studies have been able to find a significant gender effect (Schlosser et al. 1998).

Sex-related differences in brain responses were shown in *cognitive tasks* and cognition-related brain regions, including the *prefrontal cortex* (PFC) and *hippocampus*. Decision making processes, for example, which are primarily related to prefrontal brain regions and proved to be deficient in male patients with a PFC-lesion of the right hemisphere, whereas no deficits in the decision-making capacity was not shown in women with similar lesions. However, lesions in the left ventromedial PFC led to an impaired performance in women but not in men; following right-sided damage, however, defects were mild or absent (Tranel et al. 2005). The opposite was true in men: severe defects were found following unilateral right ventromedial PFC damage but not after left-sided damage (Tranel et al. 2005). The authors assumed that these results suggest that men and women use different strategies to solve similar problems - e.g. men may use a more holistic, gestalt-type strategy and women may use a more analytic, verbally-mediated strategy (Tranel et al. 2005). Enhanced lateralization to the left hemisphere in females was also shown during executive tasks (Bolla et al. 2004; Speck et al. 2000); male subjects, by contrast, showed bilateral activation (Speck et al. 2000) or right-sided dominance in the prefrontal cortex, parietal cortices and caudate (Bolla et al. 2004; Speck et al. 2000). Greater brain responses in males compared to females were also observed during a word generation task, e.g. in the left and right dorsolateral prefrontal cortex, the right inferior parietal lobe and the cingulate (Bell et al. 2006). During memory recall, females demonstrated a greater bilateral regional blood flow in temporal regions (Ragland et al. 2000). In spatial attention tasks there were no functional differences between male and female subjects in spite of a better performance by men (Bell et al. 2006). On the other hand, the variability of task performance was not always mirrored in differences in brain activation (Bell et al. 2006).

There is some evidence demonstrating that the *hippocampus*, a region which is primarily associated with learning and memory, differs significantly between male and female subjects regarding their anatomical structure: the hippocampus is larger in women than men when adjusted for total brain size (Goldstein et al. 2001), many neurotransmitter systems (Madeira and Lieberman 1995), its reaction to chronic stress (indicated in studies with rats and monkeys (McEwen 2000)) and its functional reactivity. Corresponding to these findings about the amygdala, the hippocampal activation was significantly more left lateralized in women, and more right lateralized in men (Frings et al. 2006).

In summary, there is some evidence for increased neural responses of women compared to men in many regions of the brain including the hippocampus, amygdala, thalamus, prefrontal cortex, cingulate regions, and parietal cortex. In addition, significant differences in patterns of activation have been found between male and female subjects, for instance functional responses of the amygdala-hippocampus complex tended to be left lateralized in women and right lateralized in men.

Functional Imaging of Gender Differences in Emotion Processing and Induced Sadness

Another brain structure with growing evidence for a sexually dimorphic nature is the *amygdala* (Cahill 2003; Hamann 2005). There is some evidence that the amygdala is one of the key structures mediating differences in emotional response between men and women (Hamann 2005): emotional memories tended to be stronger for women than men. The amygdala is significantly larger in men than in women (adjusted for total brain size) (Goldstein et al. 2001) and there are significant differences in its structural relationship with other brain structures (Mechelli et al. 2005). Functional imaging studies indicated differences in the involvement of the amygdala during the processing of emotional information in women compared to men: in women, the left amygdala was related to memory for emotional material whereas in men the right amygdala was mainly involved during the same task (Cahill et al. 2001; Cahill et al. 2004; Canli et al. 2002; Mackiewicz et al. 2006). Killgore and colleagues (2001) examined processing emotional facial expressions in men and women using fMRI. The results indicated that seeing happy faces led to enhanced activation in the left amygdala in females compared to males, whereas men activated the right amygdala stronger than women (Killgore and Yurgelun-Todd 2001). Differential activations of the amygdala in female and male subjects was also elicited by the presentation of fearful faces (Schienle et al. 2005; Williams et al. 2005). Despite emotion-related differences in amygdala responses, there is also some evidence for functional dissociations during resting. One PET study of Kilpatrick and colleagues (2006) showed a hemispheric lateralization of function: amygdala activity of the right hemisphere correlated to a greater extent with responses of other brain regions in men than in women, whereas the reverse pattern was revealed for the left hemisphere (Kilpatrick et al. 2006). Altogether, these results may indicate that the laterality occurring in response to emotional stimulation may stem from differences during rest (Cahill 2006).

Differences in emotion processing are probably linked to a greater prevalence of depression (Davidson et al. 2002). Gender-related differences in neural responses to *self-induced emotions* (sadness, happiness) were determined. A PET study was conducted and male and female healthy subjects were scanned at rest and during happy, sad, and neutral states of self-induced emotions (recall of affect-appropriate life events; looking at happy, sad, and neutral faces) (George et al. 1996). At rest, women showed decreased activity of the temporal and prefrontal cortex, and increased responses of the brainstem. During transient sadness, women activated larger regions of the limbic system compared to men, despite similar self-reported changes in mood (George et al. 1996). Another study using a mood induction procedure also revealed differential cerebral correlates of emotional experience in male and female subjects: in men, stimuli inducing negative affect led to amygdala activity, whereas females failed to show similar activation patterns (Schneider et al. 2000).

Differences in male and female neural activity were demonstrated during induced emotions: processing emotional information led to enhanced neural responses of the left amygdala in women and the right amygdala in men. Also, in women induced sadness elicited increased activity of limbic brain regions.

Functional Imaging of Gender Differences in Depression

Studies about structural variations related to depression revealed inconsistent results: some studies reported no volume differences in the hippocampus and hippocampus-amygdala complex, respectively (e.g. Axelson et al. 1993; Vakili et al. 2000), others found smaller hippocampus volumes in depressed subjects compared to healthy volunteers (Bremner et al. 2000; Steffens et al. 2000; Vythilingam et al. 2002). Hastings and colleagues (2004) found a different pattern of volumetric change in male and female patients: compared to sex-matched controls, the left inferior anterior cingulate was smaller in depressed males compared to depressed females. In addition, only depressed females but not males had smaller amygdala compared to controls (Hastings et al. 2004).

The neurotransmitter serotonin (5-HT) has long been implicated in mood regulation and affective disorders (van der Veen et al. 2007). Abnormal serotonergic functions is assumed to underlie many of the cardinal symptoms of depression including mood, appetite, suicide, and cognition (Maes and Meltzer 1995). Central and peripheral markers of lowered 5-HT function were observed in depressed patients, including variations in plasma tryptophan, 5-HT receptor and 5-HT transporter binding (Maes and Meltzer 1995; Schatzberg et al. 2002). In addition, differences in pharmacodynamic effects were suggested to be the reason for sex differences in antidepressant treatment (Baca et al. 2004; Kornstein et al. 2000; Martenyi et al. 2001; Yonkers and Brawman-Mintzer 2002).

Staley and colleagues (2006) showed that the 5-HT transporter availability, measured by the $[^{123}I]\beta$-CIT uptake in the diencephalon is reduced in depressed women in an age-dependent manner, but not in men (see Figure 1, 2). Gender differences in the 5-HT transporter expression may suggest differential responses of women and men to antidepressant treatment with SSRIs. These findings match those that young women benefit more from treatment with SSRIs (Baca et al. 2004; Kornstein et al. 2000; Martenyi et al. 2001).

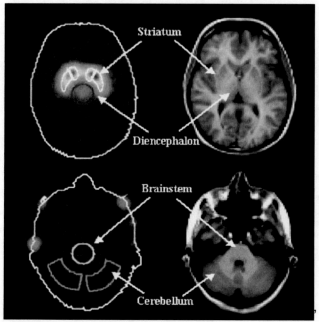

Abbreviations: [123I]β-CIT, iodine-123 2beta-carbomethoxy-3beta-(4iodophenyl)tropane; SPECT, single-photon emission computed tomography; MRI, magnetic resonance imaging.

Figure 1. *Illustration of regions of interest on an [^{123}I]β-CIT SPECT image and co-registered MRI.* The regions of interest including striatum, diencephalon, brainstem, and the background region cerebellum are illustrated on a representative [^{123}I]β-CIT image and the corresponding co-registered MRI. The regions of interest were placed on the MRI and then transferred to the SPECT scan (Reprint from Staley et al 2005; Copyright (2005) with permission from Elsevier).

Other experiments concentrated on the examination of acute tryptophan depletion on mood and neural correlates: tryptophan is the precursor of serotonin (Carpenter et al. 1998). Acute tryptophan depletion leads to a decreased 5-HT metabolism (Carpenter et al. 1998). 5-HT is suggested to be important for emotional behavior (Lucki 1998), for instance the perception of facial emotion. Tryptophan depletion studies with healthy controls without a family history of affective disorder did not find any significant effects on mood (Evers et al. 2005a; Evers et al. 2005b). Others subjects, however, do experience mood lowering effects of acute tryptophan depletion, e.g. healthy subjects with a family history of affective disorder (Neumeister et al. 2002) and patients with remitted depression (Booij et al. 2002; Neumeister et al. 2004). A study of van der Veen and colleagues (2007) explored the emotion perception capacity of female subjects with a positive history of depression using fMRI. Depletion led to the expected lowering of mood in female subjects with a positive history of depression. A strong mood lowering effect was associated with less accurate performance in faces expressing a negative emotion and stronger responses of the right amygdala to fearful faces in comparison to happy faces (van der Veen et al. 2007). The authors concluded that tryptophan depletion probably elicited a stronger impact on the expressed negative emotion leading to more interference during the task and a stronger amygdala response. Altogether, the results indicated that for women the effect of acute tryptophan depletion on mood, emotion recognition and amygdala responses depended on their family history of depression (van der Veen et al. 2007).

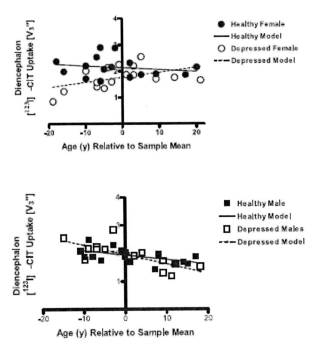

Abbreviations: $[^{123}I]\beta$-CIT, iodine-123 2beta-carbomethoxy-3beta-(4iodophenyl)tropane.

Figure 2: *Scatter plot of diencephalon $[^{123}I]\beta$-CIT uptake in healthy and depressed subjects by sex.* Individual V_3 values for each healthy and depressed patient are plotted as a function of the age for healthy and depressed women (top) and healthy and depressed men (bottom). Linear regression analysis demonstrated that diencephalon $[^{123}I]\beta$-CIT uptake is decreased in depressed women as compared to healthy women in an age-specific manner. In contrast, $[^{123}I]\beta$-CIT uptake did not differ between depressed and healthy men through their lifespan (Reprint from Staley et al 2005; Copyright (2005) with permission from Elsevier).

So far, there are no studies exploring functional deficits in depressed male and female patients. Depression-related functional alterations and gender-related changes in neural activity seem to be associated with various congruent brain regions, e.g. the amygdala-hippocampus complex and the prefrontal cortex. Hence, these regions appear to be crucial for depression and gender-related particularities.

References

Amaral, DG; Price, JL; Pitkanen, A; Carmichael, ST. Anatomical organization of the primate amygdaloid complex. In Agleton, JP, ed., *The Amygdala: Neurobiological Aspects of Emotione, Memory, and Mental Dysfunction.* Wiley-Liss, 1992.

Audenaert, K; Goethals, I; Van Laere, K; Lahorte, P; Brans, B; Versijpt, J; Vervaet, M; Beelaert, L; Van Heeringen, K; Dierckx, R. SPECT neuropsychological activation procedure with the Verbal Fluency Test in attempted suicide patients. *Nucl. Med. Commun.* (2002) 23(9):907-16.

Axelson, DA; Doraiswamy, PM; McDonald, WM; Boyko, OB; Tupler, LA; Patterson, LJ; Nemeroff, CB; Ellinwood, EH, Jr.; Krishnan, KR. Hypercortisolemia and hippocampal changes in depression. *Psychiatry Res.* (1993) 47(2):163-73.

Baca, E; Garcia-Garcia, M; Porras-Chavarino, A. Gender differences in treatment response to sertraline versus imipramine in patients with nonmelancholic depressive disorders. *Prog. Neuropsychopharmacol. Biol. Psychiatry* (2004) 28(1):57-65.

Barch, DM; Sheline, YI; Csernansky, JG; Snyder, AZ. Working memory and prefrontal cortex dysfunction: specificity to schizophrenia compared with major depression. *Biol. Psychiatry* (2003) 53(5):376-84.

Baxter, LR, Jr.; Schwartz, JM; Phelps, ME; Mazziotta, JC; Guze, BH; Selin, CE; Gerner, RH; Sumida, RM. Reduction of prefrontal cortex glucose metabolism common to three types of depression. *Arch. Gen. Psychiatry* (1989) 46(3):243-50.

Bell, EC; Willson, MC; Wilman, AH; Dave, S; Silverstone, PH. Males and females differ in brain activation during cognitive tasks. *Neuroimage* (2006) 30(2):529-38.

Bench, CJ; Frackowiak, RS; Dolan, RJ. Changes in regional cerebral blood flow on recovery from depression. *Psychol. Med.* (1995) 25(2):247-61.

Bolla, KI; Eldreth, DA; Matochik, JA; Cadet, JL. Sex-related differences in a gambling task and its neurological correlates. *Cereb. Cortex* (2004) 14(11):1226-32.

Booij, L; Van der Does, W; Benkelfat, C; Bremner, JD; Cowen, PJ; Fava, M; Gillin, C; Leyton, M; Moore, P; Smith, KA; Van der Kloot, WA. Predictors of mood response to acute tryptophan depletion. A reanalysis. *Neuropsychopharmacology* (2002) 27(5):852-61.

Bremner, JD; Narayan, M; Anderson, ER; Staib, LH; Miller, HL; Charney, DS. Hippocampal volume reduction in major depression. *Am. J. Psychiatry* (2000) 157(1):115-8.

Brody, AL; Saxena, S; Silverman, DH; Alborzian, S; Fairbanks, LA; Phelps, ME; Huang, SC; Wu, HM; Maidment, K; Baxter, LR, Jr. Brain metabolic changes in major depressive disorder from pre- to post-treatment with paroxetine. *Psychiatry Res.* (1999) 91(3):127-39.

Brody, AL; Saxena, S; Stoessel, P; Gillies, LA; Fairbanks, LA; Alborzian, S; Phelps, ME; Huang, SC; Wu, HM; Ho, ML; Ho, MK; Au, SC; Maidment, K; Baxter, LR, Jr. Regional brain metabolic changes in patients with major depression treated with either paroxetine or interpersonal therapy: preliminary findings. *Arch. Gen. Psychiatry* (2001) 58(7):631-40.

Buchel, C; Dolan, RJ; Armony, JL; Friston, KJ. Amygdala-hippocampal involvement in human aversive trace conditioning revealed through event-related functional magnetic resonance imaging. *J. Neurosci.* (1999) 19(24):10869-76.

Buchsbaum, MS; Wu, J; Siegel, BV; Hackett, E; Trenary, M; Abel, L; Reynolds, C. Effect of sertraline on regional metabolic rate in patients with affective disorder. *Biol. Psychiatry* (1997) 41(1):15-22.

Cahill, L. Sex- and hemisphere-related influences on the neurobiology of emotionally influenced memory. *Prog. Neuropsychopharmacol. Biol. Psychiatry* (2003) 27(8):1235-41.

Cahill, L. Why sex matters for neuroscience. *Nat. Rev. Neurosci.* (2006) 7(6):477-84.

Cahill, L; Haier, RJ; White, NS; Fallon, J; Kilpatrick, L; Lawrence, C; Potkin, SG; Alkire, MT. Sex-related difference in amygdala activity during emotionally influenced memory storage. *Neurobiol Learn Mem* (2001) 75(1):1-9.

Cahill, L; Uncapher, M; Kilpatrick, L; Alkire, MT; Turner, J. Sex-related hemispheric lateralization of amygdala function in emotionally influenced memory: an FMRI investigation. *Learn Mem* (2004) 11(3):261-6.

Canli, T; Desmond, JE; Zhao, Z; Gabrieli, JD. Sex differences in the neural basis of emotional memories. *Proc Natl Acad Sci U S A* (2002) 99(16):10789-94.

Carpenter, LL; Anderson, GM; Pelton, GH; Gudin, JA; Kirwin, PD; Price, LH; Heninger, GR; McDougle, CJ. Tryptophan depletion during continuous CSF sampling in healthy human subjects. *Neuropsychopharmacology* (1998) 19(1):26-35.

Cowan, RL; Frederick, BB; Rainey, M; Levin, JM; Maas, LC; Bang, J; Hennen, J; Lukas, SE; Renshaw, PF. Sex differences in response to red and blue light in human primary visual cortex: a bold fMRI study. *Psychiatry Res* .(2000) 100(3):129-38.

Damasio, AR; Grabowski, TJ; Bechara, A; Damasio, H; Ponto, LL; Parvizi, J; Hichwa, RD. Subcortical and cortical brain activity during the feeling of self-generated emotions. *Nat. Neurosci.* (2000) 3(10):1049-56.

Davidson, RJ; Irwin, W; Anderle, MJ; Kalin, NH. The neural substrates of affective processing in depressed patients treated with venlafaxine. *Am. J. Psychiatry* (2003) 160(1):64-75.

Davidson, RJ; Pizzagalli, D; Nitschke, JB; Putnam, K. Depression: perspectives from affective neuroscience. *Annu. Rev. Psychol.* (2002) 53:545-74.

Davis, M; Whalen, PJ. The amygdala: vigilance and emotion. *Mol. Psychiatry* (2001) 6(1):13-34.

Deckersbach, T; Dougherty, DD; Rauch, SL. Functional imaging of mood and anxiety disorders. *J. Neuroimaging.* (2006) 16(1):1-10.

Drevets, WC. Functional neuroimaging studies of depression: the anatomy of melancholia. *Annu. Rev. Med.* (1998) 49:341-61.

Drevets, WC. Neuroimaging studies of mood disorders. *Biol .Psychiatry* (2000) 48(8):813-29.

Drevets, WC. Neuroimaging and neuropathological studies of depression: implications for the cognitive-emotional features of mood disorders. *Curr. Opin. Neurobiol* .(2001) 11(2):240-9.

Drevets, WC; Bogers, W; Raichle, ME. Functional anatomical correlates of antidepressant drug treatment assessed using PET measures of regional glucose metabolism. *Eur. Neuropsychopharmacol.* (2002) 12(6):527-44.

Drevets, WC; Price, JL; Simpson, JR, Jr.; Todd, RD; Reich, T; Vannier, M; Raichle, ME. Subgenual prefrontal cortex abnormalities in mood disorders. *Nature* (1997) 386(6627):824-7.

Ebert, D; Feistel, H; Barocka, A. Effects of sleep deprivation on the limbic system and the frontal lobes in affective disorders: a study with Tc-99m-HMPAO SPECT. *Psychiatry Res.* (1991) 40(4):247-51.

Elliott, R; Baker, SC; Rogers, RD; O'Leary, DA; Paykel, ES; Frith, CD; Dolan, RJ; Sahakian, BJ. Prefrontal dysfunction in depressed patients performing a complex planning task: a study using positron emission tomography. *Psychol. Med.* (1997) 27(4):931-42.

Elliott, R; Rubinsztein, JS; Sahakian, BJ; Dolan, RJ. The neural basis of mood-congruent processing biases in depression. *Arch. Gen. Psychiatry* (2002) 59(7):597-604.

Esposito, G; Van Horn, JD; Weinberger, DR; Berman, KF. Gender differences in cerebral blood flow as a function of cognitive state with PET. *J. Nucl. Med.* (1996) 37(4):559-64.

Evers, EA; Cools, R; Clark, L; van der Veen, FM; Jolles, J; Sahakian, BJ; Robbins, TW. Serotonergic modulation of prefrontal cortex during negative feedback in probabilistic reversal learning. *Neuropsychopharmacology* (2005a) 30(6):1138-47.

Evers, EA; Tillie, DE; van der Veen, FM; Lieben, CK; Jolles, J; Deutz, NE; Schmitt, JA. Effects of a novel method of acute tryptophan depletion on plasma tryptophan and cognitive performance in healthy volunteers. *Psychopharmacology (Berl)* (2005b) 178(1):92-9.

Fink, GR; Markowitsch, HJ; Reinkemeier, M; Bruckbauer, T; Kessler, J; Heiss, WD. Cerebral representation of one's own past: neural networks involved in autobiographical memory. *J. Neurosci.* (1996) 16(13):4275-82.

Fischer, H; Fransson, P; Wright, CI; Backman, L. Enhanced occipital and anterior cingulate activation in men but not in women during exposure to angry and fearful male faces. *Cogn Affect Behav Neurosci* (2004) 4(3):326-34.

Frings, L; Wagner, K; Unterrainer, J; Spreer, J; Halsband, U; Schulze-Bonhage, A. Gender-related differences in lateralization of hippocampal activation and cognitive strategy. *Neuroreport* (2006) 17(4):417-21.

Galynker, II; Cai, J; Ongseng, F; Finestone, H; Dutta, E; Serseni, D. Hypofrontality and negative symptoms in major depressive disorder. *J. Nucl. Med.* (1998) 39(4):608-12.

George, MS; Ketter, TA; Parekh, PI; Herscovitch, P; Post, RM. Gender differences in regional cerebral blood flow during transient self-induced sadness or happiness. *Biol. Psychiatry* (1996) 40(9):859-71.

George, MS; Ketter, TA; Post, RM. SPECT and PET imaging in mood disorders. *J. Clin. Psychiatry* (1993) 54 Suppl:6-13.

Georgopoulos, AP; Whang, K; Georgopoulos, MA; Tagaris, GA; Amirikian, B; Richter, W; Kim, SG; Ugurbil, K. Functional magnetic resonance imaging of visual object construction and shape discrimination : relations among task, hemispheric lateralization, and gender. *J. Cogn. Neurosci.* (2001) 13(1):72-89.

Goldstein, JM; Seidman, LJ; Horton, NJ; Makris, N; Kennedy, DN; Caviness, VS, Jr.; Faraone, SV; Tsuang, MT. Normal sexual dimorphism of the adult human brain assessed by in vivo magnetic resonance imaging. *Cereb. Cortex* (2001) 11(6):490-7.

Gur, RC; Alsop, D; Glahn, D; Petty, R; Swanson, CL; Maldjian, JA; Turetsky, BI; Detre, JA; Gee, J; Gur, RE. An fMRI study of sex differences in regional activation to a verbal and a spatial task. *Brain Lang* (2000) 74(2):157-70.

Gur, RC; Gur, RE; Obrist, WD; Hungerbuhler, JP; Younkin, D; Rosen, AD; Skolnick, BE; Reivich, M. Sex and handedness differences in cerebral blood flow during rest and cognitive activity. *Science* (1982) 217(4560):659-61.

Hama, S; Yamashita, H; Shigenobu, M; Watanabe, A; Kurisu, K; Yamawaki, S; Kitaoka, T. Post-stroke affective or apathetic depression and lesion location: left frontal lobe and bilateral basal ganglia. *Eur. Arch. Psychiatry Clin. Neurosci.* (2007) 257(3):149-52.

Hamann, S. Sex differences in the responses of the human amygdala. *Neuroscientist* (2005) 11(4):288-93.

Harvey, PO; Fossati, P; Pochon, JB; Levy, R; Lebastard, G; Lehericy, S; Allilaire, JF; Dubois, B. Cognitive control and brain resources in major depression: an fMRI study using the n-back task. *Neuroimage* (2005) 26(3):860-9.

Hastings, RS; Parsey, RV; Oquendo, MA; Arango, V; Mann, JJ. Volumetric analysis of the prefrontal cortex, amygdala, and hippocampus in major depression. *Neuropsycho pharma- cology* (2004) 29(5):952-9.

Johnstone, T; van Reekum, CM; Urry, HL; Kalin, NH; Davidson, RJ. Failure to regulate: counterproductive recruitment of top-down prefrontal-subcortical circuitry in major depression. *J. Neurosci* .(2007) 27(33):8877-84.

Kennedy, SH; Evans, KR; Kruger, S; Mayberg, HS; Meyer, JH; McCann, S; Arifuzzman, AI; Houle, S; Vaccarino, FJ. Changes in regional brain glucose metabolism measured with positron emission tomography after paroxetine treatment of major depression. *Am. J. Psychiatry* (2001) 158(6):899-905.

Killgore, WD; Yurgelun-Todd, DA. Sex differences in amygdala activation during the perception of facial affect. *Neuroreport* (2001) 12(11):2543-7.

Kilpatrick, LA; Zald, DH; Pardo, JV; Cahill, LF. Sex-related differences in amygdala functional connectivity during resting conditions. *Neuroimage* (2006) 30(2):452-61.

Kornstein, SG; Schatzberg, AF; Thase, ME; Yonkers, KA; McCullough, JP; Keitner, GI; Gelenberg, AJ; Davis, SM; Harrison, WM; Keller, MB. Gender differences in treatment response to sertraline versus imipramine in chronic depression. *Am. J. Psychiatry* (2000) 157(9):1445-52.

Lane, RD; Reiman, EM; Bradley, MM; Lang, PJ; Ahern, GL; Davidson, RJ; Schwartz, GE. Neuroanatomical correlates of pleasant and unpleasant emotion. *Neuropsychologia* (1997) 35(11):1437-44.

Lee, TM; Liu, HL; Chan, CC; Fang, SY; Gao, JH. Neural activities associated with emotion recognition observed in men and women. *Mol .Psychiatry* (2005) 10(5):450-5.

Lee, TM; Liu, HL; Hoosain, R; Liao, WT; Wu, CT; Yuen, KS; Chan, CC; Fox, PT; Gao, JH. Gender differences in neural correlates of recognition of happy and sad faces in humans assessed by functional magnetic resonance imaging. *Neurosci. Lett* .(2002) 333(1):13-6.

Leppanen, JM. Emotional information processing in mood disorders: a review of behavioral and neuroimaging findings. *Curr. Opin. Psychiatry* (2006) 19(1):34-9.

Levin, JM; Ross, MH; Mendelson, JH; Mello, NK; Cohen, BM; Renshaw, PF. Sex differences in blood-oxygenation-level-dependent functional MRI with primary visual stimulation. *Am J. Psychiatry* (1998) 155(3):434-6.

Liotti, M; Mayberg, HS; Brannan, SK; McGinnis, S; Jerabek, P; Fox, PT. Differential limbic--cortical correlates of sadness and anxiety in healthy subjects: implications for affective disorders. *Biol. Psychiatry* (2000) 48(1):30-42.

Lucki, I. The spectrum of behaviors influenced by serotonin. *Biol. Psychiatry* (1998) 44(3):151-62.

Mackiewicz, KL; Sarinopoulos, I; Cleven, KL; Nitschke, JB. The effect of anticipation and the specificity of sex differences for amygdala and hippocampus function in emotional memory. *Proc. Natl. Acad. Sci .U S A* (2006) 103(38):14200-5.

Madeira, MD; Lieberman, AR. Sexual dimorphism in the mammalian limbic system. *Prog. Neurobiol.* (1995) 45(4):275-333.

Maes, M; Meltzer, H. The serotonin hypothesis of major depression. In Bloom, FE, and Kupfer, D, eds., *Psychopharmacology: The Fourth Generation of Progress*. Raven Press Ltd, 1995.

Martenyi, F; Dossenbach, M; Mraz, K; Metcalfe, S. Gender differences in the efficacy of fluoxetine and maprotiline in depressed patients: a double-blind trial of antidepressants with serotonergic or norepinephrinergic reuptake inhibition profile. *Eur Neuropsychopharmacol* (2001) 11(3):227-32.

Matsuo, K; Kato, N; Kato, T. Decreased cerebral haemodynamic response to cognitive and physiological tasks in mood disorders as shown by near-infrared spectroscopy. *Psychol.Med* .(2002) 32(6):1029-37.

Mayberg, HS. Limbic-cortical dysregulation: a proposed model of depression. *J Neuropsychiatry Clin. Neurosci.* (1997) 9(3):471-81.

Mayberg, HS; Brannan, SK; Mahurin, RK; Jerabek, PA; Brickman, JS; Tekell, JL; Silva, JA; McGinnis, S; Glass, TG; Martin, CC; Fox, PT. Cingulate function in depression: a potential predictor of treatment response. *Neuroreport* (1997) 8(4):1057-61.

Mayberg, HS; Brannan, SK; Tekell, JL; Silva, JA; Mahurin, RK; McGinnis, S; Jerabek, PA. Regional metabolic effects of fluoxetine in major depression: serial changes and relationship to clinical response. *Biol. Psychiatry* (2000) 48(8):830-43.

Mayberg, HS; Lewis, PJ; Regenold, W; Wagner, HN, Jr. Paralimbic hypoperfusion in unipolar depression. *J. Nucl. Med.* (1994) 35(6):929-34.

Mayberg, HS; Liotti, M; Brannan, SK; McGinnis, S; Mahurin, RK; Jerabek, PA; Silva, JA; Tekell, JL; Martin, CC; Lancaster, JL; Fox, PT. Reciprocal limbic-cortical function and negative mood: converging PET findings in depression and normal sadness. *Am. J. Psychiatry* (1999) 156(5):675-82.

Mayberg, HS; Lozano, AM; Voon, V; McNeely, HE; Seminowicz, D; Hamani, C; Schwalb, JM; Kennedy, SH. Deep brain stimulation for treatment-resistant depression. *Neuron* (2005) 45(5):651-60.

McEwen, BS. The neurobiology of stress: from serendipity to clinical relevance. *Brain Res* (2000) 886(1-2):172-189.

Mechelli, A; Friston, KJ; Frackowiak, RS; Price, CJ. Structural covariance in the human cortex. *J. Neurosci* .(2005) 25(36):8303-10.

Neumeister, A; Konstantinidis, A; Stastny, J; Schwarz, MJ; Vitouch, O; Willeit, M; Praschak-Rieder, N; Zach, J; de Zwaan, M; Bondy, B; Ackenheil, M; Kasper, S. Association between serotonin transporter gene promoter polymorphism (5HTTLPR) and behavioral responses to tryptophan depletion in healthy women with and without family history of depression. *Arch. Gen .Psychiatry* (2002) 59(7):613-20.

Neumeister, A; Nugent, AC; Waldeck, T; Geraci, M; Schwarz, M; Bonne, O; Bain, EE; Luckenbaugh, DA; Herscovitch, P; Charney, DS; Drevets, WC. Neural and behavioral responses to tryptophan depletion in unmedicated patients with remitted major depressive disorder and controls. *Arch. Gen. Psychiatry* (2004) 61(8):765-73.

Pizzagalli, D; Pascual-Marqui, RD; Nitschke, JB; Oakes, TR; Larson, CL; Abercrombie, HC; Schaefer, SM; Koger, JV; Benca, RM; Davidson, RJ. Anterior cingulate activity as a predictor of degree of treatment response in major depression: evidence from brain electrical tomography analysis. *Am. J. Psychiatry* (2001) 158(3):405-15.

Ragland, JD; Coleman, AR; Gur, RC; Glahn, DC; Gur, RE. Sex differences in brain-behavior relationships between verbal episodic memory and resting regional cerebral blood flow. *Neuropsychologia* (2000) 38(4):451-61.

Rogers, MA; Kasai, K; Koji, M; Fukuda, R; Iwanami, A; Nakagome, K; Fukuda, M; Kato, N. Executive and prefrontal dysfunction in unipolar depression: a review of neuropsychological and imaging evidence. *Neurosci Res.* (2004) 50(1):1-11.

Rose, EJ; Simonotto, E; Ebmeier, KP. Limbic over-activity in depression during preserved performance on the n-back task. *Neuroimage* (2006) 29(1):203-15.

Rubin, E; Sackeim, HA; Prohovnik, I; Moeller, JR; Schnur, DB; Mukherjee, S. Regional cerebral blood flow in mood disorders: IV. Comparison of mania and depression. *Psychiatry Res.* (1995) 61(1):1-10.

Sackeim, HA; Prohovnik, I; Moeller, JR; Brown, RP; Apter, S; Prudic, J; Devanand, DP; Mukherjee, S. Regional cerebral blood flow in mood disorders. I. Comparison of major depressives and normal controls at rest. *Arch Gen Psychiatry* (1990) 47(1):60-70.

Schatzberg, AF; Garlow, SJ; Nemeroff, CB. Molecular and cellular mechanisms in depression. In Davis, KL, Charney, D, Coyle, JT, and Nemerhoff, C, eds., *Neuropsychopharma-cology, The Fifth Generation in Progress.* Lippincott Williams and Wilkins, 2002.

Schienle, A; Schafer, A; Stark, R; Walter, B; Vaitl, D. Gender differences in the processing of disgust- and fear-inducing pictures: an fMRI study. *Neuroreport* (2005) 16(3):277-80.

Schlosser, R; Hutchinson, M; Joseffer, S; Rusinek, H; Saarimaki, A; Stevenson, J; Dewey, SL; Brodie, JD. Functional magnetic resonance imaging of human brain activity in a verbal fluency task. *J. Neurol. Neurosurg. Psychiatry* (1998) 64(4):492-8.

Schneider, F; Habel, U; Kessler, C; Salloum, JB; Posse, S. Gender differences in regional cerebral activity during sadness. *Hum. Brain Mapp* .(2000) 9(4):226-38.

Siegle, GJ; Steinhauer, SR; Thase, ME; Stenger, VA; Carter, CS. Can't shake that feeling: event-related fMRI assessment of sustained amygdala activity in response to emotional information in depressed individuals. *Biol. Psychiatry* (2002) 51(9):693-707.

Slosman, DO; Chicherio, C; Ludwig, C; Genton, L; de Ribaupierre, S; Hans, D; Pichard, C; Mayer, E; Annoni, JM; de Ribaupierre, A. (133)Xe SPECT cerebral blood flow study in a healthy population: determination of T-scores. *J. Nucl. Med.*(2001) 42(6):864-70.

Speck, O; Ernst, T; Braun, J; Koch, C; Miller, E; Chang, L. Gender differences in the functional organization of the brain for working memory. *Neuroreport* (2000) 11(11):2581-5.

Steffens, DC; Byrum, CE; McQuoid, DR; Greenberg, DL; Payne, ME; Blitchington, TF; MacFall, JR; Krishnan, KR. Hippocampal volume in geriatric depression. *Biol. Psychiatry* (2000) 48(4):301-9.

Surguladze, S; Brammer, MJ; Keedwell, P; Giampietro, V; Young, AW; Travis, MJ; Williams, SC; Phillips, ML. A differential pattern of neural response toward sad versus happy facial expressions in major depressive disorder. *Biol. Psychiatry* (2005) 57(3):201-9.

Thomas, KM; Drevets, WC; Dahl, RE; Ryan, ND; Birmaher, B; Eccard, CH; Axelson, D; Whalen, PJ; Casey, BJ. Amygdala response to fearful faces in anxious and depressed children. *Arch. Gen. Psychiatry* (2001) 58(11):1057-63.

Tomarken, AJ; Davidson, RJ. Frontal brain activation in repressors and nonrepressors. *J Abnorm. Psychol* .(1994) 103(2):339-49.

Tranel, D; Damasio, H; Denburg, NL; Bechara, A. Does gender play a role in functional asymmetry of ventromedial prefrontal cortex? *Brain* (2005) 128(Pt 12):2872-81.

Vakili, K; Pillay, SS; Lafer, B; Fava, M; Renshaw, PF; Bonello-Cintron, CM; Yurgelun-Todd, DA. Hippocampal volume in primary unipolar major depression: a magnetic resonance imaging study. *Biol. Psychiatry* (2000) 47(12):1087-90.

van der Veen, FM; Evers, EA; Deutz, NE; Schmitt, JA. Effects of acute tryptophan depletion on mood and facial emotion perception related brain activation and performance in healthy women with and without a family history of depression. *Neuropsychopharmacology* (2007) 32(1):216-24.

Vasic, N; Wolf, RC; Walter, H. [Executive functions in patients with depression. The role of prefrontal activation]. *Nervenarzt* (2007) 78(6):628, 630-2, 634-6 passim.

Videbech, P; Ravnkilde, B. Hippocampal volume and depression: a meta-analysis of MRI studies. *Am. J .Psychiatry* (2004) 161(11):1957-66.

Videbech, P; Ravnkilde, B; Gammelgaard, L; Egander, A; Clemmensen, K; Rasmussen, NA; Gjedde, A; Rosenberg, R. The Danish PET/depression project: performance on Stroop's test linked to white matter lesions in the brain. *Psychiatry Res* .(2004) 130(2):117-30.

Vythilingam, M; Heim, C; Newport, J; Miller, AH; Anderson, E; Bronen, R; Brummer, M; Staib, L; Vermetten, E; Charney, DS; Nemeroff, CB; Bremner, JD. Childhood trauma associated with smaller hippocampal volume in women with major depression. *Am. J. Psychiatry* (2002) 159(12):2072-80.

Wagner, G; Sinsel, E; Sobanski, T; Kohler, S; Marinou, V; Mentzel, HJ; Sauer, H; Schlosser, RG. Cortical inefficiency in patients with unipolar depression: an event-related FMRI study with the Stroop task. *Biol .Psychiatry* (2006) 59(10):958-65.

Weiss, E; Siedentopf, CM; Hofer, A; Deisenhammer, EA; Hoptman, MJ; Kremser, C; Golaszewski, S; Felber, S; Fleischhacker, WW; Delazer, M. Sex differences in brain activation pattern during a visuospatial cognitive task: a functional magnetic resonance imaging study in healthy volunteers. *Neurosci. Lett* .(2003) 344(3):169-72.

Williams, LM; Barton, MJ; Kemp, AH; Liddell, BJ; Peduto, A; Gordon, E; Bryant, RA. Distinct amygdala-autonomic arousal profiles in response to fear signals in healthy males and females. *Neuroimage* (2005) 28(3):618-26.

Yonkers, KA; Brawman-Mintzer, O. The pharmacologic treatment of depression: is gender a critical factor? *J. Clin.. Psychiatry* (2002) 63(7):610-5.

Index

B

C

E

F

G

H

I

J

K

L

M

N

O

P

Q

R

S

W

X

Y